PEARSON EDEXCEL INTERNATIONAL GCSE (9–1)

MATHEMATICS A

Student Book 1

David Turner
Ian Potts

Published by Pearson Education Limited, 80 Strand, London, WC2R 0RL.

www.pearsonglobalschools.com

Copies of official specifications for all Edexcel qualifications may be found on the website: https://qualifications.pearson.com

Text © Pearson Education Limited 2016
Edited by Lyn Imeson
Answers checked by Laurice Suess
Designed by Cobalt id
Typeset by Cobalt id
Original illustrations © Pearson Education Limited 2016
Illustrated by © Cobalt id
Cover design by Pearson Education Limited
Picture research by Ann Thomson
Cover photo/illustration © Shutterstock.com: Filip Fuxa

The rights of David Turner and Ian Potts to be identified as authors of this work have been asserted by them in accordance with the Copyright, Designs and Patents Act 1988.

First published 2016

23
IMP 18

British Library Cataloguing in Publication Data
A catalogue record for this book is available from the British Library

ISBN 978 0 435 18144 4

Printed by Neografia in Slovakia

Dedicated to Viv Hony who started the whole project.

Grateful for contributions from Jack Barraclough, Chris Baston, Ian Bettison, Sharon Bolger, Phil Boor, Ian Boote, Judith Chadwick, Tony Cushen, Tara Doyle, Kath Hipkiss, Ian Jacques, Catherine Murphy, Su Nicholson, Naomi Norman, Diane Oliver, Katherine Pate, Glyn Payne, Jenny Roach, Carol Roberts, Peter Sherran, Robert Ward-Penny and our Development Editor: Gwen Burns.

Websites
There are links to relevant websites in this book. In order to ensure that the links are up to date and that the links work we have made the links available on our website at www.pearsonhotlinks.co.uk. Search for ISBN 978 0 435 18144 4.

Endorsement Statement

In order to ensure that this resource offers high-quality support for the associated Pearson qualification, it has been through a review process by the awarding body. This process confirms that this resource fully covers the teaching and learning content of the specification or part of a specification at which it is aimed. It also confirms that it demonstrates an appropriate balance between the development of subject skills, knowledge and understanding, in addition to preparation for assessment.

Endorsement does not cover any guidance on assessment activities or processes (e.g. practice questions or advice on how to answer assessment questions), included in the resource nor does it prescribe any particular approach to the teaching or delivery of a related course.

While the publishers have made every attempt to ensure that advice on the qualification and its assessment is accurate, the official specification and associated assessment guidance materials are the only authoritative source of information and should always be referred to for definitive guidance.

Pearson examiners have not contributed to any sections in this resource relevant to examination papers for which they have responsibility.

Examiners will not use endorsed resources as a source of material for any assessment set by Pearson. Endorsement of a resource does not mean that the resource is required to achieve this Pearson qualification, nor does it mean that it is the only suitable material available to support the qualification, and any resource lists produced by the awarding body shall include this and other appropriate resources.

UNIT 4

UNIT 5

ABOUT THIS BOOK

This two-book series is written for students following the Pearson Edexcel International GCSE (9-1) Maths A Higher Tier specification. There is a Student Book for each year of the course.

The course has been structured so that these two books can be used in order, both in the classroom and for independent learning.

Each book contains five units of work. Each unit contains five sections in the topic areas: *Number, Algebra, Graphs, Shape and Space, Sets* and *Handling Data*.

In each unit, there are concise explanations and worked examples, plus numerous exercises that will help you build up confidence.

Parallel exercises, non-starred and starred, are provided, to bring together basic principles before being challenged with more difficult questions. These are supported by parallel revision exercises at the end of each chapter.

Challenges, which provide questions applying the basic principles in unusual situations, feature at the back of the book along with *Fact Finders* which allow you to practise comprehension of real data.

Points of Interest put the maths you are about to learn in a real-world context.

Learning Objectives show what you will learn in each lesson.

Basic Principles outline assumed knowledge and key concepts from the beginning.

Transferable Skills are highlighted to show what skill you are using and where.

Activities are a gentle way of introducing a topic.

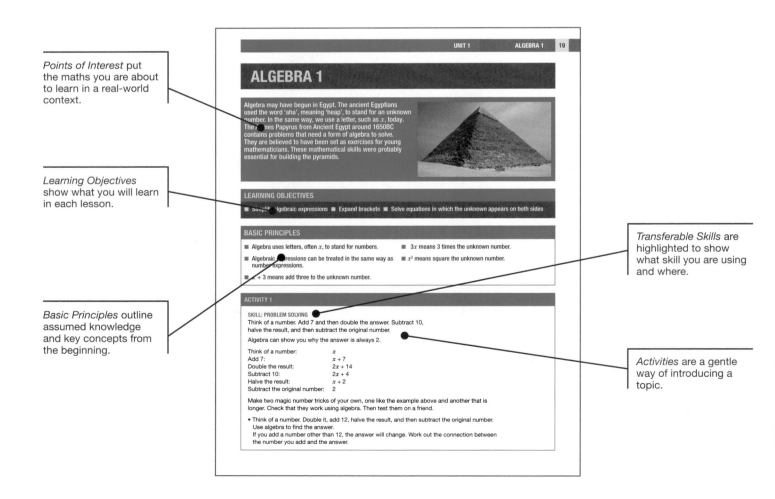

UNIT 1   ALGEBRA 1   19

ALGEBRA 1

Algebra may have begun in Egypt. The ancient Egyptians used the word 'aha', meaning 'heap', to stand for an unknown number. In the same way, we use a letter, such as x, today. The Rhines Papyrus from Ancient Egypt around 1650BC contains problems that need a form of algebra to solve. They are believed to have been set as exercises for young mathematicians. These mathematical skills were probably essential for building the pyramids.

LEARNING OBJECTIVES

■ Simplify algebraic expressions ■ Expand brackets ■ Solve equations in which the unknown appears on both sides

BASIC PRINCIPLES

■ Algebra uses letters, often x, to stand for numbers.

■ Algebraic expressions can be treated in the same way as number expressions.

■ $x + 3$ means add three to the unknown number.

■ $3x$ means 3 times the unknown number.

■ x^2 means square the unknown number.

ACTIVITY 1

SKILL: PROBLEM SOLVING

Think of a number. Add 7 and then double the answer. Subtract 10, halve the result, and then subtract the original number.

Algebra can show you why the answer is always 2.

Think of a number:	x
Add 7:	$x + 7$
Double the result:	$2x + 14$
Subtract 10:	$2x + 4$
Halve the result:	$x + 2$
Subtract the original number:	2

Make two magic number tricks of your own, one like the example above and another that is longer. Check that they work using algebra. Then test them on a friend.

• Think of a number. Double it, add 12, halve the result, and then subtract the original number. Use algebra to find the answer.
  If you add a number other than 12, the answer will change. Work out the connection between the number you add and the answer.

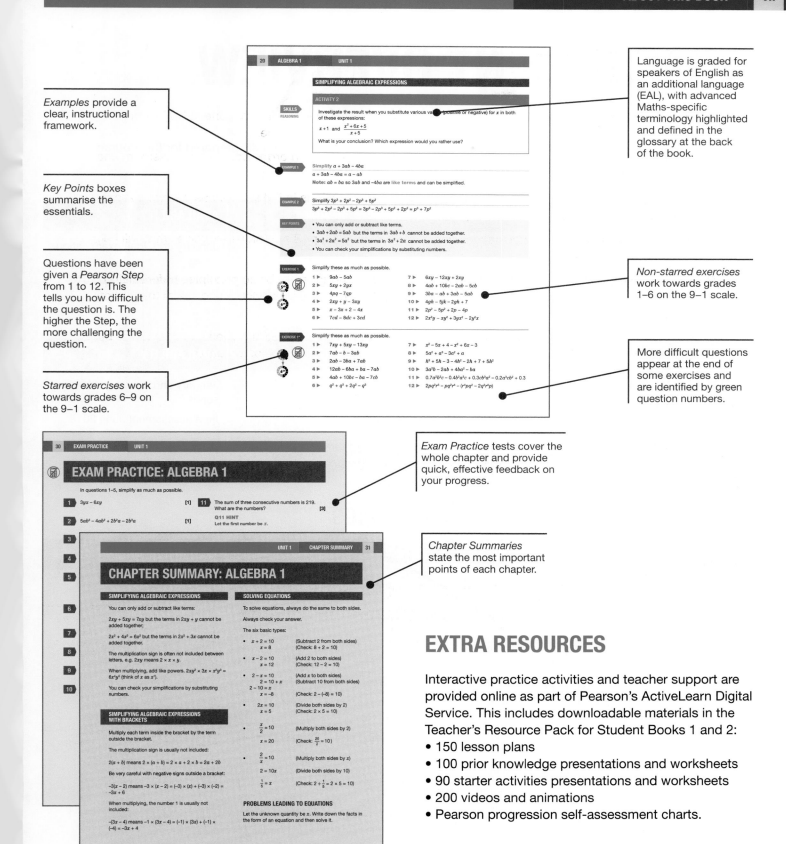

Examples provide a clear, instructional framework.

Key Points boxes summarise the essentials.

Questions have been given a *Pearson Step* from 1 to 12. This tells you how difficult the question is. The higher the Step, the more challenging the question.

Starred exercises work towards grades 6–9 on the 9–1 scale.

Language is graded for speakers of English as an additional language (EAL), with advanced Maths-specific terminology highlighted and defined in the glossary at the back of the book.

Non-starred exercises work towards grades 1–6 on the 9–1 scale.

More difficult questions appear at the end of some exercises and are identified by green question numbers.

Exam Practice tests cover the whole chapter and provide quick, effective feedback on your progress.

Chapter Summaries state the most important points of each chapter.

EXTRA RESOURCES

Interactive practice activities and teacher support are provided online as part of Pearson's ActiveLearn Digital Service. This includes downloadable materials in the Teacher's Resource Pack for Student Books 1 and 2:
• 150 lesson plans
• 100 prior knowledge presentations and worksheets
• 90 starter activities presentations and worksheets
• 200 videos and animations
• Pearson progression self-assessment charts.

ASSESSMENT OVERVIEW

The following tables give an overview of the assessment for this course.

We recommend that you study this information closely to help ensure that you are fully prepared for this course and know exactly what to expect in the assessment.

PAPER 1	PERCENTAGE	MARK	TIME	AVAILABILITY
HIGHER TIER MATHS A Written examination paper Paper code 4MA1/3H Externally set and assessed by Pearson Edexcel	50%	100	2 hours	January and June examination series First assessment June 2018

PAPER 2	PERCENTAGE	MARK	TIME	AVAILABILITY
HIGHER TIER MATHS A Written examination paper Paper code 4MA1/4H Externally set and assessed by Pearson Edexcel	50%	100	2 hours	January and June examination series First assessment June 2018

ASSESSMENT OBJECTIVES AND WEIGHTINGS

ASSESSMENT OBJECTIVE	DESCRIPTION	% IN INTERNATIONAL GCSE
AO1	Demonstrate knowledge, understanding and skills in number and algebra: • numbers and the numbering system • calculations • solving numerical problems • equations, formulae and identities • sequences, functions and graphs	57–63%
AO2	Demonstrate knowledge, understanding and skills in shape, space and measures: • geometry and trigonometry • vectors and transformation geometry	22–28%
AO3	Demonstrate knowledge, understanding and skills in handling data: • statistics • probability	12–18%

ASSESSMENT SUMMARY

The Pearson Edexcel International GCSE (9–1) in Mathematics (Specification A) **Higher Tier** requires students to demonstrate application and understanding of the following topics.

NUMBER
- Use numerical skills in a purely mathematical way and in real-life situations.

ALGEBRA
- Use letters as equivalent to numbers and as variables.
- Understand the distinction between expressions, equations and formulae.
- Use algebra to set up and solve problems.
- Demonstrate manipulative skills.
- Construct and use graphs.

GEOMETRY
- Use the properties of angles.
- Understand a range of transformations.
- Work within the metric system.
- Understand ideas of space and shape.
- Use ruler, compasses and protractor appropriately.

STATISTICS
- Understand basic ideas of statistical averages.
- Use a range of statistical techniques.
- Use basic ideas of probability.

Students should also be able to demonstrate **problem-solving skills** by translating problems in mathematical or non-mathematical contexts into a process or a series of mathematical processes.

Students should be able to demonstrate **reasoning skills** by
- making deductions and drawing conclusions from mathematical information
- constructing chains of reasoning
- presenting arguments and proofs
- interpreting and communicating information accurately.

CALCULATORS

Students will be expected to have access to a suitable electronic calculator for both examination papers. The electronic calculator to be used by students attempting **Higher Tier** examination papers (3H and 4H) should have these functions as a minimum:

$+, -, \times, \div, x^2, \sqrt{x},$ memory, brackets, $x^y, x^{\frac{1}{y}}, \bar{x}, \Sigma x, \Sigma fx,$ standard form, sine, cosine, tangent and their inverses.

PROHIBITIONS

Calculators with any of the following facilities are prohibited in all examinations:
- databanks
- retrieval of text or formulae
- QWERTY keyboards
- built-in symbolic algebra manipulations
- symbolic differentiation or integration.

UNIT 1

1 is not a prime number. Any number multiplied by 1 is itself. Computer systems use the binary system that contains only two numbers (1 and 0) which represent numbers and instructions. It is also the most likely first number to appear in a list of numerical data as first described by Benford's Law.

NUMBER 1

The word fraction comes from the Latin 'fractio' which means 'to break'. Fractions in Ancient Egypt always had the top number as 1, such as $\frac{1}{3}$, $\frac{1}{4}$ and $\frac{1}{5}$, but it was very difficult to do calculations with them. In ancient Rome, fractions were written using words, not numbers, so calculations were also very difficult then. In India by about 500 AD fractions were being written with one number above the other but without a line. Around the year 1200 AD, the Ancient Arabs added the line to make fractions as we know them today.

LEARNING OBJECTIVES

- Add and subtract fractions and mixed numbers ■ Multiply and divide fractions and mixed numbers

- Solve problems involving fractions

BASIC PRINCIPLES

- **Sign** of answer when multiplying or dividing:

$$+ \times + = + \qquad + \times - = - \qquad - \times + = - \qquad - \times - = +$$
$$+ \div + = + \qquad + \div - = - \qquad - \div + = - \qquad - \div - = +$$

- Finding **common factors**: Common factors of 12 and 8 are 2 and 4.

- Finding lowest **common denominator** when adding and subtracting fractions: Lowest common denominator of 6 and 4 is 12.

- The value of a fraction is not changed if the top and bottom are multiplied or divided by the same number:

$$\frac{1}{2} = \frac{3 \times 1}{3 \times 2} = \frac{3}{6} \qquad \frac{4}{10} = \frac{2 \times 2}{2 \times 5} = \frac{2}{5}$$

- Converting **mixed numbers** to fractions: $1\frac{2}{3} = \frac{5}{3}$

WORKING WITH FRACTIONS

Fraction calculations can be done on a calculator. In Unit 2, calculations are done with fractions like $\frac{x}{4}$. Since these cannot be done on a calculator, it is important that you can do fraction calculations without a calculator.

SIMPLIFYING FRACTIONS

A fraction has been simplified when the **numerator** (the top number) and the denominator (the bottom number) are expressed as whole numbers with no common factors.

EXAMPLE 1

SKILLS

ANALYSIS

Simplify

a $\dfrac{28}{42}$

b $\dfrac{0.8}{1.6}$

a $\dfrac{28}{42} = \dfrac{2 \times 14}{2 \times 21} = \dfrac{2 \times 7}{3 \times 7} = \dfrac{2}{3}$

b $\dfrac{0.8}{1.6} = \dfrac{0.8 \times 10}{1.6 \times 10} = \dfrac{8}{16} = \dfrac{8 \times 1}{8 \times 2} = \dfrac{1}{2}$

Example 2 shows how to write decimals as fractions.

EXAMPLE 2

SKILLS

ANALYSIS

Change   a   0.4   b   0.025   to fractions.

a $0.4 = \dfrac{4}{10} = \dfrac{2}{5}$

b $0.025 = \dfrac{25}{1000} = \dfrac{5 \times 5}{5 \times 5 \times 40} = \dfrac{1}{40}$

To write a fraction as a decimal, divide the top number by the bottom number.

EXAMPLE 3

SKILLS

ANALYSIS

Change   a $\dfrac{2}{5}$ b $\dfrac{5}{8}$ to decimals

a $2 \div 5 = 0.4$ (using a calculator or **long division**)

b $5 \div 8 = 0.625$ (using a calculator or long division)

KEY POINTS

• Always simplify fractions.

• When working with mixed numbers, convert to **improper fractions** first.

EXERCISE 1

Simplify these.

1 ▶ $\dfrac{8}{12}$ 3 ▶ $\dfrac{15}{45}$ 5 ▶ $\dfrac{0.6}{1.2}$

2 ▶ $\dfrac{16}{24}$ 4 ▶ $\dfrac{56}{84}$ 6 ▶ $\dfrac{0.9}{2.7}$

Copy and complete this table, giving fractions in their lowest terms.

	FRACTION	DECIMAL
7 ▶	$\dfrac{4}{5}$	
8 ▶	$\dfrac{3}{8}$	
9 ▶		0.75
10 ▶		0.2

Change each of these to a mixed number.

11 ▶ $\dfrac{8}{3}$ 12 ▶ $\dfrac{13}{4}$ 13 ▶ $\dfrac{17}{5}$ 14 ▶ $\dfrac{19}{7}$

Change each of these to an improper fraction.

15 ▶ $2\frac{1}{3}$ **16** ▶ $3\frac{3}{5}$ **17** ▶ $1\frac{5}{6}$ **18** ▶ $5\frac{6}{7}$

19 ▶   Write 18 minutes as a fraction of an hour in its simplest form.

20 ▶   Craig buys a ring for $500. He sells it for $750. Write the selling price as a fraction of the cost price in its simplest form.

EXERCISE 1*

Simplify and write each of these as a single fraction.

1 ▶ $\frac{6}{21}$ **3** ▶ $\frac{15}{90}$ **5** ▶ $\frac{0.7}{1.4}$

2 ▶ $\frac{14}{21}$ **4** ▶ $\frac{105}{165}$ **6** ▶ $\frac{1.2}{3.2}$

Copy and complete this table, giving fractions in their lowest terms.

	FRACTION	DECIMAL
7 ▶	$\frac{5}{16}$	
8 ▶	$\frac{3}{40}$	
9 ▶		0.35
10 ▶		0.375

Change each of these to a mixed number.

11 ▶ $\frac{13}{3}$ **12** ▶ $\frac{11}{5}$ **13** ▶ $\frac{23}{7}$ **14** ▶ $\frac{19}{4}$

Change each of these to an improper fraction.

15 ▶ $4\frac{2}{3}$ **16** ▶ $6\frac{3}{7}$ **17** ▶ $8\frac{2}{5}$ **18** ▶ $20\frac{8}{9}$

19 ▶   Elliot scores 65 out of 80 in a Maths test. Write this as a fraction in its simplest form.

20 ▶   Rendell cycles 42 km at an average speed of 18 km/hr. Find the time taken, giving your answer as a fraction of an hour in its simplest form.

MULTIPLYING FRACTIONS

If you do not know why one-half of one-third is the same as
one-half multiplied by one-third, read the next example.

EXAMPLE 4

SKILLS

PROBLEM
SOLVING

Ella has a bar of chocolate. Her mother says she can eat one-half of one-third of the bar.
How much does Ella eat?

When Ella unwraps the bar, she finds it has six squares.

One-third of the bar is two squares.

Half of this is one square.

So one-half of one-third of the bar is one square or one-sixth.

This is the same as one-half multiplied by one-third. $\frac{1}{2} \times \frac{1}{3} = \frac{1}{6}$

ACTIVITY 1

SKILLS

PROBLEM
SOLVING

If Ella is eats one-half of two-thirds of the bar, how many squares does she eat?

Is this the same as $\frac{1}{2} \times \frac{2}{3}$?

Note that $\frac{1}{2} \times \frac{2}{3}$ can be calculated in two ways:

a Multiply top and bottom then **cancel down**: $\frac{1}{2} \times \frac{2}{3} = \frac{2}{6} = \frac{1}{3}$

b Cancel the 2s, then multiply: $\frac{1}{\cancel{2}} \times \frac{\cancel{2}}{3} = \frac{1}{3}$

You can do the calculation in both ways, however the second method is usually more efficient.

Write mixed numbers as improper fractions before doing a calculation. If possible, divide by
common factors before multiplying. Treat whole numbers as fractions, e.g. $5 = \frac{5}{1}$

EXAMPLE 5

Work out   a $1\frac{2}{3} \times \frac{4}{5}$ b $5 \times \frac{3}{10}$

a $1\frac{2}{3} \times \frac{4}{5} = \frac{\cancel{5}}{3} \times \frac{4}{\cancel{5}} = \frac{4}{3} = 1\frac{1}{3}$ b $5 \times \frac{3}{10} = \frac{\cancel{5}}{1} \times \frac{3}{\cancel{10}_2} = \frac{3}{2} = 1\frac{1}{2}$

KEY POINTS

- The word 'of' means 'multiplied by'.
- Convert mixed numbers into improper fractions before multiplying.
- If possible, divide by common factors before multiplying.
- Treat whole numbers as fractions, e.g. $5 = \frac{5}{1}$.

EXERCISE 2

Giving your answers as fractions in their lowest terms, work out

1 ▶ $\frac{5}{18} \times 3$ **3 ▶** $1\frac{3}{4} \times \frac{4}{7}$ **5 ▶** $0.8 \times \frac{5}{16}$ **7 ▶** $\frac{2}{5} \times \frac{3}{7} \times \frac{5}{6}$

2 ▶ $\frac{4}{5} \times \frac{3}{8}$ **4 ▶** $1\frac{1}{3} \times 1\frac{1}{2}$ **6 ▶** $\frac{8}{9} \times 0.75$ **8 ▶** $\frac{3}{7} \times \frac{5}{6} \times 1\frac{5}{9} \times 1\frac{3}{15}$

9 ▶ Three-sevenths of the songs in Riley's music library are rock songs. Of the rock songs, seven-ninths feature a guitar solo. What fraction of the songs in Riley's music library are rock songs featuring a guitar solo?

10 ▶ Imogen was doing her music practice for one-quarter of an hour. For two-thirds of that time she was practising her scales. For what fraction of an hour did she practise her scales?

EXERCISE 2*

Giving your answers as fractions in their lowest terms or as mixed numbers where appropriate, work out

1 ▶ $\frac{4}{5} \times \frac{15}{16}$ **3 ▶** $3\frac{3}{8} \times 1\frac{1}{9}$ **5 ▶** $\frac{3}{4} \times \frac{8}{7} \times \frac{21}{27} \times \frac{1}{4}$ **7 ▶** $\frac{a^2}{b} \times \frac{b}{a}$

2 ▶ $1\frac{1}{4} \times \frac{1}{5}$ **4 ▶** $8\frac{1}{4} \times 4\frac{4}{11}$ **6 ▶** $8\frac{2}{3} \times \frac{7}{13} \times 1\frac{2}{7}$ **8 ▶** $\frac{b}{a^2} \times \frac{b}{a} \times \frac{a^3}{b^2}$

9 ▶ Lucas divides his pizza into three equal pieces for himself and his two friends. His friend Teddy eats $\frac{5}{8}$ of his piece for lunch and a further $\frac{2}{5}$ of what remains for dinner. What fraction of the original pizza did Teddy eat for dinner?

10 ▶ In a factory, two-thirds of the floor area is taken up by the production line. Out of the remaining floor area, three-fifths is taken up by office space. The rest is warehouse space. The warehouse space occupies 2000 m². Work out the floor area of the production line.

DIVIDING FRACTIONS

To divide by a fraction, turn the fraction upside down and multiply. The next two examples explain this rule. The word 'reciprocal' is used for turning a fraction upside down.

Half of Ella's chocolate bar is divided equally into three for three friends.
How much does each friend receive?

Half of Ella's bar is three squares of chocolate.

When divided in three, each friend receives one square or one-sixth of the original bar.

So $\frac{1}{2} \div 3 = \frac{1}{6}$

By writing 3 as $\frac{3}{1}$ you can see that the rule works: $\frac{1}{2} \div \frac{3}{1} = \frac{1}{2} \times \frac{1}{3} = \frac{1}{6}$

$2 \div \frac{1}{3}$ means how many thirds are in two whole units.

Ella has two bars of chocolate.

Both bars are divided into thirds.
How many blocks of chocolate are there?

One-third of a bar consists of two squares.

There are six blocks of one-third of a bar.

So $2 \div \frac{1}{3} = 6$

By writing 2 as $\frac{2}{1}$ you can see that the rule works: $\frac{2}{1} \div \frac{1}{3} = \frac{2}{1} \times \frac{3}{1} = \frac{6}{1} = 6$

Dividing by a fraction is the same as multiplying by the reciprocal of that fraction.

To find the reciprocal of a fraction, swap the numerator and the denominator.

Work out   **a** $1\frac{2}{3} \div \frac{5}{6}$ **b** $9 \div 1\frac{1}{5}$ **c** $2\frac{2}{3} \div 4$

a $1\frac{2}{3} \div \frac{5}{6} = \frac{5}{3} \times \frac{6}{5} = \frac{2}{1} = 2$

b $9 \div 1\frac{1}{5} = \frac{9}{1} \div \frac{6}{5} = \frac{9}{1} \times \frac{5}{6} = \frac{15}{2} = 7\frac{1}{2}$

c $2\frac{2}{3} \div 4 = \frac{8}{3} \div \frac{4}{1} = \frac{8}{3} \times \frac{1}{4} = \frac{2}{3}$

• To divide by a fraction, turn the fraction upside down and multiply.

EXERCISE 3

Giving your answers as fractions in their lowest terms or as mixed numbers where appropriate, work out

1 ▶ $\frac{3}{4} \div \frac{7}{8}$ 3 ▶ $\frac{12}{25} \div 4$ 5 ▶ $6 \div 1\frac{1}{3}$ 7 ▶ $1\frac{1}{3} \div 2\frac{2}{5}$

2 ▶ $\frac{3}{10} \div \frac{4}{5}$ 4 ▶ $9 \div \frac{3}{4}$ 6 ▶ $1\frac{4}{5} \div 6$ 8 ▶ $2\frac{1}{2} \div 2\frac{1}{4}$

9 ▶ Mia cuts up a piece of wood $4\frac{1}{2}$ m long into pieces measuring $\frac{3}{4}$ m long. How many pieces are there?

10 ▶ A bottle contains $2\frac{1}{4}$ litres of water. How many glasses of volume $\frac{3}{16}$ litre can it fill?

EXERCISE 3*

Giving your answers as fractions in their lowest terms or as mixed numbers where appropriate, work out

1 ▶ $\frac{2}{43} \div \frac{20}{21}$ 3 ▶ $16 \div \frac{2}{7}$ 5 ▶ $2\frac{1}{3} \div 2\frac{4}{5}$ 7 ▶ $13\frac{1}{2} \div 2\frac{1}{4}$

2 ▶ $\frac{8}{15} \div \frac{6}{5}$ 4 ▶ $3\frac{1}{9} \div 14$ 6 ▶ $3\frac{3}{7} \div 2\frac{1}{7}$ 8 ▶ $1\frac{3}{7} \div \frac{6}{35}$

9 ▶ A roll of ribbon is $32\frac{1}{2}$ cm long. How many pieces $1\frac{1}{4}$ cm long can be cut from the roll?

10 ▶ Dylan's cow produces $21\frac{1}{3}$ litres of milk per day. The milk is put into bottles with a volume of $2\frac{1}{3}$ litres. How many bottles does Dylan need each week to bottle all the milk?

ADDING AND SUBTRACTING FRACTIONS

This can only be done if the denominators are the same.

EXAMPLE 9

SKILLS

PROBLEM SOLVING

Ella eats one-half of her bar of chocolate and then eats a further third. What fraction of the bar has she eaten?

Half the bar is 3 squares.

One-third of the bar is 2 squares.

One-half plus one-third equals five-sixths or $\frac{1}{2} + \frac{1}{3} = \frac{3}{6} + \frac{2}{6} = \frac{5}{6}$

EXAMPLE 10   Work out $\frac{3}{4}+\frac{1}{6}$

$$\frac{3}{4}+\frac{1}{6}=\frac{9}{12}+\frac{2}{12}=\frac{9+2}{12}=\frac{11}{12}$$

EXAMPLE 11   Work out $\frac{3}{4}-\frac{2}{5}$

$$\frac{3}{4}-\frac{2}{5}=\frac{15}{20}-\frac{8}{20}=\frac{15-8}{20}=\frac{7}{20}$$

EXAMPLE 12   Work out $3\frac{1}{3}-1\frac{3}{4}$

$$3\frac{1}{3}-1\frac{3}{4}=\frac{10}{3}-\frac{7}{4}=\frac{40}{12}-\frac{21}{12}=\frac{40-21}{12}=\frac{19}{12}=1\frac{7}{12}$$

KEY POINTS
- To add or subtract fractions, put them over a common denominator.
- Less work is needed if the common denominator is the lowest one.

EXERCISE 4   Giving your answers as fractions in their lowest terms or as mixed numbers where appropriate, work out

1 ▶ $\frac{2}{7}+\frac{4}{7}$ 5 ▶ $\frac{3}{8}+\frac{7}{12}$ 9 ▶ $2\frac{5}{6}+1\frac{3}{4}$

2 ▶ $\frac{4}{9}-\frac{1}{9}$ 6 ▶ $\frac{5}{6}-\frac{3}{4}$ 10 ▶ $3\frac{7}{8}+4\frac{1}{4}$

3 ▶ $\frac{5}{6}-\frac{1}{3}$ 7 ▶ $3\frac{1}{4}+1\frac{1}{6}$ 11 ▶ $5\frac{3}{10}-2\frac{11}{20}$

4 ▶ $\frac{11}{20}-\frac{3}{10}$ 8 ▶ $4\frac{3}{5}-2\frac{1}{2}$ 12 ▶ $36\frac{3}{8}-32\frac{7}{12}$

13 ▶ Li does one-quarter of her homework before dinner and a further one-third after dinner. What fraction of her homework remains undone?

14 ▶ A chemical consists of four compounds, A, B, C and D. $\frac{1}{6}$ is A, $\frac{2}{5}$ is B, $\frac{1}{10}$ is C and the rest is D. What fraction of the chemical is D?

EXERCISE 4*   Giving your answers as fractions in their lowest terms or as mixed numbers where appropriate, work out

1 ▶ $\frac{1}{3}+\frac{5}{12}$ 5 ▶ $\frac{1}{5}+\frac{3}{10}+\frac{9}{20}$ 9 ▶ $7\frac{2}{3}-1\frac{1}{6}$

2 ▶ $\frac{1}{4}+\frac{9}{20}$ 6 ▶ $\frac{1}{4}+\frac{3}{20}-\frac{1}{40}$ 10 ▶ $4\frac{7}{9}-3\frac{1}{3}$

3 ▶ $\frac{5}{6}-\frac{7}{30}$ 7 ▶ $4\frac{1}{2}+3\frac{1}{6}$ 11 ▶ $7\frac{2}{3}-\frac{8}{9}$

4 ▶ $\frac{11}{15}-\frac{3}{20}$ 8 ▶ $6\frac{2}{5}+7\frac{1}{3}$ 12 ▶ $6\frac{1}{12}-4\frac{7}{10}$

13 ▶ Tonia and Trinny are twins. Their friends give them identical cakes for their birthday. Tonia eats $\frac{1}{8}$ of her cake and Trinny eats $\frac{1}{6}$ of her cake. How much cake is left?

14 ▶ A part has broken on a machine and needs to be replaced. The replacement part must be between $7\frac{1}{18}$ cm and $7\frac{1}{6}$ cm long in order to fit. The diagram shows the replacement part.

Will this part fit the machine? You must explain your answer.

ORDER OF OPERATIONS

The answer to $3 + 4 \times 2$ depends on whether the addition or multiplication is done first.

So that everybody gets the same answer to a calculation, there are rules for the order of operations. (Examples of operations: addition, subtraction, multiplication and division.)

The mnemonic BIDMAS will help you remember the correct order.

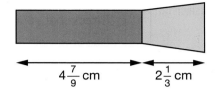

KEY POINT

- First   B   Brackets
- Second   I   Indices
- Third   DM   Division and/or Multiplication, working from left to right
- Fourth   AS   Addition and/or Subtraction, working from left to right

EXAMPLE 13

Evaluate $7 - 3 \div (5 - 2) \times 2^2 + 5$

SKILLS

INTERPRETATION

The part of the expression being worked out at each step is highlighted in yellow.

$7 - 3 \div (5 - 2) \times 2^2 + 5 = 7 - 3 \div 3 \times 2^2 + 5$ Brackets

$7 - 3 \div 3 \times 2^2 + 5 = 7 - 3 \div 3 \times 4 + 5$ Indices

$7 - 3 \div 3 \times 4 + 5 = 7 - 1 \times 4 + 5$ Division and/or Multiplication, working l to r.

$7 - 1 \times 4 + 5 = 7 - 4 + 5$ Division and/or Multiplication, working l to r.

$7 - 4 + 5 = 3 + 5$ Addition and/or Subtraction, working l to r.

$3 + 5 = 8$ Addition and/or Subtraction, working l to r.

ACTIVITY 2

SKILLS

INTERPRETATION

Without using your calculator, work out $2 + 3 \times 4$ and $3 \times 4 + 2$.

Check that your calculator gives the correct answer of 14 to $2 + 3 \times 4$ and to $3 \times 4 + 2$.

Use your calculator to check that $7 - 3 \div (5 - 2) \times 22 + 5 = 8$ (as in Example 13).

The line in a fraction acts like brackets. $\dfrac{1+2}{3}$ means $\dfrac{(1+2)}{3}$

EXAMPLE 14

Work out $\dfrac{16 - 4 \times 3}{6 \div 3 \times 2}$

SKILLS

INTERPRETATION

The part of the expression being worked out at each step is highlighted in yellow.

$\dfrac{16 - 4 \times 3}{6 \div 3 \times 2}$ means $\dfrac{(16 - 4 \times 3)}{(6 \div 3 \times 2)} = \dfrac{(16 - 12)}{(2 \times 2)} = \dfrac{4}{4} = 1$

EXERCISE 5

Work out the following.

1 ▶ $12 + 4 \times 2$ 4 ▶ $12 - 2^2 \times 3$ 7 ▶ $3 + 2 \div (7 - 9) \times (5 \times 2 - 6)$

2 ▶ $(12 + 4) \times 2$ 5 ▶ $(8 - 3 \times 2)^2$ 8 ▶ $\dfrac{4 + 4^2}{6 \div 3 \times 2}$

3 ▶ $11 - 3^2$ 6 ▶ $5 + (5 \times 2)^2 \div 5$

9 ▶   Insert brackets in this expression to make it correct: $4 \times 5 - 3 + 2 = 10$

10 ▶   Insert brackets and symbols into this expression to make it correct: $7 \quad 5 \quad 3 = 6$

EXERCISE 5*

Evaluate the following.

1 ▶ $4 + 6 \times (2^2 + 5) \div 3 - 10$

2 ▶ $2 - 5 \div (8 - 3) \times 2 + 8$

3 ▶ $125 \div (7 \times 4 - 23)^2 \div 5$

4 ▶ $\dfrac{3}{4} \div \dfrac{9}{10} \times \dfrac{4}{5} \div \dfrac{2}{3}$

5 ▶ $1 + 10 \div 5 \times 11 - 3^2 \div 3$

6 ▶ $(3 \times 4 \div 2^2 + 3) \times (6 \div 3 \times 5 - 5 \times 2 + 1) - 5$

7 ▶ $\dfrac{1 + 4 \times 2}{6 - 1 \times 2} \div \dfrac{12 \div 2^2}{8 \div 2 \times 2}$

8 ▶ $\dfrac{\dfrac{2}{3} \times \dfrac{1}{4} + \dfrac{3}{4} \div \dfrac{9}{10}}{1 + 5 \times \dfrac{3}{5} - \dfrac{6}{7} \div \dfrac{3}{7}}$

9 ▶   Insert brackets in this expression to make it correct:
$8 - 2 + 1 \times 5 - 3 = 2$

10 ▶   Insert brackets and symbols in this expression to make it correct:
$8 \quad 6 \quad 2 \quad 4 = 5$

SIGNIFICANT FIGURES AND DECIMAL PLACES

If a piece of wood is to be cut 35.784 mm long then this measurement is too accurate to mark out and cut, so 35.784 would be **rounded** to a suitable **degree of accuracy**. Numbers can be rounded to a certain number of **significant figures** or **decimal places**.

SIGNIFICANT FIGURES (s.f.)

The first s.f. is the first non-zero digit in the number, counting from the left.

EXAMPLE 15

SKILLS

INTERPRETATION

Highlight the first s.f. of the following numbers.

a 27 400   **b** 0.123   **c** 0.000 583

The first s.f. is highlighted in yellow.

a 27 400   **b** 0.123   **c** 0.000 583

For example, when rounding to 2 s.f., look at the third s.f. If this is greater than or equal to 5 then round the second figure up. If rounding to 3 s.f., look at the fourth s.f. and so on.

EXAMPLE 16

SKILLS

INTERPRETATION

Write   **a** 1361   **b** 1350   **c** 1349 **correct to** 2 s.f.

a 3rd s.f. is 6. $6 \geq 5$ so 3 rounds up to 4 $\Rightarrow$ 1361 = 1400 (2 s.f.)
(1361 is closer to 1400 than 1300)

b 3rd s.f. is 5. $5 \geq 5$ so 3 rounds up to 4 $\Rightarrow$ 1350 = 1400 (2 s.f.)
(1350 is midway between 1400 and 1300 but we round up in this case)

c 3rd s.f. is 4. $4 < 5$ so 3 is not rounded up $\Rightarrow$ 1349 = 1300 (2 s.f.)
(1349 is closer to 1300 than 1400)

EXAMPLE 17

SKILLS

INTERPRETATION

Write   **a** 0.001 361   **b** 0.001 35   **c** 0.001 349 correct to 2 s.f.

a 3rd s.f. is 6. $6 \geq 5$ so 3 rounds up to 4 $\Rightarrow$ 0.001 361 = 0.0014 (2 s.f.)
(0.001 361 is closer to 0.0014 than 0.0013)

b 3rd s.f. is 5. $5 \geq 5$ so 3 rounds up to 4 $\Rightarrow$ 0.001 35 = 0.0014 (2 s.f.)
(0.001 35 is midway between 0.0014 and 0.0013 but we round up in this case)

c 3rd s.f. is 4. $4 < 5$ so 3 is not rounded up $\Rightarrow$ 0.001 349 = 0.0013 (2 s.f.)
(0.001 349 is closer to 0.0013 than 0.0014)

DECIMAL PLACES (d.p.)

Count after the decimal point (going from left to right).
Rounding up or down follows the same rules as for s.f.

EXAMPLE 18

SKILLS

INTERPRETATION

Write   **a** 7.1361   **b** 0.135   **c** 0.0349 correct to 2 d.p.

a 3rd d.p. is 6. 6 ≥ 5 so 3 rounds up to 4 ⇒ 7.1361 = 7.14 (2 d.p.)
(7.1361 is closer to 7.14 than 7.13)

b 3rd d.p. is 5. 5 ≥ 5 so 3 rounds up to 4 ⇒ 0.135 = 0.14 (2 d.p.)
(0.135 is midway between 0.14 and 0.13 but we round up in this case)

c 3rd d.p. is 4. 4 < 5 so 3 is not rounded up ⇒ 0.0349 = 0.03 (2 d.p.)
(0.0349 is closer to 0.03 than 0.04)

This table shows $\pi = 3.141\,592\,654\ldots$ rounded to various degrees of accuracy.

DEGREE OF ACCURACY	SIGNIFICANT FIGURES	DECIMAL PLACES
5	3.1416	3.141 59
3	3.14	3.142
1	3	3.1

ACTIVITY 3

SKILLS

INTERPRETATION

Use your calculator instruction book to find out how to:

• convert fractions to decimals and decimal to fractions

• round to a certain number of significant figures or decimal places.

Check by using the examples in this chapter.

KEY POINTS

• The first significant figure is the first non-zero digit in the number, counting from the left.

• For decimal places, count after the decimal point (going from left to right).

• If the next number is greater than or equal to 5, then round up.

EXERCISE 6

Write correct to 1 significant figure.

1 ▶   783

2 ▶   87 602

Write correct to 3 significant figures.

3 ▶   3738

4 ▶   80 290

Write correct to 2 significant figures.

5 ▶   0.439

6 ▶   0.555

Write correct to 3 significant figures.

7 ▶   0.5057

8 ▶   0.1045

Write correct to 2 decimal places.

9 ▶   34.777

10 ▶   0.654

Write correct to 1 decimal place.

11 ▶   3.009

12 ▶   9.09

13 ▶ The speed of light is 299 792 458 m/s.
Write this speed correct to   **a** 3 s.f.   **b** 6 s.f.

14 ▶ The **diameter** of a human hair is given as 0.0185 mm.
Write this diameter correct to   **a** 2 d.p.   **b** 2 s.f.

15 ▶ Pablo Picasso's 'Women of Algiers' sold at auction in New York for $179 365 000.
Write this price correct to 4 s.f.

16 ▶ The distance round the equator is 40 075 km. Write this distance correct to 1 s.f.

EXERCISE 6*

Write correct to 1 significant figure.

1 ▶   10.49

2 ▶   5049

Write correct to 3 significant figures.

3 ▶   45.703

4 ▶   89 508

Write correct to 2 significant figures.

5 ▶   0.0688

6 ▶   0.006 78

Write correct to 3 significant figures.

7 ▶   0.049 549

8 ▶   0.000 567 9

Write correct to 2 decimal places.

9 ▶   8.997

10 ▶   2.0765

Write correct to 1 decimal place.

11 ▶   6.96

12 ▶   78.1818

13 ▶ Write 0.000 497 5 correct to   **a** 3 d.p.   **b** 3 s.f.

14 ▶ Write $\sqrt{2}$ correct to   **a** 6 d.p.   **b** 6 s.f.

15 ▶ Only 10 bottles of a very exclusive and expensive perfume are made.
They are sold for the price of $12 721.89 per ounce.
Write this price correct to   **a** 1 s.f   **b** 1 d.p.

16 ▶ The Bohr radius is a physical constant of value 0.000 000 052 917 721 092 mm. Write the Bohr radius correct to   **a** 7 d.p.   **b** 7 s.f.

EXERCISE 7

REVISION

Give all answers, where appropriate, as fractions in their lowest terms.

1 ▶ Simplify   **a** $\dfrac{12}{18}$ **b** $\dfrac{1.2}{18}$

2 ▶ Calculate   **a** $2\dfrac{1}{6} \times \dfrac{3}{26}$ **b** $3\dfrac{1}{5} \div 1\dfrac{3}{5}$

3 ▶ Calculate   **a** $2\dfrac{2}{5} + \dfrac{1}{4}$ **b** $2\dfrac{3}{4} - 1\dfrac{9}{10} + 1\dfrac{1}{5}$

4 ▶ Calculate   **a** $10 - 3 \times 2$ **b** $6 - 3 \div 3 \times 4$ **c** $8 \div (3 - 1)^2 \times 2$

5 ▶ Insert brackets in this expression to make it correct: $12 \div 4 + 2 + 3 = 5$

6 ▶ Insert brackets and symbols in this expression to make it correct: $3 \quad 5 \quad 2 = 4$

7 ▶   Write 12.000 497 5 correct to   **a** 5 d.p.   **b** 5 s.f

8 ▶   The age of the Earth is 4.543 billion years. Write 4.543 correct to   **a** 1 d.p.   **b** 1 s.f.

9 ▶   Geela has 20 litres of yoghurt that she wants to put into pots containing $1\frac{1}{4}$ litres each. How many pots can she fill?

10 ▶   Gill wears a device that counts the number of steps she takes every day. One day she did one-fifteenth of her steps before breakfast, a further half walking into town and another one-tenth walking round the supermarket.

    a What fraction of her steps were not taken yet?

    b That day the device recorded 12 000 steps. How many steps were not taken yet?

EXERCISE 7*

REVISION

Give all answers, where appropriate, as fractions in their lowest terms.

1 ▶   Simplify   **a** $\frac{21}{63}$ **b** $\frac{0.21}{63}$

2 ▶   Calculate   **a** $\frac{14}{15} \div 1\frac{2}{5}$ **b** $5\frac{1}{3} \div 4\frac{12}{13}$

3 ▶   Calculate   **a** $2\frac{3}{4} - 1\frac{1}{5}$ **b** $1\frac{1}{8} - 1\frac{11}{12} + 1\frac{5}{6}$

4 ▶   Calculate   **a** $25 \div (1 + 2^2)^2 \times 2$

                b $5 + 12 \div 6 \times 2 - 18 \div 3^2$ **c** $\frac{2 + 2 \times 2}{16 - 3 \times 4} \div \frac{27 \div 3^2}{8 \div 2 \times 2}$

5 ▶   Insert brackets in this expression to make it correct: $2 \times 3 + 3 \div 3 = 3$

6 ▶   Insert brackets and symbols in this expression to make it correct: 7   2   2   3 = 6

7 ▶   Write 8.999 49 correct to   **a** 3 d.p.   **b** 3 s.f.

8 ▶   An important number in mathematics is Euler's number, $e = 2.718\,281\,828\,459\,0...$ Write Euler's number correct to   **a** 8 s.f   **b** 8 d.p.

9 ▶   Holly drinks $2\frac{4}{5}$ litres of water each day. The water comes in $1\frac{2}{5}$ litre bottles. How many bottles does Holly drink in a week?

10 ▶   Jake's computer has two hard drives that can store the same amount of data. One drive is $\frac{3}{8}$ full while the other is $\frac{2}{5}$ full.

    a What fraction of the total amount of storage space is empty?

    b Each hard drive can store 750 gigabytes of data. Jake wants to download 150 gigabytes of data. Does he have enough space? Explain your answer.

EXAM PRACTICE: NUMBER 1

Give all answers where appropriate as fractions or mixed numbers in their lowest terms.

1 ▶ Simplify   **a** $\frac{14}{42}$ **b** $\frac{140}{42}$ **c** $\frac{1.4}{42}$ **[3]**

2 ▶ Calculate   **a** $\frac{5}{12} \times 1\frac{1}{15}$ **b** $5\frac{1}{4} \div \frac{7}{8}$ **[4]**

3 ▶ Calculate $\frac{4}{9} + 1\frac{3}{4} - 1\frac{1}{12}$ **[3]**

4 ▶ Calculate   **a** $3 + 2 \times (1 + 4)^2$

               b $\frac{1}{2} + \frac{1}{2} \div \frac{5}{6}$ **[4]**

5 ▶ A recent survey has found that the Great Wall of China is more than twice as long as was previously thought. Its length is now given as 21 196.18 km.

Write this length
a correct to 1 d.p.   **b** correct to 1 s.f.   **[2]**

6 ▶ The planning rules for a housing development state that $\frac{1}{3}$ of the houses should have three bedrooms, $\frac{3}{8}$ should have four bedrooms, $\frac{1}{24}$ should be executive homes and the rest should have two bedrooms.

    a What fraction of the houses have two bedrooms?

    b If 24 houses have two bedrooms, how many houses are on the development?   **[5]**

7 ▶ Olivia's fish tank contains $42\frac{2}{3}$ litres of water. She is emptying it out using a scoop which holds $1\frac{1}{3}$ litres of water. How many full scoops will it take to empty the tank?   **[4]**

[Total 25 marks]

CHAPTER SUMMARY: NUMBER 1

WORKING WITH FRACTIONS

Always simplify fractions to their lowest terms: $\frac{4}{6} = \frac{2 \times 2}{2 \times 3} = \frac{2}{3}$.

The word 'of' means the same as 'multiplied by': $\frac{1}{2}$ of $\frac{1}{3} = \frac{1}{2} \times \frac{1}{3} = \frac{1}{6}$

Convert mixed numbers into improper fractions: $2\frac{1}{4} = \frac{9}{4}$

Treat whole numbers as fractions, e.g. $5 = \frac{5}{1}$

To divide by a fraction, turn the fraction upside down and multiply: $\frac{1}{3} \div \frac{1}{2} = \frac{1}{3} \times \frac{2}{1} = \frac{2}{3}$

To add or subtract fractions, put them over a common denominator: $\frac{1}{4} - \frac{1}{6} = \frac{3-2}{12} = \frac{1}{12}$

ORDER OF OPERATIONS (BIDMAS)

- First   B   Brackets
- Second   I   Indices
- Third   DM   Division and/or Multiplication, working from left to right
- Fourth   AS   Addition and/or Subtraction, working from left to right

The part of the expression being worked out at each step is highlighted in yellow.

$5 + (2 + 1)^2 \times 4 = 5 + 32 \times 4$	Brackets
$5 + 3^2 \times 4 = 5 + 9 \times 4$	Indices
$5 + 9 \times 4 = 5 + 36$	Division and/or Multiplication
$5 + 36 = 41$	Addition and/or Subtraction

Note that calculators use the correct order of operations.

SIGNIFICANT FIGURES AND DECIMAL PLACES

The first significant figure is the first non-zero digit in the number, counting from the left.

The first s.f. is highlighted in yellow.

a 3400   b 0.367   c 0.008 45

For decimal places, count after the decimal point (going from left to right).

The third d.p. is highlighted in yellow.

a 12.3456   b 0.000 73

For example, when rounding to 2 s.f., look at the third s.f. If this is greater than or equal to 5 then round the second figure up. If rounding to 3 s.f., look at the fourth s.f. and so on.

2499 = 2000 (1 s.f.),   2499 = 2500 (2 s.f.),   0.2499 = 0.2 (1 d.p.),   0.2499 = 0.25 (2 d.p.)

ALGEBRA 1

Algebra may have begun in Egypt. The ancient Egyptians used the word 'aha', meaning 'heap', to stand for an unknown number. In the same way, we use a letter, such as x, today. The Ahmes Papyrus from Ancient Egypt around 1650BC contains problems that need a form of algebra to solve. They are believed to have been set as exercises for young mathematicians. These mathematical skills were probably essential for building the pyramids.

LEARNING OBJECTIVES

■ Simplify algebraic expressions   ■ Expand brackets   ■ Solve equations in which the unknown appears on both sides

BASIC PRINCIPLES

■ Algebra uses letters, often x, to stand for numbers.

■ Algebraic expressions can be treated in the same way as number expressions.

■ $x + 3$ means add three to the unknown number.

■ $3x$ means 3 times the unknown number.

■ x^2 means square the unknown number.

ACTIVITY 1

SKILL: PROBLEM SOLVING

Think of a number. Add 7 and then double the answer. Subtract 10, halve the result, and then subtract the original number.

Algebra can show you why the answer is always 2.

Think of a number:	x
Add 7:	$x + 7$
Double the result:	$2x + 14$
Subtract 10:	$2x + 4$
Halve the result:	$x + 2$
Subtract the original number:	2

Make two magic number tricks of your own, one like the example above and another that is longer. Check that they work using algebra. Then test them on a friend.

• Think of a number. Double it, add 12, halve the result, and then subtract the original number. Use algebra to find the answer.
  If you add a number other than 12, the answer will change. Work out the connection between the number you add and the answer.

SIMPLIFYING ALGEBRAIC EXPRESSIONS

ACTIVITY 2

SKILLS
REASONING

Investigate the result when you substitute various values (positive or negative) for x in both of these expressions:

$$x + 1 \quad \text{and} \quad \frac{x^2 + 6x + 5}{x + 5}$$

What is your conclusion? Which expression would you rather use?

EXAMPLE 1

Simplify $a + 3ab - 4ba$

$a + 3ab - 4ba = a - ab$

Note: $ab = ba$ so $3ab$ and $-4ba$ are **like terms** and can be simplified.

EXAMPLE 2

Simplify $3p^3 + 2p^2 - 2p^3 + 5p^2$

$3p^3 + 2p^2 - 2p^3 + 5p^2 = 3p^3 - 2p^3 + 5p^2 + 2p^2 = p^3 + 7p^2$

KEY POINTS

- You can only add or subtract like terms.
- $3ab + 2ab = 5ab$ but the terms in $3ab + b$ cannot be added together.
- $3a^2 + 2a^2 = 5a^2$ but the terms in $3a^2 + 2a$ cannot be added together.
- You can check your simplifications by substituting numbers.

EXERCISE 1

Simplify these as much as possible.

1 ▶ $9ab - 5ab$
2 ▶ $5xy + 2yx$
3 ▶ $4pq - 7qp$
4 ▶ $2xy + y - 3xy$
5 ▶ $x - 3x + 2 - 4x$
6 ▶ $7cd - 8dc + 3cd$

7 ▶ $6xy - 12xy + 2xy$
8 ▶ $4ab + 10bc - 2ab - 5cb$
9 ▶ $3ba - ab + 3ab - 5ab$
10 ▶ $4gh - 5jk - 2gh + 7$
11 ▶ $2p^2 - 5p^2 + 2p - 4p$
12 ▶ $2x^2y - xy^2 + 3yx^2 - 2y^2x$

EXERCISE 1*

Simplify these as much as possible.

1 ▶ $7xy + 5xy - 13xy$
2 ▶ $7ab - b - 3ab$
3 ▶ $2ab - 3ba + 7ab$
4 ▶ $12ab - 6ba + ba - 7ab$
5 ▶ $4ab + 10bc - ba - 7cb$
6 ▶ $q^2 + q^3 + 2q^2 - q^3$

7 ▶ $x^2 - 5x + 4 - x^2 + 6x - 3$
8 ▶ $5a^2 + a^3 - 3a^2 + a$
9 ▶ $h^3 + 5h - 3 - 4h^2 - 2h + 7 + 5h^2$
10 ▶ $3a^2b - 2ab + 4ba^2 - ba$
11 ▶ $0.7a^2b^3c - 0.4b^2a^3c + 0.3cb^3a^2 - 0.2a^3cb^2 + 0.3$
12 ▶ $2pq^2r^5 - pq^2r^4 - (r^4pq^2 - 2q^2r^5p)$

SIMPLIFYING ALGEBRAIC EXPRESSIONS WITH BRACKETS

EXAMPLE 3

Simplify $4r \times 5t$

$4r \times 5t = 20rt$

EXAMPLE 4

Simplify $(3b)^2 \times 3b$

$(3b)^2 \times 3b = 3b \times 3b \times 3b = 27b^3$

KEY POINTS

- The multiplication sign is often not included between letters, e.g. $3ab$ means $3 \times a \times b$.
- When multiplying, add like **powers** $3a^2b \times 2a^5b^4 \times a = 6a^8b^5$ (think of a as a^1).

EXERCISE 2

Simplify these.

1 ▶ $3 \times 2a$ 4 ▶ $5a^3 \times 3a^2$ 7 ▶ $2a^2 \times b^2$ 10 ▶ $(2a)^2 \times 5a$

2 ▶ $2x \times x$ 5 ▶ $2t \times 3s$ 8 ▶ $2y \times 2y \times y$

3 ▶ $3x \times x^2$ 6 ▶ $4r \times s^2$ 9 ▶ $2x^2 \times 3 \times 2x$

EXERCISE 2*

Simplify these.

1 ▶ $8a \times a^2$ 6 ▶ $5abc \times 2ab^2c^3 \times 3ac$

2 ▶ $5x^3 \times 3y^2 \times x$ 7 ▶ $7x \times 2y^2 \times (2y)^2$

3 ▶ $a^2 \times 2a^4 \times 3a$ 8 ▶ $2xy^2 \times 3x^2y + 4x^3y^3$

4 ▶ $(3y)^2 \times 2y$ 9 ▶ $x^2y^3 \times 3xy - 2x^3y^2$

5 ▶ $6xy^2 \times 2x^3 \times 3xy$ 10 ▶ $(2ab)^2 \times 5a^2b^4 - 2a^2b^5 \times 3a^2b$

EXPANDING BRACKETS

To simplify an expression with brackets, first multiply each term inside the bracket by the term outside the bracket, then simplify. This is called **expanding** the brackets.

EXAMPLE 5

Simplify $2(3 + x)$.

$2(3 + x) = 2 \times 3 + 2 \times x = 6 + 2x$

The diagram helps to show that $2(3 + x) = 6 + 2x$.

The area of the whole rectangle is $2(3 + x)$.

The area of rectangle A is 6.

The area of rectangle B is $2x$.

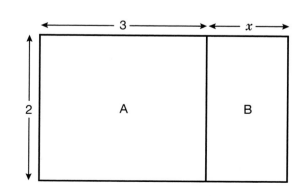

- Multiply each term inside the bracket by the term outside the bracket.

- The multiplication sign is usually left out:
  $3(x + y)$ means $3 \times (x + y) = 3 \times x + 3 \times y = 3x + 3y$

- Be very careful with negative signs outside a bracket:
  $-2(a - 3)$ means $-2 \times (a - 3) = (-2) \times (a) + (-2) \times (-3) = -2a + 6$

- When multiplying, the number 1 is usually left out:
  $-(2x + 3)$ means $-1 \times (2x + 3) = (-1) \times (2x) + (-1) \times (3) = -2x - 3$

EXERCISE 3

Remove the brackets and simplify these if possible.

1 ▶ $5(2 + 3a)$ 6 ▶ $3a + 2(a + 2b)$

2 ▶ $2(b - 4c)$ 7 ▶ $3(t - 4) - 6$

3 ▶ $-3(2a + 8)$ 8 ▶ $7x - (x - y)$

4 ▶ $-4(3 - x)$ 9 ▶ $0.4(x - 3y) + 0.5(2x + 3y)$

5 ▶ $-(a - 2b)$ 10 ▶ $1.1(a + 3) - 5(3 - 0.2a)$

EXERCISE 3*

Remove the brackets and simplify these if possible.

1 ▶ $4(3m - 2)$ 6 ▶ $0.4(2 - x) - (x + 3)$

2 ▶ $2(x - y + z)$ 7 ▶ $\frac{3}{4}(4x - 8y) - \frac{3}{5}(15x - 5y)$

3 ▶ $5(3a + b - 4c)$ 8 ▶ $5x - 7y - 0.4(x - 2y + z)$

4 ▶ $\frac{1}{2}(4x - 6y + 8)$ 9 ▶ $0.3(2a - 6b + 1) - 0.4(3a + 6b - 1)$

5 ▶ $5x - 3(2x - y)$ 10 ▶ $0.3x(0.2x - y) - 4y(x + 0.3y) + 0.5x(y - x)$

SOLVING EQUATIONS

If is often easier to solve mathematical problems using algebra. Let the unknown quantity be x and then write down the facts in the form of an equation. There are six basic types of equation:

$x + 3 = 12$ $x - 3 = 12$ $3 - x = 12$

$3x = 12$ $\dfrac{x}{3} = 12$ $\dfrac{3}{x} = 12$

Solving an equation means having only x on one side of the equation.

EXAMPLE 6

Solve $x + 3 = 12$ for x.

$x + 3 = 12$ (Subtract 3 from both sides)

$\quad x = 9$ (Check: $9 + 3 = 12$)

EXAMPLE 7

Solve $x - 3 = 12$ for x.

$x - 3 = 12$ (Add 3 to both sides)

$\quad x = 15$ (Check: $15 - 3 = 12$)

EXAMPLE 8

Solve $3 - x = 12$ for x.

$3 - x = 12$	(Add x to both sides)
$3 = 12 + x$	(Subtract 12 from both sides)
$-12 + 3 = x$	
$x = -9$	(Check: $3 - (-9) = 12$)

EXAMPLE 9

Solve $3x = 12$ for x.

$3x = 12$	(Divide both sides by 3)
$x = 4$	(Check: $3 \times 4 = 12$)

EXAMPLE 10

Solve $\dfrac{x}{3} = 12$ for x.

$\dfrac{x}{3} = 12$	(Multiply both sides by 3)
$x = 36$	(Check: $36 \div 3 = 12$)

EXAMPLE 11

Solve $\dfrac{3}{x} = 12$ for x.

$\dfrac{3}{x} = 12$	(Multiply both sides by x)
$3 = 12x$	(Divide both sides by 12)
$\dfrac{1}{4} = x$	(Check: $3 \div \dfrac{1}{4} = 12$)

KEY POINTS

- To solve equations, do the same thing to both sides.
- Always check your answer.

EXERCISE 4

Solve these for x.

1 ▶ $5x = 20$ 5 ▶ $3 = \dfrac{36}{x}$ 9 ▶ $3.8 = \dfrac{x}{7}$

2 ▶ $x + 5 = 20$ 6 ▶ $20 - x = 5$ 10 ▶ $x + 9.7 = 11.1$

3 ▶ $x - 5 = 20$ 7 ▶ $5x = 12$ 11 ▶ $13.085 - x = 12.1$

4 ▶ $\dfrac{x}{5} = 20$ 8 ▶ $x - 3.8 = 9.7$ 12 ▶ $\dfrac{34}{x} = 5$

EXERCISE 4*

Solve these for x.

1 ▶ $23.5 + x = 123.4$ 3 ▶ $39.6 = x - 1.064$ 5 ▶ $7.89 = \dfrac{67}{x}$

2 ▶ $7.6x = 39$ 4 ▶ $45.7 = \dfrac{x}{12.7}$ 6 ▶ $40.9 - x = 2.06$

EXAMPLE 12

Solve $3x - 5 = 7$ for x.

$3x - 5 = 7$	(Add 5 to both sides)
$3x = 12$	(Divide both sides by 3)
$x = 4$	(Check: $3 \times 4 - 5 = 7$)

EXAMPLE 13 ▶ Solve $4(x + 3) = 20$ for x.

$4(x + 3) = 20$	(Divide both sides by 4)
$x + 3 = 5$	(Subtract 3 from both sides)
$x = 2$	(Check: $4(2 + 3) = 20$)

EXAMPLE 14 ▶ Solve $2(x + 3) = 9$ for x.

$2(x + 3) = 9$	(**Multiply out** the bracket)
$2x + 6 = 9$	(Subtract 6 from both sides)
$2x = 3$	(Divide both sides by 2)
$x = \frac{3}{2}$	(Check: $2\left(\frac{3}{2} + 3\right) = 9$)

EXERCISE 5 ▶ Solve these for x.

1 ▶ $2x + 4 = 10$

2 ▶ $4x + 5 = 1$

3 ▶ $12x - 8 = -32$

4 ▶ $15x - 11 = -41$

5 ▶ $2(x + 3) = 10$

6 ▶ $5(x - 2) = 30$

7 ▶ $5 - x = 4$

8 ▶ $9 = 3 - x$

9 ▶ $12 = 2 - x$

10 ▶ $2(6 - 3x) = 6$

11 ▶ $3(6 - 2x) = 12$

12 ▶ $4(2 - x) = 16$

13 ▶ $6(3 - x) = 24$

14 ▶ $3(x - 5) = -13$

EXERCISE 5* ▶ Solve these for x.

1 ▶ $5x - 3 = 17$

2 ▶ $27 = 3(x - 2)$

3 ▶ $7(x - 3) = -35$

4 ▶ $12(x + 5) = 0$

5 ▶ $9(x + 4) = 0$

6 ▶ $-7 = 9 + 4x$

7 ▶ $5 - 4x = -15$

8 ▶ $8 - 7x = -6$

9 ▶ $34 = 17(2 - x)$

10 ▶ $39 = 13(4 - x)$

11 ▶ $9(x + 4) = 41$

12 ▶ $5(10 - 3x) = 30$

13 ▶ $7(2 - 5x) = 49$

14 ▶ $6(4 - 7x) = 36$

EQUATIONS WITH x ON BOTH SIDES

EXAMPLE 15

Solve $7x - 3 = 3x + 5$ for x.

$7x - 3 = 3x + 5$	(Subtract $3x$ from both sides)
$7x - 3x - 3 = 5$	(Add 3 to both sides)
$4x = 5 + 3$	(Simplify)
$4x = 8$	(Divide both sides by 4)
$x = 2$	(Check: $7 \times 2 - 3 = 3 \times 2 + 5 = 11$)

EXAMPLE 16

Solve $5x + 6 = 3(10 - x)$ for x.

$5x + 6 = 3(10 - x)$	(Multiply out the bracket)
$5x + 6 = 30 - 3x$	(Add $3x$ and subtract 6 from both sides)
$5x + 3x = 30 - 6$	(Simplify)
$8x = 24$	(Divide both sides by 8)
$x = 3$	(Check: $5 \times 3 + 6 = 3(10 - 3) = 21$)

EXERCISE 6

Solve these for x.

1 ▶ $8x - 3 = 4x + 1$ 5 ▶ $7x - 5 = 9x - 13$ 9 ▶ $6 + 2x = 6 - 3x$

2 ▶ $5x - 6 = 3x + 2$ 6 ▶ $2x + 7 = 5x + 16$ 10 ▶ $8x + 9 = 6x + 8$

3 ▶ $2x + 5 = 5x - 1$ 7 ▶ $5x + 1 = 8 - 2x$

4 ▶ $4x + 3 = 6x - 7$ 8 ▶ $14 - 3x = 10 - 7x$

EXERCISE 6*

Solve these for x.

1 ▶ $3x + 8 = 7x - 8$ 6 ▶ $5(x + 1) = 4(x + 2)$

2 ▶ $7x + 5 = 5x + 1$ 7 ▶ $8(x + 5) = 10(x + 3)$

3 ▶ $5x + 7 = 9x + 1$ 8 ▶ $3(x - 5) = 7(x + 4) - 7$

4 ▶ $4x + 3 = 7 - x$ 9 ▶ $3.1(4.8x - 1) - 3.9 = x + 1$

5 ▶ $15x - 4 = 10 - 3x$ 10 ▶ $8.9(x - 3.5) + 4.2(3x + 2.3) = 4.7x$

NEGATIVE SIGNS OUTSIDE BRACKETS

EXAMPLE 17

Solve $2(3x + 1) - (2x - 5) = 15$ for x.

$2(3x + 1) - (2x - 5) = 15$	(Remove brackets)
$6x + 2 - 2x + 5 = 15$	(Simplify)
$4x + 7 = 15$	(Subtract 7 from both sides)
$4x = 8$	(Divide both sides by 4)
$x = 2$	(Check: $2(3 \times 2 + 1) - (2 \times 2 - 5) = 15$)

KEY POINT

- $-(2x-5)$ means $-1 \times (2x-5) = (-1) \times (2x) + (-1) \times (-5) = -2x + 5$

EXERCISE 7

Solve these for x.

1 ▶ $3(x-2) - 2(x+1) = 5$ 6 ▶ $3(3x+2) - 4(3x-3) = 0$

2 ▶ $4(x-1) - 3(x+2) = 26$ 7 ▶ $4(3x-1) - (x-2) = 42$

3 ▶ $3(2x+1) - 2(2x-1) = 11$ 8 ▶ $2(2x-1) - (x+5) = 5$

4 ▶ $9(x-2) - 3(2x-3) = 12$ 9 ▶ $4(3-5x) - 7(5-4x) + 3 = 0$

5 ▶ $2(5x-7) - 6(2x-3) = 0$ 10 ▶ $5(3x-2) - 9(2+4x) - 7 = 0$

EXERCISE 7*

Solve these for x.

1 ▶ $5(x-3) - 4(x+1) = -11$ 6 ▶ $5(6x+2) - 7(3x-5) - 72 = 0$

2 ▶ $9(x-2) - 7(x+1) = -15$ 7 ▶ $-2(x+3) - 6(2x-4) + 108 = 0$

3 ▶ $4(3x+5) - 5(2x+6) = 0$ 8 ▶ $-3(x-2) - 5(3x-2) + 74 = 0$

4 ▶ $3(5x-4) - 3(2x-1) = 0$ 9 ▶ $7(5x-3) - 10 = 2(3x-5) - 3(5-7x)$

5 ▶ $3(3x+1) - 8(2x-3) + 1 = 0$ 10 ▶ $4(7+3x) - 5(6-7x) + 1 = 8(1+4x)$

PROBLEMS LEADING TO EQUATIONS

Let the unknown quantity be x. Write down the facts in the form of an equation and then solve it.

EXAMPLE 18

The sum of three **consecutive** numbers is 219. What are the numbers?

Let the first number be x. Then the next two numbers are $(x + 1)$ and $(x + 2)$.

$$x + (x + 1) + (x + 2) = 219$$
$$3x + 3 = 219$$
$$3x = 216$$
$$x = 72$$

So the three numbers are 72, 73 and 74. (Check: $72 + 73 + 74 = 219$)

EXAMPLE 19

SKILLS

REASONNING

Find the value of x and the **perimeter** of this **isosceles triangle**.

As the triangle is isosceles

$$4x + 2 = 7x - 4$$
$$2 + 4 = 7x - 4x$$
$$6 = 3x$$
$$x = 2$$

Check: $4 \times 2 + 2 = 7 \times 2 - 4 = 10$

The sides are 10, 10 and 6 so the perimeter is 26.

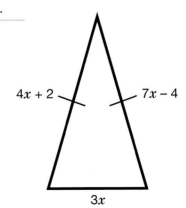

EXERCISE 8

1 ▶ The sum of two consecutive numbers is 477. What are the numbers?
(Let the first number be x.)

2 ▶ Find x and the size of each angle
in this triangle.

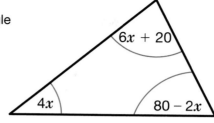

3 ▶ Find the value of x and the
perimeter of this rectangle.

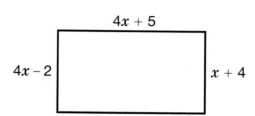

4 ▶ The result of doubling a certain number and adding 17 is the same as trebling (multiplying by 3) that number and adding 4. What is the number?

5 ▶ A kind teacher gives you 20 cents for every question you get right, but you have to pay the teacher 10 cents for every question you get wrong. After 30 questions you have made a profit of $1.80.

   a Form an equation with x representing the number of questions you got right.

   b Solve your equation to find how many questions you got right.

6 ▶ A cup of tea costs 10 cents less than a cup of coffee, while a cup of hot chocolate costs 20 cents more than a cup of coffee. Three cups of coffee, five cups of tea and two cups of hot chocolate cost $8.90.

   a Form an equation with x representing the price of a cup of coffee.

   b Solve your equation to find the price of a cup of coffee.

EXERCISE 8*

1 ▶ The sum of three consecutive even numbers is 222. Find the numbers.

2 ▶ John and Amelia have a baby daughter, Sonia. John is 23 kg heavier than Amelia, who is four times as heavy as Sonia. Their combined weight is 122 kg. How heavy is each person?

3 ▶ A father is three times as old as his son. In 14 years' time, he will be twice as old as his son. How old is the father now?

4 ▶ Lakshmi is trying to throw basketballs through hoops at a fair. If a ball goes through a hoop, she receives 50p, but if it does not she has to pay 20p for the shot. After 15 shots, Lakshmi finds she has made a profit of £1.20. How many times did Lakshmi successfully throw a ball through a hoop?

5 ▶ Aidan is doing a multiple-choice test with 20 questions. He scores 3 marks for a correct answer and loses 1 mark if the answer is incorrect. Aidan answers all the questions and scores 40 marks. How many questions has he answered correctly?

6 ▶ Freddie the frog is climbing up a well. Every day he climbs up 3 m but some nights he falls asleep and slips back 4 m. At the start of the sixteenth day, he has climbed a total of 29 m. On how many nights was he asleep?

EXERCISE 9

REVISION

Simplify these as much as possible.

1 ▶ $x + 2x + 3 - 5$

2 ▶ $3ba - ab + 3ab - 4ba$

3 ▶ $2a \times 3$

4 ▶ $2a \times a$

5 ▶ $a^2 \times a$

6 ▶ $2a^2 \times a^2$

7 ▶ $2a \times 2a \times a^2$

8 ▶ $7a - 4a(b + 3)$

9 ▶ $4(x + y) - 3(x - y)$

Solve these equations.

10 ▶ $2(x - 1) = 12$

11 ▶ $7x - 5 = 43 - 3x$

12 ▶ $5 - (x + 1) = 3x - 4$

13 ▶ Find three consecutive numbers whose sum is 438.

14 ▶ The perimeter of a rectangle is 54 cm. One side is x cm long and the other is 6 cm longer.

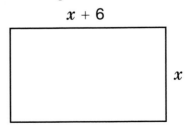

$x + 6$

x

a Form an equation involving x.

b Solve the equation and write down the length of each of the sides.

EXERCISE 9*   **REVISION**

Simplify these as much as possible.

1 ▶ $6xy^2 - 3x^2y - 2y^2x$

3 ▶ $p - (p - (p - (p - 1)))$

2 ▶ $2xy^2 \times x^2y$

4 ▶ $xy(x^2 + xy + y^2) - x^2(y^2 - xy - x^2)$

Solve these equations.

5 ▶ $4 = \dfrac{x}{5}$

7 ▶ $43 - 2x = 7 - 8x$

6 ▶ $4 = \dfrac{5}{x}$

8 ▶ $1.3 - 0.3x = 0.2x + 0.3$

9 ▶ $0.6(x + 1) + 0.2(6 - x) = x - 0.6$

10 ▶   The length of a conference room is one and a half times its width. There is a carpet in the centre of the room. The length of the carpet is twice its width. This leaves a 3 m wide border around the edges of the carpet. Find the area of the carpet.

11 ▶   Two years ago, my age was four times the age of my son.
Eight years ago, my age was ten times the age of my son. Find the age of my son now.

12 ▶   A river flows at 2 m/s. Juan's boat can travel twice as fast down the river as it can go up the river. How fast can the boat go in still water?

13 ▶   Matt wants to buy a television. If he pays cash, he gets a discount of 7%. If he pays with a loan he has to pay an extra 10% in interest. The difference between the two methods is $49.98. Find the cost of the television.

EXAM PRACTICE: ALGEBRA 1

In questions 1–5, simplify as much as possible.

1 ⟩ $3yx - 6xy$ **[1]**

2 ⟩ $5ab^3 - 4ab^2 + 2b^2a - 2b^3a$ **[1]**

3 ⟩ $4b^2 \times 2b^4$ **[1]**

4 ⟩ $4p \times (2p)^3$ **[1]**

5 ⟩ $9x - (2y - x)$ **[2]**

In questions 6–10, solve for x.

6 ⟩ $3 = \dfrac{x}{36}$ **[2]**

7 ⟩ $3 = \dfrac{36}{x}$ **[2]**

8 ⟩ $8(5 - 2x) = 24$ **[2]**

9 ⟩ $3x + 5 = 29 - 9x$ **[2]**

10 ⟩ $2(x - 2) - (x - 3) = 3$ **[2]**

11 ⟩ The sum of three consecutive numbers is 219.
What are the numbers?   **[3]**

Q11 HINT
Let the first number be x.

12 ⟩ If AB is a straight line, find x and the size of
each angle.   **[3]**

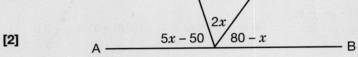

13 ⟩ The diagram shows an isosceles triangle. Find the
value of x and the perimeter of the triangle.   **[3]**

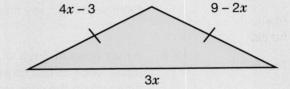

[Total 25 marks]

CHAPTER SUMMARY: ALGEBRA 1

SIMPLIFYING ALGEBRAIC EXPRESSIONS

You can only add or subtract like terms:

$2xy + 5xy = 7xy$ but the terms in $2xy + y$ cannot be added together;

$2x^2 + 4x^2 = 6x^2$ but the terms in $2x^2 + 3x$ cannot be added together.

The multiplication sign is often not included between letters, e.g. $2xy$ means $2 \times x \times y$.

When multiplying, add like powers. $2xy^2 \times 3x \times x^2y^3 = 6x^4y^5$ (think of x as x^1).

You can check your simplifications by substituting numbers.

SIMPLIFYING ALGEBRAIC EXPRESSIONS WITH BRACKETS

Multiply each term inside the bracket by the term outside the bracket.

The multiplication sign is usually not included:

$2(a + b)$ means $2 \times (a + b) = 2 \times a + 2 \times b = 2a + 2b$

Be very careful with negative signs outside a bracket:

$-3(x - 2)$ means $-3 \times (x - 2) = (-3) \times (x) + (-3) \times (-2) = -3x + 6$

When multiplying, the number 1 is usually not included:

$-(3x - 4)$ means $-1 \times (3x - 4) = (-1) \times (3x) + (-1) \times (-4) = -3x + 4$

SOLVING EQUATIONS

To solve equations, always do the same to both sides.

Always check your answer.

The six basic types:

- $x + 2 = 10$ — (Subtract 2 from both sides)
  $x = 8$ — (Check: $8 + 2 = 10$)

- $x - 2 = 10$ — (Add 2 to both sides)
  $x = 12$ — (Check: $12 - 2 = 10$)

- $2 - x = 10$ — (Add x to both sides)
  $2 = 10 + x$ — (Subtract 10 from both sides)
  $2 - 10 = x$
  $x = -8$ — (Check: $2 - (-8) = 10$)

- $2x = 10$ — (Divide both sides by 2)
  $x = 5$ — (Check: $2 \times 5 = 10$)

- $\frac{x}{2} = 10$ — (Multiply both sides by 2)
  $x = 20$ — (Check: $\frac{20}{2} = 10$)

- $\frac{2}{x} = 10$ — (Multiply both sides by x)
  $2 = 10x$ — (Divide both sides by 10)
  $\frac{1}{5} = x$ — (Check: $2 \div \frac{1}{5} = 2 \times 5 = 10$)

PROBLEMS LEADING TO EQUATIONS

Let the unknown quantity be x. Write down the facts in the form of an equation and then solve it.

GRAPHS 1

The cost, C cents, of telephoning for m minutes is given by $C = 10m + 50$ and is shown on the graph of C against m.

The picture is much easier to understand than the algebraic expression.

Every time you graph an equation you are using the work of René Descartes (1596–1650), a French philosopher who connected algebra to geometry, therefore giving a picture to algebra. Graphs are sometimes called Cartesian graphs in his honour.

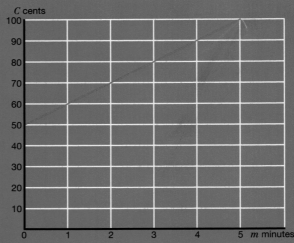

LEARNING OBJECTIVES

- Find the gradient of a line through two points
- Find the gradient and y-intercept of a straight line from its equation
- Compare two straight-line graphs using their equations
- Draw and interpret real-life graphs
- Plot graphs of straight lines with equations $ax + by = c$

BASIC PRINCIPLES

- Points on a graph are given by two numbers in brackets separated by a comma, for example (2, 3). All points are measured from the origin O.

- The x-axis is horizontal, the y-axis is vertical.

- The first number gives the distance from O in the x direction.

- The second number gives the distance from O in the y direction.

- These numbers can be positive or negative.

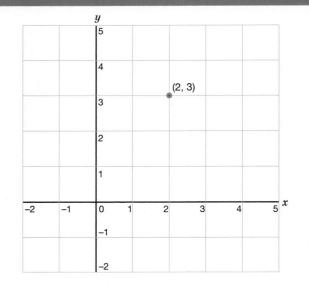

GRADIENT OF A STRAIGHT LINE

The pictures show some steep slopes. The slope of a line is its **gradient**.

The larger the gradient, the steeper the slope.

The letter m is usually used for the gradient.

For a straight line $m = \dfrac{\text{change in the } y \text{ coordinates}}{\text{change in the } x \text{ coordinates}} = \dfrac{\text{'rise'}}{\text{'run'}}$

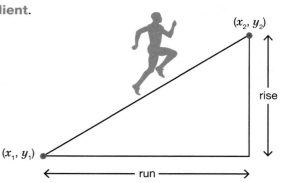

If the straight line joins the points (x_1, y_1) and (x_2, y_2) then 'rise' $= y_2 - y_1$ and 'run' $= x_2 - x_1$

The gradient is given by the formula $m = \dfrac{y_2 - y_1}{x_2 - x_1}$

EXAMPLE 1

SKILLS

PROBLEM SOLVING

Find the gradient of the straight line joining A (1, 2) to B (3, 6).

First draw a diagram.

The gradient is $\dfrac{\text{rise}}{\text{run}} = \dfrac{4}{2} = 2$ (a positive gradient).

Or use the formula with $x_1 = 1$, $y_1 = 2$, $x_2 = 3$, $y_2 = 6$

$m = \dfrac{6-2}{3-1} = \dfrac{4}{2} = 2$

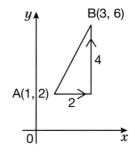

EXAMPLE 2

SKILLS

PROBLEM SOLVING

HINT

Do not use a ruler to measure the rise and run in case the x and y scales are different.

Find the gradient of the graph.

Choose two points on the graph and work out the rise and run.

The gradient is $\dfrac{\text{rise}}{\text{run}} = \dfrac{-2}{4} = -\dfrac{1}{2}$ (a negative gradient).

Or use the formula. The two points chosen are (2, 3) and (6, 1) so

$m = \dfrac{1-3}{6-2} = \dfrac{-2}{4} = -\dfrac{1}{2}$

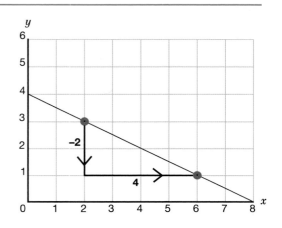

KEY POINTS

- Gradient $m = \dfrac{\text{'rise'}}{\text{'run'}}$

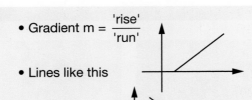

- Lines like this   have a positive gradient.

- Lines like this   have a negative gradient.

- Parallel lines have the same gradient.

- Always draw a diagram.

EXERCISE 1   Find the gradient of the straight line joining A to B.

1 ▶

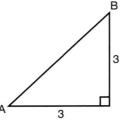

2 ▶

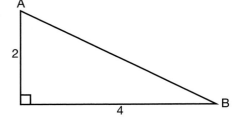

3 ▶   A is (1, 3) and B is (2, 6)

4 ▶   A is (–4, –1) and B is (4, 1)

5 ▶   A is (–2, 2) and B is (2, 1)

6 ▶   Find the gradient of the graph.   **7 ▶**   Find the gradient of the graph.

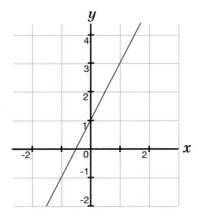

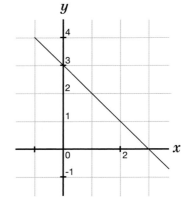

8 ▶   A ladder reaches 12 m up a vertical wall and has a gradient of 4.
How far is the bottom of the ladder from the wall?

9 ▶   After take-off, an aeroplane climbs in a straight
line with a gradient of $\dfrac{1}{5}$.
When it has reached a height of 2000 m, how far
has it gone horizontally?

10 ▶   The roof of this garden shed has a gradient of 0.35.
Find the height of the shed.

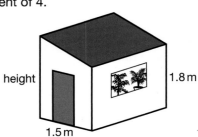

height   1.8 m

1.5 m

11 ▶ The seats at a football stadium are on a slope with gradient of $\frac{1}{2}$.
What is the height (h) of the bottom seats?

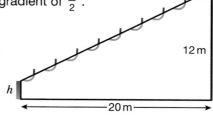

12 ▶ A road has a gradient of $\frac{1}{15}$ for 90 m.

Then there is a horizontal section 130 m long.

The final section has a gradient of $\frac{1}{25}$ for 200 m.

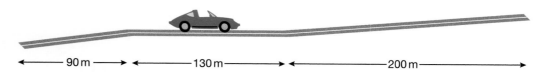

    a Find the total height gained from start to finish.
    b What is the average gradient from start to finish?

---

1 ▶ Find the gradient of the straight line joining A (−4, −1) to B (4, 2).

2 ▶ Find the gradient of the straight line joining A (−3, 2) to B (4, −4).

3 ▶ Find the gradient of the graph.

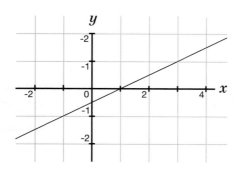

4 ▶ Find the gradient of the graph.

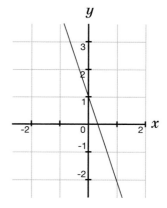

5 ▶ The line joining A (1, 4) to B (5, p) has a gradient of $\frac{1}{2}$. Find the value of p.

6 ▶ The masts for the Millennium Dome were held up during construction by wire ropes as shown in the diagram.

A is 106 m above the ground, C is vertically below A, the gradient of AB is 1 and CD is 53 m.

    a Find the gradient of AD.
    b Find the length of BD.

7 ▶ Antonio enjoys mountain biking. He has found that the maximum gradient which he can cycle up is 0.3 and the maximum gradient he can safely descend is 0.5. Antonio's map has a scale of 2 cm to 1 km with contours every 25 m. What is the minimum distance between the contours (lines on a map showing the height of land) on his map that allows him to go

    a up-hill   **b** down-hill?

8 ▶ A crane is lifting a boat suspended by wire ropes AB and AD.
The point C is vertically below A, and BC measures 5 m.

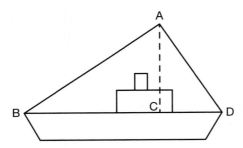

    a The gradient of AB is 0.8. How high is A above C?

    b The gradient of AD is –1.25. What is the length of the boat?

9 ▶ Do the points (1, 2), (51, 27) and (91, 48) lie on a straight line? Give reasons for your answer.

10 ▶ Find an algebraic expression for the gradient of the straight line joining A (p, q) to B (r, s).

11 ▶ The line joining (3, p) to (7, –4p) is parallel to the line joining (–1, –3) to (3, 7). Find p.

12 ▶ The gradient of the line joining (4, q) to (6, 5) is twice the gradient of the line joining (0, 0) to (4, q). Find q.

13 ▶ One of the world's tallest roller coasters is in Blackpool, England. The maximum drop is 65 m over a horizontal distance of 65 m in two sections. The first section has a gradient of 3 and the second section has a gradient of $\frac{1}{2}$.

How high is the point A above the ground?

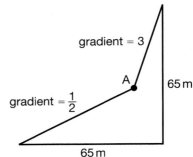

ACTIVITY 1

Find the gradient of the line AB.

Find the gradient of AB as the point B moves closer and closer to the point C.

Put your results in a table. What is the gradient of the horizontal line AC?

Find the gradient of AB as the point A moves closer and closer to the point C.

Put your results in a table. What is the gradient of the vertical line BC?

PLOTTING STRAIGHT-LINE GRAPHS

ACTIVITY 2

SKILL: REASONING

Plotted here are the six graphs:

a $y = x + 1$ **b** $y = -x + 1$ **c** $y = 2x - 1$ **d** $y = -2x + 1$ **e** $y = 3x - 1$ **f** $y = \frac{1}{2}x + 2$

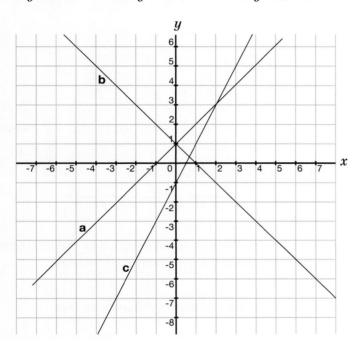
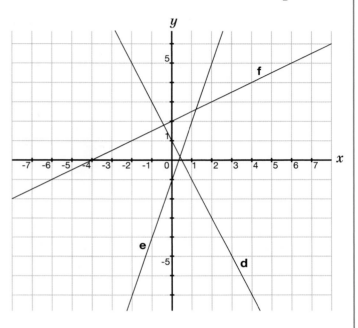

Copy and complete the table. (The 'y-intercept' is the value of y where the line crosses the y-axis.)

EQUATION	GRADIENT	y-INTERCEPT
$y = x + 1$		
$y = -x + 1$		
$y = 2x - 1$		
$y = -2x + 1$		
$y = 3x - 1$		
$y = \frac{1}{2}x + 2$		
$y = mx + c$		

Can you see a connection between the number in front of x and the gradient?

Can you see a connection between the number at the end of the equation and the y-intercept?

REAL-LIFE STRAIGHT-LINE GRAPHS

These graphs simply replace x and y with **variables** which represent real-life values such as weight, length, time, speed etc.

If a uniform **rate** is given, it is often necessary to produce the equation.

When drawing a graph of two variables, p against q, it is normal practice to draw the first named variable (p) on the vertical axis.

EXAMPLE 3

SKILLS

INTERPRETATION

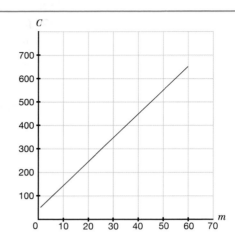

The cost of phoning is 10 cents per minute plus 50 cents. Write down an equation for the total cost, $C, for phoning for m minutes if the minimum is 1 minute and the maximum is 60 minutes.

$C = 10m + 50$ \qquad $1 \le m \le 60$

Usually the graph would be drawn with C on the vertical axis and m on the horizontal axis.

KEY POINTS

- The graph of $y = mx + c$ is a straight line with gradient m and y-intercept c.
- If the points do not lie on a straight line, then there is a mistake in the table of values.
- It is usual to use only three or four widely spaced points in the table of values.

EXERCISE 2

1 ▶ a Copy and complete the table of values for $y = 2x - 3$.

x	−2	−1	0	1	2	3
y		−5			1	

b Draw the graph of $y = 2x - 3$ for $-2 \le x \le 3$.

c Find the gradient and y-intercept of the graph.

d Use your graph to estimate the value of y when x is 0.6. Why is it an estimate?

2 ▶ Choose from these equations:

a the line with the steepest gradient

b the line with negative gradient

c the pair of parallel lines.

$y = 2x + 3$ \qquad $y = 3x - 9$

$y = x + 8$ \qquad $y = 4x - 2$

$y = -3x + 5$ \qquad $y = 2x - 4$

3 ▶ In a Physics lesson, Chantelle adds weights to a spring and carefully measures the extension. She finds that the weight, y g is related to the extension, x cm by the formula

$y = 0.5x + 1$ for $0 \le x \le 20$.

Q3a HINT
Find only three points.

    a Draw the graph of y against x for $0 \le x \le 20$.

    b Use this graph to find the

       (i) weight for a 17 cm extension
       (ii) extension produced by a 5 g weight.

    c What would Chantelle's formula predict for the spring's extension for a 1 kg weight? Comment on your answer.

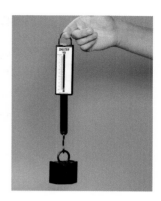

4 ▶ A monkey puzzle tree can grow up to 40 m and can live for 1000 years. Idris plants a monkey puzzle tree in his school playground and calculates that the tree's height, y m, is related to the time, t years, after it was planted, by the formula

$y = 0.9t + 1$ for $0 \le t \le 10$.

    a Draw a graph of y against t for $0 \le t \le 10$.

    b Use this graph to find

       (i) the height of the tree when it is planted and after 20 months
       (ii) when the tree is 5.5 m high.

    c Idris realises that the school's playground will be totally in shadow when the tree is 19 m tall. Use the formula to find out when this will happen and comment on your answer.

5 ▶ The depth of water, d m, in an African desert well during the dry season, in the first t days of December, is given by the formula

$d = -0.3t + 10$ for $0 \le t \le 30$.

    a Draw a graph of d against t for $0 \le t \le 30$.

    b Use this graph to find

       (i) the depth of water in the well on 25 December
       (ii) the date when the water is 7 m deep.

    c According to the formula, when will the well be dry? Comment on your answer.

6 ▶ Tatiana buys a new refrigerator and switches it on at midday. The air temperature inside the freezer, T (°C), t hours after she switches it on, is given by the formula

$T = -4t + 15$ for $0 \le t \le 6$.

    a Draw a graph of T against t for $0 \le t \le 6$.

    b Use this graph to find

       (i) the freezer temperature before she turns it on
       (ii) the times when the freezer temperature is 0°C and −5°C.

    c Use the formula to find the freezer temperature at 7:30pm on that day. Comment on your answer.

EXERCISE 2*

1 ▶ **a** Copy and complete the table of values for $y = \frac{1}{2}x + 1$ and $y = \frac{1}{2}x - 2$.

x	−2	0	2	4
$y = \frac{1}{2}x + 1$				
$y = \frac{1}{2}x - 2$				

b Draw both graphs on one set of axes for $-2 \le x \le 4$.

c What are the gradient and y-intercept of each graph?

d The lines are extended in both directions. Will they ever meet? Give a reason for your answer.

2 ▶ The population of mosquitoes, N thousands, in a small mangrove swamp, after the first t days of June is given by the formula

$N = 2t + 30$ for $0 \le t \le 10$.

a Draw the graph of N against t for $0 \le t \le 10$.

b Use this graph to find

  (i) the number of mosquitoes on 2 June
  (ii) the date when the mosquito population is 46 000.

c The mosquito population at the end of June is 18% greater than the population on 10 June. Find the mosquito population on 30 June.

3 ▶ The cost of car hire in Paris by 'Vite-Voitures' is €40 per day plus a single payment at the start of the hire period of €60.

a Write down the formula for the total cost of hiring a car, €C, for t days.

b Draw the graph of C against t for $0 \le t \le 7$.

c Use this graph to find the

  (i) cost of hiring a car for 6 days
  (ii) number of days when the car hire cost is €180.

4 ▶ The value of Ziyana's Smart Phone, $$V$ hundreds, loses value at a rate of $150 per year after she bought it for $900.

a Write down the formula for the value of the Smart Phone $$V$ after x years.

b Draw the graph of V against x for $0 \le x \le 5$.

c Use the graph to find

  (i) the value of the Smart Phone after 30 months
  (ii) when the Smart Phone is worth $300.

d When will Ziyana's Smart Phone be worth nothing?

5 ▶ Seth owns two electric cars, a Zenith and a Bubble.

Zenith: Bought for £25 000 and loses a value (**depreciates**) of £5000 per year.

Bubble: Bought for £10 000 and depreciates at £2000 per year.

a Write down the formula for the value, £V thousands, for each car after x years.

b Draw the graphs of V against x for both cars on the same axes for $0 \le x \le 5$.

c Use the graphs to find the time when Seth's cars

     (i) are worth the same value

     (ii) have a difference in value of £9000.

GRAPHS OF $ax + by = c$

The graph of $3x + 4y = 12$ is a straight line. The equation can be rearranged as $y = -\frac{3}{4}x + 3$ showing it is a straight line with gradient $-\frac{3}{4}$ and y-intercept (0, 3). The easiest way to plot the graph is to find where the graph crosses the axes.

EXAMPLE 4	Draw the graph $x + 2y = 8$.
SKILLS	Find where the line crosses the axes.
INTERPRETATION	Substituting $y = 0$ gives $x = 8 \Rightarrow$ (8, 0) lies on the line.

Substituting $x = 0$ gives $y = 4 \Rightarrow$ (0, 4) lies on the line.

Join the points with a straight line.

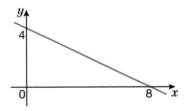

KEY POINTS

• $ax + by = c$ is a straight line.

• To draw the graph, find where it crosses the axes.

EXERCISE 3

Find where each graph crosses the axes and draw the graph.

1 ▶ $2x + y = 6$ **2 ▶** $3x + 2y = 12$ **3 ▶** $x - 2y = 4$ **4 ▶** $4y - 3x = 24$

5 ▶   A firm selling plants has found that the number sold (N thousand) is related to the price (£P) by the formula $6P + N = 90$.

     a Draw the graph of N against P for $0 \le N \le 90$.
       (Put N on the vertical axis and P on the horizontal axis.)

     b Use your graph to find the price when 30 000 plants were sold.

     c Use your graph to find the number sold if the price is set at £8.

     d Use your graph to find the price if 90 000 plants were sold. Is this a sensible value?

EXERCISE 3*

Find where each graph crosses the axes and draw the graph.

1 ▶ $6x - 3y = 36$ **2 ▶** $4y + 6x = 21$ **3 ▶** $7y - 2x = 21$ **4 ▶** $6x - 7y = -21$

5 ▶ Eduardo has started playing golf. In golf, the lower the score, the better. To try to reduce his score, he has lessons with a professional. He keeps a record of his progress.

Week (W)	5	10	20	30
Score (H)	22	21	20	19

a Plot these points on a graph of H against W.
   Draw in the best straight line.

b What was Eduardo's score before he started lessons?

c Find the gradient and y-intercept of the line and write down the equation of the line in the form $ax + by = c$.

d To enter a trial for the team, Eduardo needs to have a score below 12. Use your equation to find how many weeks it will take Eduardo to reduce his score to 12. Do you think this is a reasonable value? Give a reason for your answer.

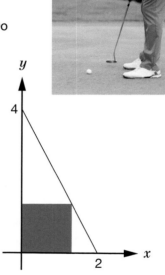

6 ▶ The line $ax + by = c$ has no y-intercept.
Can you say anything about the values of a, b or c?

7 ▶ The top of a ladder is 4 m up a vertical wall, the bottom is 2 m from the wall. The coordinate axes are the wall and the horizontal ground.

a Find the equation representing the ladder.

b A square box just fits under the ladder. Find the coordinates of the point where the box touches the ladder.

STRAIGHT-LINE CONVERSION GRAPHS

A graph gives an easy way of converting from one unit to another.

EXAMPLE 5

SKILLS

MODELLING

a In May, £1 was worth €1.38. Draw a conversion graph to convert £0 to £100 into euros.

b Use your graph to convert

   (i) £60 to euros

   (ii) €120 to British pounds.

a £100 is worth €138, £0 is worth €0. Plot both points on a graph and join with a straight line.

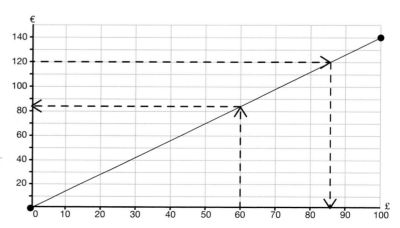

b The arrows show how to use the conversion graph.

(i) £60 is approximately €83.   (ii) €120 is approximately £87.

• A conversion graph is an easy way of converting from one unit to another.

• Because **readings** are taken from a graph, the answers are not exact.

• Not all conversion graphs pass through the origin.

EXERCISE 4

1 ▶ The graph shows the conversion from euros (€) to the Japanese yen (¥).

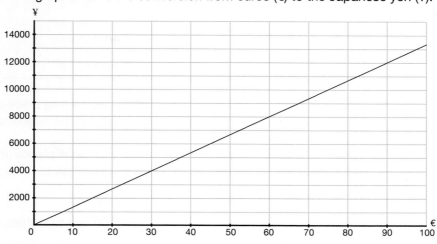

a Convert €90 to yen.   b Convert ¥8000 to euros.

c A shop in Japan says that it will accept euros. Adam pays with a €100 note for a camera that costs ¥6000. How many yen should he receive in change?

2 ▶ The graph shows the cost per month of using units of electricity.

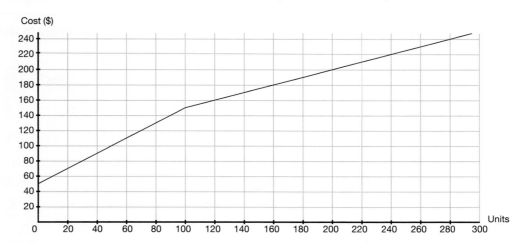

a What is the cost per month of using 80 units of electricity?

b Zak's bill is $210. How many units of electricity did he use?

c The next month Zak's bill is $50. How many units of electricity did he use?

3 ▶   The graph shows the cooking time needed to roast some lamb.

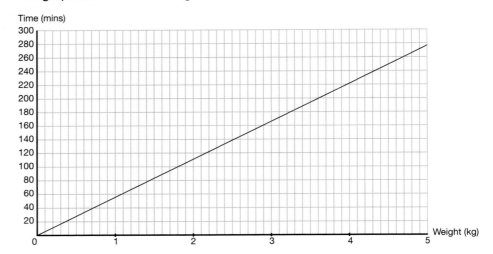

a How long (in hours and mins) will it take to roast a 4 kg piece of lamb?

b Mary has 1 hour 40 mins to cook a meal. What is the largest piece of lamb that she can cook in this time?

c Does the graph give sensible answers for very small pieces of lamb? Suggest how the graph could be improved for very small pieces of lamb.

4 ▶   1 foot (plural 'feet') is equivalent to 0.305 metres.

a Draw a conversion graph to convert up to 100 feet to metres, plotting feet on the horizontal axis.

b Mala estimates the height of a tree as 26 m. What height is this in feet?

Q4d HINT
Use your answer
to part c.

c Convert 20 feet to metres.

d Convert 2 feet to metres.

EXERCISE 4*

1 ▶   The graph shows the conversion from miles per hour (mph) to kilometres per hour (km/h).

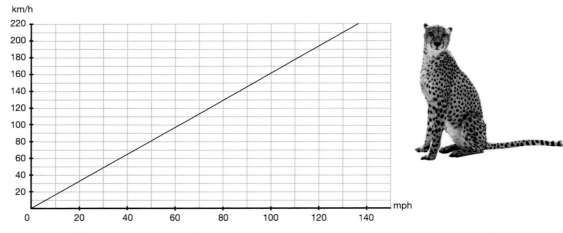

a The speed limit on rural roads in France is 90 km/h. What is this speed in mph?

b Cheetahs can run up to 75 mph. What is this speed in km/h?

c The world land speed record is 763 mph. What is this speed approximately in km/h?

2 ▶ Sherlock Holmes makes the following remark in one of his early adventures: 'The height of a man, in nine cases out of ten, can be told from the length of his stride.' ('Stride' is the length of someone's step). The graph shows Sherlock's conversion.

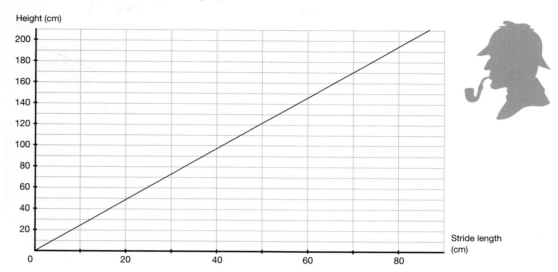

a Estimate the height of a person with a stride length of 55 cm.
b A person is 1.75 m tall. What is their expected stride length?
c The police find some footprints that are 210 cm apart. What can they work out from this?

3 ▶ The graph shows one prediction of the connection between the increase of CO_2 in the atmosphere in parts per million (ppm) and the overall global temperature rise.

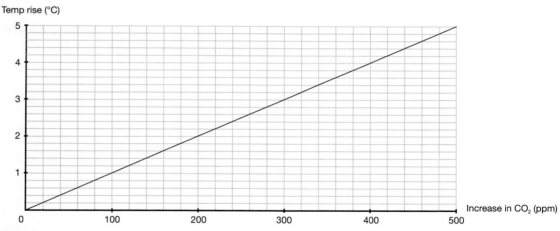

a If the CO_2 increases by 360 ppm, what is the predicted rise in temperature?
b From 1980 to 2000 the temperature rise was 0.4°C. What was the increase in CO_2?
c Experts want to limit the temperature rise to 2°C. What is the maximum increase in CO_2 that is allowed?

4 ▶ When Sophia was young, petrol in the UK was sold in gallons. It is now sold in litres, and 1 litre is equivalent to 0.22 gallons. To help Sophia buy petrol, her grandson has drawn a conversion chart.

a Draw a conversion graph to convert up to 20 litres to gallons, plotting litres on the horizontal axis.
b Sophia wants to buy 4 gallons of petrol. How many litres is this?
c Sophia's emergency can of petrol holds 5 litres. How many gallons is this?
d Sophia puts 50 litres of petrol in her car. How many gallons is this?

EXERCISE 5 ▶   REVISION

6th
8th

1 ▶ Find the gradient of the straight line joining A to B when

   a A is (3, 4), B is (5, 8)

   b A is (–1, 2), B is (1, 0)

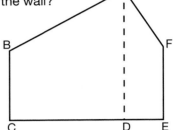

2 ▶ The bottom of a ladder is 1.5 m from the base of a vertical wall. The gradient of the ladder is 3. How far up does the top of the ladder touch the wall?

3 ▶ An architect is designing a roof on a building. The cross-section is shown in the diagram. The point D is vertically below A. BC and FE are 3 m and CD is 5 m.

   a The gradient of AB is 0.8. How high is A above C?

   b The gradient of AF is –1.25. What is the width of the building?

4 ▶ **a** Draw the graph of $3x + 5y = 15$ for $0 \leq x \leq 6$ and $0 \leq y \leq 6$.

   b What is the gradient of the graph?

5 ▶ The cost, C, of hiring a car for d days when on holiday is given by $C = 20d + 50$.

   a Draw a graph of C against d for $0 \leq d \leq 7$.

   b What is the initial charge before you add on the daily hire charge?

   c Liam has $160 to spend on car hire. For how many days can he hire a car?

   d What is the cost of hiring a car for 14 days?

6 ▶ There is a connection between the length of a person's forearm and their height. This connection is shown on the conversion graph.

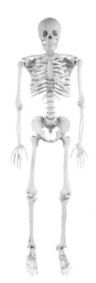

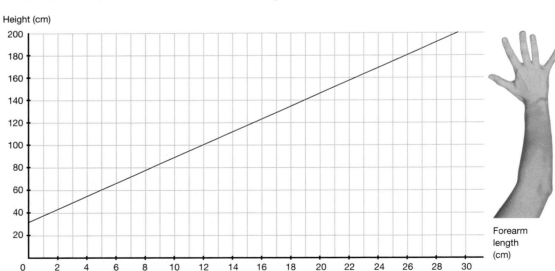

   a Archaeologists discover an incomplete skeleton with a forearm length of 23 cm. Estimate the height of the complete skeleton.

   b Wayne thinks a forearm with length 18 cm came from a skeleton of height 180 cm. Is this likely? Give a reason to support your answer.

EXERCISE 5*   **REVISION**

1 ▶ The Leaning Tower of Pisa is 55 m high, and the gradient of its lean is 11. By how many metres does the top overhang the bottom?

2 ▶ Show that joining the points A (–5, 2), B (–1, 5), C (5.6, –0.5), D (1, –3) makes a **trapezium**.

3 ▶ Find b such that the line from the origin to (3, 4b) is parallel to the line from the origin to (b, 3).

4 ▶ Find the gradient of the straight line joining (1, 2 + 4p) to (1 – 2p, 2).

5 ▶ Temperature (F) in degrees Fahrenheit is related to temperature (C) in degrees Celsius by the formula

$$F = \tfrac{9}{5}C + 32$$

    a Draw a graph of F against C for $-50 \le C \le 40$.

    b Use your graph to estimate

        (i) 80°F in °C
        (ii) 25°C in °F
        (iii) –22°F in °C.

    c Use your graph to find which temperature has the same value in both degrees Fahrenheit and degrees Celsius.

6 ▶ In a recipe book, the time for fast roasting (F) in a hot oven is given as 20 minutes plus 40 minutes per kg (K). The time for slow roasting (S) in a moderate oven is given as 35 minutes plus 75 minutes per kg.

    a Write down the equations relating

        (i) F to K
        (ii) S to K.

    b Draw both graphs on the same axes for $0 \le K \le 6$.

    c Use your graphs to estimate the cooking time for a

        (i) 2.5 kg piece of meat (slow roasting)
        (ii) 3 kg piece of meat (fast roasting).

    d What was the weight of a piece of meat that took 3 hours 45 mins to cook in a hot oven?

    e A 2 kg piece of meat is put in the oven at 11am. By mistake, the temperature is set halfway between hot and moderate. By drawing a third line on your graph, estimate when the piece of meat will be cooked.

EXAM PRACTICE: GRAPHS 1

1 Find the gradient of the line joining the following points.

  a A (2, 3) and B (5, 9)
  b C (–2, –3) and D (–5 , 9)   **[4]**

2 A steep cliff has a gradient of 9.
What is the value of h?   **[3]**

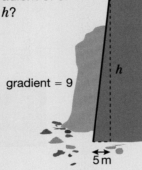

gradient = 9

h

5 m

3 Bicycle hire in San Francisco costs \$$c$ for t hours and is given by the formula

$c = 4t + 5$ for $1 \le t \le 10$.

  a Draw the graph of c against t for $1 \le t \le 10$.

Q3a HINT
Only three points are needed.

  b What is the gradient of this graph?
  c Use the graph to find how long a bicycle was hired for when the cost was \$37.   **[6]**

4 Jules has a watch pedometer which counts how many steps (S) he walks in a day. He has measured his step length as 0.7 m.

  a Draw a conversion graph of the distance walked (L) against S to convert up to 10 000 steps into metres.
  b Use your graph to find how far Jules walked when he walked 8500 steps.
  c Jules' mother recommends he walks 6 km per day. How many steps is this?   **[6]**

5 A small party balloon has a maximum volume of 500 cm³. Unfortunately, it has a leak that allows 10 cm³ of air to escape every second.

  a Write down an equation for the volume (v cm³) of the party balloon, t secs after it starts to leak.
  b Draw the graph of v against t for $0 \le t \le 50$.
  c Use this graph to find the time when the balloon is 25% full.   **[6]**

[Total 25 marks]

CHAPTER SUMMARY: GRAPHS 1

GRADIENT OF A STRAIGHT LINE

Positive gradient

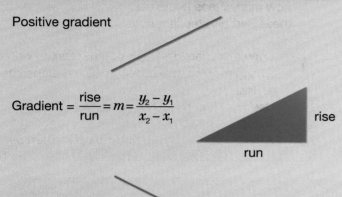

$$\text{Gradient} = \frac{\text{rise}}{\text{run}} = m = \frac{y_2 - y_1}{x_2 - x_1}$$

Negative gradient

Parallel lines have the same gradient.

Horizontal lines have a gradient of 0.

Vertical lines have an infinite gradient.

PLOTTING STRAIGHT-LINE GRAPHS

GRAPHS OF $y = mx + c$

The equation of any straight line can be expressed in this form where m is the gradient and c is the y-intercept.

When plotting a straight line, three widely separated points are enough.

$y = -2x + 5$ has a gradient of -2 and crosses the y-axis at $(0, 5)$.

REAL-LIFE STRAIGHT-LINE GRAPHS

These graphs replace x and y with variables which represent real-life values such as weight, length, time, speed etc.

If a uniform rate is given, then the graph is a straight line.

When drawing a graph of two variables, for example p against q, it is normal practice to draw the first named variable (p) on the vertical axis.

GRAPHS OF $ax + by = c$

These equations can be rearranged to find the gradient (m) and the y-intercept (c).

To plot, simply substitute $x = 0$ then $y = 0$ to produce two points.

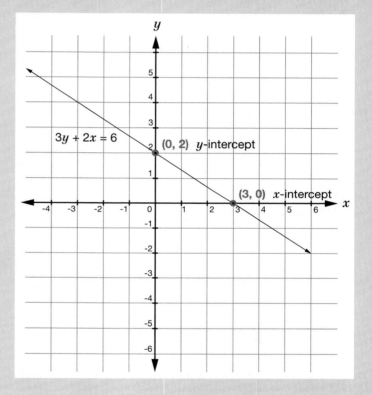

Plot $2x + 3y = 6$:

$x = 0 \Rightarrow 3y = 6 \Rightarrow y = 2$ also $y = 0 \Rightarrow 2x = 6 \Rightarrow x = 3$

$(0 , 2)$ and $(3, 0)$ are the two points on the axes.

STRAIGHT-LINE CONVERSION GRAPHS

A conversion graph is an easy way of converting from one unit to another, for example converting from pounds to dollars.

Because readings are taken from a graph, the answers are not exact.

Not all conversion graphs pass through the origin.

SHAPE AND SPACE 1

The architects who designed The Izadi Tower in Tehran used an incredible range of geometrical shapes and patterns in its complex construction. We will study many of these shapes in this section on geometry.

LEARNING OBJECTIVES

- Obtain and use the sum of angles in a triangle

- Obtain and use the property that the exterior angle of a triangle is equal to the sum of the two opposite interior angles

- Use the properties of special triangles to solve geometrical problems

- Obtain and use the sum of angles in a quadrilateral

- Use the properties of quadrilaterals to solve geometrical problems

- Calculate the sum of the interior angles of a polygon

- Know and use the sum of the exterior angles of a polygon

- Use the angles of polygons to solve geometrical problems

- Use and interpret maps and scale drawings

- Solve problems involving bearings

- Construct triangles using a ruler and compasses

- Construct the perpendicular bisector of a line

- Construct the bisector of an angle

- Construct angles using a ruler and compasses

- Recognise similar shapes

- Use the ratio of corresponding sides to work out scale factors

- Find missing lengths on similar shapes

BASIC PRINCIPLES

- Angles on a straight line.

$a + b = 180°$

- Vertically opposite angles.

$a = c, b = d$

- Parallel lines.

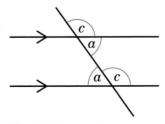

Alternate angles a are equal

Corresponding angles c are equal

- Lines of symmetry. If a shape is folded along a line of symmetry, both halves will match exactly.

Line of symmetry

- **Rotational symmetry**. If a shape has rotational symmetry then it still looks the same after a rotation of less than one turn. This propeller can be rotated to three different positions and still look the same. In maths, we would say that it has rotational symmetry of order 3.

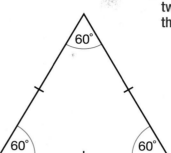

- **Equilateral triangle**. All three sides are the same length and all three angles are 60°.

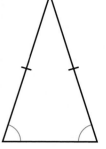

- **Isosceles triangle**. Two sides are the same length and two angles are the same.

TRIANGLES

The angle **sum** of a triangle is 180°.

PROOF

ABC is any triangle.

Through B draw a line parallel to AC.

(1) $d + b + e = 180°$ (angles on a straight line)

(2) $d = a$ (alternate angles)

(3) $e = c$ (alternate angles)

Substituting (2) & (3) into (1) gives $a + b + c = 180°$.

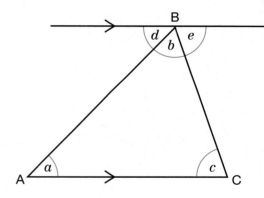

| EXAMPLE 1 | One angle of a triangle is 60°. What is the sum of the other two angles? |

SKILLS

REASONING

$a + b + 60 = 180°$

$\Rightarrow a + b = 120°$

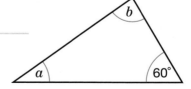

INTERIOR AND EXTERIOR ANGLES

When one side of a triangle is extended, the **exterior angle** is formed.

interior angle

exterior angle

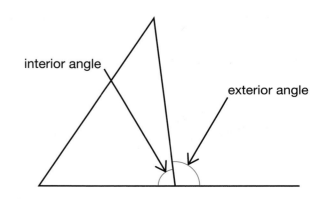

ACTIVITY 1

HINT
Look back at
Example 1.

Copy and complete the table for each of the triangles below.

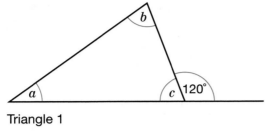

Triangle 1

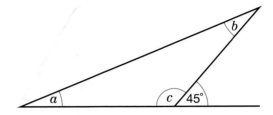

Triangle 2

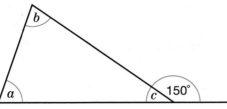

Triangle 3

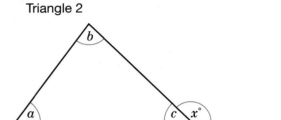

Triangle 4

	Exterior angle	c	$a + b$
Triangle 1	120°		
Triangle 2	45°		
Triangle 3	150°		
Triangle 4	$x°$		

What do you notice about the sum of the two opposite **interior angles**, $a + b$?

Activity 1 shows that the exterior angle of a triangle equals the sum of the opposite angles.
Writing out the calculations for triangle 4 including reasons would give a proof of this result.

ANGLE SUM OF THE EXTERIOR ANGLES OF A TRIANGLE

Imagine you are walking around a triangular field ABC.

Start at A, facing B.

Walk to B then turn anti-clockwise through angle b to face C.

Walk to C then turn anti-clockwise through angle c to face A.

Walk to A then turn anti-clockwise through angle a to face B again.

You have turned through 360°.

You have also turned through $a + b + c$.

So $a + b + c = 360°$.

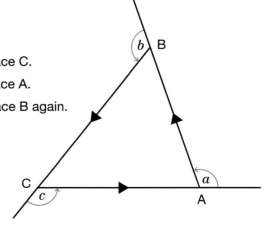

SPECIAL TRIANGLES

Some triangles have special names and properties.

A dotted line in the diagrams shows an **axis of symmetry**.

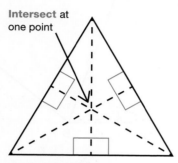

Intersect at one point

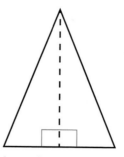

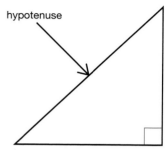

hypotenuse

Equilateral triangle
All sides are equal
All angles are 60°
Dotted lines go to the **mid-points**
of the sides and are at right angles
Rotational symmetry of order 3

Isosceles triangle
Two sides are equal
Two angles are equal
Dotted line goes to the
mid-point of the side and
is at right angles
No rotational symmetry

Right-angled triangle
One angle is 90°
The **hypotenuse** is the
longest side
No axis of symmetry
No rotational symmetry

It is possible to have a right-angled isosceles triangle which has an axis of symmetry.

ACTIVITY 2

Draw a right-angled isosceles triangle.

Mark in the axis of symmetry.

An isosceles triangle can always be split down the line of symmetry into two equal right-angled triangles. This is very important for solving problems using Pythagoras' Theorem or trigonometry later in the book.

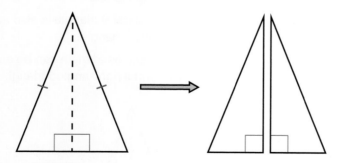

EXAMPLE 2

EXAMPLE 2

SKILLS

REASONING

ABC and BCD are isosceles triangles.

AB is parallel to CD.

∠ACE is 140°.

Find the angle marked x.

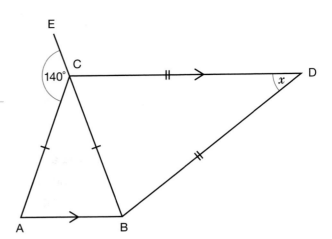

∠ACE is an exterior angle of △ABC

⇒ ∠CAB + ∠ABC = 140°

∠CAB = ∠ABC   (△ABC is isosceles)

⇒ ∠ABC = 70°

∠ABC = ∠BCD   (alternate angles)

∠BCD = ∠CBD = 70°   (△BCD is isosceles)

⇒ angle x = 40°   (angle sum of triangle)

EXAMPLE 3

SKILLS

REASONING

Work out the size of angle ABC.

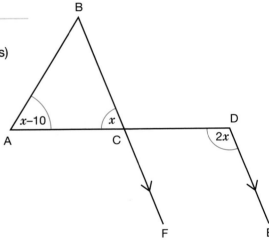

∠FCD = x (vertically opposite angles)

∠FCD + ∠CDE = 180°   (interior angles of parallel lines)

⇒ 3x = 180 ⇒ x = 60°

⇒ ∠BAC = 50°   (∠BAC = x − 10)

⇒ ∠ABC = 70°   (angle sum of a triangle)

KEY POINTS

- The angle sum of a triangle is 180°.

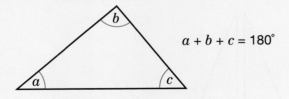

$a + b + c = 180°$

- The exterior angle of a triangle equals the sum of the opposite interior angles.

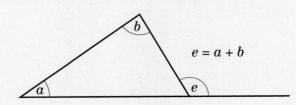

$e = a + b$

- The sum of the exterior angles of a triangle is 360°.

- An equilateral triangle is also an isosceles triangle.

- An isosceles triangle can be split into two equal right-angled triangles.

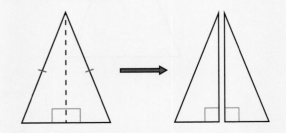

- When doing problems, mark any angles you work out on a neat **sketch** of the diagram.

EXERCISE 1

1 ▶ Work out the sizes of the angles marked with a letter.

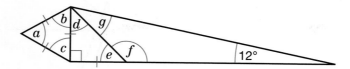

2 ▶ ABC and CDE are straight lines. AE is parallel to BD.

Work out the size of

a AB̂D **b** BD̂C **c** AÊC **d** AĈE

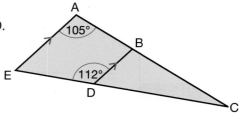

3 ▶ Work out the size of each angle marked with a letter.

a

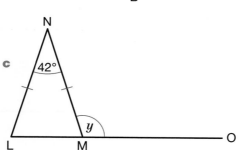

b

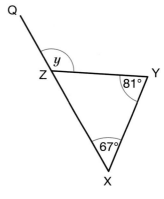

c

4 ▶ AB is parallel to CD.

EG = FG

AÊG = 110°

Calculate the size of DĜH.

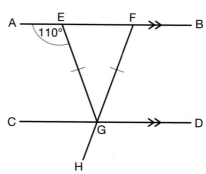

5 ▶ ABC is a triangle.
D is a point on AC.
Find the size of angle ACB.

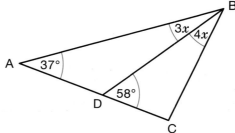

6 ▶   Angle AFC = $x°$ and angle ACB = $y°$.

   a What is the value of x?

   b What is the value of y?

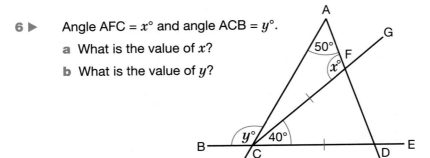

---

1 ▶   ABC and CDE are straight lines. AE is parallel to BD.

   Work out the size of

   a AB̂D   **b** AÊD   **c** BD̂C   **d** AĈE

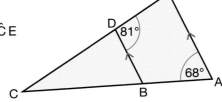

2 ▶   Work out the size of each angle marked with a letter.

a

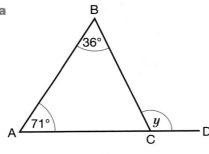

c

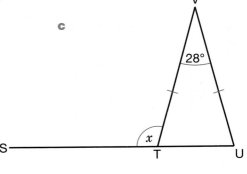

b

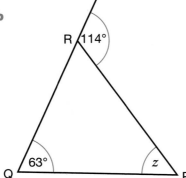

d

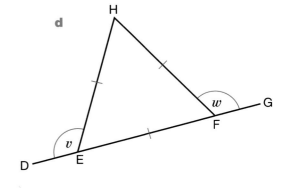

3 ▶   CDEF is a straight line.
AB is parallel to CF. DE = AE.

Calculate the size of the angle marked x.
You must give reasons for your answer.

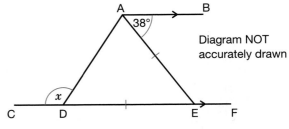

Diagram NOT accurately drawn

4 ▶   Work out the size of angle QSP. Give reasons for your **working**.

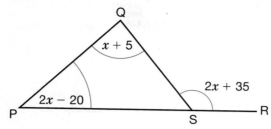

5 ▶   An isosceles triangle has one angle of 50 degrees.
Work out the angles of the two possible triangles.

6 ▶   In an isosceles triangle, one angle is three times the size of the other two angles.
Work out the size of each angle.

QUADRILATERALS

INTERIOR ANGLES

A **quadrilateral** can always be split into two triangles.

The angle sum of each triangle is 180°.

So the angle sum of the quadrilateral is 360°.

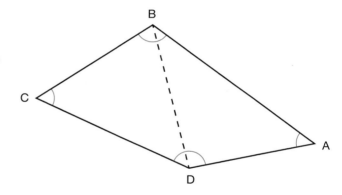

EXTERIOR ANGLES

In the same way that you imagined walking around a triangular field, imagine walking around a quadrilateral field ABCD.

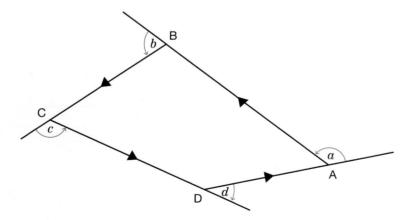

Again you turn anti-clockwise through 360°.

So $a + b + c + d = 360°$

The sum of the exterior angles of a quadrilateral is 360°.

SPECIAL QUADRILATERALS

The diagrams show quadrilaterals with special names and properties.

A dotted line in the diagrams shows an axis of symmetry.

Square

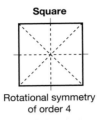

Rotational symmetry
of order 4

Rectangle

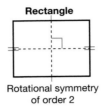

Rotational symmetry
of order 2

Kite

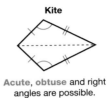

Acute, obtuse and right
angles are possible.

Rhombus

Rotational symmetry
of order 2

Parallelogram

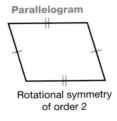

Rotational symmetry
of order 2

Trapezium

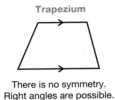

There is no symmetry.
Right angles are possible.

Isosceles trapezium

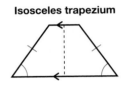

Note: the square, rhombus and rectangle have parallel sides. This is not shown on the diagrams since it would make them too confusing.

EXAMPLE 4

SKILLS

REASONING

ABCD is a quadrilateral with angles as shown.

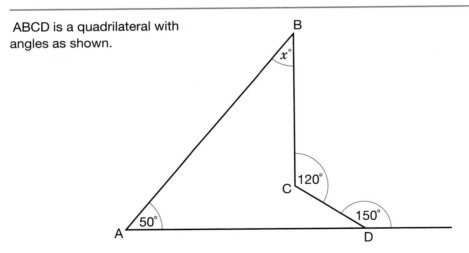

a Find angle x.

b Show that BC is **perpendicular** to AD.

---

a $\angle ADC = 30°$ (angles on a straight line add up to 180°)

$\angle DCB = 240°$ (angles at a point **sum** to 360°)

$x = 360 - 50 - 30 - 240 = 40°$ (internal angles of a quadrilateral sum to 360°)

b   Extend BC to meet AD at point E.

Then AEB = 90° (angle sum of a triangle is 180°)

⇒ BC is perpendicular to AD.

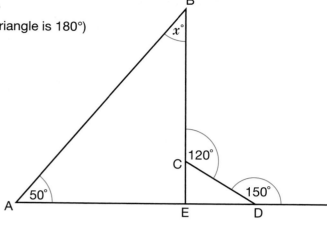

EXAMPLE 5

In this quadrilateral, angles PQR and QRS are equal.

Angles QRS is $1\frac{1}{2}$ times the size of angle PSR.

Angle PSR is twice the size of angle QPS.

Find the size of angle QPS.

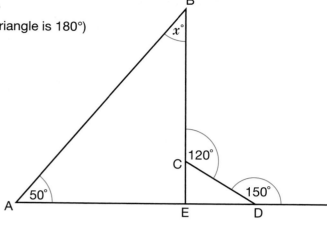

Let angle QPS be x.

Angle PSR = $2x$

Angle QRS = $1\frac{1}{2} \times 2x = 3x$

Angle PQR = angle QRS = $3x$

Angles in the quadrilateral PQRS = $x + 2x + 3x + 3x = 9x$

Angles in a quadrilateral sum to 360°.

So, $9x = 360°$

$x = \frac{360°}{9} = 40°$

Angle QPS = 40°

KEY POINTS

- The sum of the interior angles of a quadrilateral is 360°.
- The sum of the exterior angles of a quadrilateral is 360°.

EXERCISE 2

1 ▶   Name a quadrilateral with no lines of symmetry and rotational symmetry of order two.

2 ▶   The diagram shows a kite. Find the size of angle a.

3 ▶ Work out the size of

a angle DAB

b ∠AZY

c MN̂K

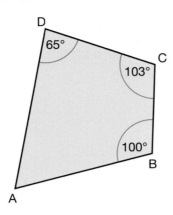
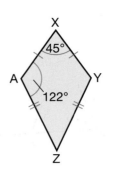
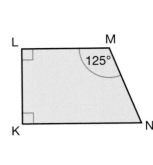

4 ▶ Work out the size of angle ABC. Give reasons for your working.

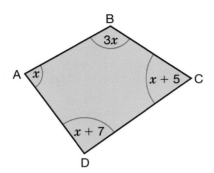

5 ▶ ABCD is a parallelogram.
CDE is an isosceles triangle.
ADEF is a straight line. Angle BAD = 64°.
Work out the size of angle CEF.
Give reasons for your working.

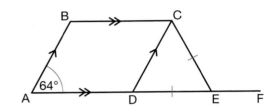

6 ▶ Work out the size of angle ABD.
Give reasons for your working.

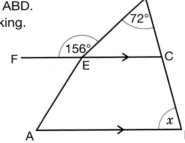

EXERCISE 2*

1 ▶ Name a quadrilateral with one line of symmetry and no rotational symmetry.

2 ▶ The four angles of a quadrilateral are 90°, $3x + 15°$, $x + 25°$ and $x + 55°$. Find x.

3 ▶ ABCD is an isosceles trapezium. BCE is an isosceles triangle.
DCEF is a straight line. Angle BEF = 132°.
Work out the size of angle DAB. Give reasons for your working.

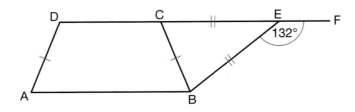

4 ▶   Work out the size of angle ACB. Give reasons for your working.

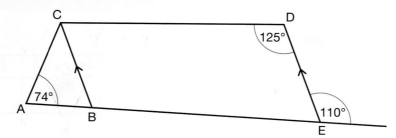

5 ▶   In this quadrilateral, angles PQR and QRS are equal.

Angle PSR is $\frac{4}{7}$ angle QRS.

Angle QPS is $\frac{6}{7}$ angle QRS.

   a   Find angle PSR.

   b   Show that angle QPS is a right angle.

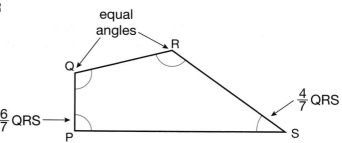

6 ▶   **a**   The diagonals of a rectangle intersect at 76°.
         Find the angle that a diagonal makes with a longer side of the rectangle.

   b   The diagonals of a rectangle intersect at x°.
         Find the angle that a diagonal makes with a longer side of the rectangle.

POLYGONS

INTERIOR ANGLES

Polygons can always be divided into triangles.

The diagram shows a hexagon divided into four triangles.

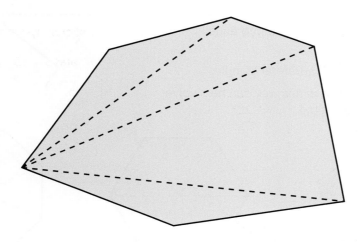

ACTIVITY 3

Copy and complete the table.

NAME	Quadrilateral	Pentagon	Hexagon	Heptagon	Octagon	n-gon
NUMBER OF SIDES	4		6			n
NUMBER OF TRIANGLES	2		4			

You can now see that an n-sided polygon can be divided into $(n-2)$ triangles
⇒ the angle sum is $(n-2) \times 180°$.

If the polygon is regular, then the interior angles are all equal.

Each interior angle is $\dfrac{(n-2) \times 180}{n} = \dfrac{180n - 360}{n} = 180 - \dfrac{360}{n}$ degrees.

EXTERIOR ANGLES

Imagine walking around a field that is the shape of an n-sided polygon.

You will still turn through 360°.

The sum of the exterior angles of a polygon is 360° no matter how many sides it has.

If the polygon is regular, then the exterior angles are all the same and they equal $\dfrac{360°}{n}$

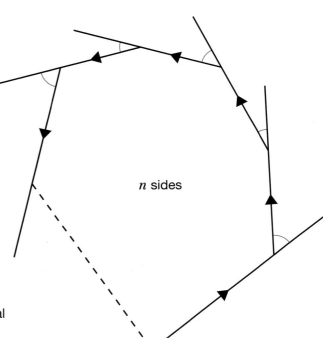

n sides

DIVIDING REGULAR POLYGONS

All regular polygons can be divided into equal isosceles triangles.

The hexagon divides into equilateral triangles.

Dividing a regular polygon in this way can help solve many mathematical problems.

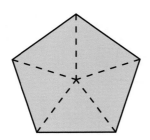
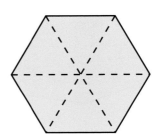
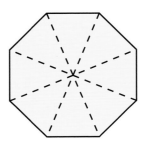

ACTIVITY 4

A regular octagon is divided into equal isosceles triangles.

Work out the angles of these triangles.

EXAMPLE 6

A regular polygon has twelve sides. Find the size of each exterior and interior angle.

SKILLS

REASONING

The exterior angle is $\dfrac{360}{n} = \dfrac{360}{12} = 30°$

The interior angle is $180 - \dfrac{360}{n} = 180 - 30 = 150°$

Note: the interior and exterior angles sum to 180°.

EXAMPLE 7

The interior angle of a regular polygon is 162°. How many sides does it have?

SKILLS

REASONING

The exterior angle is $180 - 162 = 18°$

The exterior angle is $18 = \dfrac{360}{n} \Rightarrow n = \dfrac{360}{18} = 20$

The polygon has 20 sides.

KEY POINTS

- An n-sided polygon can be divided into $n - 2$ triangles.

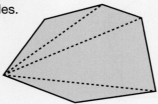

- The sum of the interior angles of a polygon is $(n - 2) \times 180°$.

- The sum of the exterior angles of a polygon is 360° no matter how many sides it has.

- All regular polygons can be divided into equal isosceles triangles.

- For a regular polygon

$180 - \dfrac{360}{5} = 108°$

$\dfrac{360}{5} = 72°$

External angle $= \dfrac{360°}{n}$

Interior angle $= 180 - \dfrac{360}{n}$ degrees.

EXERCISE 3

1 ▶ For each irregular polygon work out

(i) the sum of the interior angles

(ii) the size of the angle marked with a letter.

a
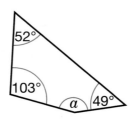

b
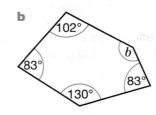

c
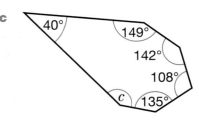

2 ▶ For each of the following shapes, work out the size of

(i) the angle sum   (ii) the interior angle.

a a regular hexagon   b a regular pentagon   c an 18-sided regular polygon.

3 ▶ For each polygon, work out the number of sides from the sum of its interior angles.

a 1620°   b 2160°   c 2700°   d 3960°

4 ▶ Each interior angle of a regular polygon is 140 degrees.
How many sides does the polygon have?

5 ▶ Point F lies on the mid-point of CD. Find the size of angle x.

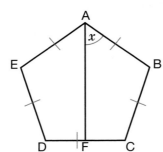

6 ▶ ABCDEFGH is a regular octagon.
PAE is a straight line.
Angle PAB = $y°$.
Work out the value of y.

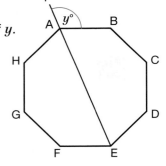

EXERCISE 3*

1 ▶ The sum of the interior angles of a regular polygon is $180(n - 2)$ degrees.
How many sides does the polygon have?

2 ▶ Marco claims that he has drawn a regular polygon with an interior angle of 145°.
Prove that this is impossible.

3 ▶ The diagram shows a regular pentagon and a regular octagon.

Calculate the size of the angle marked x.

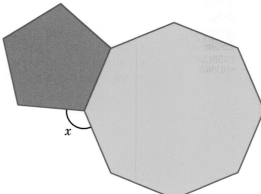

4 ▶ Garry wants to put a path in his garden. The shape of each paving stone is an isosceles trapezium. The path will follow a complete circle. If there are 20 stones, what is the size of angle x?

5 ▶ The interior angle of a regular polygon is seven times as large as the exterior angle. How many sides does the polygon have?

6 ▶ There are two polygons. The larger one has three times as many sides as the smaller one. Its angle sum is four times as big. How many sides does the smaller polygon have?

CONSTRUCTIONS

Constructions of various shapes can be done accurately with a ruler and **compasses**. Architects used to use this technique when producing accurate scale drawings of their building plans.

BEARINGS AND SCALE DRAWINGS

Scale drawings show a real object with accurate sizes reduced or enlarged (scaled) by a **scale factor**.

KEY POINTS

Bearings are measured

- clockwise
- from north.

A is on a bearing of 300° from B.
B is on a bearing of 120° from A.

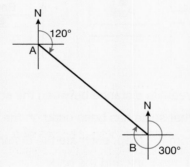

EXAMPLE 8

SKILLS

PROBLEM SOLVING

A map has a **scale** of 1:50 000.

What is the real-life distance in kilometres for 6 cm on the map?

Map   Real life

$$\times6 \left(\begin{array}{c} 1 : 50\,000 \\ 6 : 300\,000 \end{array} \right) \times6$$

6 cm represents 6 × 50 000 = 300 000 cm — Convert cm to m.
300 000 cm ÷ 100 = 3000 m
3000 m ÷ 1000 = 3 km — Convert to km.

EXERCISE 4

1 ▶   **a** On a scale drawing, 1 cm represents 2 m. What does 10 cm on the drawing represent?
   b On a map, 1 cm represents 10 km. What is the length on the map for a real-life distance of 25 km?

2 ▶   **a** Make an accurate scale drawing of this triangular garden. Use a scale of 1 cm to 1.5 m.
   b What is the **perimeter** of the real-life garden?

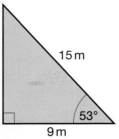

3 ▶   Describe the bearing of B from A.

a

b

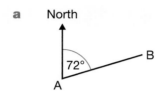

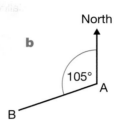

4 ▶   Here is a map of a town.

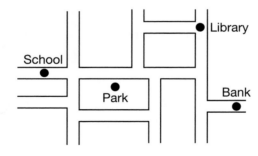

The real-life distance between the school and the library in a straight line is 480 m.

a What scale has been used on the map?

b From the map, estimate the distance (in a straight line) between

   (i) the bank and the park
   (ii) the bank and the school.

c John can walk 100 m in 40 seconds. How long will it take him to walk from the library to the school? Write your answer in minutes.

EXERCISE 4*

1 ▶   The distance between Manchester Airport and Luton Airport is 215 km.

The bearing of Luton Airport from Manchester Airport is 135°.

Make an accurate scale map of the locations of the two airports, using a scale of 1 cm to 40 km.

2 ▶   **a** Calculate the distance in km between

    (i) Galway and Sligo   **(ii)** Dublin and Belfast.

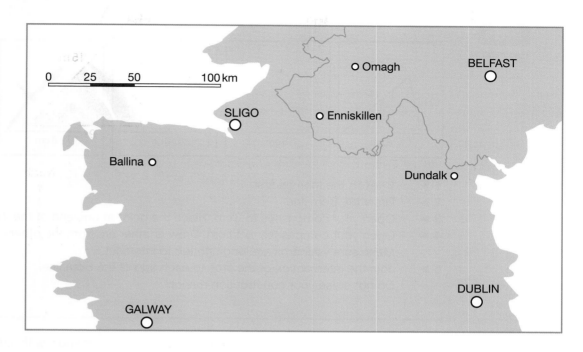

b Which place is 180 km from Dublin and 150 km from Belfast?

3 ▶   The scale on a map is 1 : 25 000.

    a On the map, the distance between two schools is 10 cm. Work out the real-life distance between the schools. Give your answer in km.

    b The real-life distance between two farms is 4 km. Work out the distance between the farms on the map. Give your answer in cm.

4 ▶   The bearing of Palermo Airport (in Italy) from Paris Airport is 143°.

Calculate the bearing of Paris Airport from Palermo Airport.

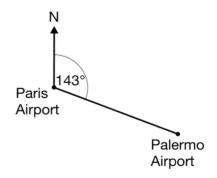

Q4 HINT

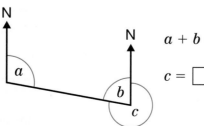

$a + b = \boxed{}$ (co-interior angles)

$c = \boxed{} - b$ (angles around a point)

CONSTRUCTING TRIANGLES

Construct a triangle with sides 11 cm, 8 cm and 6 cm.

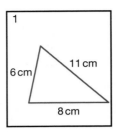 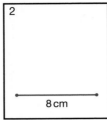 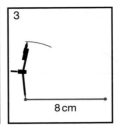 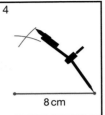 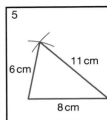

1 ▶ **Sketch** the triangle first.

2 ▶ Draw the 8 cm line.

3 ▶ Open your compasses to 6 cm. Place the point at one end of the 8 cm line. Draw an **arc**.

4 ▶ Open your compasses to 11 cm. Draw another arc from the other end of the 8 cm line. Make sure your arcs are long enough to intersect.

5 ▶ Join the intersection of the arcs to each end of the 8 cm line. Do not erase your construction marks.

EXERCISE 5

1 ▶ Follow these instructions to accurately construct a triangle with sides 6 cm, 7 cm and 10 cm.

a
Use a ruler to draw the 10 cm side accurately.

b
The 6 cm side starts at the left-hand end of this line. Open your compasses to exactly 6 cm and draw an arc from the left-hand end of the line.

c
Open your compasses to exactly 7 cm and draw an arc from the other end.

d
Use the point where the arcs cross to create the finished triangle.

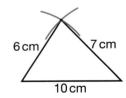

2 ▶ Construct this triangle.

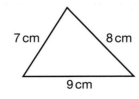

3 ▶ Construct an accurate drawing of this triangle.

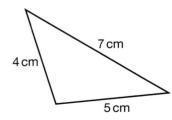

4 ▶ Construct each triangle ABC.
  a AB = 5 cm, BC = 6 cm, AC = 7 cm
  b AB = 10 cm, AC = 5 cm, CB = 6 cm
  c AB = 8.5 cm, BC = 4 cm, AC = 7.5 cm

5 ▶ Construct an equilateral triangle with sides 6.5 cm. Check the angles using a **protractor**.

6 ▶ Explain why it is impossible to construct a triangle with sides 6 cm, 4.5 cm, 11 cm.

EXERCISE 5*

5th

1 ▶ Construct an accurate scale drawing of this skateboard ramp. Use a scale of 1 cm to 20 cm.

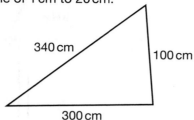

340 cm

100 cm

300 cm

2 ▶ The diagram shows the end elevation of a house roof.

Using a scale of 1 cm to 2 m, construct an accurate scale drawing of this elevation.

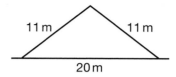

11 m   11 m

20 m

Q3 HINT

A net is a two-dimensional pattern that you cut and fold to make a three-dimensional shape.

6th

3 ▶ This chocolate box is in the shape of a **tetrahedron**. Each face is an equilateral triangle with side length 24 cm. Construct an accurate net for the box. Use a scale of 1 cm to 4 cm.

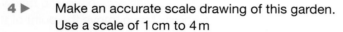

4 ▶ Make an accurate scale drawing of this garden. Use a scale of 1 cm to 4 m

A tree can be planted between 10 m and 4 m from corner C. It must be planted at least 14 m from the house. Accurately shade the region where the tree could be planted.

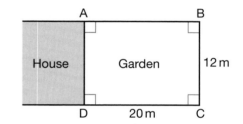

A   B

House   Garden   12 m

D   20 m   C

7th

5 ▶ This map shows two villages, Reethi and Rakariya.

A company is going to build a warehouse. The warehouse will be less than 30 km from Reethi and less than 50 km from Rakariya.

On a copy of the map, sketch the region where the company can build the warehouse.

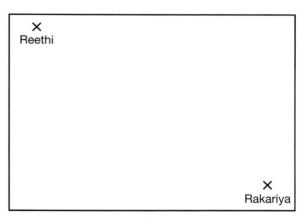

✕
Reethi

✕
Rakariya

Scale: 1 cm represents 10 km

6 ▶ Three radio stations can transmit signals up to 100 km.

a Using a scale of 1 cm to 20 km, construct a triangle with the radio stations at the corners of the triangle.

b Shade the region where someone could hear all three radio stations.

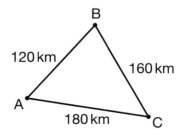

B

120 km   160 km

A

180 km   C

PERPENDICULAR BISECTOR

A perpendicular bisector is a line that cuts another line in half at right angles.

EXAMPLE 10

SKILLS

REASONING

Draw a line 9 cm long. Construct its perpendicular **bisector**.

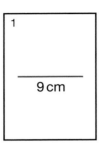 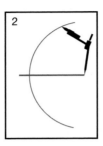 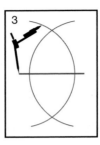 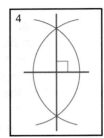

1 ▶ Use a ruler to draw the line.

2 ▶ Open your compasses to more than half the length of the line.
Place the point on one end of the line and draw an arc above and below.

3 ▶ Keeping the compasses open to the same distance, move the point of the compasses to the other end of the line and draw a similar arc.

4 ▶ Join the points where the arcs intersect. Do not erase your construction marks.
This vertical line is the perpendicular bisector.

EXERCISE 6

1 ▶ Draw a line 12 cm long. Follow these instructions to construct the perpendicular bisector.

a
Draw the line.
Open your compasses
to more than half the
length of the line.

12 cm

b
Draw the
first arc.

c
Draw the
second arc.

d
Draw the
perpendicular
bisector.

2 ▶ Draw a line 7 cm long. Construct the perpendicular bisector.

3 ▶ Draw a line 10 cm long. Construct the perpendicular bisector using a ruler and compasses.

4 ▶ a Draw a line **segment** AB 7 cm long. Construct the perpendicular bisector of AB.
b Use a ruler and protractor to check that it **bisects** your line at right angles.
c Mark any point P on your perpendicular bisector. Measure its distance from A and from B.

EXERCISE 6*

1 ▶ Two ships, S and T, are 50 m apart.
a Using a scale of 1 cm to 5 m, draw an accurate scale drawing of the ships.
b A lifeboat is **equidistant** (of equal distance) from both ships.
Construct a line to show where the lifeboat could be.
How can you find a point the same distance from A as from B?

2 ▶ Follow these instructions to draw the perpendicular from point P not on the line to the line AB.

    a Draw a line segment AB and point P not on the line.

    b Open your compasses and draw an arc with centre P. Label the two points where it intersects the line AB S and T.

    c Construct the perpendicular bisector of the line ST.

    d What is the shortest distance from P to AB?

3 ▶ Follow these instructions to construct the perpendicular at point P on a line.

    a Draw a line segment and point P on the line.

    b Open your compasses. Put the point on P and draw arcs on the line on either side of point P.
Label the points where they intersect the line X and Y.

    c Construct the perpendicular bisector.

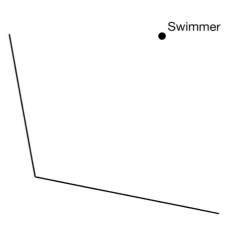

4 ▶ A swimmer wants to swim the shortest distance to the edge of a swimming pool. The scale is 1 cm to 5 m.

    a Trace the diagram and construct the shortest path for the swimmer to swim to each side of the swimming pool.

    b Work out the difference in the distances.

    c The swimmer swims 2 m every second. How long would the shortest distance take?

ANGLE BISECTOR

An angle bisector cuts an angle in half.

EXAMPLE 11

Draw an angle of 80°. Construct the angle bisector.

SKILLS

REASONING

1	2	3	4	5
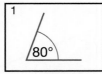	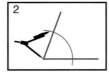	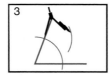		

1 ▶ Draw an angle of 80° using a protractor.

2 ▶ Open your compasses and place the point at the vertex of the angle. Draw an arc that crosses both arms (lines) of the angle.

3 ▶ Keep the compasses open to the same distance. Move them to one of the points where the arc crosses an arm. Make an arc in the middle of the angle.

4 ▶ Do the same for where the arc crosses the other arm.

5 ▶ Join the vertex of the angle to the point where the two small arcs intersect. Do not erase your construction marks. This line is the angle bisector.

EXERCISE 7

1 ▶ Use a protractor to draw an angle of 70°.
Follow these instructions to construct the angle bisector.

a
Draw the
angle.

b
Draw an arc
from the vertex
of the angle.

c
Draw another arc
between the two
sides of the angle.

d
Draw a second
arc.

e
Draw the angle
bisector.

2 ▶ For each angle
(i) draw the angle
(ii) construct the angle bisector using a ruler and compasses
(iii) check your two smaller angles using a protractor.

a
b

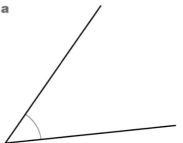
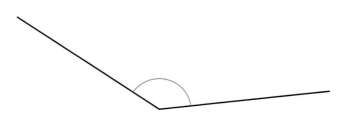

3 ▶ Use a ruler and compasses to construct these angles.
a 90°   **b** 45°

4 ▶ Use a ruler and compasses to construct these angles.
a 60°   **b** 30°

EXERCISE 7*

1 ▶ A gardener wants to divide a rectangular
garden into two sections.
The triangular section will be a terrace and
the rest of the garden will be grass.

a Make a scale drawing of the rectangular
garden. Use a scale of 1 cm to 4 m.
b Use a ruler and compasses to construct
an angle of 30°.
c Calculate the area of the terrace.

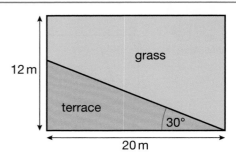

2 ▶ **a** Use a ruler, protractor and compasses
to construct the triangle ABC.
b Construct a line that is perpendicular
to AB and passes through C.
c Calculate the area of the triangle to the
nearest cm².

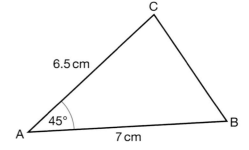

3 ▶ Construct this trapezium made from equilateral triangles using a ruler and compasses.

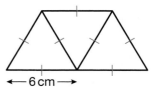

← 6 cm →

 4 ▶   **a** Construct a triangle with sides 5 cm, 8 cm and 10 cm.
b Construct the bisector of each angle.
c The angle bisectors cross at the same point. Label this point O.
d Construct the perpendicular to one of the sides from the point you found in part **c**. Label the point where the perpendicular meets the side A.
e Draw a circle with **radius** OA. What do you notice about your circle?

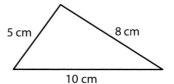

SIMILAR TRIANGLES

• **Similar triangles** have these properties.

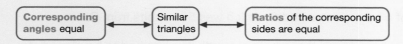

If any one of these facts is true, then the other two must also be true.

ACTIVITY 5

SKILLS

REASONING

Measure each of the angles in these three triangles.

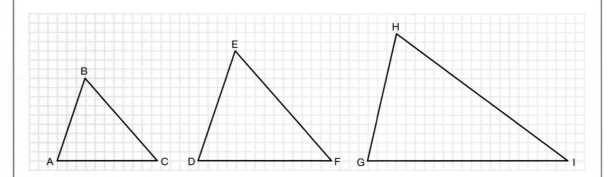

You should find that the corresponding angles in triangles ABC and DEF are equal.
This is because these two triangles are similar in shape.
Now measure each of the nine sides, then use your measurements to calculate these ratios.

$$\frac{AC}{DF} \quad \frac{AB}{DE} \quad \frac{BC}{EF} \quad \frac{AB}{GH} \quad \frac{AC}{GI} \quad \frac{EF}{HI}$$

You should find that only the first three ratios give the same result.
This is because only triangles ABC and DEF are similar in shape.

EXAMPLE 12

SKILLS

REASONING

Which of these triangles are similar to each other?

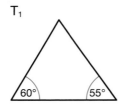

T₁

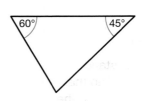

T₂

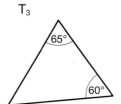

T₃

The angle sum of a triangle is 180°.

Therefore in T₁ the angles are 55°, 60° and 65°, in T₂ the angles are 45°, 60° and 75°, and in T₃ the angles are 55°, 60° and 65°.

Therefore the triangles T₁ and T₃ are similar.

EXAMPLE 13

SKILLS

PROBLEM SOLVING

The ancient Egyptians used similar triangles to work out the heights of their pyramids. The unit they used was the cubit, a measure based on the length from a person's elbow to their fingertips.

The shadow of a pyramid reached C, which was 500 cubits from B.

An Egyptian engineer found that a pole of length 4 cubits had to be placed at Y, 20 cubits from C, for its shadow to reach C as well. What was the height of the pyramid AB?

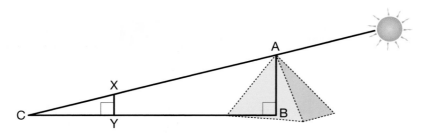

As AB and XY are both vertical, the triangles CAB and CXY are similar in shape.

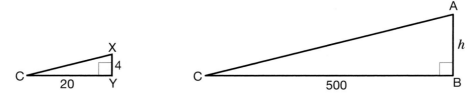

So the ratios of their corresponding sides are equal.

$$\frac{AB}{XY} = \frac{CB}{CY} \qquad \frac{AB}{4} = \frac{500}{20} = 25 \qquad AB = 4 \times 25 = 100$$

So the height of the pyramid is 100 cubits.

ACTIVITY 6

SKILLS

ADAPTIVE LEARNING

To find the height of a wall AB, place a mirror on the ground at any point R.

An observer stands in line with the wall at point Y so that the top of the wall can be seen in the mirror.

Explain why the triangles ABR and YXR are similar in shape.

Show that the ratio of the corresponding sides is given by

$$\frac{AB}{XY} = \frac{AR}{RY}$$

Use this method to find out the height of your classroom or some other tall object.

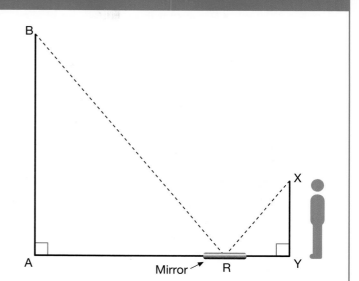

Repeat the experiment by placing the mirror in various positions. Describe your method, and comment on the accuracy of your results.

Use the method of Example 13 to check some of your measurements. Compare the two methods.

EXAMPLE 14

SKILLS

REASONING

Find x and y.

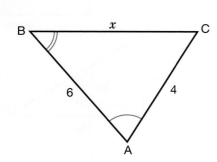

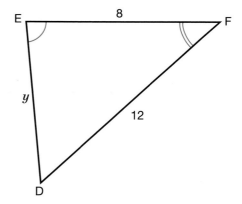

$\hat{A} = \hat{E}, \hat{B} = \hat{F}, \hat{C} = \hat{D}$ Therefore △ ABC is similar to △ DEF.

$\Rightarrow \dfrac{AB}{EF} = \dfrac{AC}{DE} = \dfrac{BC}{DF} \Rightarrow \dfrac{6}{8} = \dfrac{4}{y} = \dfrac{x}{12}$ Corresponding sides are in the same ratio.

$\Rightarrow \dfrac{6}{8} = \dfrac{x}{12}$ $\Rightarrow 6 \times 12 = 8 \times x$ $\Rightarrow x = 9$

$\Rightarrow \dfrac{6}{8} = \dfrac{4}{y}$ $\Rightarrow 6 \times y = 8 \times 4$ $\Rightarrow y = 5\dfrac{1}{3}$

If solving similar triangles for side length:

- Prove that the triangles are similar – all three angles must be the same.

- Identify the corresponding sides – these will be opposite the same angle – and write them as ratios in a consistent order.

- Some diagrams may be easier to work with if they are redrawn in the same orientation (each vertex facing the same way).

EXERCISE 8

1 ▶ For each pair of similar triangles

    (i) name the three pairs of corresponding sides   **(ii)** state which pairs of angles are equal.

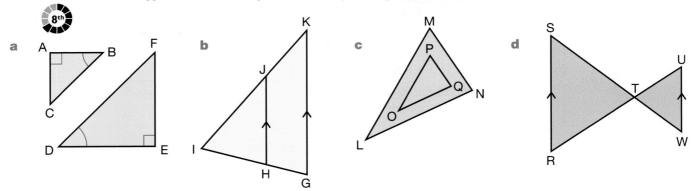

2 ▶ Which of these triangles are similar to triangle A?

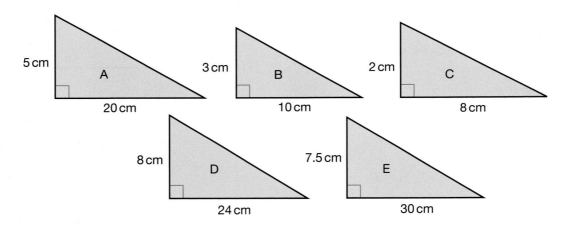

3 ▶ Triangle A is similar to triangle B.

    a Work out the scale factor of A to B by comparing the given side lengths.

    The perimeter of triangle A is 12 cm.

    b What is the perimeter of triangle B?

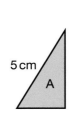 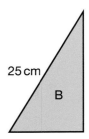

Q4 HINT
Sketch the triangles in the same orientation.

4 ▶ All these shapes are similar. Work out the lengths marked with letters.

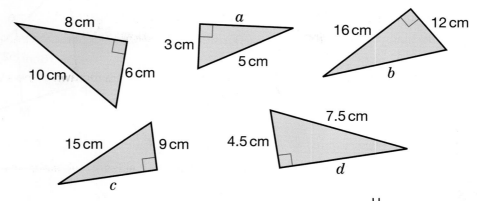

5 ▶ Triangle CDE is similar to triangle FGH.

∠CDE = ∠FGH

Calculate the length of

a FG   **b** FH

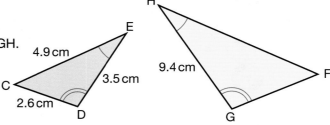

EXERCISE 8*

1 ▶ Are triangles ABE and CDE similar? Explain.

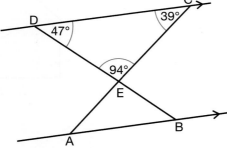

Give reasons for your answers.

Q1 HINT
Find the angles in triangle AEB.

Q2 HINT
Mark equal angles.

2 ▶ **a** Show that triangles PQR and RST are similar.

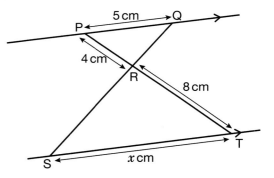

b Find the missing length x.

Q3 HINT
Draw the triangles separately.

3 ▶ **a** Explain why triangles FGH and FJK are similar.

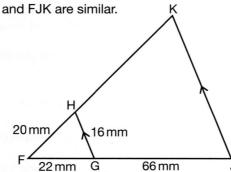

b Calculate the length HK.
c Calculate the length JK.

4 ▶ Calculate the height of The Shard, a very tall building in London, using similar triangles.

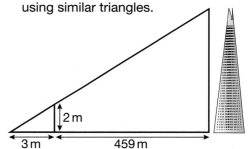

5 ▶   **a** Find the sizes of angle PQN and angle LMN.

   b Explain why triangle LMN is similar to triangle LPQ.

   c Find the length of LQ.

   d Find the length of NQ.

   e Find the length of MP.

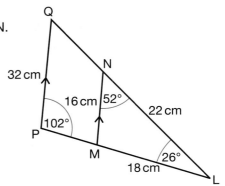

EXERCISE 9   **REVISION**

1 ▶   Work out the sizes of the angles marked with letters.

a
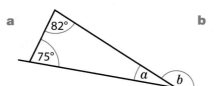

b
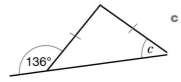

c
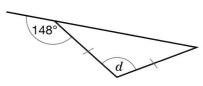

2 ▶   AFB and CHD are parallel lines.
EFD is a straight line.
Work out the size of the angle marked x.

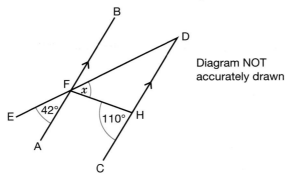

Diagram NOT accurately drawn

3 ▶   Find the size of angle a.

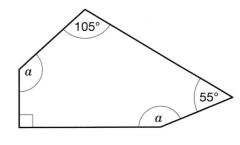

4 ▶   **a** How many sides does this regular polygon have?
   b A regular polygon has 18 sides. What is the size of its exterior angle?

5 ▶   Use compasses and a ruler to construct an **equilateral triangle** of sides 7 cm.

6 ▶   Use compasses and a ruler to construct the perpendicular bisector of the line AB where AB = 8 cm.

7 ▶   A ship sails for 24 km on a bearing of 060°. It then turns and sails for 18 km on a bearing of 160°.
   a Use a scale of 10 cm to 30 km to draw an accurate scale drawing of the journey of the ship.
   b How far is the ship from its starting point to the nearest kilometre?
   c On what bearing should the ship sail, to return to its starting point?

8 ▶ **a** Prove that triangle ABE is similar to triangle ACD.

　　b Work out length CD.

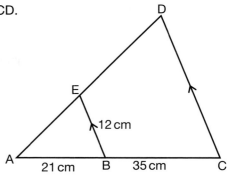

REVISION

1 ▶ Triangle BDC is an isosceles triangle.
Triangle ACE is a right-angled triangle.

Show that triangle ABC is an equilateral triangle.

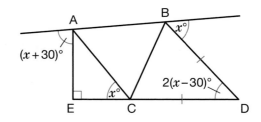

2 ▶ AB, BC and CD are three sides of a regular octagon.

Find the size of angle BAC. Give reasons for your answer.

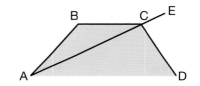

3 ▶ Work out the size of each unknown exterior angle in this polygon.

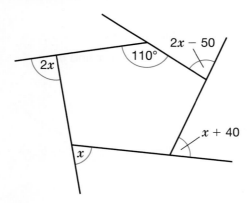

4 ▶ One side of a regular hexagon ABCDEF forms the side of a regular polygon with n sides.

Angle GAF = 105°. Work out the value of n.

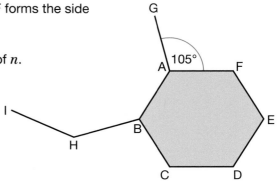

5 ▶ In a party game, a valuable prize is hidden within a triangle formed by an oak tree (O), an apple tree (A) and a plum tree (P).

    a Given that OA = 16 m, AP = 18 m and OP = 20 m, construct the triangle OPA using a scale of 1 cm = 2 m.

    b The prize is equidistant from the apple tree and the plum tree and 12 m from the oak tree. By careful construction find the distance of the prize from the plum tree.

6 ▶ The rectangle ABCD represents a map of an area 30 m × 60 m. A mobile phone mast, M, is to be placed so that it is equidistant from A and B and 20 m from point E, so that BE : EC = 1 : 2.

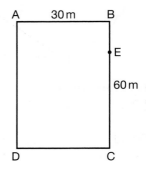

    a Draw the map using a scale of 1 cm = 5 m.

    b Showing your construction lines clearly, find the shortest distance of M from D.

Q7 HINT
Draw each bearing from the north line clockwise.
Make sure the bearing lines are long enough so that they meet.

7 ▶ The diagram shows the position of two boats, B and C.

Boat T is on a bearing of 060° from boat B.

Boat T is on a bearing of 285° from boat C.

    a Draw an accurate diagram to show the position of boat T.

    b Mark the position of boat T with a cross (X). Label it T.

8 ▶ **a** Show that PQR and RST are similar triangles.

    b Work out the missing lengths in the diagram, x and y.

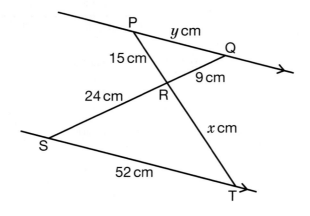

EXAM PRACTICE: SHAPE AND SPACE 1

1 ABC and CDE are straight lines.
AE is parallel to BD.

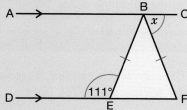

Work out the size of
a AB̂D   b AÊD   c AĈE   [3]

2 ABC and DEF are straight lines.
AC is parallel to DF. BE = BF.

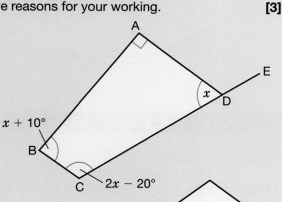

Calculate the size of the angle marked x.
You must give reasons for your answer.   [3]

3 Work out the size of angle ADE.
Give reasons for your working.   [3]

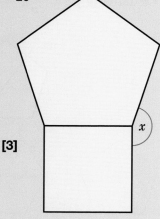

4 The diagram shows a regular pentagon and a square.

Calculate the size of the angle marked x.
You must show all your working.   [3]

5 a The scale of the map is 1 : 1 000 000.
Calculate the distance in km between
(i) St Peter Port and St Helier
(ii) St Helier and Carteret.
b Which town is 57 km from Cherbourg?   [4]

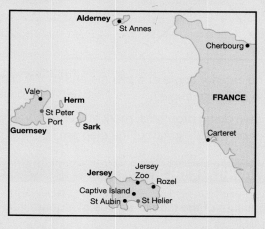

6 Using compasses and a ruler, construct
a an angle of 45°
b the perpendicular bisector of an 8 cm line.   [2]

7 Calculate the height of the Statue of Liberty using similar triangles.   [2]

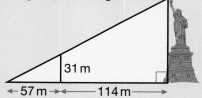

8 a Find the sizes of angles PQN and LMN.

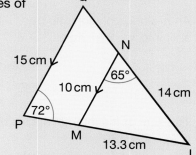

b Explain why triangle LMN is similar to triangle LPQ.
c Find the length of LQ.
d Find the length of NQ.
e Find the length of MP.   [5]

[Total 25 marks]

CHAPTER SUMMARY: SHAPE AND SPACE 1

TRIANGLES

The angle sum of a triangle is 180°.

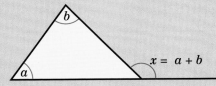

The exterior angle of a triangle equals the sum of the opposite angles.

When doing problems, mark any angles you work out on a neat sketch of the diagram.

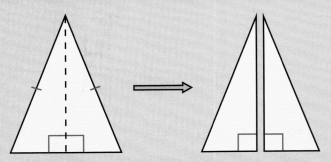

An isosceles triangle can be divided into two equal right-angled triangles.

QUADRILATERALS

The sum of the interior angles of a quadrilateral is 360°.

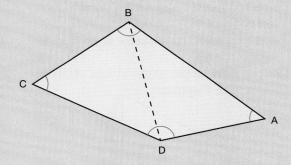

The sum of the exterior angles of a quadrilateral is 360°.
$a + b + c + d = 360°$

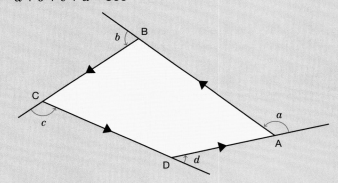

POLYGONS

An n-sided polygon can be split into $n - 2$ triangles.

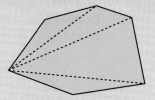

For a regular polygon

• External angle $= \dfrac{360°}{n}$ • Interior angle $= 180 - \dfrac{360°}{n}$

The sum of the internal angles of a polygon is $(n - 2) \times 180°$.

The sum of the exterior angles of a polygon is 360° no matter how many sides it has.

All regular polygons can be divided into equal isosceles triangles.

$180 - \dfrac{360}{5} = 108°$

$\dfrac{360}{5} = 72°$

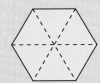

CONSTRUCTIONS

CONSTRUCTING TRIANGLES

Construct a triangle with sides 11 cm, 8 cm and 6 cm.

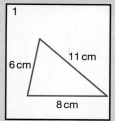
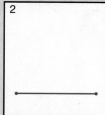
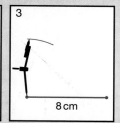
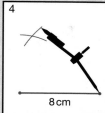
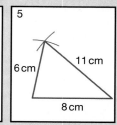

PERPENDICULAR BISECTOR

A perpendicular bisector is a line that cuts another line in half at right angles.
Draw a line 9 cm long. Construct its perpendicular bisector.

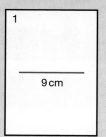

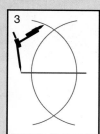
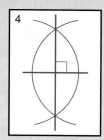

ANGLE BISECTOR

An angle bisector cuts an angle in half.
Draw an angle of 80°. Construct the angle bisector.

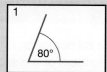
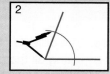
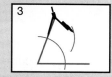
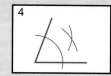
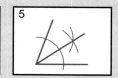

SIMILAR TRIANGLES

Similar triangles have these properties.

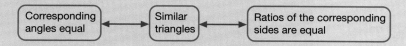

Corresponding angles equal ↔ Similar triangles ↔ Ratios of the corresponding sides are equal

If any one of these facts is true, then the other two must also be true.

If solving similar triangles for side length:

• Prove that the triangles are similar – all 3 angles must be the same.

• Identify the corresponding sides – these will be opposite the same angle – and write them as ratios in a consistent order.

• Some diagrams may be easier to work with if they are redrawn in the same orientation (each vertex facing the same way).

SETS 1

The idea of a set is simple but powerful. The theory of sets is mainly due to the work of the German mathematician, Georg Cantor (1845–1918). His work resulted in arguments and disagreements since it was so counter-intuitive (against common sense). Cantor faced many fierce personal attacks by the mathematical establishment. In later years he suffered from chronic depression, possibly due to these attacks, and he died in poverty. By the 1920s his ideas were generally accepted and led to great advances in mathematics.

LEARNING OBJECTIVES

■ Use set notation ■ Use Venn diagrams to represent sets

BASIC PRINCIPLES

■ Recognise different types of numbers (odd, even, prime, square, …).

■ Know the properties of triangles and quadrilaterals.

■ Understand multiples and factors of numbers.

SET NOTATION

A set is a collection of objects which are called the elements or members of the set. The objects can be numbers, animals, ideas, colours, in fact anything you can imagine. A set can be described by listing all the members of the set, or by giving a rule to describe the members. The list or rule is enclosed by braces (curly brackets) {}.

EXAMPLE 1

A set described by the list

{Anne, Nikos, Bob}

is the set consisting of the three people called Anne, Nikos and Bob.

EXAMPLE 2

A set described by the rule {even numbers between 1 and 11} is the set consisting of the five numbers 2, 4, 6, 8, 10.

Sets are often labelled by a single capital letter.

A = {odd numbers between 2 and 10} means A is the set consisting of the four numbers 3, 5, 7, 9.

The number of elements in the set A is $n(A)$, so $n(A) = 4$.

Sets can be infinite in size, for example the set of **prime numbers**.

Membership of a set is indicated by the symbol $\in$ and non-membership by the symbol $\notin$.

EXAMPLE 3

If E = {2, 8, 4, 6, 10} and F = {even numbers between 1 and 11}, then $n(E) = 5$, $n(F) = 5$; in other words, both E and F have the same number of elements.

$3 \notin E$ means 3 is not a member of the set E.

$6 \in F$ means 6 is a member of the set F.

E = F because both E and F have the same members.

The order of listing the members does not matter.

The empty set, $\varnothing$ or {}, is the set with no members.

EXAMPLE 4

Give two examples of the empty set.

• The set of people you know over 4 m tall.

• The set of odd **integers** divisible by two.

KEY POINTS

• A set is a collection of objects, described by a list or a rule.　A = {1, 3, 5}
• Each object is an element or member of the set.　$1 \in A, 2 \notin A$
• Sets are equal if they have exactly the same elements.　B = {5, 3, 1}, B = A
• The number of elements of set A is given by $n(A)$.　$n(A) = 3$
• The empty set is the set with no members.　{} or $\varnothing$

EXERCISE 1

1 ▶ Write down two more members of these sets.
 a {carrot, potato, pea, ...}
 b {red, green, blue, ...}
 c {a, b, c, d, ...}
 d {1, 3, 5, 7, ...}

2 ▶ List the members of these sets.
 a {days of the week}
 b {square numbers less than 101}
 c {subjects you study at school}
 d {prime numbers less than 22}

3 ▶ Describe the following sets by a rule.

   a {a, b, c, d}

   b {Tuesday, Thursday}

   c {1, 4, 9, 16}

   d {2, 4, 6, 8, …}

4 ▶ Which of these statements are true?

   a cat ∈ {animals with two legs}

   b square ∉ {**parallelograms**}

   c 1 ∈ {prime numbers}

   d 2 ∉ {odd numbers}

5 ▶ Which of these are examples of the empty set?

   a The set of men with no teeth.

   b The set of months of the year with 32 days

   c The set of straight lines drawn on the surface of a sphere

   d The set of prime numbers between 35 and 43

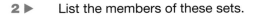

EXERCISE 1*

1 ▶ Write down two more members of these sets.

   a {Venus, Earth, Mars, …}

   b {triangle, square, hexagon, …}

   c {hydrogen, iron, aluminium, …}

   d {1, 4, 9, 16, …}

2 ▶ List the members of these sets.

   a {all possible means of any two elements of 1, 3, 5}

   b {different digits of 11^4}

   c {all factors of 35}

   d {**powers** of 10 with values greater than 5 and less than one million}

3 ▶ Describe the following sets by a rule.

   a {Spring, Summer, Autumn, Winter}

   b {circle, ellipse, **parabola**, hyperbola}

   c {1, 2, 4, 8, 16}

   d {(3, 4, 5), (5, 12, 13), (7, 24, 25), …}

4 ▶ Which of these statements are true?

   a Everest ∈ {mountains over 2000 m high}

   b 2000 ∉ {leap years: years with 366 days}

   c $2x + 3y = 5$ ∈ {equations with straight-line graphs}

   d −2 ∈ {solutions of $x^3 - 2x^2 = 0$}

5 ▶ Which of these are examples of the empty set?

   a The set of kangaroos with three legs

   b The set which has the numeral zero as its only member

   c The set of **common factors** of 11 and 13

   d The set of real solutions of $x^2 = -1$

VENN DIAGRAMS

Sets can be shown in a diagram called a Venn diagram after the English mathematician John Venn (1834–1923). The members of the set are shown within a closed curve.

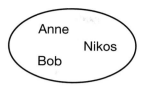
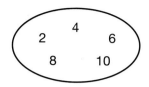

When the number of elements is large, a closed curve is drawn and labelled to indicate the set.

If S = {striped cats} then the Venn diagram is

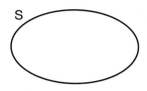

If C = {cats in the world}, S and C can be shown on a Venn diagram as

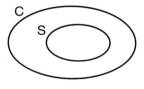

Set S is shown inside set C because every member of S is also a member of C.

S is called a **subset** of C. This is written as S ⊂ C.

EXAMPLE 5

A = {1, 2, 3, 4, 5, 6, 7, 8, 9}

a List the subset O = {odd numbers}

b List the subset P = {prime numbers}

c Is Q = {8, 4, 6} a subset of A?

d Is R = {0, 1, 2, 3} a subset of A?

---

a O = {1, 3, 5, 7, 9}

b P = {2, 3, 5, 7}

c Q ⊂ A because every member of Q is also a member of A.

d R ⊄ A because the element 0 is a member of R but it is not a member of A.

If the earlier problem was only about cats in this world, then we call the set C the universal set (ℰ). The universal set contains all the elements in a particular problem. It is shown as a rectangle.

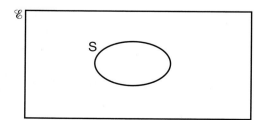

If the problem was only about cats in Rome, then ℰ = {cats in Rome}; the Venn diagram does not change. If there are 10 000 cats in Rome, and 1000 are striped cats, these numbers can be entered on the Venn diagram. The diagram shows that there are 9000 non-striped cats outside S. This set is denoted by S′ and is called the **complement** of S.

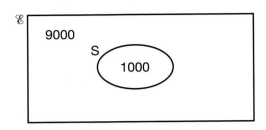
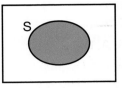
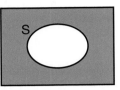

S shown shaded   S′ shown shaded

INTERSECTION OF SETS

Sets can overlap. Let M = {male cats}. S and M overlap because some cats are both striped and male. S and M are shown on the Venn diagram.

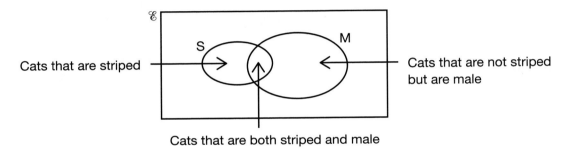

Cats that are striped   Cats that are not striped but are male

Cats that are both striped and male

The set of cats that are both striped and male is where the sets S and M overlap. It is called the intersection of the two sets S and M and is written S ∩ M.

EXAMPLE 6

SKILLS

REASONING

ℰ = {all positive integers less than 10}, P = {prime numbers less than 10} and O = {odd numbers less than 10}.

a   Show this information on a Venn diagram.

b   Find the set P ∩ O and n(P ∩ O).

c   List P′.

a

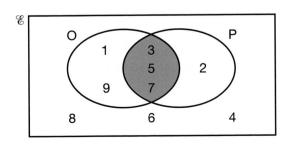

b   The set P ∩ O is shown shaded on the Venn diagram.

From the Venn diagram P ∩ O = {3, 5, 7} and n(P ∩ O) = 3.

c   P′ is every element not in P so P′ = {1, 4, 6, 8, 9}.

KEY POINTS

- The universal set, $\mathscr{E}$, contains all the elements being considered in a particular problem.

- B is a subset of A, B ⊂ A, if every member of B is a member of A.

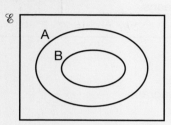

- The complement of set A, A′, is the set of all elements not in A.

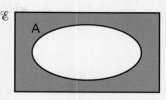

- The intersection of A and B, A ∩ B, is the set of elements which are in both A and B.

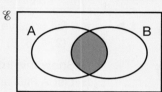

EXERCISE 2

1 ▶ In the Venn diagram, $\mathscr{E}$ = {pupils in a class}, C = {pupils who like chocolate} and S = {pupils who like sweets}.

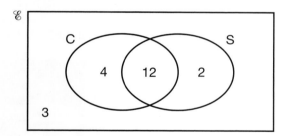

a How many pupils like chocolate?
b Find n(S) and express what this means in words.
c Find n(C ∩ S) and express what this means in words.
d How many pupils are there in the class?

2 ▶ On the Venn diagram, $\mathscr{E}$ = {people at a party}, T = {people wearing tee shirts} and J = {people wearing jeans}.

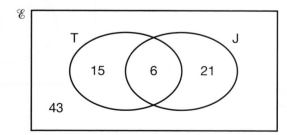

How many people
a were wearing tee shirts and jeans
b were wearing tee shirts but not jeans
c were not wearing jeans
d were at the party?

3 ▶ ℰ = {a, b, c, d, e, f, g, h, i, j}, A = {a, c, e, g, i}, B = {c, d, e, f}.
   a Show this information on a Venn diagram.
   b List A ∩ B and find n(A ∩ B).
   c Does A ∩ B = B ∩ A?
   d Is B ⊂ A? Give a reason for your answer.

4 ▶ ℰ = {all cars in the world}, P = {pink cars}, R = {Rolls-Royce cars}.
   a Describe the set P ∩ R in words.
   b Describe the set R′ in words.
   c If P ∩ R = ∅, describe what this means.

EXERCISE 2*

1 ▶ ℰ = {all positive integers less than 12},
   A = {2, 4, 6, 8, 10}, B = {4, 5, 6, 7, 8}.

   a Show this information on a Venn diagram.
   b List A ∩ B and find n(A ∩ B).
   c Does A ∩ B = B ∩ A?
   d List (A ∩ B)′.
   e Is A ∩ B a subset of A?

2 ▶ ℰ = {all positive integers less than 12}, E = {1, 2, 3, 4}, F = {5, 6, 7, 8}.
   a Show this information on a Venn diagram.
   b List E ∩ F.
   c If E ∩ F = ∅ what can you say about the sets E and F?

3 ▶ R is the set of roses in a flower shop and W is the set of white flowers in the same shop.

   a Show this information on a Venn diagram.
   b Describe the set R ∩ W in words.
   c If R ∩ W = ∅, what can you say?

4 ▶ On the Venn diagram, ℰ = {ice creams in Marco's restaurant}, C = {ice creams containing chocolate} and N = {ice creams containing nuts}. n(C) = 53 and n(N) = 36.

   a Copy and complete the Venn diagram.
   b How many ice creams contain chocolate but no nuts?
   c How many ice creams contain chocolate or nuts but not both?
   d How many ice creams are there in the restaurant?

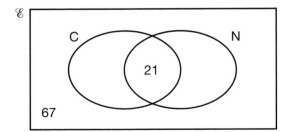

5 ▶ Show that a set of 3 elements has 8 subsets including ∅. Find a rule giving the number of subsets (including ∅) for a set of n elements.

6 ▶ A = {multiples of 2}, B = {multiples of 3}, C = {multiples of 5}.
If $n(A \cap B \cap C) = 1$ what can you say about ℰ?

UNION OF SETS

The union of two sets A and B is the set of elements that belong to A or to B or to both A and B, and is written A ∪ B.

EXAMPLE 7

ℰ = {all positive integers less than 10}, P = {prime numbers less than 10} and
O = {odd numbers less than 10}.

a Show this information on a Venn diagram.
b Find the set P ∪ O and $n(P \cup O)$.

a The set P ∪ O is shown shaded in the Venn diagram.

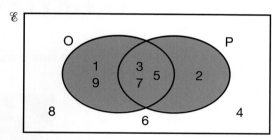

b From the Venn diagram P ∪ O = {1, 2, 3, 5, 7, 9} and $n(P \cup O) = 6$

KEY POINT

• The union of A and B, A ∪ B, is the set of elements which are in A or B or both.

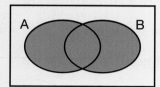

EXERCISE 3

1 ▶ ℰ = {all positive integers less than 10}, A = {1, 3, 5, 7, 9}, B = {3, 4, 5, 6}.

a Show this information on a Venn diagram.

b List A ∪ B and find $n(A \cup B)$.

c Does A ∪ B = B ∪ A?

d List (A ∪ B)'.

e Is A ∪ B a subset of A?

2 ▶ ℰ = {letters of the alphabet}, V = {vowels}, A = {a, b, c, d, e}.

     a Show this information on a Venn diagram.
     b List V ∩ A.
     c Describe V′.
     d List V ∪ A.

3 ▶ ℰ = {all triangles}, I = {isosceles triangles},
R = {right-angled triangles}.

     a Show this information on a Venn diagram.
     b **Sketch** a member of I ∩ R.
     c Describe I ∩ R in words.
     d Describe I ∩ R′ in words.

4 ▶ For sets A and B, $n(A) = 15$, $n(B) = 10$, $n(A ∩ B) = 4$. Find $n(A ∪ B)$.

EXERCISE 3*

1 ▶ ℰ = {all positive integers less than 10}, E = {2, 4, 6, 8}, O = {1, 3, 5, 7, 9}.
     a Show this information on a Venn diagram.
     b List E ∪ O.
     c If $n(E) + n(O) = n(E ∪ O)$ what does this tell you about the sets E and O?
     d If $(E ∪ O)′ = ∅$ what does this tell you about E and O?

2 ▶ In Joe's Pizza Parlour, O is the set of pizzas
containing olives and C is the set of pizzas
containing cheese.

     a Describe O ∪ C in words.
     b Describe O ∩ C in words.
     c If $(O ∪ C)′ = ∅$, what can you say?

3 ▶ For sets A and B, $n(A) = 10$, $n(B) = 16$, $n(A ∪ B) = 20$. Find $n(A ∩ B)$.

4 ▶ If $n(A) = n(A ∪ B)$ what can you say about the sets A and B?

5 ▶ Does $n(A) + n(B) = n(A ∪ B) + n(A ∩ B)$ for all possible sets A and B?

EXERCISE 4

REVISION

1 ▶ List these sets.
     a {square numbers between 2 and 30}
     b {all factors of 24}
     c {set of vowels in the word 'mathematics'}
     d {set of months of the year containing 30 days}

2 ▶ Describe these sets by a rule.
     a {2, 3, 5, 7}
     b {32, 34, 36, 38}
     c {Saturday, Sunday}
     d {a, e, i, o, u}

3 ▶ ℰ = {all positive integers}, P = {prime numbers}, E = {even numbers}, O = {odd numbers}.
Say which of these are true or false.
  a 51 ∈ P
  b P is a subset of O
  c E ∩ O = ∅
  d E ∪ O = ℰ

4 ▶ ℰ = {positive integers less than 11}, A = {multiples of 2}, B = {multiples of 4}.
  a Show this information on a Venn diagram.
  b List the set A′ and describe it in words.
  c Find n(B′).
  d Is B ⊂ A? Explain your answer.

5 ▶ ℰ = {members of an expedition to the South Pole},
A = {people born in Africa}, F = {females}.
  a Show this information on a Venn diagram.
  b Describe A ∪ F
  c The leader ∈ A ∩ F. What can you say about
  the leader?

6 ▶ For two sets A and B, n(A ∩ B) = 3, n(B) = 8, n(A ∪ B) = 12. Find n(A).

EXERCISE 4*   **REVISION**

1 ▶ List these sets.
  a {multiples of 4 less than 20}
  b {colours of the rainbow}
  c {arrangements of the letters CAT}
  d {all pairs of **products** of 1, 2, 3}

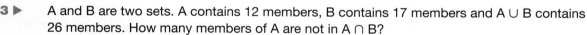

2 ▶ Describe the following sets by a rule.
  a {1, 2, 3, 4, 6, 12}
  b {1, 1, 2, 3, 5}
  c {Hearts, Clubs, Diamonds, Spades}
  d {**tetrahedron**, **cube**, **octahedron**, **dodecahedron**, **icosahedron**}

3 ▶ A and B are two sets. A contains 12 members, B contains 17 members and A ∪ B contains
26 members. How many members of A are not in A ∩ B?

4 ▶ ℰ = {all **polygons**}, F = {polygons with four sides}
and R = {regular polygons}.
  a Show this information on a Venn diagram.
  b Describe F ∩ R.
  c Describe F ∩ R′.
  d Draw an 'x' in your Venn diagram indicating
  where a square would be.

5 ▶ For two sets A and B, n(A ∩ B) = 4, n(B) = 9, n(A ∪ B)′ = 6
and n(B′) = 13. Find n(A).

6 ▶ ℰ = {positive integers less than 30}, P = {multiples of 4},
Q = {multiples of 5}, R = {multiples of 6}.
  a List P ∩ Q.
  b x ∈ P ∩ R. List the possible values of x.
  c Is it true that Q ∩ R = ∅? Explain your answer.

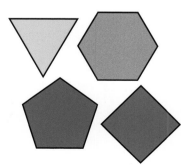

EXAM PRACTICE: SETS 1

1 Which of these statements are true?

  a Jupiter $\notin$ {Solar System}

  b triangle $\in$ {polygons}

  c $y = x + 1 \in$ {equations with straight-line graphs}

  d $3 \notin$ {odd numbers}   **[4]**

2 $\mathscr{E}$ = {all the clothes in a shop}, J = {jeans} and Y = {yellow clothes}.

  a Describe the set Y′ in words.

  b Describe the set J ∩ Y in words.

  c If J ∩ Y = ∅, describe what this means.   **[5]**

3 In the Venn diagram, $\mathscr{E}$ = {animals in a field}, B = {black animals} and S = {sheep}.

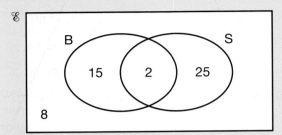

  a How many animals are there in the field?

  b How many non-black sheep are there?

  c Find n(B ∪ S) and express what this means in words.

  d How many black animals are there?   **[6]**

4 $\mathscr{E}$ = {positive integers less than 13}, E = {even integers}, F = {multiples of 4} and T = {multiples of 3}.

  a List the sets E′, E ∩ T and F ∩ T.

  b Give descriptions of the sets E′, E ∩ T and F ∩ T.   **[6]**

5 For two sets A and B, n(A ∩ B) = 3, n(A) = 6, n(B′) = 10 and $n(\mathscr{E})$ = 18. Find n(B).   **[4]**

[Total 25 marks]

CHAPTER SUMMARY: SETS 1

SET NOTATION

A set is a collection of objects, described by a list or a rule.

Each object is an element or member of the set.

Sets are equal if they have exactly the same elements.

The number of elements of set A is given by $n(A)$.

The empty set, {} or $\varnothing$, is the set with no members.

$A = \{1, 3, 5\}$

$1 \in A, 2 \notin A$

$B = \{5, 3, 1\}, B = A$

$n(A) = 3$

VENN DIAGRAMS

The universal set, $\mathscr{E}$, contains all the elements being considered in a particular problem.

B is a subset of A, $B \subset A$, if every member of B is also a member of A.

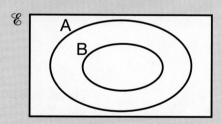

The complement of set A, A′, is the set of all elements not in A.

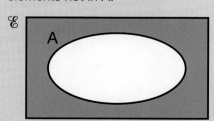

The intersection of A and B, $A \cap B$, is the set of elements which are in both A and B.

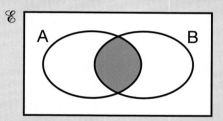

The union of A and B, $A \cup B$, is the set of elements which are in A or B or both.

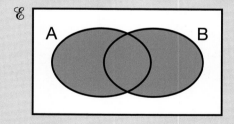

UNIT 2

2 is the first and only even prime number. $\sqrt{2}$ cannot be written as an exact fraction; this defines it as an irrational number. If n is a whole number (integer) bigger than 0, the value of $n^2 + n$ is always divisible by 2. Fermat's Last Theorem states that there are no integers x, y, z which have a solution to $x^n + y^n = z^n$ when n is bigger than 2.

NUMBER 2

The smallest measurable thing in the Universe is the *Planck length* which if written in full is
0.000 000 000 000 000 000 000 000 000 000 000 016 2 metres.

The size of the observable universe is approximately a giant
sphere of diameter 880 000 000 000 000 000 000 000 000 000 metres.

These numbers can both be written more
conveniently in a simpler format called standard
form. The first length is 1.62×10^{-35} m and the
second measurement is 8.8×10^{26} m.

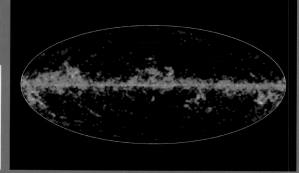

Max Planck (1858–1947) ▶

LEARNING OBJECTIVES

- Write a number in standard form
- Calculate with numbers in standard form
- Work out a percentage increase and decrease
- Solve real-life problems involving percentages

BASIC PRINCIPLES

- $10^2 \times 10^3 = 10^5$ $\Rightarrow$ $10^m \times 10^n = 10^{m+n}$

- $10^2 \div 10^3 = \dfrac{1}{10^1} = 10^{-1}$ $\Rightarrow$ $10^m \div 10^n = 10^{m-n}$

- $(10^3)^2 = 10^6$ $\Rightarrow$ $(10^m)^n = 10^{mn}$

STANDARD FORM

Standard form is used to express large and small numbers more efficiently.

KEY POINT

- **Standard form** is always written as $a \times 10^b$, where a is between 1 and 10, but is never equal to
  10 and b is an **integer** which can be positive or negative.

STANDARD FORM WITH POSITIVE INDICES

EXAMPLE 1

Write 8 250 000 in standard form.

SKILLS

$8 250 000 = 8.25 \times 1 000 000 = 8.25 \times 10^6$

REASONING

EXAMPLE 2

SKILLS

REASONING

SKILLS

ADAPTIVE
LEARNING

Write 3.75×10^5 as an ordinary number.

$3.75 \times 10^5 = 3.75 \times 100\,000 = 375\,000$

ACTIVITY 1

In the human brain, there are about $100\,000\,000\,000$ neurons, and over the human lifespan $1\,000\,000\,000\,000\,000$ neural connections are made.

Write these numbers in standard form.

Calculate the approximate number of neural connections made per second in an average human lifespan of 75 years.

EXERCISE 1

Write each of these in standard form.

1 ▶	456	**3 ▶**	123.45	**5 ▶**	568	**7 ▶**	706.05
2 ▶	67.8	**4 ▶**	67 million	**6 ▶**	38.4	**8 ▶**	123 million

Write each of these as an ordinary number.

9 ▶	4×10^3	**11 ▶**	4.09×10^6	**13 ▶**	5.6×10^2	**15 ▶**	7.97×10^6
10 ▶	5.6×10^4	**12 ▶**	6.789×10^5	**14 ▶**	6.5×10^4	**16 ▶**	9.876×10^5

17 ▶ The approximate area of all the land on Earth is 10^8 square miles. The area of the British Isles is 10^5 square miles. How many times larger is the Earth's area?

18 ▶ The area of the surface of the largest known star is about 10^{15} square miles. The area of the surface of the Earth is about 10^{11} square miles. How many times larger is the star's area?

Calculate these, and write each answer in standard form.

19 ▶	$(2 \times 10^4) \times (4.2 \times 10^5)$	**21 ▶**	$(4.5 \times 10^{12}) \div (9 \times 10^{10})$
20 ▶	$(6.02 \times 10^5) \div (4.3 \times 10^3)$	**22 ▶**	$(2.5 \times 10^4) + (2.5 \times 10^5)$

EXERCISE 1*

Write each of these in standard form.

1 ▶	45 089	**3 ▶**	29.83 million
2 ▶	87 050	**4 ▶**	0.076 54 billion

Q4 HINT
1 billion = 10^9

Calculate these, and write each answer in standard form.

5 ▶ 10×10^2

8 ▶   10 million $\div 10^6$

11 ▶ $10^7 \div 10^7$

6 ▶ $(10^3)^2$

9 ▶ $10^{12} \times 10^9$

12 ▶ $\dfrac{10^{12}}{1 \text{ million}}$

7 ▶ $\dfrac{10^9}{10^4}$

10 ▶ $(10^2)^4$

Calculate these, and write each answer in standard form.

13 ▶ $(5.6 \times 10^5) + (5.6 \times 10^6)$

15 ▶ $(3.6 \times 10^4) \div (9 \times 10^2)$

14 ▶ $(4.5 \times 10^4) \times (6 \times 10^3)$

16 ▶ $(7.87 \times 10^4) - (7.87 \times 10^3)$

Calculate these, and write each answer in standard form.

17 ▶ $(4.5 \times 10^5)^3$

19 ▶ $10^{12} \div (4 \times 10^7)$

21 ▶ $10^9 - (3.47 \times 10^7)$

18 ▶ $(3 \times 10^8)^5$

20 ▶ $(3.45 \times 10^8) + 10^6$

22 ▶ $10^{16} \div (2.5 \times 10^{12})$

You will need the information in this table to answer Questions 23, 24 and 25.

CELESTIAL BODY (OBJECT IN SPACE)	APPROXIMATE DISTANCE FROM EARTH (MILES)
Sun	10^8
Saturn	10^9
Andromeda Galaxy (nearest major galaxy)	10^{19}
Quasar OQ172 (one of the remotest objects known)	10^{22}

Copy and complete these sentences.

23 ▶   The Andromeda Galaxy is … times further away from the Earth than Saturn.

24 ▶   The quasar OQ172 is … times further away from the Earth than the Andromeda Galaxy.

25 ▶   To make a scale model showing the distances of the four bodies from the Earth, a student marks the Sun 1 cm from the Earth. How far along the line should the other three celestial bodies (objects in space) be placed?

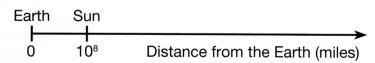

STANDARD FORM WITH NEGATIVE INDICES

ACTIVITY 2

SKILLS

ADAPTIVE LEARNING

Copy and complete the table.

DECIMAL FORM	FRACTION FORM OR MULTIPLES OF 10	STANDARD FORM
0.1	$\dfrac{1}{10} = \dfrac{1}{10^1}$	1×10^{-1}
	$\dfrac{1}{100} = \dfrac{1}{10^2}$	
0.001		
0.0001		
		1×10^{-5}

KEY POINT

- $10^{-n} = \dfrac{1}{10^n}$

EXAMPLE 3

Write these **powers** of 10 as decimal numbers: **a** 10^{-2} **b** 10^{-6}

SKILLS

REASONING

a $10^{-2} = \dfrac{1}{10^2} = \dfrac{1}{100} = 0.01$

b $10^{-6} = \dfrac{1}{10^6} = \dfrac{1}{1000000} = 0.000001$

ACTIVITY 3

SKILLS

ADAPTIVE LEARNING

Write down the **mass** of each of the first three objects in grams

- in ordinary numbers

- in standard form.

Copy and complete these statements.

- A house mouse is … times heavier than a pigmy shrew. 10^{22} kg

- A shrew is … times heavier than a grain of sand.

- A grain of sand is 100 000 times lighter than a …

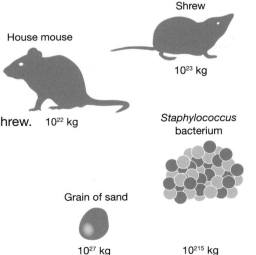

Shrew

House mouse

10^{23} kg

Staphylococcus bacterium

Grain of sand

10^{27} kg 10^{215} kg

- A shrew is 10 000 times heavier than a …

- A … is 100 million times heavier than a …

- A house mouse is … 10 000 billion times heavier than a …

EXAMPLE 4

SKILLS

REASONING

Write 0.987 in standard form.

Write the number between 1 and 10 first.

$$0.987 = 9.87 \times \frac{1}{10} = 9.87 \times 10^{-1}$$

To display this on your calculator, press [9] [·] [8] [7] [×] [×10ˣ] [(−)] [1]

EXAMPLE 5

SKILLS

REASONING

Write 3.75 × 10⁻³ as an ordinary number.

Write the number between 1 and 10 first.

$$3.75 \times 10^{-3} = 3.75 \times \frac{1}{10^3} = 0.00375$$

EXERCISE 2

Write each number in standard form.

1 ▶	0.1	**3 ▶**	0.001	**5 ▶**	$\frac{1}{1000}$	**7 ▶**	10
2 ▶	0.01	**4 ▶**	0.0001	**6 ▶**	$\frac{1}{100}$	**8 ▶**	1

Write each number as an ordinary number.

9 ▶	10^{-3}	**11 ▶**	1.2×10^{-3}	**13 ▶**	10^{-6}	**15 ▶**	4.67×10^{-2}
10 ▶	10^{-5}	**12 ▶**	8.7×10^{-1}	**14 ▶**	10^{-4}	**16 ▶**	3.4×10^{-4}

Write each number in standard form.

17 ▶	0.543	**19 ▶**	0.007	**21 ▶**	0.67	**23 ▶**	100
18 ▶	0.0708	**20 ▶**	0.0009	**22 ▶**	0.000 707	**24 ▶**	1000

Write each as an ordinary number.

25 ▶ $10^{-2} \times 10^{4}$ **27 ▶** $10^{2} \div 10^{-2}$ **29 ▶** $(3.2 \times 10^{-2}) \times (4 \times 10^{3})$

26 ▶ $10^{3} \times 10^{-1}$ **28 ▶** $10^{3} \div 10^{-3}$ **30 ▶** $(2.4 \times 10^{-2}) \div (8 \times 10^{-1})$

EXERCISE 2*

Write each as an ordinary number.

1 ▶ $10^{3} \times 10^{-2}$ **3 ▶** $10^{-2} + 10^{-3}$ **5 ▶** $10^{-4} \times 10^{2}$ **7 ▶** $10^{-3} + 10^{-4}$

2 ▶ $10^{-1} \times 10^{-2}$ **4 ▶** $10^{-1} - 10^{-3}$ **6 ▶** $10^{-3} \times 10^{-1}$ **8 ▶** $10^{-3} - 10^{-1}$

Write each number in standard form.

9 ▶ $10 \div 10^{-2}$ **11 ▶** $10^{-1} \div 10^{-2}$ **13 ▶** $10^{3} \div 10^{-1}$ **15 ▶** $10^{-2} \div 10^{-4}$

10 ▶ $10^{2} \div 10^{-2}$ **12 ▶** $10^{-4} \div 10^{-3}$ **14 ▶** $10^{-1} \div 10^{3}$ **16 ▶** $10^{-5} \div 10^{-2}$

Write each number in standard form.

17 ▶ $(4 \times 10^{2})^{-2}$ **21 ▶** $(5 \times 10^{2})^{-2}$

18 ▶ $(4 \times 10^{-2})^{2}$ **22 ▶** $(5 \times 10^{-2})^{2}$

19 ▶ $(6.9 \times 10^{3}) \div 10^{-4}$ **23 ▶** $(4.8 \times 10^{2}) \div 10^{-3}$

20 ▶ $10^{-3} \div (2 \times 10^{-2})$ **24 ▶** $10^{-2} \div (5 \times 10^{-3})$

You will need this information to answer Questions 25, 26 and 27.

Cough virus 9.144×10^{-6} mm **diameter**

Human hair 5×10^{-2} mm diameter

Pin 6×10^{-1} mm diameter

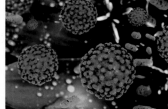

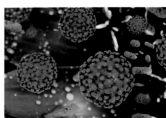

25 ▶ How many viruses, to the nearest thousand, can be placed in a straight line across the width of a human hair?

26 ▶ How many viruses, to the nearest thousand, can be placed in a straight line across the width of a pin?

27 ▶ The **radius** of the nucleus of a hydrogen atom is 5.3×10^{-13} mm. How many hydrogen atoms would fit in a straight line across the width of a human hair?

28 ▶ The average mass of a grain of sand is 10^{-4} g. How many grains of sand are there in 2 kg?

29 ▶ Find a sensible method to work out $(3.4 \times 10^{23}) + (3.4 \times 10^{22})$ without a calculator.

30 ▶ A molecule of water is a very small thing, so small that its volume is 10^{-27} m³.

    a How many molecules are there in 1 m³ of water?
    If you wrote your answer in full, how many zero digits would there be?

    b If you assume that a water molecule is in the form of a **cube**, show that its side
    length is 10^{-9} m.

    c If a number of water molecules were placed touching each other in a straight line,
    how many would there be in a line 1 cm long?

    d The volume of a cup is 200 cm³.
    How many molecules of water would the cup hold?

    e If all the molecules in the cup were placed end to end in a straight line, how long
    would the line be?

    f Take the **circumference** of the Earth to be 40 000 km.
    How many times would the line of molecules go around the Earth?

PERCENTAGES

Percentages are numbers without a dimension that help us make
fast judgements. Values are scaled to be out of 100. Percentages
appear frequently in everyday life. They can be used to compare
quantities and work out a percentage change such as profit or loss.

x AS A PERCENTAGE OF y

EXAMPLE 6

Calculate $5 as a percentage of $80.

SKILLS

REASONING

Express the **ratio** as a fraction and multiply by 100.

$5 as a percentage of $80 $= \frac{5}{80} \times 100 = 6.25\%$

KEY POINT

- To calculate x as a percentage of y: $\dfrac{x}{y} \times 100$

x PERCENT OF y

EXAMPLE 7

Calculate 5% of 80 kg.

SKILLS

REASONING

1% of 80 kg $= \frac{80}{100}$ so 5% $= 5 \times \frac{80}{100} = 80 \times \frac{5}{100} = 80 \times 0.05 = 4$ kg

KEY POINT

• To calculate x percent of y: 1% of $y = \dfrac{y}{100}$ so $x\%$ of $y = x \times \dfrac{y}{100} = y \times \left(\dfrac{x}{100}\right)$

The $\left(\dfrac{x}{100}\right)$ part of the last expression is the **multiplying factor**.

5% of a quantity can be found by using a multiplying factor of 0.05.

95% of a quantity can be found by using a multiplying factor of 0.95 and so on.

PERCENTAGE CHANGE

EXAMPLE 8

SKILLS

REASONING

Olive measures Salma's height as 95 cm. Some time later she measures her height as 1.14 m.

Work out the percentage increase in Salma's height.

Percentage change $= \dfrac{\text{value of change}}{\text{original value}} \times 100 = \dfrac{114 - 95}{95} \times 100 = +20\%$

Salma's height has changed by $+20\%$.

To compare units it is necessary to be consistent. In the above example, centimetres were the units used.

EXAMPLE 9

SKILLS

REASONING

Kerry improves her 400 m running time from 72 s to 63 s.

What was Kerry's percentage improvement?

Percentage change $= \dfrac{\text{value of change}}{\text{original value}} \times 100 = \dfrac{72 - 63}{72} \times 100 = -12.5\%$

Kerry's time has changed by -12.5%.

KEY POINT

• Percentage change $= \dfrac{\text{value of change}}{\text{original value}} \times 100$

EXERCISE 3

1 ▶ Find €12 as a percentage of €60.

2 ▶ Find 15 km as a percentage of 120 km.

3 ▶ Find $180 as a percentage of $3600.

4 ▶ Find 2500 kg as a percentage of 62 500 kg.

5 ▶ Find 5% of 110 km/h.

6 ▶ Find 15% of 80°C.

7 ▶ Find 30% of 420 m².

8 ▶ Find 70% of 24 hrs.

9 ▶ Pavel's pocket money increases from €12 per week to €15 per week. Work out the percentage increase in his pocket money.

10 ▶ India's swimming time decreases from 32 s to 24 s. Work out the percentage decrease in her time.

EXERCISE 3*

1 ▶ Find 175p as a percentage of £35.

2 ▶ Find 2.5 km as a percentage of 15 000 m.

3 ▶ Find $25 000 as a percentage of $1 million.

4 ▶ Find 375 g as a percentage of 15 kg.

5 ▶ Find 15% of the area of a square of side 12 cm.

6 ▶ Find 85% of the volume of a cube of side 12 cm.

7 ▶ Find 2.5% of 10% of 1×10^6 m³.

8 ▶ Find 90% of 36% of 2.5×10^3 db (decibels).

9 ▶ What is the percentage error in using $\frac{22}{7}$ as an approximation to π ?

10 ▶ Find the percentage change in the 100 m sprint World Records for the

   a Men's record since 1891

   b Women's record since 1922.

MEN'S 100 m SPRINT WORLD RECORD		
Year	Time	Holder
1891	10.80 s	Cary, USA
2009	9.58 s	Bolt, Jamaica

WOMEN'S 100 m SPRINT WORLD RECORD		
Year	Time	Holder
1922	13.60 s	Mejzlikova, Czechoslovakia
1988	10.49 s	Griffith-Joyner, USA

PERCENTAGE INCREASE AND DECREASE

To increase a value by $R\%$ it is necessary to have the original value plus $R\%$.

Therefore, we multiply it by a **factor** of $(1 + \dfrac{R}{100})$.

EXAMPLE 10

SKILLS

REASONING

In 2015, the Kingda Ka Roller Coaster at Six Flags (USA) had the largest vertical drop of 139 m. If the designers want to increase this height by 12%, what will the new height be?

New height = original height $\times (1 + \dfrac{12}{100}) = 139 \times 1.12 = 155.68$ m

To decrease a value by $R\%$ it is necessary to have the original value minus $R\%$.

Therefore, we multiply it by a factor of $(1 - \dfrac{R}{100})$.

EXAMPLE 11

SKILLS

REASONING

In 2015, the world record for the 100 m swimming butterfly in the female Paralympian S12 class was held by Joanna Mendak (Poland) with a time of 65.1 secs.

If this world record is reduced by 5%, what will the new time be?

New time = original time $\times (1 - \dfrac{5}{100}) = 65.1 \times 0.95 = 61.845$ s $= 61.85$ s (2 d.p.)

Note: this is the same calculation as finding 95% of the original time, so reducing a quantity by 25% is the same as finding 75% of the value and so on.

KEY POINTS

• To increase a quantity by $R\%$, multiply it by $1 + \dfrac{R}{100}$

• To decrease a quantity by $R\%$, multiply it by $1 - \dfrac{R}{100}$

PERCENTAGE CHANGE	MULTIPLYING FACTOR
+25%	1.25
+75%	1.75
−25%	0.75
−75%	0.25

PERCENTAGE INCREASE AND DECREASE

If a quantity gains value over time it has **appreciated** or gone through an inflation. It can happen for a number of reasons, often a *greater demand* or a *smaller supply* can push prices up. Houses, rare antiques and rare minerals are typical examples.

If a quantity loses value over time it has **depreciated** or gone through a deflation. It can happen for a number of reasons, often a *smaller demand* or a *greater supply* can push prices down. Cars, oil and some toys are typical examples.

EXERCISE 4

1 ▶　Copy and complete the following table.

ORIGINAL VALUE	PERCENTAGE INCREASE	MULTIPLYING FACTOR	NEW VALUE
20	5		
180	95		
360		1.30	
2500		1.70	

2 ▶　Copy and complete the following table.

ORIGINAL VALUE	PERCENTAGE DECREASE	MULTIPLYING FACTOR	NEW VALUE
20	5		
180	95		
360		0.70	
2500		0.30	

3 ▶　Increase $1500 by

　　a 1%　　　b 99%　　　c 10%　　　d 90%

4 ▶　Decrease 500 kg by

　　a 1%　　　b 99%　　　c 10%　　　d 90%

5 ▶　An Emperor Penguin weighs 40 kg and gains 70% of its weight before losing its feathers so that it can survive the extreme temperatures of Antarctica. Find the penguin's weight just before it loses its feathers.

6 ▶　A bottlenose dolphin weighs 650 kg while carrying its baby calf. After it gives birth to the calf its weight is reduced by 4%. Find the dolphin's weight just after giving birth.

7 ▶　Madewa pays $12 000 into an investment and it appreciates by 12% after one year. Find the value of Madewa's investment after a year.

8 ▶ Iris buys a new car for $45 000 and it depreciates by 12% after one year. Find the value of Iris' car after a year.

9 ▶ A rare sculpture is worth €120 000 and appreciates by 8% p.a. Find the value of the sculpture after one year.

10 ▶ A rare stamp is worth €2500 and depreciates by 8% p.a. Find the value of the stamp after one year.

EXERCISE 4*

1 ▶ Copy and complete the following table.

ORIGINAL VALUE	PERCENTAGE INCREASE	MULTIPLYING FACTOR	NEW VALUE
60 secs			75 secs
50 kg			80 kg
		1.25	125 km/h
	20		1500 m

2 ▶ Copy and complete the following table.

ORIGINAL VALUE	PERCENTAGE DECREASE	MULTIPLYING FACTOR	NEW VALUE
75 secs			60 secs
80 kg			50 kg
120 km/h		0.60	
1500 m	20		

3 ▶ A $24 box of luxury chocolates is sold in Canada where the inflation **rate** is 2% p.a. Find the new price of these chocolates in Canada after a year.

4 ▶ The cost of oil is $45 per barrel (a standard unit) and the price goes through a deflation rate of 12% p.a. Find the new price of a barrel after one year.

5 ▶ A Persian rug is worth £5750. It goes through an increase of 5% followed by a second increase of 12%. Find the price of the rug after the second increase.

6 ▶ A super-size hi-definition TV costs £7500. It goes through a decrease of 10% followed by a second decrease of 12% in the sales. Find the price of the TV after the second decrease.

7 ▶ The temperature in Doha, Qatar on 1 June is 40°C. Over the next two days this temperature increases by 10% followed by a decrease of 10%. Find the temperature in Doha on 3 June.

8 ▶ A loud clap of thunder is measured at a noise level of 120 decibels (the unit for measuring sound). The next two thunderclaps register a decrease of 20% followed by a 25% increase in noise level. How loud, in decibels, is the third thunderclap?

9 ▶ A circular drop of oil has a radius of 10 cm. If this radius increases by 5% then by 10% and finally by 15%, find the new area of the circle. (Area of circle $A = \pi r^2$)

10 ▶ A circular drop of oil has a diameter of 10 cm. If this diameter decreases by 5% then by 10% and finally by 15%, find the new circumference of the circle. (Circumference of circle $= 2\pi r$)

EXERCISE 5   **REVISION**

1 ▶ Write 275 000 in standard form.

2 ▶ Write 0.0275 in standard form.

3 ▶ Write 3.5×10^3 as an ordinary number.

4 ▶ Write 3.5×10^{-3} as an ordinary number.

5 ▶ Find 18% of $360 000.

6 ▶ Write 240 m as a percentage of 12 000 m.

7 ▶ Luke's salary changes from €75 000 p.a. to €100 000 p.a. Find the percentage increase in Luke's salary.

8 ▶ Mari's watch gains 3 minutes every hour. Find the percentage error in Mari's watch at the end of one hour.

9 ▶ Increase $350 by 17.5%.

10 ▶ Decrease $350 by 17.5%.

EXERCISE 5*   **REVISION**

1 ▶   Write $(4.5 \times 10^3) \times (5 \times 10^3)$ as an ordinary number.

2 ▶   Write $0.1 + 0.02 + 0.003$ in standard form.

3 ▶   Write $5.3 \times 10^4 + 5.3 \times 10^3$ as an ordinary number.

4 ▶   Write $\dfrac{2.5 \times 10^3 \times 6 \times 10^2}{3 \times 10^{-6}}$ in standard form.

5 ▶   Find 15% of the **perimeter** of a square of area $1024\,m^2$.

6 ▶   Write a time of 1 second as a percentage of 1 day. Express your answer in standard form to 3 s.f.

7 ▶   When Fredrick buys a cup of coffee he is given change of €1.65 when he should have received €1.50. Find the percentage error.

8 ▶   Find the percentage error in x when it is estimated to be y and $y > x$.

9 ▶   Erika's toy ski chalet is valued at €450. Its value increases by 10% then decreases by 10% the year after. What is the value of Erika's toy after these two changes?

10 ▶   Akintade makes the following purchases and sales:

   a   He buys a jewel for $180, then sells it for $216. Find his percentage profit.

   b   He buys a toy car for $150, then sells it for $120. Find his percentage loss.

EXAM PRACTICE: NUMBER 2

1 Write the following numbers in standard form.

a 4500
b 3 million
c 0.0075
d a quarter   [4]

2 Write the following as ordinary numbers.

a 1.2×10^3
b 5.8×10^6
c 4.5×10^{-1}
d 9.3×10^{-3} [4]

3 Write the following in standard form to 3 s.f.

a $(2.5 \times 10^2) \times (1.7 \times 10^5)$

b $\dfrac{7.3 \times 10^6}{2.1 \times 10^3}$

c $(7.3 \times 10^5) + (7.3 \times 10^4)$ [6]

4 The human body contains about 60% water. How many kg of water are contained in a 75 kg man?   [2]

5 Between 2010 and 2015 the human population of India grew from 1.21×10^9 to 1.29×10^9. The world population in 2015 was 7.39 billion.

Find the percentage

a of the world population that lived in India in 2015
b change in the Indian population from 2010 to 2015.   [4]

6 A square has its side length increased by 10%. Find the percentage increase in the area of the square.   [2]

7 The Womens' World Record Marathon time has improved by 34.82% from Dale Grieg's (UK) time of 3 hrs 27 mins 45 s in 1964 to Paula Radcliffe's (UK) time in 2003. Find Paula Radcliffe's World Record time.   [3]

[Total 25 marks]

CHAPTER SUMMARY: NUMBER 2

STANDARD FORM

Standard form is used to express large and small numbers more efficiently.

A number in standard form looks like this:

$$2.5 \times 10^6$$

↑   ↑

This part is written as a number between 1 and 10.   This part is written as a power of 10.

For negative powers of 10: $10^{-n} = \dfrac{1}{10^n}$

It is always written as $a \times 10^b$, where $1 \le a < 10$ and b is an integer which can be positive or negative.

$1000 = 1 \times 10^3$, $0.001 = 1 \times 10^{-3}$ are two numbers written in standard form.

$10^m \times 10^n = 10^{m+n}$
$10^m \div 10^n = 10^{m-n}$
$(10^m)^n = 10^{mn}$

PERCENTAGES

To calculate x as a percentage of y: $\dfrac{x}{y} \times 100$

To calculate x percent of y:

1% of $y = \dfrac{y}{100}$ so $x\%$ of $y = x \times \dfrac{y}{100} = y \times \left(\dfrac{x}{100}\right)$

The $\left(\dfrac{x}{100}\right)$ part of the last expression is the multiplying factor.

5% of a quantity can be found by using a multiplying factor of 0.05.

95% of a quantity can be found by using a multiplying factor of 0.95 and so on.

$1\% = \frac{1}{100} = 0.01$ $10\% = \frac{10}{100} = \frac{1}{10} = 0.1$

$50\% = \frac{50}{100} = \frac{1}{2} = 0.5$ $75\% = \frac{75}{100} = \frac{3}{4} = 0.75$

PERCENTAGE CHANGE

Percentage change $= \dfrac{\text{value of change}}{\text{original value}} \times 100$

Per annum (p.a.) is frequently used and means per year.

PERCENTAGE INCREASE AND DECREASE

To increase a quantity by $R\%$, multiply it by $1 + \dfrac{R}{100}$

To decrease a quantity by $R\%$, multiply it by $1 - \dfrac{R}{100}$

PERCENTAGE CHANGE	MULTIPLYING FACTOR
+5%	1.05
+95%	1.95
−5%	0.95
−95%	0.05

ALGEBRA 2

You might think that 9999 is the largest number that can be written using just four digits, however, we can write much larger numbers using index notation. A 15-year-old person has been alive for about 5×10^8 seconds, the universe is about 10^{17} seconds old and the number of atoms in the observable universe has been estimated at 10^{80}. It is amazing that four digits can represent such an incredibly large number!

LEARNING OBJECTIVES

- Multiply and divide algebraic fractions

- Add and subtract algebraic fractions

- Solve equations with roots and powers

- Use the rules of indices (to simplify algebraic expressions)

- Solve inequalities and show the solution on a number line

BASIC PRINCIPLES

- Simplifying number fractions: $\quad \frac{9}{12} = \frac{3}{4}$, $\qquad \frac{2}{3} \div \frac{1}{3} = \frac{2}{3} \times \frac{3}{1} = 2$, $\qquad \frac{2}{3} + \frac{1}{4} = \frac{8+3}{12} = \frac{11}{12}$

- Solving equations means doing the same to both sides to get the unknown on one side by itself.

- $10^4 = 10 \times 10 \times 10 \times 10$

- $x < y$ means 'x is less than y' or 'y is greater than x'.

- $x \geq y$ means 'x is greater than or equal to y' or 'y is less than or equal to x'.

SIMPLIFYING ALGEBRAIC FRACTIONS

Algebraic fractions are simplified in the same way as number fractions.

MULTIPLICATION AND DIVISION

EXAMPLE 1

Simplify $\dfrac{4x}{6x}$

$$\frac{{}^2\cancel{4}x}{{}_3\cancel{6}x} = \frac{2\cancel{x}^1}{3\cancel{x}_1} = \frac{2}{3}$$

EXAMPLE 2

Simplify $\dfrac{3x^2}{6x}$

$$\frac{3x^2}{6x} = \frac{{}^1\cancel{3} \times x \times {}^1\cancel{x}}{{}_2\cancel{6} \times {}_1\cancel{x}} = \frac{x}{2}$$

EXAMPLE 3

Simplify $\left(27xy^2\right) \div (60x)$

$$\left(27xy^2\right) \div (60x) = \frac{27xy^2}{60x} = \frac{{}^9\cancel{27} \times {}^1\cancel{x} \times y \times y}{{}_{20}\cancel{60} \times {}_1\cancel{x}} = \frac{9y^2}{20}$$

EXERCISE 1

Simplify these.

1 ▶ $\dfrac{4x}{x}$

5 ▶ $\dfrac{3ab}{6a}$

9 ▶ $\dfrac{12x}{3x^2}$

2 ▶ $\dfrac{6y}{2}$

6 ▶ $(9a) \div (3b)$

10 ▶ $\dfrac{8ab^2}{4ab}$

3 ▶ $(6x) \div (3x)$

7 ▶ $\dfrac{12c^2}{3c}$

11 ▶ $\dfrac{3a}{15ab^2}$

4 ▶ $\dfrac{12a}{4b}$

8 ▶ $\dfrac{4a^2}{8a}$

12 ▶ $(3a^2b^2) \div (12ab^2)$

EXERCISE 1*

Simplify these.

1 ▶ $\dfrac{5y}{10y}$

5 ▶ $\dfrac{10b}{5b^2}$

9 ▶ $(3a^2) \div (12ab^2)$

2 ▶ $\dfrac{12a}{6ab}$

6 ▶ $(18a) \div (3ab^2)$

10 ▶ $\dfrac{abc^3}{(abc)^3}$

3 ▶ $(3xy) \div (12y)$

7 ▶ $\dfrac{3a^2b^2}{6ab^3}$

11 ▶ $\dfrac{150a^3b^2}{400a^2b^3}$

4 ▶ $\dfrac{3a^2}{6a}$

8 ▶ $\dfrac{15abc}{5a^2b^2c^2}$

12 ▶ $\dfrac{45x^3y^4z^5}{150x^5y^4z^3}$

EXAMPLE 4

Simplify $\dfrac{3x^2}{y} \times \dfrac{y^3}{x}$

$$\dfrac{3x^2}{y} \times \dfrac{y^3}{x} = \dfrac{3 \times x \times {}^1\cancel{x}}{{}_1\cancel{y}} \times \dfrac{{}^1\cancel{y} \times y \times y}{{}_1\cancel{x}} = 3xy^2$$

EXAMPLE 5

Simplify $\dfrac{2x^2}{y} \div \dfrac{2x}{5y^3}$

$$\dfrac{2x^2}{y} \div \dfrac{2x}{5y^3} = \dfrac{{}^1\cancel{2} \times x \times {}^1\cancel{x}}{{}_1\cancel{y}} \times \dfrac{5 \times {}^1\cancel{y} \times y \times y}{{}_1\cancel{2} \times {}_1\cancel{x}} = 5xy^2$$

KEY POINT

- To divide by a fraction, turn the fraction upside down and multiply.

$$\dfrac{a}{b} \div \dfrac{c}{d} = \dfrac{a}{b} \times \dfrac{d}{c} = \dfrac{ad}{bc}$$

EXERCISE 2

Simplify these.

$1 \blacktriangleright \quad \dfrac{3x}{4} \times \dfrac{5x}{3}$

$5 \blacktriangleright \quad \dfrac{3x}{4} \div \dfrac{x}{8}$

$9 \blacktriangleright \quad \dfrac{2x}{y^2} \div \dfrac{x}{y}$

$2 \blacktriangleright \quad \dfrac{x^2 y}{z} \times \dfrac{xz^2}{y^2}$

$6 \blacktriangleright \quad 4 \div \dfrac{8}{ab}$

$10 \blacktriangleright \quad \dfrac{5ab}{c^2} \div \dfrac{10a}{c}$

$3 \blacktriangleright \quad \dfrac{x^2}{y} \times \dfrac{z}{x^2} \times \dfrac{y}{z}$

$7 \blacktriangleright \quad \dfrac{2b}{3} \div 4$

$4 \blacktriangleright \quad \dfrac{4c \times 7c^2}{7 \times 5c}$

$8 \blacktriangleright \quad \dfrac{2x}{3} \div \dfrac{2x}{3}$

EXERCISE 2*

Simplify these.

$1 \blacktriangleright \quad \dfrac{4a}{3} \times \dfrac{5a}{2} \times \dfrac{3a}{5}$

$5 \blacktriangleright \quad \dfrac{15x^2 y}{z} \div \dfrac{3xz}{y^2}$

$2 \blacktriangleright \quad \dfrac{3x^2 y}{z^3} \times \dfrac{z^2}{xy}$

$6 \blacktriangleright \quad \dfrac{2x}{y} \times \dfrac{3y}{4x} \times \dfrac{2y}{3}$

$3 \blacktriangleright \quad \dfrac{45}{50} \times \dfrac{p^2}{q} \times \dfrac{q^3}{p}$

$7 \blacktriangleright \quad \left(\dfrac{x}{2y}\right)^3 \times \dfrac{2x}{3} \div \dfrac{2}{9y^2}$

$4 \blacktriangleright \quad \dfrac{3x}{y} \div \dfrac{6x^2}{y}$

$8 \blacktriangleright \quad \dfrac{\sqrt{a^3 b^2}}{6a^3} \times \dfrac{3a^5 b}{\left(a^3 b^2\right)^2} \div \dfrac{ab}{\sqrt{a^3 b^2}}$

ADDITION AND SUBTRACTION

EXAMPLE 6

Simplify $\dfrac{a}{4} + \dfrac{b}{5}$

$\dfrac{a}{4} + \dfrac{b}{5} = \dfrac{5a + 4b}{20}$

EXAMPLE 7

Simplify $\dfrac{3x}{5} - \dfrac{x}{3}$

$\dfrac{3x}{5} - \dfrac{x}{3} = \dfrac{9x - 5x}{15} = \dfrac{4x}{15}$

EXAMPLE 8

Simplify $\dfrac{2}{3b} + \dfrac{1}{2b}$

$\dfrac{2}{3b} + \dfrac{1}{2b} = \dfrac{4 + 3}{6b} = \dfrac{7}{6b}$

EXAMPLE 9

Simplify $\dfrac{3 + x}{7} - \dfrac{x - 2}{3}$

$\dfrac{3 + x}{7} - \dfrac{x - 2}{3} = \dfrac{3(3 + x) - 7(x - 2)}{21} = \dfrac{9 + 3x - 7x + 14}{21} = \dfrac{23 - 4x}{21}$

Remember to use brackets here. Note **sign** change.

EXERCISE 3 Simplify these.

1 ▶ $\dfrac{x}{3} + \dfrac{x}{4}$ **3 ▶** $\dfrac{a}{3} + \dfrac{b}{4}$ **5 ▶** $\dfrac{2a}{7} + \dfrac{3a}{14}$ **7 ▶** $\dfrac{2a}{3} - \dfrac{a}{2}$

2 ▶ $\dfrac{a}{3} - \dfrac{a}{4}$ **4 ▶** $\dfrac{2x}{3} - \dfrac{x}{4}$ **6 ▶** $\dfrac{a}{4} + \dfrac{b}{3}$ **8 ▶** $\dfrac{a}{4} + \dfrac{2b}{3}$

EXERCISE 3* Simplify these.

1 ▶ $\dfrac{x}{6} + \dfrac{2x}{9}$ **5 ▶** $\dfrac{3}{2b} + \dfrac{4}{3b}$ **9 ▶** $\dfrac{x-3}{3} + \dfrac{x+5}{4} - \dfrac{2x-1}{6}$

2 ▶ $\dfrac{2a}{3} - \dfrac{3a}{7}$ **6 ▶** $\dfrac{2}{d} + \dfrac{3}{d^2}$ **10 ▶** $\dfrac{a}{a-1} - \dfrac{a-1}{a}$

3 ▶ $\dfrac{2x}{5} + \dfrac{4y}{7}$ **7 ▶** $\dfrac{2-x}{5} + \dfrac{3-x}{10}$

4 ▶ $\dfrac{3a}{4} + \dfrac{a}{3} - \dfrac{5a}{6}$ **8 ▶** $\dfrac{y+3}{5} - \dfrac{y+4}{6}$

SOLVING EQUATIONS WITH ROOTS AND POWERS

EXAMPLE 10 Solve $3x^2 + 4 = 52$.

$3x^2 + 4 = 52$ (Subtract 4 from both sides)

$\quad 3x^2 = 48$ (Divide both sides by 3)

$\quad\ \ x^2 = 16$ (Square root both sides)

$\quad\ \ \ x = \pm 4$

Check: $3 \times 16 + 4 = 52$

Note: -4 is also an answer because $(-4) \times (-4) = 16$.

EXAMPLE 11 Solve $5\sqrt{x} = 50$.

$5\sqrt{x} = 50$ (Divide both sides by 5)

$\quad \sqrt{x} = 10$ (Square both sides)

$\quad\ \ x = 100$

Check: $5 \times \sqrt{100} = 50$

EXAMPLE 12   Solve $\dfrac{\sqrt{x+5}}{3} = 1$.

$\dfrac{\sqrt{x+5}}{3} = 1$ (Multiply both sides by 3)

$\sqrt{x+5} = 3$ (Square both sides)

$x + 5 = 9$ (Subtract 5 from both sides)

$x = 4$

Check: $\dfrac{\sqrt{4+5}}{3} = 1$

KEY POINT   • To solve equations, do the same operations to both sides.

EXERCISE 4   Solve these equations.

1 ▶ $4x^2 = 36$ **5 ▶** $2x^2 + 5 = 23$ **9 ▶** $\sqrt{x} + 27 = 31$

2 ▶ $\dfrac{x^2}{3} = 12$ **6 ▶** $5x^2 - 7 = -2$ **10 ▶** $4\sqrt{x} + 4 = 40$

3 ▶ $x^2 + 5 = 21$ **7 ▶** $\dfrac{x+12}{5} = 5$

4 ▶ $\dfrac{x^2}{2} + 5 = 37$ **8 ▶** $\dfrac{x^2+4}{5} = 4$

EXERCISE 4*   Solve these equations.

  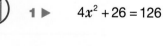

1 ▶ $4x^2 + 26 = 126$ **5 ▶** $\sqrt{\dfrac{x-3}{4}} + 5 = 6$ **9 ▶** $\sqrt{\dfrac{3x^2+5}{2}} + 4 = 8$

2 ▶ $\dfrac{x^2}{7} - 3 = 4$ **6 ▶** $\dfrac{40 - 2x^2}{2} = 4$ **10 ▶** $\sqrt{3 + \dfrac{\left(4 + \sqrt{x+3}\right)^2}{6}} = 3$

3 ▶ $\dfrac{x^2 - 11}{7} = 10$ **7 ▶** $22 = 32 - \dfrac{2x^2}{5}$

4 ▶ $1 = \dfrac{\sqrt{x+4}}{2}$ **8 ▶** $(3 + x)^2 = 169$

POSITIVE INTEGER INDICES

$10 \times 10 \times 10 \times 10$ is written in a shorter form as 10^4. In the same way, $a \times a \times a \times a$ is written as a^4.

To help you to understand how the rules of indices work, look carefully at these examples.

KEY POINTS

OPERATION	EXAMPLE	RULES
Multiplying	$a^4 \times a^2 = (a \times a \times a \times a) \times (a \times a) = a^6 = a^{4+2}$	Add the indices $(a^m \times a^n = a^{m+n})$
Dividing	$a^4 \div a^2 = \dfrac{a \times a \times a \times a}{a \times a} = a^2 = a^{4-2}$	Subtract the indices $(a^m \div a^n = a^{m-n})$
Raising to a **power**	$(a^4)^2 = (a \times a \times a \times a) \times (a \times a \times a \times a) = a^8 = a^{4 \times 2}$	Multiply the indices $(a^m)^n = a^{mn}$

EXAMPLE 13

Use the rules of indices to simplify $6^3 \times 6^4$. Then use your calculator to check the answer.

$6^3 \times 6^4 = 6^7 = 279\,936$ (Add the indices)

EXAMPLE 14

Simplify $9^5 \div 9^2$.

$9^5 \div 9^2 = 9^3 = 729$ (Subtract the indices)

EXAMPLE 15

Simplify $(4^2)^5 = 4^{10}$.

$(4^2)^5 = 4^{10} = 1\,048\,576$ (Multiply the indices)

Some answers become very large after only a few multiplications.

EXERCISE 5

Use the rules of **indices** to simplify these. Then use your calculator to calculate the answer.

1 ▶ $2^4 \times 2^6$ 3 ▶ $2^{10} \div 2^4$ 5 ▶ $\left(2^3\right)^4$

2 ▶ $4^3 \times 4^4$ 4 ▶ $\dfrac{7^{13}}{7^{10}}$ 6 ▶ $\left(6^2\right)^4$

Use the rules of indices to simplify these.

7 ▶ $a^3 \times a^2$ 　　**9** ▶ $(e^2)^3$ 　　**11** ▶ $\dfrac{c^8}{c^3}$ 　　**13** ▶ $2a^3 \times 3a^2$

8 ▶ $c^6 \div c^2$ 　　**10** ▶ $a^2 \times a^3 \times a^4$ 　　**12** ▶ $2 \times 6 \times a^4 \times a^2$ 　　**14** ▶ $2(e^4)^2$

EXERCISE 5* Use the rules of indices to simplify these. Then use your calculator to calculate the answer. Give your answers **correct** to 3 **significant figures** and in **standard form**.

1 ▶ $6^6 \times 6^6$ 　　**2** ▶ $7^{12} \div 7^6$ 　　**3** ▶ $\left(8^3\right)^4$ 　　**4** ▶ $4(4^4)^4$

Use the rules of indices to simplify these.

5 ▶ $a^5 \times a^3 \times a^4$ 　　**9** ▶ $3(2j^3)^4$ 　　**13** ▶ $\dfrac{12b^8}{6b^4} + 6b^4$

6 ▶ $(12c^9) \div (4c^3)$ 　　**10** ▶ $3m(2m^2)^3$ 　　**14** ▶ $\dfrac{b^4 + b^4 + b^4 + b^4 + b^4 + b^4}{b^4}$

7 ▶ $5(e^2)^4$ 　　**11** ▶ $3a^2(3a^2)^2$

8 ▶ $(2g^4)^3$ 　　**12** ▶ $\dfrac{2a^8 + 2a^8}{2a^8}$

INEQUALITIES

NUMBER LINES

EXAMPLE 16 These are examples of how to show **inequalities** on a number line.

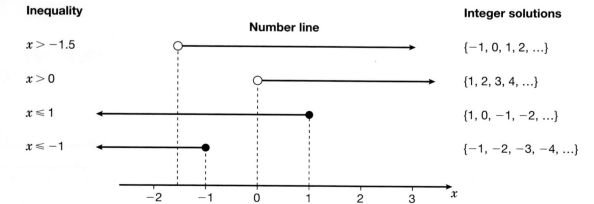

Inequality	Number line	Integer solutions
$x > -1.5$		$\{-1, 0, 1, 2, ...\}$
$x > 0$		$\{1, 2, 3, 4, ...\}$
$x \leqslant 1$		$\{1, 0, -1, -2, ...\}$
$x \leqslant -1$		$\{-1, -2, -3, -4, ...\}$

SOLVING LINEAR INEQUALITIES

Inequalities are solved in the same way as algebraic equations, EXCEPT that when multiplying or dividing by a negative number, the inequality sign is reversed.

EXAMPLE 17

Solve the inequality $4 < x \leq 10$. Show the result on a number line.

$4 < x \leq 10$ (Split the inequality into two parts)

$4 < x$ and $x \leq 10$

$x > 4$ and $x \leq 10$

Note: x cannot be equal to 4.

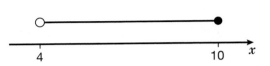

EXAMPLE 18

Solve the inequality $4 \geq 13 - 3x$. Show the result on a number line.

$4 \geq 13 - 3x$ (Add $3x$ to both sides)

$3x + 4 \geq 13$ (Subtract 4 from both sides)

$3x \geq 9$ (Divide both sides by 3)

$x \geq 3$

EXAMPLE 19

Solve the inequality $5 - 3x < 1$. List the four smallest **integers** in the solution set.

$5 - 3x < 1$ (Subtract 5 from both sides)

$-3x < -4$ (Divide both sides by –3, so reverse the inequality sign)

$x > \dfrac{-4}{-3}$

$x > 1\dfrac{1}{3}$

So the four smallest integers are 2, 3, 4 and 5.

EXAMPLE 20

Solve the inequality $x \leq 5x + 1 < 4x + 5$. Show the inequality on a number line.

$x \leq 5x + 1 < 4x + 5$ (Split the inequality into two parts)

a $x \leq 5x + 1$ (Subtract $5x$ from both sides)

$-4x \leq 1$ (Divide both sides by –4, so reverse the inequality sign)

$x \geq -\dfrac{1}{4}$

b $5x + 1 < 4x + 5$ (Subtract $4x$ from both sides)

$x + 1 < 5$ (Subtract 1 from both sides)

$x < 4$

KEY POINTS

- $x > 4$ means that x cannot be equal to 4.
- $x \geq 4$ means that x can be equal to 4 or greater than 4.

- When finding the solution set of an inequality:

  Collect up the algebraic term on one side.

  When multiplying or dividing both sides by a negative number, reverse the inequality sign.

EXERCISE 6

Insert the correct symbol, <, > or =.

1 ▶ $-3 \boxed{} 3$ **2 ▶** $30\% \boxed{} \frac{1}{3}$ **3 ▶** $-3 \boxed{} -4$ **4 ▶** $0.3 \boxed{} \frac{1}{3}$

5 ▶   Write down the inequalities represented by this number line.

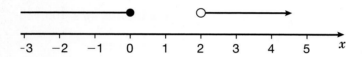

6 ▶   Write down the single inequality represented by this number line.

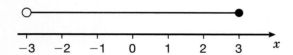

Solve the inequality, and show the result on a number line.

7 ▶ $x - 3 > 2$ **10 ▶** $10 \geq 13 - 2x$ **13 ▶** $2(x + 3) < x + 6$

8 ▶ $x - 3 \leq 1$ **11 ▶** $4x \geq 3x + 9$ **14 ▶** $5(x - 1) > 2(x + 2)$

9 ▶ $4 < 7 - x$ **12 ▶** $6x + 3 < 2x + 19$

Solve these inequalities.

15 ▶ $3 > x + 5$ **18 ▶** $x - 4 \geq 3x$

16 ▶ $-2x \leq 10$ **19 ▶** $2(x - 1) \leq 5x$

17 ▶ $3 > 2x + 5$ **20 ▶** $2(x - 3) \leq 5(x + 3)$

Solve these inequalities. List the integers in each solution set.

21 ▶ $4 < x \leq 6$ **24 ▶** $2 \leq 2x < x + 5$

22 ▶ $2 < x \leq 4.5$ **25 ▶** $4 < 2x + 1 \leq 7$

23 ▶ $-1 < x \leq 1.5$

EXERCISE 6*

1 ▶ Write down the inequalities represented by this number line.

Explain why your two answers cannot be combined into a single inequality.

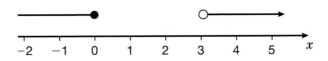

Solve the inequality and show the result on a number line.

2 ▶ $3x \leq x + 5$

3 ▶ $5x + 3 < 2x + 19$

4 ▶ $3(x + 3) < x + 12$

5 ▶ $2(x - 1) > 7(x + 2)$

6 ▶ $\dfrac{x}{2} - 3 \geq 3x - 8$

7 ▶ $-7 < 3x - 2 \leq 11$

8 ▶ $x < 2x + 1 \leq 7$

9 ▶ Find the largest **prime number** y that **satisfies** $4y \leq 103$.

10 ▶ List the integers that satisfy both the inequalities.

$-3 \leq x < 4$ and $x > 0$

11 ▶ Solve the inequality, then list the four largest integers in the solution set.

$\dfrac{x + 1}{4} \geq \dfrac{x - 1}{3}$

EXERCISE 7

REVISION

Simplify these.

1 ▶ $\dfrac{3y}{y}$

2 ▶ $\dfrac{4x}{4}$

3 ▶ $\dfrac{9x^2}{3x}$

4 ▶ $\dfrac{2a}{3} \times \dfrac{6}{a}$

5 ▶ $\dfrac{6b}{4} \div \dfrac{3b}{2a}$

6 ▶ $\dfrac{10x^2}{3} \times \dfrac{9}{5x}$

7 ▶ $\dfrac{y}{4} + \dfrac{y}{5}$

8 ▶ $\dfrac{x}{3} - \dfrac{x}{5}$

9 ▶ $\dfrac{2a}{5} + \dfrac{b}{10}$

Solve these.

10 ▶ $\dfrac{x^2}{2} + 2 = 10$

11 ▶ $\dfrac{x^2 + 2}{2} = 19$

12 ▶ $\sqrt{\dfrac{4 + x}{6}} = 2$

Use the rules of indices to simplify these.

13 ▶ $a^4 \times a^6$

14 ▶ $b^7 \div b^5$

15 ▶ $(c^4)^3$

Rewrite each expression and insert the correct symbol <, > or = in the box.

16 ▶ -2 ☐ -3 **17 ▶** $\dfrac{1}{8}$ ☐ $\dfrac{1}{7}$ **18 ▶** 0.0009 ☐ 0.01 **19 ▶** 0.1 ☐ 10%

20 ▶ Write down the single inequality represented by this number line.

What is the smallest integer that x can be?

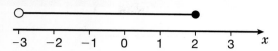

Solve the inequality and show each result on a number line.

21 ▶ $x - 4 > 1$

22 ▶ $5x \leq 3x + 9$

23 ▶ $5(x - 2) \geq 4(x - 2)$

24 ▶ Solve the inequality $x + 5 \leq 6x$.

25 ▶ List the integers in the solution set $3 \leq x < 5$.

EXERCISE 7*

REVISION

Simplify these.

1 ▶ $\dfrac{20a}{5b}$

2 ▶ $\dfrac{35x^2}{7xy}$

3 ▶ $\dfrac{12ab^2}{48a^2b}$

4 ▶ $\dfrac{2a}{b} \times \dfrac{b^2}{4a}$

5 ▶ $\dfrac{30}{xy^2} \div \dfrac{6x^2}{x^2y}$

6 ▶ $\dfrac{(3a)^2}{7b} \div \dfrac{a^3}{14b^2}$

7 ▶ $\dfrac{3a}{2} + \dfrac{a}{10}$

8 ▶ $\dfrac{2}{3b} + \dfrac{3}{4b} - \dfrac{5}{6b}$

9 ▶ $\dfrac{x+1}{7} - \dfrac{x-3}{21}$

Solve these.

10 ▶ $3x^2 + 5 = 32$

11 ▶ $2 = \dfrac{\sqrt{2x} + 2}{2}$

12 ▶ $\sqrt{100 - 4x^2} = 6$

Use the rules of indices to simplify each expression.

13 ▶ $a^5 \times a^6 \div a^7$

14 ▶ $(2b^3)^2$

15 ▶ $3c(3c^2)^3$

16 ▶ Write down the single inequality represented by the number line.

What is the smallest integer that satisfies the inequality?

Solve the inequality and show each result on a number line.

17 ▶ $7x + 3 < 2x - 19$

18 ▶ $2(x - 1) < 5(x + 2)$

19 ▶ $\dfrac{x-2}{5} \geq \dfrac{x-3}{3}$

20 ▶ Find the largest prime number y which satisfies $3y - 11 \leq 103$.

21 ▶ List the integers which satisfy both these inequalities simultaneously.

$-3.5 < x < 3$ and $4x + 1 \leq x + 2$

EXAM PRACTICE: ALGEBRA 2

In questions 1–6, simplify as much as possible.

1 $\dfrac{12xy^2}{3x}$ **[1]**

2 $(5xy^2) \div (15x^2y)$ **[1]**

3 $\dfrac{a}{b^3} \times \dfrac{ab}{c} \times \dfrac{b^2c}{a^2}$ **[1]**

4 $\dfrac{3x^2}{y^2} \div \dfrac{x^2}{y}$ **[1]**

5 $\dfrac{x}{4} - \dfrac{x}{6}$ **[2]**

6 $\dfrac{x}{9} + \dfrac{2x}{3}$ **[2]**

In questions 7–9, solve for x.

7 $2x^2 + 13 = 63$ **[3]**

8 $\dfrac{x^2 - 11}{7} = 10$ **[3]**

9 $\dfrac{\sqrt{x+4}}{4} = 1$ **[2]**

10 Simplify

a $3(q^3)^2$

b $p^5 \div p^3$

c $x^8 \times x^{12}$ **[3]**

11 Solve the inequality $10 \le 7 - x$ and show the result on a number line. **[3]**

12 List the integer solutions of $3 \le 3x < x + 6$. **[3]**

[Total 25 marks]

CHAPTER SUMMARY: ALGEBRA 2

SIMPLIFYING ALGEBRAIC FRACTIONS

$$\frac{5a}{4b_2} \times \frac{2b}{3} = \frac{5a}{6} \qquad \frac{5a}{12} + \frac{2b}{3} = \frac{5a+8b}{12} \qquad \frac{5a}{12} - \frac{2b}{3} = \frac{5a-8b}{12}$$

To divide by a fraction, turn the fraction upside down and multiply.

$$\frac{5a}{12} \div \frac{2b}{3} = \frac{5a}{12_4} \times \frac{3}{2b} = \frac{5a}{8b}$$

POSITIVE INTEGER INDICES

When multiplying, add the indices.

$$a^m \times a^n = a^{m+n}$$

When dividing, subtract the indices.

$$a^m \div a^n = a^{m-n}$$

When raising to a power, multiply the indices.

$$(a^m)^n = a^{mn}$$

SOLVING EQUATIONS WITH ROOTS AND POWERS

The way to solve equations is to isolate the unknown letter by systematically doing the same operation to both sides.

Always check your answer.

Solve $3x^2 - 4 = 71$

$3x^2 - 4 = 71$	(Add 4 to both sides)
$3x^2 = 75$	(Divide both sides by 3)
$x^2 = 25$	(Square root both sides)
$x = \pm 5$	(Note there are two answers)

Check: $3 \times (\pm 5)^2 - 4 = 71$

Solve $\dfrac{\sqrt{y+3}}{4} - 2 = 1$

$\dfrac{\sqrt{y+3}}{4} - 2 = 1$	(Add 2 to both sides)
$\dfrac{\sqrt{y+3}}{4} = 3$	(Multiply both sides by 4)
$\sqrt{y+3} = 12$	(Square both sides)
$y + 3 = 144$	(Subtract 3 from both sides)
$y = 141$	

Check: $\dfrac{\sqrt{141+3}}{4} - 2 = 1$

INEQUALITIES

Inequalities are solved in the same way as algebraic equations, EXCEPT that when multiplying or dividing by a negative number the inequality sign is reversed.

$2(x - 3) \le 5(x - 3)$	(Expand brackets)
$2x - 6 \le 5x - 15$	(Add 15 to both sides)
$2x + 9 \le 5x$	(Subtract $2x$ from both sides)
$9 \le 3x$	(Divide both sides by 3)

$3 \le x$ or $x \ge 3$

$x > 3$ means that x cannot be equal to 3.

$x \ge 3$ means that x can be equal to 3 or greater than 3.

A solid circle means

$\ge$ 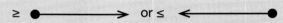 or $\le$

An open circle means

$>$ 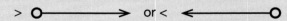 or $<$

GRAPHS 2

Whether a graph is a straight line or not can be a matter of life and death. When the polio vaccine was being developed, a researcher plotted data on infectiousness of the vaccine and found the points fell on a straight line. Scientists were convinced that the graph when continued would be straight and that after nine days' treatment the vaccine would be totally safe. However they were wrong and many people died or contracted polio as a result.

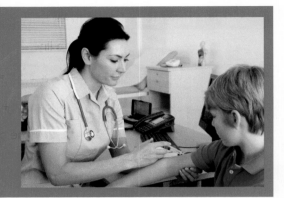

LEARNING OBJECTIVES

- Find the equation of a line
- Sketch graphs using the gradient and intercepts
- Solve a pair of simultaneous equations using a graph

BASIC PRINCIPLES

- For a straight line, m is the **gradient**

$$m = \frac{\text{change in the } y \text{ coordinates}}{\text{change in the } x \text{ coordinates}} = \frac{\text{'rise'}}{\text{'run'}}$$

- The equation $y = mx + c$ represents a straight line with gradient m and y **intercept** c.

- The equation $ax + by = c$ also represents a straight line. It is most easily plotted by finding where it crosses the x and y axes.

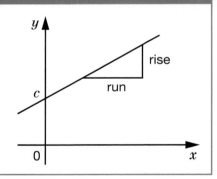

STRAIGHT-LINE GRAPHS

FINDING THE EQUATION OF A STRAIGHT-LINE GRAPH

EXAMPLE 1

Find the equation of the straight line with gradient 2 that passes through the point (1, 3).

The general form is $y = mx + c$

The gradient, m, is 2 $\Rightarrow y = 2x + c$

(1, 3) lies on the line. Substitute $x = 1$ and $y = 3$ to find c.

$3 = 2 \times 1 + c \Rightarrow c = 1$

The equation is $y = 2x + 1$.

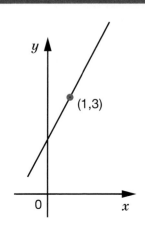

EXAMPLE 2

Find the equation of the straight line passing through A (2, 3) and B (6, 5).

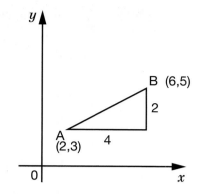

The general form is $y = mx + c$

The gradient, m, is $\frac{2}{4} = \frac{1}{2} \Rightarrow y = \frac{1}{2}x + c$

(2, 3) lies on the line. Substitute $x = 2$ and $y = 3$ to find c.

This gives $3 = \frac{1}{2} \times 2 + c \Rightarrow c = 2$

The equation is $y = \frac{1}{2}x + 2$.

Check: Substituting the coordinates of B gives $5 = \frac{1}{2} \times 6 + 2$ which is correct.

EXAMPLE 3

Find the equation of the straight line passing through A (3, 6) and the origin.

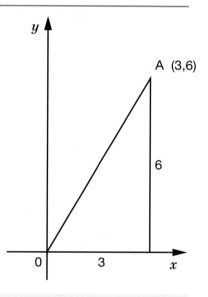

The general form is $y = mx + c$

The gradient, m, is $\frac{6}{3} = 2 \Rightarrow y = 2x + c$

(0, 0) lies on the line. Substitute $x = 0$ and $y = 0$ to find c.

This gives $0 = 2 \times 0 + c \Rightarrow c = 0$

The equation is $y = 2x$.

Check: Substituting the coordinates of A gives $6 = 2 \times 3$ which is correct.

Note: all straight lines passing through the origin will have $c = 0$.

KEY POINTS

- If the gradient is m then the equation is $y = mx + c$.
- To find c, substitute a point that lies on the line.
- If the line passes through the origin, $c = 0$ so $y = mx$.

EXERCISE 1

Find the equation of the straight line with

1 ▶ Gradient 1 passing through (2, 3)

3 ▶ Gradient –2 passing through (0, 3)

2 ▶ Gradient 0.5 passing through (4, 1)

4 ▶ Gradient –1 passing through (0, 0)

Find the equation of the straight line joining A to B when

5 ▶ A is (1, 2) and B is (3, 4)

8 ▶ A is (0, 0) and B is (6, 2)

6 ▶ A is (–2, 1) and B is (3, 6)

9 ▶ A is (–1, 5) and B is (3, 1)

7 ▶ A is (–1, –5) and B is (2, 1)

10 ▶ A is (–2, 3) and B is (4, –9)

EXERCISE 1*   Find the equation of the straight line that

1 ▶   has a gradient of 3 and passes through (–3, 3)

2 ▶   has a gradient of –0.5 and passes through (0, 0)

3 ▶   is parallel to $2y = 5x + 7$ and passes through (0, –3.5)

4 ▶   is parallel to $9x – 5y = –3$ and passes through (5, –3).

Find the equation of the straight line joining A to B when

5 ▶   A is (–2, 1) and B is (–1, 4)

6 ▶   A is (–3, 4) and B is (6, 1)

7 ▶   A is (–2, 1) and B is (3, 1).

8 ▶   a Find the equation of the straight line joining A (–10, 5) to B (8, –4).

    b What can you say about A, B and the origin?

9 ▶   A is (–8, –1), B is (–4, 1) and C is (12, 9).

    a Find the equation of the straight line joining A to B.

    b Find the equation of the straight line joining B to C.

    c What can you say about the points A, B and C?

10 ▶   AB and BC are two sides of a **parallelogram**. A is (0, 3), B is (6, 6) and C is (7, 3).
    Find the equations of the other two sides.

SKETCHING STRAIGHT-LINE GRAPHS

Sketching a straight line means showing the approximate position and slope of the line *without* plotting any points.

A straight line in the form $y = mx + c$ can be sketched by using the gradient and y-intercept.

EXAMPLE 4   Sketch these graphs.

a $y = 2x - 1$ b $y = -\frac{1}{2}x + 3$

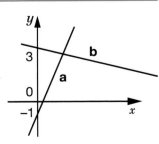

a $y = 2x - 1$ is a straight line with gradient 2 and y-intercept (0, –1).

b $y = -0.5x + 3$ is a straight line with gradient –0.5 and y-intercept (0, 3).

Graphs of the form $ax + by = c$ could be sketched by rearranging the equation as $y = ...$

It is quicker to find where the graph crosses the axes.

EXAMPLE 5

Sketch the graph $2x - 3y = 6$.

When $y = 0$, $x = 3$ so (3, 0) lies on the line.

When $x = 0$, $y = -2$ so (0, -2) lies on the line.

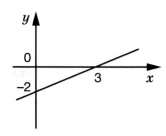

KEY POINTS

- A **sketch** is drawn roughly **to scale**, NOT plotted.
- Use the values of the gradient and intercept to sketch $y = mx + c$.
- Use where the graph crosses the axes to sketch $ax + by = c$.

EXERCISE 2

Sketch the straight lines with the given gradient and intercept.

1 ▶ Gradient = 1, intercept = 2

2 ▶ Gradient = $\frac{1}{2}$, intercept = -3

3 ▶ Gradient = -2, intercept = 1

4 ▶ Gradient = $-\frac{1}{3}$, intercept = -1

In Questions 5–8, write down the gradient and y-intercept and then sketch the graph of the equation.

5 ▶ $y = 3x + 5$

6 ▶ $y = x - 7$

7 ▶ $y = -2x + 3$

8 ▶ $y = -\frac{1}{2}x - 1$

9 ▶ Sketch $3x + 2y = 6$

10 ▶ Sketch $2x - 4y = 8$

11 ▶ Sketch $4x - 3y = -12$

12 ▶ Write down possible equations for the three lines on this sketch graph.

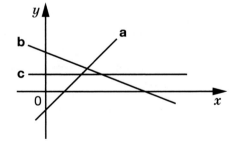

EXERCISE 2*

Write down the gradient of the graph and the intercept (or where the graph intercepts the axes), then sketch the graph.

1 ▶ $y = 5x + \frac{1}{2}$

2 ▶ $y = 4 - 2x$

3 ▶ $2y = 5 + 4x$

4 ▶ $y = -3x + \frac{5}{2}$

5 ▶ $y = 3.5x - 7$

6 ▶ $y = -2x + 10$

7 ▶ $2x - 3y = 1$

8 ▶ $4y - 2x + 3 = 0$

9 ▶ Write down possible equations for the three lines on this sketch graph.

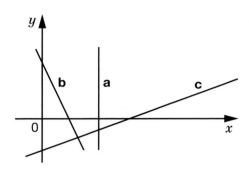

10 ▶ Sketch $ax + by = c$ for the following cases.

  a $a > 0$, $b > 0$ and $c > 0$ **b** $a > 0$, $b > 0$ and $c < 0$ **c** $a > 0$, $b < 0$ and $c > 0$

SIMULTANEOUS EQUATIONS

ACTIVITY 1

Viv is trying to decide between two internet service providers, Pineapple and Banana. Pineapple charges \$9.99/month plus 1.1 cents/minute online, while Banana charges \$4.95/month plus 1.8 cents/minute online.

If C is the cost in cents and t is the time (in minutes) online per month then the cost of using Pineapple is $C = 999 + 1.1t$, and the cost of using Banana is $C = 495 + 1.8t$.

Copy and complete this table to give the charges for Pineapple.

Time online t (minutes)	0	500	1000
Cost C (cents)			

Draw a graph of this data with t on the horizontal axis and C on the vertical axis.

Make a similar table for the Banana charges. Add the graph of this data to your previous graph.

How many minutes online per month will result in both companies charging the same amount?

When there are two unknowns, two equations are needed to solve them. These are called simultaneous equations.

In Activity 1, the **simultaneous equations** were $C = 999 + 1.1t$ and $C = 495 + 1.8t$.
The coordinates of the point of intersection of the graphs give the solution.

EXAMPLE 6

Solve the simultaneous equations $y = \frac{1}{2}x + 2$ and $y = 4 - x$ graphically.

First, make a table of values for each equation.

x	0	2	4
$y = \frac{1}{2}x + 2$	2	3	4

x	0	2	4
$y = 4 - x$	4	2	0

Next, draw accurate graphs for both equations on one set of axes.

The solution point is approximately $x = 1.3$, $y = 2.7$.

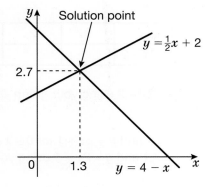

EXAMPLE 7

SKILLS

PROBLEM
SOLVING

At a craft fair stall Sarah buys two rings and three bracelets and pays $11. At the same stall Amy buys one ring and four bracelets and pays $13. How much does each item cost?

Let x be the cost of a ring and y be the cost of a bracelet.

For Sarah: $2x + 3y = 11$
For Amy: $x + 4y = 13$

The graph shows both these lines plotted.

The intersection is at $x = 1$ and $y = 3$.
Each ring costs $1 and each bracelet costs $3.

Check for Sarah: $2 \times 1 + 3 \times 3 = 11$
Check for Amy: $1 \times 1 + 4 \times 3 = 13$

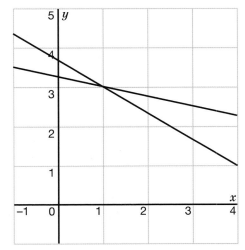

KEY POINTS

To solve simultaneous equations graphically:

- Draw the graphs for both equations on one set of axes.
- Only plot three points for a straight-line graph.
- The solution is where the graphs **intersect**.
- If the graphs do not intersect, there is no solution.
- If the graphs are the same, there is an infinite number of solutions.

EXERCISE 3

1 ▶ Copy and complete these tables, then draw both graphs on one set of axes.

x	0	2	4
$y = x + 1$			

x	0	2	4
$y = 2x - 2$			

Solve the simultaneous equations $y = x + 1$, $y = 2x - 2$ using your graph.

2 ▶ On one set of axes, draw the graphs of $y = 3x - 1$ and $y = 2x + 1$ for $0 \le x \le 6$.
Then, solve the simultaneous equations $y = 3x - 1$ and $y = 2x + 1$ using your graph.

In Questions 3 and 4, solve the simultaneous equations graphically, using $0 \le x \le 6$.

3 ▶ $y = 2x + 2$ 4 ▶ $y = \frac{1}{2}x + 1$

     $y = 3x - 1$ $y = 4 - x$

5 ▶ Logan and Max go to the fair. Logan has three rides on the Big Wheel and two rides on the Pirate Ship and spends $12. Max has five rides on the Big Wheel and one ride on the Pirate Ship and spends $13.
Let x be the cost of a Big Wheel ride and y the cost of a Pirate Ship ride.

a   Write down two equations showing what Logan and Max spent.

b   Plot these equations on one graph.

c   What does each ride cost?

6 ▶ Freya is collecting 50p and £1 coins. When she has 18 coins the value of them is £13.
Let x be the number of 50p coins and y the number of £1 coins.

Write a pair of simultaneous equations and solve them graphically to find how many 50p coins Freya has.

EXERCISE 3*

1 ▶ On one set of axes, draw the graphs of $y = 2x + 1$ and $y = 3x - 5$ for $0 \leqslant x \leqslant 6$. Then, solve the simultaneous equations $y = 2x + 1$ and $y = 3x - 5$ using your graphs.

2 ▶ Solve these simultaneous equations graphically, using $0 \leq x \leq 6$.

$$6x - 5 = 2y$$
$$3x - 7 = 6y$$

3 ▶ Solve $y = 4 - 2x$ and $6x + 3y = 18$ graphically. How many solutions are there?

4 ▶ Solve $y = \frac{1}{2}x + 3$ and $2y - x = 6$ graphically. How many solutions are there?

5 ▶ McMountain Construction is digging a tunnel in the Alps.

The mountain can be represented by $3y = 4x + 6000$ for $0 \leq x \leq 3000$ and $7y + 6x = 60\,000$ for $3000 \leq x \leq 10\,000$.

The tunnel can be represented by the line $10y + x = 30\,000$.

All the units are metres. Find the coordinates of the ends of the tunnel.

Q6 HINT
Let £x be the cost of a can of cat food and £y be the cost of a toy.

6 ▶ At the local pet shop Esme bought four cans of cat food and two bags of treats for her kitten, spending £7. Her friend Lacey bought three cans of cat food and three bags of treats, spending £6. By drawing graphs, find the cost of each item.

7 ▶ At a music festival, tickets cost either £60 or £100. 1200 tickets were sold at a total cost of £88 000. By drawing graphs, find how many £60 tickets were sold.

8 ▶ **a** Copy and complete this table to show the angle that the minute hand of a clock makes with the number 12 for various times after 12 noon.

Time after 12 noon (hours)	0	$\frac{1}{4}$	$\frac{1}{2}$	$\frac{3}{4}$	1	$1\frac{1}{4}$	$1\frac{1}{2}$	$1\frac{3}{4}$	2	$2\frac{1}{4}$	$2\frac{1}{2}$
Angle (degrees)	0		180		90						

b Use the table to draw a graph of angle against time. Show the time from 0 hours to 6 hours on the x-axis, and the angle from 0° to 360° on the y-axis.

c Draw another line on your graph to show the angle that the hour hand makes with the number 12 for various times after 12 noon.

d Use your graph to find the times between 12 noon and 6pm when the hour hand and the minute hand of the clock are in line.

EXERCISE 4

1 ▶ Find the equation of the lines with

     a gradient 2, passing through the origin   **b** gradient –3, passing through (2, 0)

2 ▶ Find the equation of the straight line joining A to B when

     a A is (3, 4) and B is (5, 8)   **b** A is (–1, 2) and B is (1, 0)

3 ▶ Sketch the following graphs.

     a $y = 3x - 3$ **b** $y = 4 - x$ **c** $2x + 5y = 10$

4 ▶ Solve $y = 2x - 3$ and $y = 3 - x$ graphically using $0 \le x \le 4$.

5 ▶ Solve $y = x + 4$ and $y = 1 - 2x$ graphically using $-3 \le x \le 1$.

6 ▶ Music downloads from Banana cost $\$x$ each, while downloads from Musedown cost $\$y$ each. Rahul downloads three songs from Banana and two from Musedown and spends $6. Mia downloads one song from Banana and four from Musedown and spends $7.

     a Write down two equations showing what Rahul and Mia spent.

     b Plot these equations on one graph.

     c What does each download cost?

EXERCISE 4*

1 ▶ Find the equation of the straight line passing through (6, 4) that is parallel to $3y = x + 21$.

2 ▶ Find the equation of the straight line joining A to B when

     a A is (–4, –1), B is (–1, –2)   **b** A is (–2, –8), B is (1, –2)

3 ▶ Sketch the following graphs.

     a $y = 3x - 2$ **b** $2y = 5 - x$ **c** $5x + 3y = 10$

4 ▶ Solve $2y + x + 3 = 0$ and $3y - x + 1 = 0$ graphically using $-4 \le x \le 2$.

5 ▶ Lewis is doing a multiple choice test of 20 questions. He gets four marks for every correct answer, but loses one mark for every answer that is wrong. Lewis answers every question and scores 50 marks. Use a graphical method to find the number of questions Lewis got wrong.

Q6 HINT

p will appear in the answer.

6 ▶ Find the equation of the straight line joining $(-2, 3 - 6p)$ to $(-2 + 2p, 3)$.

EXAM PRACTICE: GRAPHS 2

1 Find the equation of the straight line passing through A (–1, –8) and B (1, 2). **[3]**

2 A straight line passes through the origin O and the point A (4, –2).

   a Find the equation of the line OA. **[2]**

   b Find the equation of the line parallel to OA that passes through (–3, 1). **[2]**

3 Sketch the following graphs.

   a $y = 2x - 3$

   b $3x + 4y = 24$

   c $y = -x + 1$ **[6]**

4 Solve the simultaneous equations $x + y = 8$ and $y = 2x - 1$ graphically. **[6]**

Q4 HINT
Draw both x and y axes from –2 to 8.

5 At the market Theo buys six apples and four avocados and spends $14. Erin buys four apples and six avocados and spends $16. Let x be the cost of an apple and y be the cost of an avocado.

Write a pair of simultaneous equations and solve them graphically to find the cost of

   a one apple

   b one avocado. **[6]**

[Total 25 marks]

CHAPTER SUMMARY: GRAPHS 2

STRAIGHT-LINE GRAPHS

To find the equation of a straight line:

- If the gradient is m then the equation is $y = mx + c$.

- To find c substitute a point that lies on the line.

- If the line passes through the origin $c = 0$ so $y = mx$.

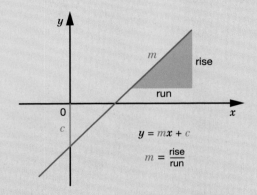

$$y = mx + c$$

$$m = \frac{\text{rise}}{\text{run}}$$

SKETCHING STRAIGHT-LINE GRAPHS

Sketch means show the position and slope of the line **without** plotting points.

A sketch is drawn roughly to scale by eye – it is not exact.

The straight line $y = mx + c$ has gradient m and crosses the y-axis at $(0, c)$.

To sketch the straight line $ax + by = c$ find where it crosses the axes.

SIMULTANEOUS EQUATIONS

To solve simultaneous equations graphically:

- Draw the graphs for both equations on one set of axes.

- Only plot three points for a straight-line graph.

- The solution is where the graphs intersect.

- If the graphs do not intersect, there is no solution.

- If the graphs are the same, there is an infinite number of solutions.

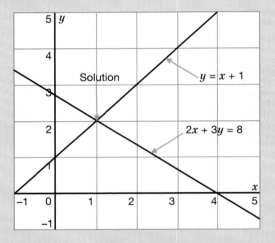

The solution to the simultaneous equations $y = x + 1$ and $2x + 3y = 8$ is $x = 1$, $y = 2$.

SHAPE AND SPACE 2

Pythagoras of Samos (570–495BC) was a well-known mathematician, scientist and religious teacher. He was inspired to study mathematics and astronomy, but also made important discoveries in astronomy, music and medicine. He set up a brotherhood (a community) with some of his followers, who practised his way of life and studied his religious ideologies. His most famous mathematical theorem was possibly known by the Babylonians in 1000BC, as well as Indian and Chinese mathematicians.

LEARNING OBJECTIVES

- Find the length of the hypotenuse in a right-angled triangle
- Find the length of a shorter side in a right-angled triangle
- Solve problems using Pythagoras' Theorem
- Use the properties of angles in a circle
- Use the properties of tangents to a circle

- Understand and use facts about chords
- Understand and use facts about the angle in a semicircle being a right angle
- Understand and use facts about angles subtended at the centre and the circumference of circles
- Understand and use facts about cyclic quadrilaterals
- Solve angle problems using circle theorems

BASIC PRINCIPLES

- Solve equations for x such as:

$$5^2 = 3^2 + x^2 \quad \Rightarrow x^2 = 5^2 - 3^2 = 16$$
$$\Rightarrow x = \sqrt{16}$$
$$\Rightarrow x = 4$$

- Straight lines can **intersect** a circle to form a **tangent**, a **diameter** or a **chord**.

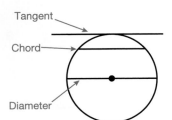

Tangent

Chord

Diameter

- A tangent touches the circle. It is **perpendicular** to the **radius** at the point of contact.

- **Isosceles triangles** frequently occur in circle theorem questions.

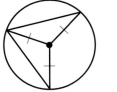

PYTHAGORAS' THEOREM

The Greek philosopher and mathematician Pythagoras found a connection between the lengths of the sides of right-angled triangles. It is probably the most famous mathematical theorem in the world.

In a right-angled triangle, the longest side is called the **hypotenuse**. It is the side opposite the right angle.

Pythagoras' Theorem states that in a right-angled triangle, the square of the hypotenuse is equal to the **sum** of the squares of the other two sides.

KEY POINT

- $a^2 = b^2 + c^2$

Side a is always the hypotenuse.

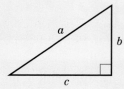

EXAMPLE 1

SKILLS

REASONING

Calculate side a.

From Pythagoras' Theorem:

$a^2 = b^2 + c^2$

$a^2 = 3^2 + 5^2$

$\quad = 34$

$a = \sqrt{34}$

$\quad a = 5.38\,\text{cm (3 s.f.)}$

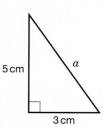

EXAMPLE 2

SKILLS

REASONING

Calculate side b.

From Pythagoras' Theorem:

$a^2 = b^2 + c^2$

$11^2 = b^2 + 8^2$

$b^2 = 11^2 - 8^2$

$\quad = 57$

$b = \sqrt{57}$

$\quad b = 7.55\,\text{cm (3 s.f.)}$

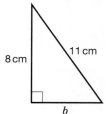

ACTIVITY 1

SKILLS

ANALYSIS

Proof of Pythagoras' Theorem

There are many elegant proofs of Pythagoras' Theorem.

One of the easiest to understand involves a square of side $(b + c)$.

Inside the large square is a smaller one of side a.

Given that the area of the large square is $(b + c)^2$ and is clearly equal to the area of the four identical triangles plus the area a^2 of the smaller square, form an equation.

Now **simplify** it to show that $a^2 = b^2 + c^2$, and therefore prove that Pythagoras was correct.

HINT $(b + c)^2 = (b + c)(b + c) = b(b + c) + c(b + c)$

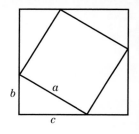

EXERCISE 1

Find length x in these right-angled triangles to 3 s.f.

1 ▶
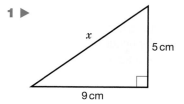

2 ▶
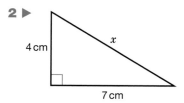

3 ▶
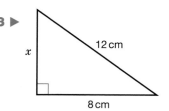

4 ▶
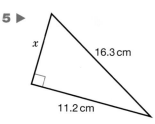

5 ▶

6 ▶
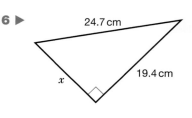

7 ▶ Find the diagonal length of a square field of side 50 m.

8 ▶ A fishing boat sails from Bastia in Corsica. It travels 15 km due east, then 25 km due south. It then returns directly to its starting point. What is the total distance the boat travels?

9 ▶ A 3.5 m ladder rests against a vertical wall. Its base is 1.5 m away from the wall.

How far up the wall is the top of the ladder?

10 ▶ A large rectangular Persian rug has a diagonal length of 12 m and a width of 6 m.

Find the length of the rug.

EXERCISE 1*

Find length a in these right-angled triangles to 3 s.f.

1 ▶
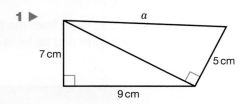

2 ▶
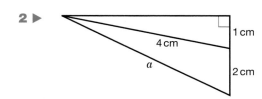

3 ▶
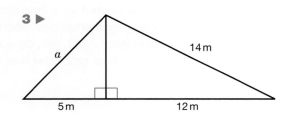

4 ▶
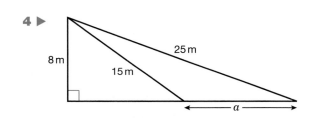

5 ▶ Calculate the distance between the points (7, 4) and (−5, −3).

6 ▶ Calculate the area of a square whose diagonals are 20 cm long.

7 ▶ Thuso sails his boat from Mogadishu directly north-east for 50 km, then directly south-east for 100 km. He then sails directly back to Mogadishu at 13:00 hrs at a speed of 25 km/h.

What time does he arrive?

8 ▶ OA = 100 m. OB = 150 m. The 100 m start of a ski jump at A has a vertical height of 50 m.

Q8a HINT
Use similar triangles.

a Find the vertical height of the 150 m starting point at B.

b Find the horizontal distance between the two starting points A and B.

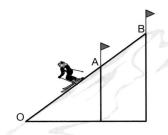

9 ▶ Let OQ = y and the circle radius = r.

Q9a HINT
Use Pythagoras' Theorem.

a Find PQ in terms of r and y.

b State why PQ = RQ.

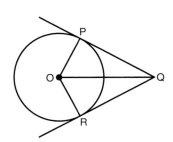

10 ▶   Find the length AB in this rectangular block.

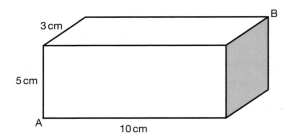

11 ▶   A fierce guard dog is tied up by a 15 m chain to a post that is 6 m from a straight path.

Over what distance along the path is a person in danger from the dog?

12 ▶   A ladder is resting against a vertical wall. Its base is 1.5 m away from the base of the wall. When Giani steps on the ladder, it falls down the wall 0.25 m and its base is now 2 m away from the wall. Find the length of the ladder.

CIRCLE THEOREMS

Circle geometry has existed for a long time. Euclid (350–300BC) was a Greek mathematician who is often called the 'Father of Geometry'. His book, called *Elements*, contained many theorems on circles that we study in this section.

ANGLES IN A SEMICIRCLE AND TANGENTS

ACTIVITY 2

Proving the result

Find the angles in circle C_1 and circle C_2.

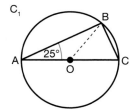
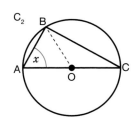

Copy and complete the table for C_1 and C_2.

Circle	$\angle$ BAO	$\angle$ ABO	$\angle$ AOB	$\angle$ BOC	$\angle$ OBC + $\angle$ OCB	$\angle$ OBC	$\angle$ ABC
C_1	25°						
C_2	$x°$						

The row for angles in circle C_2 gives a structure for a formal proof showing that 'the angles in a semicircle formed off the diameter are 90°'.

A full proof requires reasons for every stage of the calculation.

Calculations	**Reasons**
$\angle BAC = x \quad \Rightarrow \quad \angle BAO = x$	AC is diameter of C_2
$ABO = x$	$\triangle ABO$ is isosceles
$\angle BOC = 2x$	Angle sum of line $= 180°$
$\angle OBC + \angle OCB = 180° - 2x$	Angle sum of triangle $= 180°$
$\angle OBC = 90° - x$	$\triangle OBC$ is isosceles
$\angle ABC = x + (90° - x) = 90°$	As required

> **KEY POINT**
>
> - An angle in a semicircle is always a right angle.

> **KEY POINTS**
>
> ### Writing out reasons for geometrical questions
>
> - Your calculations must be supported by a reason for each step. It is helpful to label points, angles and lengths carefully.
> - It is normal practice to write calculations on the left-hand side of the page followed by reasons on the right-hand side as in Activity 2.
>
> Typical reasons:
>
> *Angle sum of a straight line = 180°*   *Angle sum around a point = 360°*
>
> *Angle sum of a triangle = 180°*   **Alternate angles** *are equal*
>
> *Isosceles triangles have equal base angles*   *Vertically opposite angles are equal*

EXERCISE 2

Find the size of each lettered angle, stating reasons for each step.

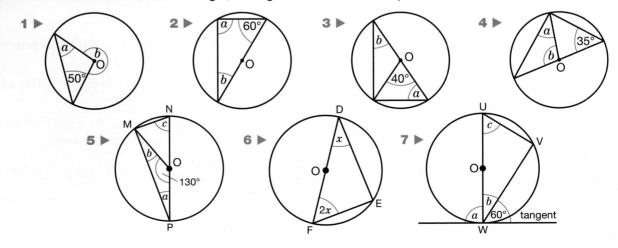

8 ▶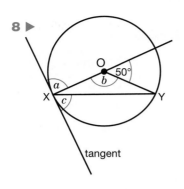

9 ▶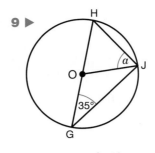

10 ▶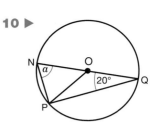

EXERCISE 2* Find the size of each lettered angle, stating reasons for each step.

1 ▶

2 ▶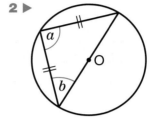

3 ▶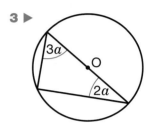

4 ▶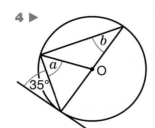

5 ▶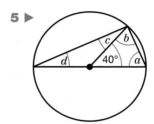

6 ▶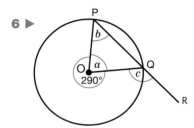

7 ▶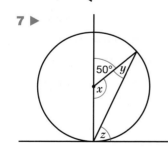

8 ▶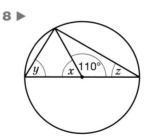

9 ▶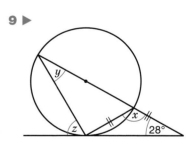

10 ▶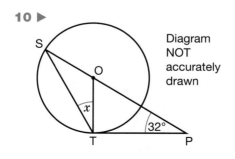

Diagram NOT accurately drawn

S and T are points on the circumference of a circle, centre O.

PT is a tangent to the circle. SOP is a straight line. Angle OPT = 32°.

Work out the size of the angle marked x.
Give reasons for your answer.

ANGLE AT CENTRE OF CIRCLE IS TWICE THE ANGLE AT CIRCUMFERENCE

ACTIVITY 3

SKILLS

ANALYSIS

Find the angles in circle C_1 and circle C_2.

Copy and complete the table for C_1 and C_2.

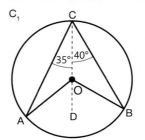

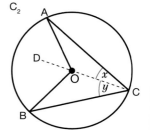

CIRCLE	∠OCA	∠OCB	∠CAO	∠AOD	∠CBD	∠BOD	∠ACB	∠AOB
C_1	35°	40°						
C_2	x	y						

If AOB = k × ACB find the value of k.

The row for angles in circle C_2 gives a structure for a formal proof showing that 'the angles **subtended** (formed) at the centre of a circle are twice the angle at the **circumference**'.

A full proof requires reasons for every stage of the calculation.

Calculations

∠OCA = x ∠OCB = y

∠CAD = x

∠AOD = $2x$

∠CBD = y

∠BOD = $2y$

∠ACB = $x + y$ ∠AOB = $2x + 2y$

∠AOB = $2 \times$ ∠ACB

Reasons

General angles chosen

ΔOAC is isosceles

Angle sum of line = 180°

ΔOBC is isosceles

Angle sum of line = 180°

As required

KEY POINT

- The angle subtended at the centre of a circle is twice the angle at the circumference.

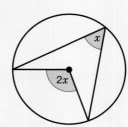

EXAMPLE 3

SKILLS

REASONING

Show that ∠ADB = ∠ACB, namely that 'the angles in the same segment are equal'.

Chord AB splits the circle into two segments. Points C and D are in the same **segment**.

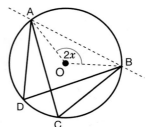

Calculations	Reasons
∠AOB = 2x	General angle chosen
∠ADB = x	Angle at centre of circle = 2 × angle at circumference
∠ACB = x	Angle at centre of circle = 2 × angle at circumference
∠ABD = ∠ACB	As required

EXAMPLE 4

SKILLS

REASONING

Show that ∠ABC + ∠ADC = 180°, namely that 'the sum of the opposite angles of a cyclic **quadrilateral** = 180°'.

ABCD is a cyclic quadrilateral with OA and OC as radii of the circle.

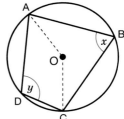

Calculations	Reasons
∠ABC = x	General angle chosen
∠ADC = y	General angle chosen
∠AOC = 2x	Angle at centre of circle = 2 × angle at circumference
∠AOC = 2y (reflex angle)	Angle at centre of circle = 2 × angle at circumference
2x + 2y = 360°	Angle sum at a point = 360°
x + y = 180°	As required

Angle sum of a quadrilateral = 360°, so sum of the remaining two angles = 180°.

KEY POINTS

- Angles in the same segment are equal.
- Opposite angles of a cyclic quadrilateral (a quadrilateral with all four **vertices** on the circumference of a circle) sum to 180°.

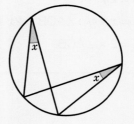

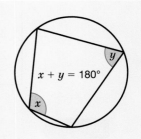

EXERCISE 3

Find the size of each lettered angle, stating reasons for each step.

1 ▶
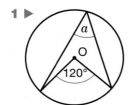

2 ▶
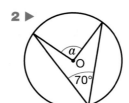

3 ▶
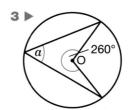

4 ▶
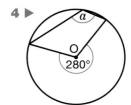

5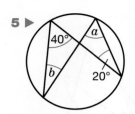

6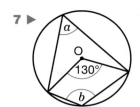

7

8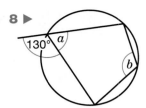

9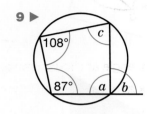

10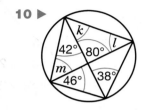

 EXERCISE 3*

Find the size of each lettered angle, stating reasons for each step.

1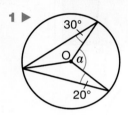

2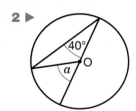

3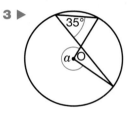

4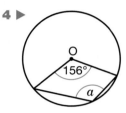

5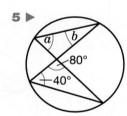

6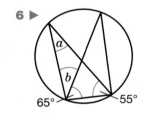

7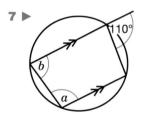

8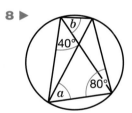

9 ▶ A, B, C and D are points on the circumference of a circle, centre O.

Angle AOC = y.

Find the size of angle ABC in terms of y.

Give a reason for each stage of your working.

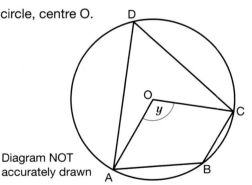

Diagram NOT accurately drawn

10 ▶ A and B are points on the circumference of a circle, centre O. AT is a tangent to the circle.
Angle TAB = 58°. Angle BTA = 41°.

Calculate the size of angle OBT.

Give a reason for each stage of your working.

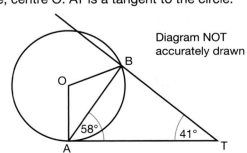

Diagram NOT accurately drawn

EXERCISE 4 **REVISION**

1 ▶ Find length x in each of these triangles.

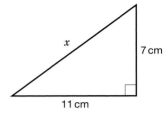

a

x

7 cm

11 cm

b

15 cm

x

10 cm

2 ▶ Find the diagonal length of a square of area 1000 cm².

3 ▶ The diagram shows the side of a shed. Find

a the height of the door AB

b the area of the entire side of the shed.

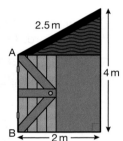

2.5 m

A

4 m

B

2 m

4 ▶ O is the centre of a circle.
OBC is an **equilateral triangle**.
Angle ABC = 130°.

Work out the size of angle a, angle b and angle c.

Give reasons for your answers.

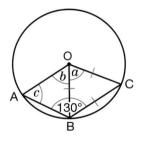

O

b a

C

A c

130°

B

5 ▶ O is the centre of a circle. Angle BAC = $3x$ and angle ACB = $2x$.

Work out the actual size of each angle in the triangle ABC.

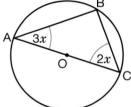

B

A $3x$

O

$2x$

C

6 ▶ O is the centre of a circle.
A, B and C are points on the circumference.
Angle BOC = 40° and angle AOB = 70°.

Prove that AC **bisects** angle OCB.

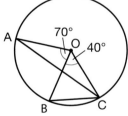

A

70°

O 40°

B C

7 ▶ O is the centre of a circle. A, B, C and D are points on the circumference.
Angle ABC = 114°.

Work out the size of angle COD.

Give a reason for each step of your working.

A

O

B 114°

D

C

8 ▶ O is the centre of a circle.
A, B, C and D are points on the circumference.
Angle BAD = 150°.

Prove that triangle OBD is equilateral.

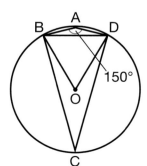

B A D

150°

O

C

EXERCISE 4*

REVISION

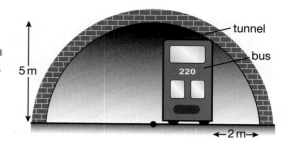

1 ▶ A tunnel has a semicircular **cross-section** and a diameter of 10 m. If the roof of a bus just touches the roof of the tunnel when the bus is 2 m from one side, how high is the bus?

2 ▶ Calculate the height of an equilateral triangle which has the same area as a circle of circumference 10 cm.

3 ▶ O is the centre of a circle. AT is a tangent and AB is a chord. Angle AOB = 124°.

Work out the size of angle BAT.

Give reasons for each step of your working.

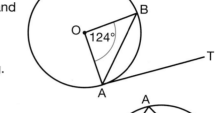

4 ▶ O is the centre of a circle. A, B, C and D are points on the circumference of the circle. Angle BCD = 110°.

Work out the size of angle BOD.

Give reasons for each step of your working.

5 ▶ O is the centre of a circle. A, B, C and D are points on the circumference of the circle. Angle ADB = 19°.

Work out the size of

a angle ABD

b angle ACB.

Give reasons for each step of your working.

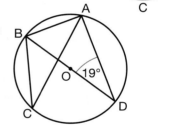

6 ▶ O is the centre of a circle. AC is a diameter.

Work out the actual size of angle BAC.

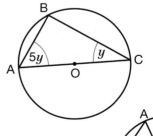

7 ▶ In the diagram, points A, B, C and D lie on the circumference of a circle centre O.

a Prove that angle BAO + angle CDO = angle BOC.

b Explain why all the angles at the edge of the circle are equal.

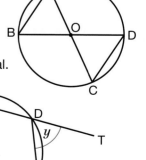

8 ▶ In the diagram, ABCD is a cyclical quadrilateral.

Prove that $x + y = 180°$.

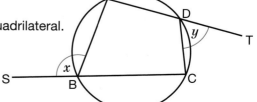

EXAM PRACTICE: SHAPE AND SPACE 2

1 A ramp is used to go up one step.
The ramp is 3 m long. The step is 30 cm high.

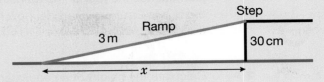

How far away from the step (*x*) does the ramp start?

Give your answer in metres, to the nearest centimetre.

Q1 HINT
Convert lengths to the same units.   [3]

2 Work out the size of each angle marked with a letter.
Give a reason for each step of your working.

a

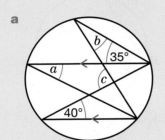

b

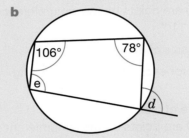

c

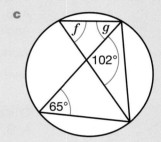

[14]

3 TBP and TCQ are tangents to the circle with centre O.
Point A lies on the circumference of the circle.

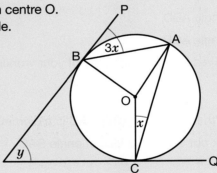

Prove that *y* = 4*x*.

Give reasons for any statements
you make.

[5]

4 Find the area of an equilateral triangle of perimeter 30 cm.   [3]

[Total 25 marks]

CHAPTER SUMMARY: SHAPE AND SPACE 2

PYTHAGORAS' THEOREM

$$a^2 = b^2 + c^2$$

Side a is always the hypotenuse.

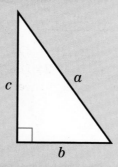

CIRCLE THEOREMS

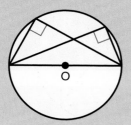
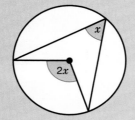
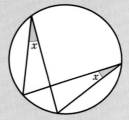
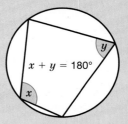

An angle in a semicircle is always a right angle.

The angle subtended at the centre of a circle is twice the angle at the circumference.

Angles in the same segment are equal.

Opposite angles of a cyclic quadrilateral (a quadrilateral with all four vertices on the circumference of a circle) sum to 180°

WRITING OUT REASONS FOR GEOMETRICAL QUESTIONS

Your calculations must be supported by a reason for each step. It is helpful to label points, angles and lengths carefully.

It is normal practice to write calculations on the left-hand side of the page followed by reasons on the right-hand side.

Typical reasons:
Angle sum of a straight line = 180°
Angle sum of a triangle = 180°
Isosceles triangles have equal base angles
Angle sum around a point = 360°
Alternate angles are equal
Vertically opposite angles are equal

HANDLING DATA 1

'There are three kinds of lies: lies, dreadful lies, and statistics' is a statement sometimes made when talking about the persuasive power of statistics. If you wish to avoid being misled by advertising claims, politicians and spin doctors, then a knowledge of statistics and its misuse is an essential skill in the modern world.

▲ Benjamin Disraeli (1804 –1872)

LEARNING OBJECTIVES

- Use pie charts and frequency polygons
- Construct and use two-way tables
- Identify misleading graphs
- Decide which average is best for a set of data

BASIC PRINCIPLES

- Data can be in the form of numbers or categories (e.g. colour).

- Data is often collected by using a tally chart.

- Data is displayed by using diagrams such as **pie charts**, **bar charts**, and **pictograms**.

- The **mean**, **median** and **mode** are all different averages.

- The mean of a set of values $= \dfrac{\text{total of the set of values}}{\text{total number of values}}$.

- The median is the middle value when the data is written in ascending (increasing) order.

- The mode is the most frequent value.

STATISTICAL INVESTIGATION AND COLLECTING DATA

Statistics involves making sense of data, recognising patterns or trends and then possibly making predictions. Frequently a lot of data is obtained from **samples**. Statisticians are people who prepare and analyse statistics. They try to present this data in a way that the human mind can understand. This is done by finding averages to represent all the data, or by drawing diagrams that make it easy to understand what the data means. The conclusions are compared with the real world; more samples may be taken to improve any predictions.

Specify problem and plan

Interpret, discuss and predict

Collect data

Process and represent data

TYPES OF DATA

Data can be in categories, such as eye colour, or it can be numeric (numbers). Data in categories is called categorical data.

Numeric data can be either discrete or continuous.

Discrete data can only take certain values. For example, the number of students in a class could be 20 or 21 but not 20.5.

Continuous data can take any value (within a **range**). For example, a student's height could be 1.5 m or 1.6 m or 1.534 m or any number you can think of (within the range of possible heights for humans).

EXAMPLE 1

SKILLS

ANALYSIS

Classify the following data as discrete, continuous or categorical.

a Score in a soccer game

b Length of a leaf

c Time to run a race

d Number of cars in a car park

e Colour of cars in a car park

a Discrete (you cannot score 2.3 in a soccer game)

b Continuous (a leaf could have any length within a range)

c Continuous (the time could be any value within a range)

d Discrete (you cannot have 6.5 cars in the car park)

e Categorical (there are no numbers involved)

KEY POINTS

- Discrete data is counted.
- Continuous data is measured.
- Categorical data cannot be counted or measured.

This chapter will only deal with discrete and categorical data. Continuous data is covered later in the book.

Frequently large amounts of data have to be collected, so it is important to have an easy and accurate system for doing this.

A tally chart is a good way to collect and organise the data. Using the tally system to record your results is faster than writing out words or figures. The tally chart also gives an idea of the shape of the distribution.

EXAMPLE 2

SKILLS

ANALYSIS

This tally chart shows how to record eye colour in a class of students.

EYE COLOUR	TALLY	FREQUENCY
Brown	卌 卌 卌 III	18
Blue	IIII	4
Green	II	2
Other		0
	Total	24

A vertical mark (tally) is made for each student with a particular eye colour. For the fifth student in a category a diagonal line is made instead of a vertical line, this makes it easy to count the number in each category. The total frequency should be the same as the number of students questioned.

  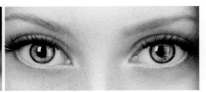

EXAMPLE 3

SKILLS

ANALYSIS

This tally chart shows how data can be grouped. Four to eight groups usually give good results.

The data is runs scored by a cricket team.

RUNS SCORED	TALLY	FREQUENCY
0–9	卌 卌 II	12
10–19	卌 卌 卌 III	18
20–29	卌 卌 IIII	14
30–39	卌 III	8
	Total	52

KEY POINTS

- Draw a neat table, deciding how to group the data if necessary.
- Make a vertical tally mark for each piece of data in the group.
- The fifth tally mark is a diagonal line through the four vertical tally marks.

EXERCISE 1

1 ▶ Classify the following data as discrete, continuous or categorical.

    a Brand of car   **d** Life of batteries in hours

    b Number of TV programs watched   **e** Pet preference

    c Number of children in a family   **f** Distance travelled to school

2 ▶ The day after a school event a group of pupils was asked to give it a grade from A to E, A being excellent and E being terrible. The following results were collected.

D, B, E, E, C, A, E, B, A, B, E, A, B, D, A, D, D, A, D, B, A, D, E, C, E, A, E, E, A, A

    a Construct a tally chart for the data.

    b How many pupils were in the survey?

    c Can you draw any conclusions about the event?

3 ▶   **a** Make a tally chart for the eye colour of students in your class.

    b Can you draw any conclusions from your data?

4 ▶   **a** Ask all the students in your class to name their lucky number between 1 and 10.

    b Record your results on a tally chart.

    c Can you draw any conclusions from your data?

EXERCISE 1*

1 ▶ Classify the following data as discrete, continuous or categorical.

    a Weight of potatoes   **d** Length of phone call

    b Types of pizza   **e** Hair colour

    c Shoe size   **f** Number of times a student is late for school

2 ▶ Tara suspects that a die lands on certain numbers more often than others. She throws it 50 times with the following results.

6 1 4 4 2 5 4 1 2 3 4 3 2 4 1 2 6 3 2 6 6 6 6 1 4 5 6 4 6 4 2 6 3 1 2 2 6 5 4 3 1 6 6 2 5 5 2 1 4 5

    a Construct a tally chart for the data.

    b Comment on Tara's suspicions.

3 ▶   a Make a tally chart for the shoe size and gender of students in your class.

   b Make two more tally charts, one showing girls' shoe sizes, the other boys' shoe sizes.

   c Can you draw any conclusions from your data?

4 ▶   a Use the **random** number generator on your calculator to generate 50 single-digit random numbers.

   b Construct a tally chart for the data.

   c Comment on whether the data appears random or not.

PRESENTING DATA

PICTOGRAMS

A pictogram shows the frequencies using pictures.

EXAMPLE 4

SKILLS

ANALYSIS

Draw a pictogram for this eye colour data.

EYE COLOUR	FREQUENCY
Brown	18
Blue	4
Green	2
Total	24

One picture of an eye is chosen to represent a frequency of 2.

Eye colour	Key ◉ = 2 people
Brown	◉ ◉ ◉ ◉ ◉ ◉ ◉ ◉ ◉
Blue	◉ ◉
Green	◉

A pictogram is visually appealing and conveys a good overall feel of the data. However, sometimes it is difficult to read the frequencies accurately.

PIE CHARTS

A pie chart is a good way of representing proportions. The angle of each sector represents the proportion.

EXAMPLE 5

SKILLS

ANALYSIS

Draw a pie chart for this eye colour data.

The **working** is most easily done using a table. Work out the total angle to check the answer.

EYE COLOUR	FREQUENCY	PROPORTION	ANGLE
Brown	18	$\frac{18}{24}$	$\frac{18}{24} \times 360° = 270°$
Blue	4	$\frac{4}{24}$	$\frac{4}{24} \times 360° = 60°$
Green	2	$\frac{2}{24}$	$\frac{2}{24} \times 360° = 30°$
Total	24	1	360°

Eye colour

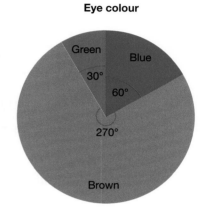

BAR CHARTS

A bar chart shows the frequency by the length of a bar.

EXAMPLE 6

SKILLS

ANALYSIS

Draw a bar chart for this eye colour data.

EYE COLOUR	FREQUENCY
Brown	18
Blue	4
Green	2
Total	24

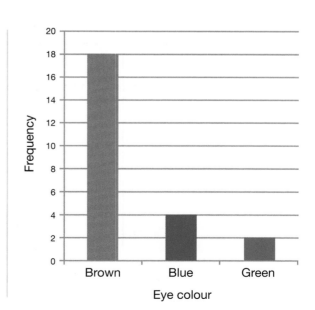

All bar charts for categorical and discrete data have gaps between the bars.

TWO-WAY TABLES

A two-way table shows how data falls into different categories.

A survey of eye colour in Class A and Class B was made. Display the results in a two-way table.

EYE COLOUR	BROWN	BLUE	GREEN	TOTAL
Class A	18	4	2	24
Class B	7	12	5	24
Total	25	16	7	48

Totals are often included to help further calculations.

The totals make it easy to see, for example, that the class sizes were the same.

COMPARATIVE BAR CHARTS

Comparative bar charts can be used to compare the distributions of two sets of data.

Draw a comparative bar chart to illustrate the data of Example 7.

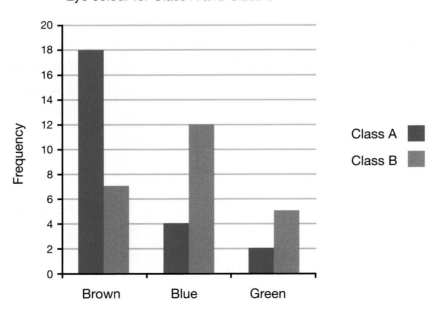

EXERCISE 2

1 ▶ Charlie keeps a record of the number of cans of cola he drinks in a week.

DAY	Monday	Tuesday	Wednesday	Thursday	Friday	Saturday	Sunday
FREQUENCY	2	5	3	0	1	6	2

Draw a pictogram to display these results.

2 ▶ Dima collected data on pets from students in her class.

PET	Cat	Dog	Fish	Rabbit	Other
FREQUENCY	5	3	2	4	3

Draw a bar chart to display this data.

3 ▶ Riley and Layla sell cars. The table shows the number of cars they each sold in the first four months of the year.

MONTH	January	February	March	April
RILEY	2	5	13	10
LAYLA	4	7	9	10

a Draw a comparative bar chart to illustrate this data.

b Comment on their sales figures.

4 ▶ A café owner records the drinks sold in his café on one day. The information is shown in the table.

DRINK	FREQUENCY
Hot chocolate	20
Milkshake	15
Coffee	25
Tea	30

a Work out the angles on a pie chart for each type of drink.

b Draw a pie chart to show the information.

5 ▶ Students were asked whether they were in favour of having more lockers in the school changing rooms. In Year 10, 110 of the 180 students were in favour. In Year 11, 100 of the 210 students were against the idea.

a Display this information in a table.

b The school will only buy new lockers if at least 60% of Year 10 and 11 students are in favour. Explain if the school will buy the lockers or not.

EXERCISE 2*

1 ▶ The table gives the number of thefts from cars in a town over a six-month period.

MONTH	January	February	March	April	May	June
NO. OF THEFTS	12	14	18	6	8	4

a Draw a pictogram to display these results.

b To try and reduce thefts, extra police officers were introduced during this period. When were these police officers employed?

2 ▶ Some students were asked to name their favourite sport. The results are in the table.

SPORT	Tennis	Football	Swimming	Basketball
FREQUENCY	16	26	8	15

a Draw a bar chart to illustrate these results.

b How many students were in the survey?

3 ▶ Kirsten records the number of hats sold in her shop.

	JANUARY–MARCH	APRIL–JUNE	JULY–SEPTEMBER	OCTOBER–DECEMBER
YEAR 1	470	420	510	630
YEAR 2	490	540	770	820

a Draw a comparative bar chart to illustrate this data.

b Comment on the sales of hats in Year 1 and Year 2

4 ▶ 40 students went on holiday abroad.

The table shows the number of students who visited each country.

COUNTRY	NUMBER OF STUDENTS
France	16
Spain	12
Germany	5
Italy	7

Draw an accurate pie chart to show this information

5 ▶ A clinical trial is carried out to compare the effect of two drugs for the treatment of hay fever.

One hundred people suffering from hay fever were given *either* Drug A or Drug B. After a week the patients were asked to choose one of three responses: no change, improved and much improved.

	NO CHANGE	IMPROVED	MUCH IMPROVED	TOTAL
DRUG A	10			60
DRUG B			13	
TOTAL	17	65		100

a Copy and complete the table.

b What fraction of these patients were given Drug B?

c Which drug performed best in this trial?

Give a reason for your answer.

MISLEADING DATA PRESENTATION

Diagrams can be used to present evidence to suit the point that someone wants to make.

EXAMPLE 9

SKILLS

ANALYSIS

A common technique is not to show the origin on the frequency scale of bar charts.

These two bar charts display the same information but give very different impressions!

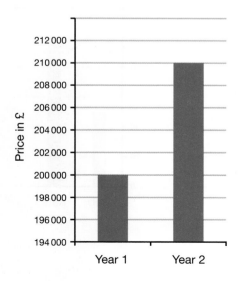

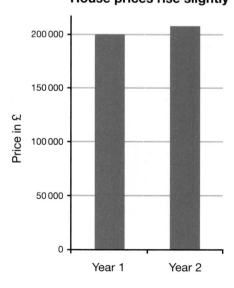

EXAMPLE 10

SKILLS

ANALYSIS

Another technique is to use an uneven scale on the vertical axis or no scale at all.

These two bar charts show the same falling sales figures. The first chart appears to show sales falling by about half whereas they have actually fallen by three-quarters!

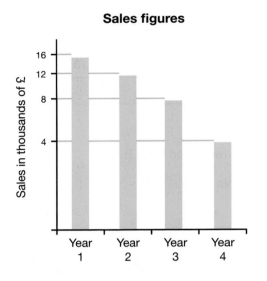

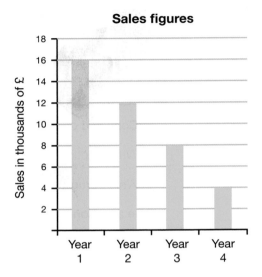

EXAMPLE 11

SKILLS

ANALYSIS

Another technique is to use area or volume rather than length to represent a frequency.

Kate collected twice as much money as Bob for charity. The first diagram suggests that Kate collected far more than double what Bob collected, though the height of Kate's bag is only double the height of Bob's bag.

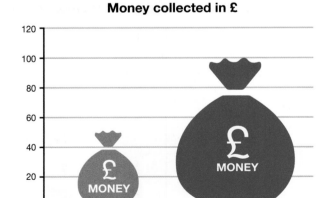

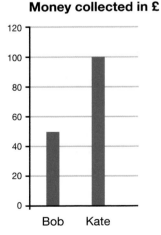

EXAMPLE 12

SKILLS

ANALYSIS

In the first pie chart, the red sector looks larger than the purple sector even though they are the same angle. This is due to the distortion when the diagram is drawn in 3-D as well as the colours chosen.

ACTIVITY 1

Do a search on the internet for 'Misuse of statistical diagrams' to find further examples of diagrams being used to misrepresent the evidence.

AVERAGES FOR DISCRETE DATA

KEY POINTS

- The mean, median and mode are all different averages.

- The mean of a set of values = $\dfrac{\text{total of the set of values}}{\text{total number of values}}$.

- The median is the middle value when the data is written in ascending (increasing) order.

- For an even number of values, the median is the mean of the middle two values.

- The mode is the most frequent value.

- It is possible to have no mode or more than one mode.

- The mode can be used for non-numerical (categorical) data.

EXAMPLE 13

SKILLS

ANALYSIS

Six children were asked how much pocket money they received. The results, in dollars, are shown in ascending order: 9 10 12 15 15 17

Find the mean, median and mode of the data.

Mean

The total of the set of values is 9 + 10 + 12 + 15 + 15 + 17 = 78.

The total number of values is 8.

The mean is $\dfrac{78}{8}$ = $9.75.

Median

The arrow shows the middle of the data: 9 10 12 ↓ 15 15 17

This is between 12 and 15, so the median is the mean of 12 and 15 which is $13.50.

Mode

15 is the most frequent value so the mode is $15.

Note: both the mean and the median are not values from the original data.

EXAMPLE 14

SKILLS

ANALYSIS

Eight students were collecting money for a school event. The mean collected per student was £18.25.

How much was collected in total?

Let the total be x.

Then $\dfrac{x}{8} = 18.25 \Rightarrow x = 8 \times 18.25 = 146$

The total collected was £146.

EXERCISE 3

Find the mean, median and mode of the following sets of data.

1 ▶ The numbers of cups of coffee Phoebe drank each day of a week were
4, 5, 0, 7, 6, 4, 2

2 ▶ The numbers of typing errors made in a day on a typing training course were
2, 16, 8, 5, 1, 3, 0, 6, 4

3 ▶ The numbers of text messages sent by a group of friends one day were
4, 6, 5, 1, 7, 0, 28, 0, 3

4 ▶ The numbers of beetles found on one plant on **consecutive** days were
7, 9, 7, 3, 9, 0, 2, 1

5 ▶ Days in the months of a leap year (a year with 366 days, when February has 29 days)

6 ▶ Lance threw a die six times. His median score was 3.5. His first five throws were
1, 5, 3, 5, 1. What was his sixth throw?

7 ▶ The mean number of emails Adele received during a week was 51. The numbers received for the first six days were 39, 57, 70, 45, 71 and 32. Find how many emails she received on the seventh day.

8 ▶ After five spelling tests, Duval's mean number of mistakes per test was 7. After the sixth test his mean per test was 6. How many mistakes did he make on his last test?

EXERCISE 3* Find the mean, median and mode of the following sets of data.

1 ▶ The numbers of TV programs watched by a group of friends over the weekend were

5, 0, 4, 9, 0, 1, 6, 0, 2

2 ▶ The lives of some batteries in hours to the nearest hour were

69, 55, 72, 44, 46, 72, 84, 86

3 ▶ The numbers of telephone calls received by a hotel on consecutive days were

45, 78, 23, 14, 89, 64, 245, 101

4 ▶ The reaction times in seconds to the nearest 0.01 s of some students were

0.22, 0.57, 0.58, 0.46, 0.90, 0.46, 0.78, 0.99

Q5 HINT
1 is not a prime number.

5 ▶ The first 10 **prime numbers**

6 ▶ The mean number of ice creams sold per day by a shop during the 31 days of January was 91. During the 28 days of February the mean was 95 per day. Find the mean number sold per day for the two-month period.

7 ▶ David recorded the number of worms found in a square metre of earth over a period of six days. He had put his data in order when a large raindrop made the middle two values on his paper impossible to read. The values were 8, 10, *, *, 17, 23. The mean of the data was 14, and the median was 13. Find the two missing values.

8 ▶ The data 1, x, 3, y, 8, z is in ascending order. The mean of the data is 5, the median is 4.5 and the mode is 3. Find x, y and z.

COMPARING THE MEAN, MEDIAN AND MODE

The mean, median and mode are all different averages of a set of data. An average is a single value that should give you some idea about all the data. For example, if you know that one batsman has a mean score of 12 and another has a mean score of 78 then you immediately have some idea about the batsmen's ability without knowing all their individual scores.

When the data is plotted as a bar chart, if the result is roughly 'bell shaped' or 'normal' then the mean, median and mode all give approximately the same answers.

If there are a few very high or very low values (both are called 'outliers') then these can distort the averages, and you need to choose which average is the best to use.

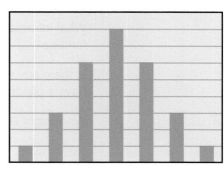

A 'bell shaped or normal' distribution

EXAMPLE 15

SKILLS

ANALYSIS

The wages per week in a small firm are

$500, $500, $650, $660, $670, $680, $3000

The mean is $951 (to the nearest dollar). The median is $660. The mode is $500.

The mode is the two lowest values and is not representative.

The mean is not very useful as it is distorted by the managing director's large salary.

The median is the best to use as it tells us most about the data.

However, it all depends on your point of view! In wage negotiations, the managing director can claim that the 'average' salary is good at $951, while the union representative can claim that the 'average' salary is poor at $500. Both are telling the truth, it all depends which 'average' you use.

	MEAN	MEDIAN	MODE
ADVANTAGES	Uses all the data	Easy to calculate Not affected by extreme values	Easy to calculate Not affected by extreme values
DISADVANTAGES	Distorted by extreme values	Does not use all the data	Does not use all the data Less representative than the mean or median
WHEN TO USE	When the data is distributed reasonably symmetrically	When there are some extreme values	For non-numerical data When the most popular value is needed

ACTIVITY 2

SKILLS

REASONING

'The average family has 2.3 children.'

Discuss whether this sentence makes sense.

What information does this sentence give about families?

Is there any way of knowing how many families have 4 children?

Who might like to know?

SHAPE OF DISTRIBUTIONS

Activity 2 shows that we often need more information than the mean can provide. We also need to know about the shape and spread of a distribution. You will learn more about this later on in this book.

EXERCISE 4

1 ▶ The annual salaries of staff who work in a cake shop are

£12 000, £12 000, £15 000, £18 000, £40 000.

  a Work out the mean, median and mode of staff salaries.

  b The company wishes to insert one of the averages of the salaries in an advertisement for new staff. Which of the averages would be the most appropriate? Give reasons for your answer.

2 ▶ State whether it is better to use the mean, median or mode for these data sets. Give reasons for your answers.

  a Time taken for five people to perform a task (in seconds): 6, 25, 26, 30, 30

  b Car colour: red, red, grey, black, black, black, blue

3 ▶ The sizes of jeans sold in a shop one day are

8, 8, 10, 10, 12, 12, 12, 12, 12, 12, 14, 14, 14, 16, 16, 18, 20, 20, 22, 22

  a Work out the mean, median and mode of the sizes.

  b The shop owner wants to order some more jeans but can only order one size. Which size should he order? Give reasons for your answer.

4 ▶ The numbers of passengers using a train service one week are recorded in the table.

DAY	NUMBER OF PASSENGERS
Monday	230
Tuesday	180
Wednesday	170
Thursday	180
Friday	210

  a Work out the mean, median and mode of the number of passengers.

  b The train company wishes to work out the average daily profit. Which average should be used to calculate an accurate figure? Give reasons for your answer.

EXERCISE 4*

1 ▶ The sizes of shoes sold in a shop during a morning are

5, 5.5, 5.5, 6, 7, 7, 7, 7, 8.5, 9, 9, 10, 11, 11.5, 12, 13

  a Work out the mean, median and mode of these shoe sizes.

  b The shop manager wishes to buy more stock but is only allowed to buy shoes of one size. Which one of these averages would be the most appropriate to use? Give reasons for your answer.

2 ▶ The annual numbers of burglaries reported in a town over the past 5 years are

45, 33, 47, 47, 93

  a Work out the mean, median and mode of the number of burglaries.

  b An insurance company bases how much it charges on the average number of burglaries. Which of the averages would be the most appropriate? Give reasons for your answer.

3 ▶ The monthly costs of heating a shop in the UK in the winter months are shown in the table.

MONTH	HEATING COST
Nov	£180
Dec	£190
Jan	£270
Feb	£240
Mar	£180

  a Work out the mean, median and mode of heating costs.

  b The shop must provide a report of expenses and day-to-day costs to its accountant. Which of the averages is the most appropriate to provide in the report? Give reasons for your answer.

4 ▶ State whether it is best to use the mean, median or mode for these data sets. Give reasons for your answers.

  a Colour of tablet case: red, blue, green, orange, blue

  b Number of customers in a shop: 12, 12, 13, 17, 19

EXERCISE 5   **REVISION**

1 ▶ The following ingredients are needed to make a strawberry smoothie:

250 g strawberries, 150 g banana, 200 g yoghurt and 120 g iced water.

Calculate the angle each ingredient would have on a pie chart, then draw the pie chart, marking the angles clearly.

2 ▶ The table gives information about the fish caught in a fishing competition.

FISH	Perch	Bream	Carp	Pike
NO. CAUGHT	23	10	39	6

Draw a bar chart to illustrate the data.

3 ▶ The table shows the number of sunny days in a four-month period over two years.

MONTH	May	June	July	August
YEAR 1	14	22	18	23
YEAR 2	16	13	8	5

a Draw a comparative bar chart to illustrate this data.

b Comment on the difference between the years.

4 ▶ A school offers three language options and two humanities options at GCSE.

Students must choose one language and one humanities option.

	FRENCH	GERMAN	MANDARIN	TOTAL
HISTORY	57		18	126
GEOGRAPHY		12		
TOTAL			35	200

a Copy and complete the table.

b What percentage of the students study Mandarin?

c Which humanities option was most popular?
Give reasons for your answer.

5 ▶ The bar chart shows the level of support for a new high speed rail link. The government claims that this provides convincing evidence that people are in favour of the plans.

a Explain why this bar chart is misleading.

b Draw a correct version. Comment on what information this provides about the level of support for the new rail link.

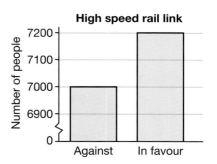

6 ▶ Find the mean, median and mode of 4, 6, 9, 1, 0, 8, 7.

7 ▶ A small factory has a managing director and seven workers. The weekly wages are $700, $700, $700, $750, $750, $800, $800 and $4000.

a Find the mean, mode and median of these wages.

b Which average best describes the weekly wages? Give reasons for your answer.

8 ▶ After six games of crazy golf, Harvey's mean score was 39.5. After seven games his mean had dropped to 39. What did Harvey score in his seventh game?

EXERCISE 5*

REVISION

1 ▶ The pie chart shows the results of a school mock election.

If Labour received 183 votes, how many pupils voted in total?

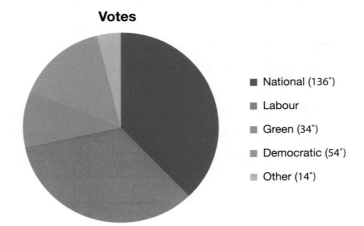

Votes

■ National (136°)

■ Labour

■ Green (34°)

■ Democratic (54°)

■ Other (14°)

2 ▶ Finley keeps a record of the cost of the gas he has used for the last 12 months.

PERIOD	June–August	September–November	December–February	March–May
COST (£)	100	220	440	280

a Draw a bar chart to illustrate this data.

Finley thinks the cost of gas will remain the same for the next 12 months. He wants to make equal monthly payments for his gas.

b Calculate to the nearest penny what Finley should pay each month for his gas.

3 ▶ The table shows the average daily hours of sunshine in Majorca and Crete over a five-month period.

MONTH	April	May	June	July	August
MAJORCA	9	9	11	11	10
CRETE	6	8	11	13	12

a Draw a comparative bar chart to illustrate this data.

b Comment on the difference between the islands.

4 ▶ A survey was carried out in a town to find out if more parking spaces were needed. Of 60 men surveyed, 23 thought there were not enough spaces. Of 60 women surveyed, 30% thought there were enough spaces. The town has equal numbers of men and women.

a Display this information in a two-way table.

b The town council will provide more parking spaces if more than 60% of residents want more parking. Will this happen?

5 ▶ A supplier of 'Nutty Oats Muesli' claims that it provides more fibre than three rival brands and uses the bar chart to support this claim.

Give *two* reasons why this diagram is misleading.

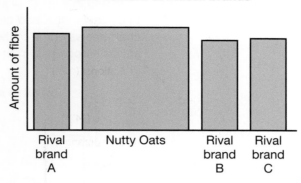

Fibre content of muesli brands

6 ▶ For two weeks Corine recorded the number of emails she receives each day.
The results were:

39, 57, 70, 45, 70, 32, 0, 51, 56, 44, 65, 31, 50, 48.

a Find the mean, mode and median of these numbers.

b Which average best describes the number of emails received each day? Give a reason for your answer.

7 ▶ A football team of 11 players has a mean height of 1.83 m. One player is injured and is replaced by a player of height 1.85 m. The new mean height of the team is now 1.84 m. What is the height of the injured player?

8 ▶ Sharonda is doing a biology project using two groups of worms. The mean length of the first group of ten worms is 8.3 cm, while the mean length of a second group of eight worms is 10.7 cm. What is the mean length of all 18 worms?

EXAM PRACTICE: HANDLING DATA 1

1 The pie chart shows the numbers of different phones in a class of students.

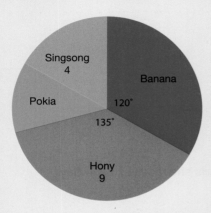

a How many Banana phones were there?

b What should the angle of the sector representing Singsong phones be?   **[3]**

2 Students in Year 11 were asked whether they walk or cycle, or walk *and* cycle to school. The bar chart shows some of the results. All 203 Year 11 students took part in the survey.

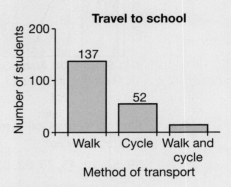

How many both walk *and* cycle to school?   **[2]**

3 The table shows the numbers of gold, silver and bronze medals won by a team in two following years.

MEDAL	GOLD	SILVER	BRONZE
YEAR 1	15	17	15
YEAR 2	29	17	19

a Draw a comparative bar chart to illustrate this data.

b Comment on the difference between the two years.

[5]

4 A fixed menu at a café offers two main course options followed by two dessert choices.
One lunchtime there were 50 customers. The table shows some information about their choices.

	CHICKEN	VEGETARIAN	TOTAL
CHEESE	15		23
ICE CREAM		5	
TOTAL			50

Copy and complete the table.   **[3]**

5 A soft drinks supplier produces a bar chart
showing sales of their soft drinks and uses it
to support the claim that sales of cola are more
than twice the sales of the other drinks.

Give *two* reasons why the diagram is
misleading.   **[2]**

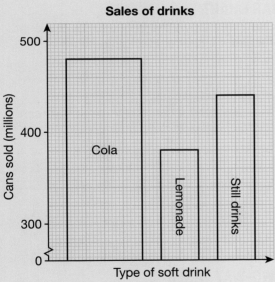

6 Find the mean, mode and median of
4, 5, 1, 7, 14, 9, 0, 6, 8.   **[3]**

7 To obtain a grade A, Youseff's mean score in
five tests must be 85 or more. Youseff has
scored 86, 94, 75 and 88 in four tests.
What is his minimum mark in the fifth test
to get a grade A?

                                                                           [3]

8 In a small town the mean number of burglaries
per day during March was 2 while the mean
number per day during April was 1.6. What was
the mean number per day during both months?
Give your answer **correct to** 3 s.f.   **[4]**

[Total 25 marks]

CHAPTER SUMMARY: HANDLING DATA 1

STATISTICAL INVESTIGATION

Discrete data is counted, e.g. Number of eggs = 4

Continuous data is measured, e.g. Speed of a bird = $\sqrt{2}$ m/s

Categorical data cannot be counted or measured, e.g. An opinion in a survey.

PRESENTING DATA

The table shows the distribution of coloured sweets bought from shop A.

COLOUR	Yellow	Green	Red	Purple
FREQUENCY	4	6	3	2

PICTOGRAM

A pictogram shows the frequencies using pictures.

Sweet colour	Key 🍬 = 1 sweet
Yellow	🍬 🍬 🍬 🍬
Green	🍬 🍬 🍬 🍬 🍬 🍬
Red	🍬 🍬 🍬
Purple	🍬 🍬

BAR CHART

A bar chart shows the frequency by the length of a bar.

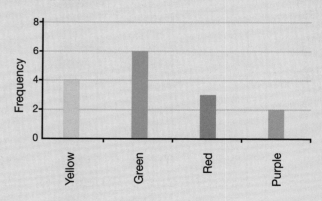

PIE CHARTS

The angle of each sector represents the proportion.

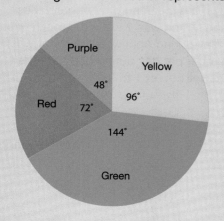

Total number of sweets is 15

For example, yellow angle is $\frac{4}{15} \times 360 = 96$ degrees

TWO-WAY TABLE

A two-way table shows how data falls into different categories. The table shows the distribution of coloured sweets bought from shop A and shop B.

COLOUR	YELLOW	GREEN	RED	PURPLE
SHOP A	4	6	3	2
SHOP B	7	2	2	4

COMPARATIVE BAR CHARTS

Comparative bar charts can be used to compare the distributions of two sets of data.

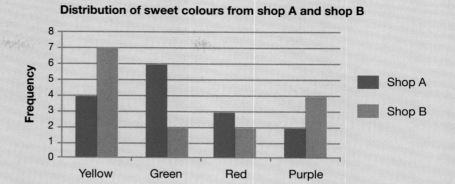

Distribution of sweet colours from shop A and shop B

MISLEADING DATA PRESENTATION

Diagrams can be used to present evidence to suit the point that someone wants to make. Some common techniques are:

• not showing the origin on the vertical axis

• using an uneven scale on the vertical axis or no scale at all

• using area or volume rather than length to represent frequency

• distortion when the diagram is drawn in 3-D.

AVERAGES FOR DISCRETE DATA

• The mean, median and mode are all different averages.

  The mean of a set of values = $\dfrac{\text{total of the set of values}}{\text{total number of values}}$ e.g. mean of 1, 2, 3, 3 is $\dfrac{9}{4} = 2\dfrac{1}{4}$.

• The median is the middle value when the data is written in ascending order, e.g. median of 1, 2, 3, 3 is 2.5.

  For an even number of values, the median is the mean of the middle two values.

• The mode is the most frequent value, e.g. mode of 1, 2, 3, 3 is 3.

  It is possible to have no mode or more than one mode.

  The mode can be used for non-numerical data.

	MEAN	**MEDIAN**	**MODE**
ADVANTAGES	Uses all the data	Easy to calculate Not affected by extreme values	Easy to calculate Not affected by extreme values
DISADVANTAGES	Distorted by extreme values	Does not use all the data	Does not use all the data Less representative than the mean or median
WHEN TO USE	When the data is distributed reasonably symmetrically	When there are some extreme values	For non-numerical data When the most typical value is needed

UNIT 3

3 is the only prime number that is one less than a perfect square number. A number is divisible by 3 when the sum of all its digits can be divided by 3. It is the first number of one of the most famous mathematical ratios, which is 3.141…

An octopus has 3 hearts!

NUMBER 3

In January 2016, the largest known prime number, $2^{74\,207\,281} - 1$, a number with 22 338 618 digits was discovered, five million digits longer than the previous largest prime number. A roll of paper 5 km long would be needed to print this number out. This largest prime number was found by the Great Internet Mersenne Prime Search (GIMPS) at Missouri University, USA. Prime numbers this large could prove useful to computing in the future for encryption.

Mersenne primes are named after a French monk, Abbé Marin Mersenne (1588–1648), who studied them in the 17th century.

LEARNING OBJECTIVES

■ Write a number as a product of its prime factors

■ Find the HCF and LCM of two (or more) numbers

■ Solve problems involving HCF and LCM

■ Compare ratios

■ Find quantities using ratios

■ Solve problems involving ratio

BASIC PRINCIPLES

Multiples

■ The multiples of 4 are 4, 8, 12, 16, …. i.e. the numbers that 4 divides into exactly.

Factors

■ The factors of 10 are 1, 2, 5 and 10. These are the only numbers that divide into 10 exactly.

■ If the only factors of a number are 1 and itself, the number is a prime number.

Prime numbers

■ These are only divisible by 1 and themselves.

■ They are 2, 3, 5, 7, 11, 13, 17, 19, 23, …

■ The number of prime numbers is infinite.

■ 1 is not a prime number.

PRIME FACTORS

Any factor of a number that is a prime number is a **prime factor**.

Any number can be written uniquely as the **product** of its prime factors.

EXAMPLE 1

SKILLS

ANALYSIS

Express 72 as a product of prime factors.

Keep dividing repeatedly by prime numbers or use your knowledge of the multiplication tables.

	72		2	72		72	= 8 × 9

$$72 = 2 \times 36$$
$$= 2 \times 2 \times 18$$
$$= 2 \times 2 \times 2 \times 9$$
$$= 2 \times 2 \times 2 \times 3 \times 3$$
$$= 2^3 \times 3^2$$

2	72
2	36
2	18
3	9
3	3
	1

$$72 = 8 \times 9$$
$$= 2^3 \times 3^2$$

$$\Rightarrow 72 = 2^3 \times 3^2$$

KEY POINTS

- Prime factors are factors that are prime numbers.
- Divide a number repeatedly by prime numbers to find the prime factors.
- The product of the prime factors is written in index form.
- There is only one way of expressing a number as a product of prime factors.

EXERCISE 1

List the first five multiples of these numbers.

1 ▶   7   **2 ▶**   6

List all the factors of these numbers.

3 ▶   12   **4 ▶**   18   **5 ▶**   30

Express each number as a product of prime factors.

6 ▶   28   **7 ▶**   70   **8 ▶**   60   **9 ▶**   96

10 ▶   The number 48 can be written in the form $2^n \times 3$. Find the value of n.

11 ▶   a Express 252 as a product of its prime factors.
          b Express 6 × 252 as a product of prime factors.

12 ▶   Hakim is making a mosaic from square tiles. The area he needs to fill measures 150 mm by 180 mm. The tiles have side lengths of 4, 6 or 8 mm and are too small to cut. Which tiles should Hakim use?

EXERCISE 1*

List the first five multiples of these numbers.

1 ▶   5   **2 ▶**   9   **3 ▶**   13

Write down, in numerical order, all the factors of these numbers.

4 ▶   75   **5 ▶**   40   **6 ▶**   54

7 ▶   Express 1155 as a product of prime factors.

8 ▶   **a** Express 399 as a product of prime factors.
          b Express 36 × 399 as a product of prime factors.

9 ▶   Write 84 as a product of prime factors. Hence write 168^2 as a product of prime factors.

10 ▶ Steve and Ian are asked to find 60 as a product of prime factors.

          Steve begins by writing 60 = 5 × 12

          Ian begins by writing 60 = 6 × 10

          a Work out a final answer for Steve.
          b Work out a final answer for Ian.
          c Express 48 as a product of prime factors starting in two different ways.

11 ▶ Harley needs to put up a fence 26 m long in his garden. Fence panels come in widths of 175 cm, 200 cm and 220 cm. Harley wants to use all the same width of panel. Which width panel should he buy to ensure they fit the length exactly?

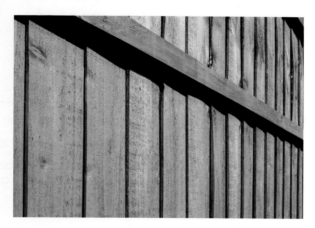

12 ▶ Find the largest number apart from 840 that is a multiple of 24 and a factor of 840.

HCF AND LCM

HCF is the Highest **Common Factor**.
It is the highest (largest) factor common to a set of numbers.

LCM is the Lowest Common Multiple.
It is the lowest (smallest) multiple common to a set of numbers.

To find the HCF or LCM of a set of numbers, first express the numbers as products of prime factors.

EXAMPLE 2

SKILLS

ANALYSIS

Find the HCF and LCM of 12 and 42.

$12 = 4 \times 3 = 2^2 \times 3$

$42 = 6 \times 7 = 2 \times 3 \times 7$

Draw a Venn diagram.

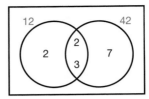

The common prime factors are in the intersection set, i.e. 2 and 3.

The highest common factor (HCF) is the intersection set numbers all multiplied together: $2 \times 3 = 6$.

The lowest common multiple (LCM) is the union set numbers all multiplied together:
$2 \times 2 \times 3 \times 7 = 84$.

Notes:

3 is a common factor, but it is not the highest common factor.

$12 \times 42 = 504$ is a common multiple, but it is not the lowest common multiple.

EXAMPLE 3

SKILLS

PROBLEM
SOLVING

A rope of length 672 cm and a rope of length 616 cm
will be cut into pieces. All the pieces must be the same length.

Find the greatest possible length of each piece.

The length must be a factor of both 672 and 616.

The greatest possible length must be the HCF of 672 and 616.

$672 = 2^5 \times 3 \times 7$, $616 = 2^3 \times 7 \times 11$, $HCF = 2^3 \times 7 = 56$

The greatest possible length is 56 cm.

EXAMPLE 4

SKILLS

PROBLEM
SOLVING

Daisy and Max both walk a whole number of steps from one side of their garden to the other.

Daisy's step length is 75 cm while Max's is 80 cm. What is the minimum length of their garden?

The length must be a multiple of 75 and 80. The minimum length must be the LCM of 75 and 80.

$75 = 3 \times 5^2$, $80 = 2^4 \times 5$, $LCM = 2^4 \times 3 \times 5^2 = 1200$

The minimum length of the garden is 1200 cm or 12 m.

KEY POINTS

- The HCF is the highest (largest) factor that is common to a set of numbers.
- The LCM is the lowest (smallest) multiple that is common to a set of numbers.
- To find the HCF or LCM, express the numbers in prime factor form in a Venn diagram.

EXERCISE 2

You may find it helpful to draw a Venn diagram for these questions.

Find the highest common factor of these numbers.

1 ▶ 6 and 8　　**2 ▶** 20 and 35　　**3 ▶** 22 and 44

Find the lowest common multiple of these numbers.

4 ▶ 2 and 3　　**5 ▶** 5 and 6　　**6 ▶** 6 and 15

7 ▶ Mahtab is filling bags with sweets. She has 18 chocolates and 27 mints. Each bag must contain the same mix of sweets and there must be no sweets left over. What is the greatest number of bags she can fill and what will be in each bag?

8 ▶ Tours at an ancient palace start at 9am. The palace tours leave every 45 minutes and the palace and garden tours leave every 75 minutes. When do both tours next leave at the same time?

Find the highest common factor of these.

9 ▶ $2x$ and $4xy$　　**10 ▶** $12y^2$ and $8xy^2$

Find the lowest common multiple of these.

11 ▶ $2a$ and $3b$　　**12 ▶** $4y$ and $3x$

EXERCISE 2*

Find the HCF and LCM of these.

1 ▶ 12 and 18　　**4 ▶** $4xy$ and $6xy$　　**7 ▶** $6x^2yz$ and $9xy^2z^2$

2 ▶ 30 and 105　　**5 ▶** x^2y and xyz　　**8 ▶** 504, 240 and 540

3 ▶ $3xy$ and $2yz$　　**6 ▶** x^3y and xy^4

9 ▶ Two numbers have an HCF of 84 and an LCM of 4620. Both numbers are larger than the HCF. Find the two numbers.

10 ▶ A new school is deciding whether their lessons should be 30, 50 or 60 minutes long. Each lesson duration fits exactly into the total teaching time of each school day.
a How long is the total teaching time of each school day?
b Could there be more than one answer? Give a reason for your answer.

11 ▶ Tom and Harry are racing go-carts. Tom takes 2 minutes 8 seconds to complete a lap while Harry takes 2 minutes to complete a lap. They both start from the start line at the same time. When will they next cross the start line together?

12 ▶ Fatima is preparing food parcels to give to charity. She has 252 tins of beans, 168 chocolate bars and 294 packets of soup. Each food parcel must contain the same, and there must be nothing left over. What is the greatest number of parcels she can prepare, and what will be in each parcel?

RATIO

Ratios are used to compare quantities (or parts). If the ratio of the quantities is given and one quantity is known, the other quantities can be found. Also, if the total quantity is known, the individual quantities can be found.

EXAMPLE 5

SKILLS

PROBLEM SOLVING

A marinade in a recipe contains rice vinegar and soy sauce in the ratio $2:3$.

How much of each ingredient is needed to make 100 ml of the marinade?

Add the numbers in the ratio together: $2 + 3 = 5$

Then $\frac{2}{5}$ of the marinade is rice vinegar and $\frac{3}{5}$ is soy sauce.

Amount of rice vinegar $= \frac{2}{5} \times 100 = 40$ ml

Amount of soy sauce $= \frac{3}{5} \times 100 = 60$ ml

Check: 40 ml + 60 ml = 100 ml

EXAMPLE 6

SKILLS

PROBLEM SOLVING

Divide £1170 in the ratio of $2:3:4$.

Add the numbers in the ratio together: $2 + 3 + 4 = 9$

Then the first part $= \frac{2}{9} \times £1170 = £260$

The second part $= \frac{3}{9} \times £1170 = £390$

The third part $= \frac{4}{9} \times £1170 = £520$

Check: £260 + £390 + £520 = £1170

Ratios stay the same if both sides are multiplied or divided by the same number.

To compare ratios write them as unit ratios, that is $1:n$ or $n:1$.

EXAMPLE 7

SKILLS

REASONING

Which is larger, $9:4$ or $23:10$?

Divide both sides of $9:4$ by 4 to give $2.25:1$

Divide both sides of $23:10$ by 10 to give $2.3:1$

So $23:10$ is larger the $9:4$

KEY POINTS

- Add the numbers in ratios together to find each proportion.
- Ratios stay the same if both sides are multiplied or divided by the same number.
- Compare ratios by writing them as unit ratios.

EXERCISE 3

1 ▶ Divide $120 in the ratio $3:5$.

2 ▶ The fuel for a machine is a mixture of 8 parts petrol to one part oil.
How much oil is needed to make 1 litre of fuel?

3 ▶ The angles of a triangle are in the ratio $1:2:3$. Find the angles.

4 ▶ Mr Chan has three daughters, An, Lien and Tao, aged 7, 8 and 10 years respectively. He shares $100 between them in the ratio of their ages. How much does Lien receive?

5 ▶ In a school there are 52 teachers and 598 students.

   a Write the student : teacher ratio in the form $n : 1$.

Another school has 85 teachers and 1020 students.

   b Which school has the larger number of teachers per student?

6 ▶ Julie and Hammad each make a glass of orange drink. Julie uses 42 ml of juice and 210 ml of lemonade. Hammad uses 30 ml of juice and 170 ml of lemonade. Who has made their drink stronger in taste?

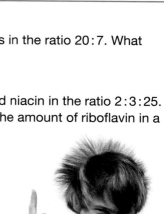

7 ▶ Archie and Bijan share some money in the ratio 7 : 11. Bijan gets £132. How much money does Archie get?

8 ▶ To make a tough adhesive, Paul mixes 5 parts of resin with 2 parts of hardener.

   a Write down the ratio of resin to hardener.

   b To fix a chair, Paul uses 9 g of hardener. How many grams of resin does he use?

   c On another project, Paul used 12 g of resin. How much hardener did he use?

EXERCISE 3*

1 ▶ Divide €350 in the ratio 1 : 6.

2 ▶ A type of cat food contains chicken bones and chicken pieces in the ratio 20 : 7. What weight of chicken pieces is needed to make 2 kg of cat food?

3 ▶ Divide 576 tonnes in the ratio 4 : 3 : 2.

4 ▶ A breakfast cereal contains the vitamins thiamin, riboflavin and niacin in the ratio 2 : 3 : 25. A bowl of cereal contains 10 mg of these vitamins. Calculate the amount of riboflavin in a bowl of cereal.

5 ▶ On Saturday at 12pm, there were 45 staff members and 375 customers in a department store.

   a Write the customer : staff ratio in the form $n : 1$.

Another department store has 70 staff members and 637 customers at the same time.

   b Which store had more customers per staff member?

6 ▶ Cheryl and Jon both make hair dye by mixing hair colourant with peroxide. Cheryl uses 750 ml of colourant and 450 ml of peroxide. Jon uses 850 ml of colourant and 650 ml of peroxide.

Who has the greater concentration of peroxide in their hair dye?

7 ▶ Jackie and Alan share the profits of their business in the ratio of the amounts they invested. Jackie invested £170 and Alan invested £150. Alan gets £18 000. How much money does Jackie get?

8 ▶ To make concrete, Ali mixes 2 parts of cement with 5 parts of sand.

   a Write down the ratio of sand to cement.

   b To lay the foundations for an extension, Ali uses 60 kg of sand. How many kilograms of cement does she use?

   c On another project, Ali used 75 kg of cement. How much sand did she use?

EXERCISE 4

REVISION

1 ▶ Express 756 as a product of its prime factors.

2 ▶ Find the HCF and LCM of 18 and 24.

3 ▶ Bella wants to tile a wall measuring 1.2 m by 2.16 m. She finds square tiles she likes with side lengths of 10 cm, 12 cm or 18 cm. Which of these tiles will fit the wall exactly?

4 ▶ Meha is buying some batteries. The shop sells D-type batteries in packs of 6 and AA-type batteries in packs of 15. Meha wishes to buy the same number of D and AA batteries. What is the smallest number of each battery type that she can buy?

5 ▶ A ribbon of length 336 cm and a ribbon of length 504 cm will be cut into pieces. All the pieces must be the same length. Find the greatest possible length of each piece.

6 ▶ Jana splits £350 between her two nieces in the ratio of their ages. Carlotta is 16 and Hannah is 12.

    a What fraction does Carlotta get?
    b What fraction does Hannah get?
    c How much money does each niece get?

7 ▶ In a school, the ratio of the number of students to the number of computers is $1 : \frac{3}{5}$.

    There are 210 computers in the school. How many students are there?

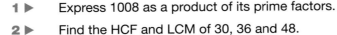

EXERCISE 4*

REVISION

1 ▶ Express 1008 as a product of its prime factors.

2 ▶ Find the HCF and LCM of 30, 36 and 48.

3 ▶ Two numbers have an LCM of 432 and an HCF of 72. Both numbers are larger than the HCF. Find the two numbers.

4 ▶ Three lighthouses flash their lights at different intervals. One flashes every 15 seconds, one every 20 seconds and one every 45 seconds. They have just all flashed their lights at the same time. How long before the next time all three lighthouses flash their lights at the same time?

5 ▶ Erin has 75 pink roses, 105 yellow roses and 45 white roses. She needs to make identical flower arrangements for a wedding and there must be no flowers left at the end. What is the greatest number of arrangements Erin can make, and what will be in each arrangement?

6 ▶ Jude wants to make lilac paint. She is going to mix red paint, blue paint and white paint in the ratios 0.8 : 1.5 : 5.7. Copy and complete the table to show how much of each colour Jude needs to make the paint quantities shown.

SIZE	BLUE	RED	WHITE
1 litre			
2.5 litres			

7 ▶ A scale model (a small model representation of a larger thing) of Tower Bridge in London is 22 cm high. The real bridge is 66 m high.

    a Work out the **scale** of the model. Write it as a ratio of real height to model height.

    The bridge is 243 m long in real life.

    b How long is the model?

EXAM PRACTICE: NUMBER 3

1 Express 1050 as a product of its prime factors. **[4]**

2 Find the HCF and LCM of 36 and 126. **[4]**

3 Two classes are given regular tests by their teachers Mr Hony and Mr Turner. Mr Hony's tests always have 30 questions, and Mr Turner's tests always have 24 questions. Both classes answer the same number of questions in a term.

a What is the smallest number of questions set in a term to make this possible?
b What is the smallest number of tests that Mr Hony's class can take? **[4]**

4 Kavi needs to prepare some gift bags with identical contents. She has 168 chocolates and 252 balloons. No items can be left at the end. What is the greatest number of bags she can prepare? **[4]**

5 Ben, who is 42, his son Terry, who is 16, and his daughter Anne, who is 14, agree to share £540 in the ratio of their ages. How much does each person receive? **[4]**

6 Saru is making some lemonade. He finds using 42 ml of lemon juice and 210 ml of water makes a tasty drink.

a Find the ratio of lemon juice to water in its simplest form.
b Saru uses 8 litres of water to make some lemonade of the same strength. What volume of lemonade does he make? **[5]**

[Total 25 marks]

CHAPTER SUMMARY: NUMBER 3

PRIME FACTORS

Prime factors are factors that are prime numbers.

Divide a number repeatedly by prime numbers to find the prime factors.

The product of the prime factors is written in index form.

There is only one way of expressing a number as a product of prime factors.

$84 = 2 \times 42 = 2 \times 2 \times 21 = 2 \times 2 \times 3 \times 7 = 2^2 \times 3 \times 7$

or

$84 = 12 \times 7 = 4 \times 3 \times 7 = 2^2 \times 3 \times 7$

HCF AND LCM

The HCF is the highest (largest) factor common to a set of numbers.

The LCM is the lowest (smallest) multiple common to a set of numbers.

To find the HCF or LCM, express the numbers in prime factor form in a Venn diagram

Find the HCF and LCM of 84 and 70.

$84 = 2^2 \times 3 \times 7$

$70 = 2 \times 5 \times 7$

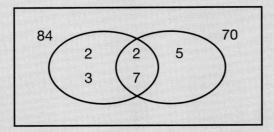

HCF is the intersection = $2 \times 7 = 14$

LCM is the union = $2^2 \times 3 \times 7 \times 5 = 420$

RATIO

Add the ratios together to find each proportion.

Ratios stay the same if both sides are multiplied or divided by the same number.

Compare ratios by writing them as unit ratios in the form $1:n$ or $n:1$.

- Divide $50 in the ratio $3:7$.

$3 + 7 = 10$

First part is $\frac{3}{10} \times 50 = 15$

Second part is $\frac{7}{10} \times 50 = 35$

$\Rightarrow$ $15 and $35

- Which is larger, $3:2$ or $13:9$?

Divide the first ratio by 2 and the second ratio by 9 to give $1.5:1$ and $1.\dot{4}:1$

Therefore $3:2$ is the larger ratio.

ALGEBRA 3

Diophantus of Alexandria is sometimes called 'the father of algebra'. He worked in Roman Egypt but very little is known about his life. His collection of books, known as the *Arithmetica*, is believed to have been completed around AD 250. They are considered to be the first books on algebra. In them, he gives methods for finding integer solutions to algebraic equations. Diophantus was the first Greek mathematician to recognise fractions as numbers.

LEARNING OBJECTIVES

- Factorise algebraic expressions
- Simplify algebraic fractions
- Solve equations involving fractions
- Solve simultaneous equations
- Solve simultaneous equations for real-life applications

BASIC PRINCIPLES

- Prime factors: $600 = 2^3 \times 3 \times 5^2$
- The lowest common denominator of 6 and 4 is 12.
- The solution of simultaneous equations is given by the intersection of their graphs.

SIMPLE FACTORISING

Expanding $2a^2b(7a - 3b)$ gives $14a^3b - 6a^2b^2$. The reverse of this process is called **factorising**. If the **common factors** are not obvious, first write out the expression to be factorised in full, writing numbers in prime factor form. Identify each term that is common to all parts, and use these terms as common factors to be placed outside the bracket.

EXAMPLE 1

Factorise $x^2 + 4x$.

$x^2 + 4x = x \times x + 4 \times x$

$\qquad = x(x + 4)$

red terms ↑ ↑ black terms

EXAMPLE 2

Factorise $6x^2 + 2x$.

$6x^2 + 2x = 2 \times 3 \times x \times x + 2 \times x$

$\qquad = 2x(3x + 1)$

red terms ↑ ↑ black terms

EXAMPLE 3

Factorise $14a^3b - 6a^2b^2$.

$14a^3b - 6a^2b^2 = 2 \times 7 \times a \times a \times a \times b - 2 \times 3 \times a \times a \times b \times b$

$= 2a^2b(7a - 3b)$

red terms ↑   ↑ black terms

• Always check your factorising by multiplying out.

EXERCISE 1

Factorise these completely.

1 ▶ $x^2 + 3x$

2 ▶ $x^2 - 4x$

3 ▶ $5a - 10b$

4 ▶ $xy - xz$

5 ▶ $2x^2 + 4x$

6 ▶ $3x^2 - 18x$

7 ▶ $ax^2 - a^2x$

8 ▶ $6x^2y - 21xy$

9 ▶ $9p^2q + 6pq$

10 ▶ $ap + aq - ar$

11 ▶ $a^2x^2 + a^3x^3$

12 ▶ $4ab^3 + 6a^2b$

EXERCISE 1*

Factorise these completely.

1 ▶ $5x^3 + 15x^4$

2 ▶ $3x^3 - 18x^2$

3 ▶ $9x^3y^2 - 12x^2y^4$

4 ▶ $x^3 - 3x^2 - 3x$

5 ▶ $\pi r^2 + 2\pi rh$

6 ▶ $abc^2 - ab^2 + a^2bc$

7 ▶ $4p^2q^2r^2 - 12pqr + 16pq^2$

8 ▶ $30x^3 + 12xy - 21xz$

9 ▶ $0.2h^2 + 0.1gh - 0.3g^2h^2$

10 ▶ $\frac{1}{8}x^3y - \frac{1}{4}xy^2 + \frac{1}{16}x^2y^2$

11 ▶ $16p^2qr^3 - 28pqr - 20p^3q^2r$

12 ▶ $ax + bx + ay + by$

13 ▶ $(x - y)^2 - (x - y)^3$

14 ▶ $x(x + 1)(x + 3)(x + 5) - x(x + 3)(x + 5)$

SIMPLIFYING FRACTIONS

To **simplify** $\frac{234}{195}$ it is easiest to factorise first.

$$\frac{234}{195} = \frac{2 \times \,^3\cancel{3}^2 \times \,^1\cancel{13}}{_1\cancel{3} \times 5 \times \,_1\cancel{13}} = \frac{6}{5}$$

Algebraic fractions are also best simplified by factorising first.

EXAMPLE 4

Simplify $\dfrac{x^2 + 5x}{x}$

$$\frac{x^2 + 5x}{x} = \frac{^1\cancel{x}(x + 5)}{_1\cancel{x}} = x + 5$$

EXAMPLE 5

Simplify $\dfrac{2a^3 - 4a^2b}{2ab - 4b^2}$

$$\frac{2a^3 - 4a^2b}{2ab - 4b^2} = \frac{^1\cancel{2}a^2(\cancel{a - 2b})}{_1\cancel{2}b(\cancel{a - 2b})} = \frac{a^2}{b}$$

EXERCISE 2

Simplify these.

1 ▶ $\dfrac{x^2 + x}{x}$ 5 ▶ $\dfrac{2r + 2s}{r + s}$ 9 ▶ $\dfrac{at - bt}{ar - br}$

2 ▶ $\dfrac{a - a^3}{a}$ 6 ▶ $\dfrac{5x - 5y}{x - y}$ 10 ▶ $\dfrac{ax - ay}{xz - zy}$

3 ▶ $\dfrac{2x + 2y}{2z}$ 7 ▶ $\dfrac{a^2 - ab}{ab}$ 11 ▶ $\dfrac{x - xy}{z - zy}$

4 ▶ $\dfrac{3a - 3b}{3c}$ 8 ▶ $\dfrac{x^2 + xy}{xy}$ 12 ▶ $\dfrac{ab - a}{bc - c}$

EXERCISE 2*

Simplify these.

1 ▶ $\dfrac{ax + ay}{a}$ 5 ▶ $\dfrac{6x^2 + 9x^4}{3x^2}$ 9 ▶ $\dfrac{(a^2 + 2ac) - (ab^2 + 2ac)}{a^2 - ab^2}$

2 ▶ $\dfrac{6a^2 + 2ab}{2a}$ 6 ▶ $\dfrac{8x^3y^2 - 24x^2y^4}{12x^2y^2}$ 10 ▶ $\dfrac{2a^2 - ab}{3a^2 - ab} \times \dfrac{3ab - b^2}{2a^2 - ab}$

3 ▶ $\dfrac{z}{z^2 + z}$ 7 ▶ $\dfrac{y^2 + y}{y + 1}$ 11 ▶ $\dfrac{1}{3x - y} \div \dfrac{1}{15x - 5y}$

4 ▶ $\dfrac{2m}{m^2 - 2m}$ 8 ▶ $\dfrac{6x^2 - 12x^2y}{3xz - 6xyz}$ 12 ▶ $\dfrac{5x^3 - 10x^2}{10x - 5x^2}$

EQUATIONS WITH FRACTIONS

Equations with fractions are easier to manage than algebraic expressions, because both sides of the equation can be multiplied by the lowest common denominator to **clear** the fractions.

EQUATIONS WITH NUMBERS IN THE DENOMINATOR

EXAMPLE 6

Solve $\dfrac{2x}{3} - 1 = \dfrac{x}{2}$

$\dfrac{2x}{3} - 1 = \dfrac{x}{2}$ (Multiply both sides by 6)

$4x - 6 = 3x$

$x = 6$

Check: $4 - 1 = 3$

EXAMPLE 7

Solve $\frac{3}{4}(x-1) = \frac{1}{3}(2x-1)$

$$\frac{3}{4}(x-1) = \frac{1}{3}(2x-1) \qquad \text{(Multiply both sides by 12)}$$

$$9x - 9 = 8x - 4$$

$$x = 5$$

Check: $\frac{3}{4}(5-1) = \frac{1}{3}(10-1) = 3$

KEY POINT

• Clear the fractions by multiplying both sides by the lowest common denominator.

EXERCISE 3

Solve these for x.

1 ▶ $\frac{3x}{4} = 6$

2 ▶ $\frac{x}{5} = -2$

3 ▶ $\frac{x}{4} = \frac{1}{2}$

4 ▶ $\frac{3x}{8} = 0$

5 ▶ $\frac{2x}{3} = -4$

6 ▶ $\frac{1}{3}(x+7) = 4$

7 ▶ $\frac{3(x-10)}{7} = -6$

8 ▶ $\frac{x}{2} - \frac{x}{3} = 1$

9 ▶ $x - \frac{2x}{7} = 10$

10 ▶ $\frac{1}{4}(x+1) = \frac{1}{5}(8-x)$

11 ▶ $\frac{3-x}{3} = \frac{2+x}{2}$

12 ▶ $\frac{x+7}{7} = \frac{1}{5}(5-x)$

13 ▶ $\left(\frac{x}{2} + 7\right)$ is three times $\left(\frac{x}{5} + 2\right)$. Find the value of x.

14 ▶   Ryan does one-third of his journey to school by car, and one-half by bus. Then he walks the final kilometre. How long is his journey to school?

EXERCISE 3*

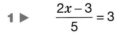

Solve these for x.

1 ▶ $\frac{2x-3}{5} = 3$

2 ▶ $\frac{3}{8}(5x-3) = 0$

3 ▶ $\frac{x+1}{5} = \frac{x+3}{6}$

4 ▶ $\frac{x+1}{7} - \frac{3(x-2)}{14} = 1$

5 ▶ $\frac{6-3x}{3} - \frac{5x+12}{4} = -1$

6 ▶ $\frac{2(x+1)}{5} - \frac{3(x+1)}{10} = x$

7 ▶ $\frac{2x-3}{2} - \frac{x-2}{3} = \frac{7}{6}$

8 ▶ $\frac{2x+1}{4} - x = \frac{3x+1}{8} + 1$

9 ▶ $4 - \frac{x-2}{2} = x + \frac{1-2x}{3}$

10 ▶ $\frac{1}{2}(1-x) - \frac{1}{3}(2+x) + \frac{1}{4}(3-x) = 1$

11 ▶ $\left(\frac{x}{14} + 3\frac{1}{2}\right)$ is twice $\left(\frac{x}{21} + 1\frac{2}{3}\right)$. Find the value of x.

12 ▶ Diophantus was a famous ancient Greek mathematician. This was written on his tomb.

> *Diophantus was a child for one-sixth of his life. After one-twelfth more, he became a man. After one-seventh more, he married, and five years later his son was born. His son lived half as long as his father and died four years before his father.*

How old was Diophantus when he died?

EQUATIONS WITH x IN THE DENOMINATOR

When the denominator contains x, the same principle of clearing fractions still applies.

EXAMPLE 8   Solve $\dfrac{3}{x} = \dfrac{1}{2}$

$$\dfrac{3}{x} = \dfrac{1}{2} \qquad \text{(Multiply both sides by } 2x\text{)}$$

$$\dfrac{3}{x} \times 2x = \dfrac{1}{2} \times 2x$$

$$6 = x$$

Check: $\dfrac{3}{6} = \dfrac{1}{2}$

EXAMPLE 9   Solve $\dfrac{4}{x} - x = 0$.

$$\dfrac{4}{x} - x = 0 \qquad \text{(Multiply both sides by } x\text{)}$$

$$\dfrac{4}{x} \times x - x \times x = 0 \times x \qquad \text{(Remember to multiply everything by } x\text{)}$$

$$4 - x^2 = 0$$

$$x^2 = 4$$

$$x = \pm 2$$

Check: $\dfrac{4}{2} - 2 = 0$ and $\dfrac{4}{-2} - (-2) = 0$

EXERCISE 4   Solve these for x.

1 ▶ $\dfrac{10}{x} = 5$ **5 ▶** $\dfrac{3}{5} = \dfrac{6}{x}$ **9 ▶** $\dfrac{5}{3x} = 1$

2 ▶ $\dfrac{12}{x} = -4$ **6 ▶** $\dfrac{8}{x} = -\dfrac{10}{3}$ **10 ▶** $\dfrac{9}{x} - x = 0$

3 ▶ $\dfrac{3}{x} = 5$ **7 ▶** $\dfrac{35}{x} = 0.7$ **11 ▶** $\dfrac{6}{7x} = 1$

4 ▶ $\dfrac{4}{x} = -\dfrac{1}{2}$ **8 ▶** $0.3 = -\dfrac{15}{2x}$ **12 ▶** $x - \dfrac{25}{x} = 0$

EXERCISE 4*

Solve these for x.

1 ▶ $\dfrac{52}{x} = 13$

5 ▶ $\dfrac{2.8}{x} = 0.7$

9 ▶ $\dfrac{1}{2x} + \dfrac{1}{3x} = 1$

2 ▶ $2.5 = -\dfrac{20}{x}$

6 ▶ $\dfrac{16}{x} = \dfrac{x}{4}$

10 ▶ $\dfrac{1}{ax} + \dfrac{1}{bx} = 1$

3 ▶ $\dfrac{15}{2x} = 45$

7 ▶ $\dfrac{12}{x} - 3x = 0$

11 ▶ $\dfrac{1}{4x} + \dfrac{1}{3x} = 1$

4 ▶ $\dfrac{8}{x} = -\dfrac{1}{8}$

8 ▶ $\dfrac{3.2}{x} - 4.3 = 5.7$

12 ▶ $\dfrac{1}{ax} - \dfrac{1}{bx} = 1$

SIMULTANEOUS EQUATIONS

If we try to solve simultaneous equations using a graph, this can take a long time and also the solutions can be inaccurate. Using algebra can be better, since this gives exact solutions, though it is impossible to solve some simultaneous equations algebraically.

There are two common ways of solving simultaneous equations using algebra; by substitution and by elimination.

SUBSTITUTION METHOD

EXAMPLE 10 ▶ A bottle and a cap together cost £1. The bottle costs 90p more than the cap.
Find the cost of the bottle.

Let b be the cost of the bottle in pence, and c be the cost of the cap in pence.
The total cost is 100p, and so

$b + c = 100$ (1)

The bottle costs 90p more than the cap, and so

$b = c + 90$ (2)

Substituting (2) into (1) gives

$(c + 90) + c = 100$
$2c = 10 \Rightarrow c = 5$

Substituting in (1) gives $b = 95$.

Therefore the bottle costs 95p and the cap costs 5p.

Check: Equation (2) gives $95 = 5 + 90$.

EXERCISE 5

Solve the following simultaneous equations by substitution.

1 ▶ $x = y + 2$
$x + 4y = 7$

5 ▶ $y = 3x + 3$
$5x + y = 11$

9 ▶ $y = 2x - 7$
$3x - y = 10$

2 ▶ $x = y + 1$
$x + 3y = 5$

6 ▶ $y = 2x + 1$
$4x + y = 13$

10 ▶ $y = 3x - 8$
$2x - y = 6$

3 ▶ $y = x + 3$
$y + 2x = 6$

7 ▶ $x = y - 3$
$x + 3y = 5$

4 ▶ $y = x + 2$
$y + 4x = 12$

8 ▶ $x = y - 4$
$x + 4y = 6$

EXERCISE 5*

Solve the following simultaneous equations by substitution.

1 ▶ $3x + 4y = 11$
$x = 15 - 7y$

5 ▶ $y = 5 - 2x$
$3x - 2y = 4$

9 ▶ $x - 2y + 4 = 0$
$5x - 6y + 18 = 0$

2 ▶ $3x + 2y = 7$
$x = 3 - y$

6 ▶ $5x - 4y = 13$
$y = 13 - 2x$

10 ▶ $x - 3y + 5 = 0$
$3x + 2y + 4 = 0$

3 ▶ $x = 7 - 3y$
$2x - 2y = 6$

7 ▶ $3x - 2y = 7$
$4x + y = 2$

4 ▶ $x = 10 - 7y$
$3x - 4y = 5$

8 ▶ $4x - 3y = 1$
$3x + y = 17$

ELIMINATION METHOD

EXAMPLE 11

Solve the simultaneous equations $2x - y = 35$, $x + y = 118$.

$$2x - y = 35 \qquad (1)$$
$$\underline{x + y = 118} \qquad (2)$$
$$3x = 153 \qquad \text{(Adding equations (1) and (2))}$$
$$x = 51$$

Substituting $x = 51$ into (1) gives $102 - y = 35 \Rightarrow y = 67$

The solution is $x = 51$, $y = 67$.

Check: Substituting $x = 51$, $y = 67$ into (2) gives $51 + 67 = 118$.

This method only works if the numbers before either x or y are of opposite **sign** and equal in value. The equations may have to be multiplied by suitable numbers to achieve this.

EXAMPLE 12

Solve the simultaneous equations $x + y = 5$, $6x - 3y = 3$.

$$x + y = 5 \qquad (1)$$
$$6x - 3y = 3 \qquad (2)$$

Multiply both sides of equation (1) by 3.

$$3x + 3y = 15 \qquad (3)$$
$$\underline{6x - 3y = 3} \qquad (2)$$
$$9x = 18 \qquad \text{(Adding equations (3) and (2))}$$
$$x = 2$$

Substituting $x = 2$ into (1) gives $2 + y = 5 \Rightarrow y = 3$

The solution is $x = 2$, $y = 3$.

Check: Substituting $x = 2$ and $y = 3$ into (2) gives $12 - 9 = 3$.

EXERCISE 6

Solve these simultaneous equations.

1 ▶
$$x + y = 8$$
$$x - y = 2$$

2 ▶
$$x + y = 2$$
$$2x - y = 1$$

3 ▶
$$x - y = 1$$
$$2x + y = 8$$

4 ▶
$$3x - y = 5$$
$$x + y = 3$$

5 ▶
$$x + y = 3$$
$$-x + y = 1$$

6 ▶
$$-x + y = 4$$
$$x + 2y = 5$$

7 ▶
$$x + 3y = 4$$
$$2y - x = 1$$

8 ▶
$$x + 4y = 2$$
$$y - x = 3$$

9 ▶
$$x + y = 0$$
$$3x - 2y = 5$$

10 ▶
$$x + 3y = 5$$
$$2x - y = -4$$

EXERCISE 6*

Solve these simultaneous equations.

1 ▶
$$x + y = 11$$
$$x - y = 5$$

2 ▶
$$x + y = 1$$
$$2x - y = 5$$

3 ▶
$$2x - y = 3$$
$$x + y = 9$$

4 ▶
$$2x + 2y = 5$$
$$3x - 2y = 10$$

5 ▶
$$3x + y = 8$$
$$3x - y = -2$$

6 ▶
$$-x + 3y = 7$$
$$x - y = 3$$

7 ▶
$$-2x + y = -2$$
$$2x - 3y = 6$$

8 ▶
$$4x + 5y = -28$$
$$-4x - 7y = 28$$

9 ▶
$$x - y = -6$$
$$y + 2x = 3$$

10 ▶
$$3x + 4y = 7$$
$$3x - 4y = -1$$

If the numbers in front of x or y are not of opposite sign, multiply by a negative number as shown in Example 13.

EXAMPLE 13

Solve the simultaneous equations $x + 2y = 8$, $2x + y = 7$.

$$x + 2y = 8 \qquad (1)$$
$$2x + y = 7 \qquad (2)$$

Multiply **both** sides of equation (2) by −2.

$$x + 2y = 8 \qquad (3)$$
$$\underline{-4x - 2y = -14} \qquad (2)$$
$$-3x = -6 \qquad \text{(Adding equations (3) and (2))}$$
$$x = 2$$

Substituting $x = 2$ into (1) gives $2 + 2y = 8 \Rightarrow y = 3$

The solution is $x = 2$, $y = 3$.

Check: Substituting $x = 2$ and $y = 3$ into equation (2) gives $4 + 3 = 7$.

Sometimes **both** equations have to be multiplied by suitable numbers, as in Example 14.

EXAMPLE 14

Solve the simultaneous equations $2x + 3y = 5$, $5x - 2y = -16$.

$$2x + 3y = 5 \qquad (1)$$
$$5x - 2y = -16 \qquad (2)$$

Multiply (1) by 2. $4x + 6y = 10 \qquad (3)$

Multiply (2) by 3. $\underline{15x - 6y = -48} \qquad (4)$

$$19x = -38 \qquad \text{(Adding equations (3) and (4))}$$
$$x = -2$$

Substituting $x = -2$ into (1) gives $-4 + 3y = 5 \Rightarrow y = 3$

The solution is $x = -2$, $y = 3$.

Check: Substituting $x = -2$ and $y = 3$ into equation (2) gives $-10 - 6 = -16$.

KEY POINTS

To solve two simultaneous equations by elimination:

- Label the equations (1) and (2).
- Choose which **variable** to eliminate.
- Multiply one or both equations by suitable numbers so that the numbers in front of the terms to be eliminated are the same and of different sign.
- Eliminate by adding the resulting equations. Solve the resulting equation.
- Substitute your answer into one of the original equations to find the other answer.
- Check by substituting both answers into the other original equation.

EXERCISE 7

Solve these simultaneous equations.

1 ▶ $3x + y = 11$
$x + y = 7$

2 ▶ $2x - y = 7$
$x - y = 3$

3 ▶ $x + 3y = 8$
$x - 2y = 3$

4 ▶ $x - 5y = 1$
$x + 3y = -5$

5 ▶ $2x + y = 5$
$3x - 2y = -3$

6 ▶ $3x + y = -5$
$5x - 3y = -13$

7 ▶ $2x + 3y = 7$
$3x + 2y = 13$

8 ▶ $3x + 2y = 5$
$6x + 5y = 8$

9 ▶ $2x + 5y = 9$
$3x + 4y = 10$

10 ▶ $3x + 4y = 11$
$5x + 6y = 17$

EXERCISE 7*

Solve these simultaneous equations.

1 ▶ $2x + y = 5$
$3x - 2y = 11$

2 ▶ $3x + y = 10$
$2x - 3y = 14$

3 ▶ $3x + 2y = 7$
$2x - 3y = -4$

4 ▶ $4x + 7y = -5$
$3x - 2y = 18$

5 ▶ $3x + 2y = 4$
$2x + 3y = 7$

6 ▶ $2x + 3y = 5$
$3x + 4y = 7$

7 ▶ $7x - 4y = 37$
$5x + 3y = 44$

8 ▶ $5x - 7y = 27$
$3x - 4y = 16$

9 ▶ $3x + 2y = 3$
$7x - 3y = 1.25$

10 ▶ $4x - 3y = 2.6$
$10x + 5y = -1$

11 ▶ $\dfrac{x}{2} + \dfrac{y}{3} = 4$
$\dfrac{y}{4} - \dfrac{x}{3} = \dfrac{1}{6}$

12 ▶ $\dfrac{x}{5} + \dfrac{y}{2} = 1$
$\dfrac{x}{2} - \dfrac{y}{8} = -3$

13 ▶ $\dfrac{a+1}{b+1} = 2$
$\dfrac{2a+1}{2b+1} = \dfrac{1}{3}$

14 ▶ $\dfrac{c+d}{c-d} = \dfrac{1}{2}$
$\dfrac{c+1}{d+1} = 2$

15 ▶ $\dfrac{2}{x} - \dfrac{1}{y} = 3$
$\dfrac{4}{x} + \dfrac{3}{y} = 16$

16 ▶ $\dfrac{2}{x} - \dfrac{3}{y} = 1$
$\dfrac{8}{x} + \dfrac{9}{y} = \dfrac{1}{2}$

HINT
For Questions
15 and 16: let

$p = \dfrac{1}{x}, q = \dfrac{1}{y}$

SOLVING PROBLEMS USING SIMULTANEOUS EQUATIONS

EXAMPLE 15

SKILLS

MODELLING

Tickets at a concert cost either £10 or £15. The total takings from sales of tickets was £8750. Sales of £10 tickets were two times the sales of £15 tickets. How many tickets were sold?

Let x be the number of £10 tickets sold, and y the number of £15 tickets sold.

The total takings was £8750, and so

$$10x + 15y = 8750$$

Divide by 5 to simplify.

$$2x + 3y = 1750 \qquad (1)$$

Sales of £10 tickets were two times the sales of £15 tickets, and so

$$x = 2y \qquad (2)$$

To check that equation (2) is correct, substitute simple numbers that obviously work, such as $x = 10$, $y = 5$.

Substituting (2) into (1) gives

$$4y + 3y = 1750$$
$$7y = 1750$$
$$y = 250$$

and so $x = 500$, from (2).

750 tickets were sold in total.

Check: In (1), $1000 + 750 = 1750$.

KEY POINTS

- Define your variables.
- Write equations to represent each sentence from the question.
- Solve the equations by using the substitution method or the elimination method. Choose the method which seems the most suitable.

EXERCISE 8

1 ▶ The **sum** of two numbers is 112 and their difference is 54. Find the two numbers.

2 ▶ Find two numbers with a **mean** of 14 and a difference of 4.

3 ▶ Two times one number added to four times another gives 34. The sum of the two numbers is 13. Find the numbers.

4 ▶ For this rectangle, find x and y and the area.

$$12x - 3y$$

$5x + 2$ | | $3x + 2y$

$$4y + 3$$

5 ▶ At McEaters, Pam bought two burgers and three colas, which cost her £3.45. Her friend Pete bought four burgers and two colas, and this cost him £4.94. Work out the cost of a burger and the cost of a cola.

6 ▶ Becky and her friend go to the fair. Becky has three rides on the rollercoaster and four rides on the water slide at a total cost of £8.10. Her friend has four rides on the rollercoaster and two rides on the water slide at a total cost of £7.80. How much is each ride?

7 ▶ A parking meter accepts only 20p coins or 50p coins. On one day, 39 coins were collected with a total value of £11.40. Find how many 50p coins were collected.

8 ▶ At a concert, tickets cost either $40 or $60. 700 tickets were sold at a cost of $33 600. Find how many $40 tickets were sold.

9 ▶ At an archery range, each shot costs 20c. If you hit the target, you receive 30c. Emma has 20 shots and makes a loss of 70c. How many hits did she get?

10 ▶ Alec is doing a test of 50 questions. He gets 2 marks for every question that is correct, but loses 1 mark for every question that is wrong. Alec answers every question and scores 67 marks. How many questions did he answer correctly?

EXAMPLE 16 ▶ Ahmed makes a camel journey of 20 km. The camel travels at 12 km/h for the first part of the journey, but then conditions become worse and the camel can only travel at 4 km/h for the second part of the journey. The journey takes 3 hours. Find the distance of each part of the journey.

Let x be the distance in km of the first part of the journey, and y be the distance in km of the second part.

$$x + y = 20 \qquad (1) \qquad \text{(Total distance is 20 km)}$$

Use the formula $\qquad \text{time} = \dfrac{\text{distance}}{\text{speed}}$

$$\frac{x}{12} + \frac{y}{4} = 3 \qquad (2) \qquad \text{(Total time taken is 3 hours)}$$

Multiply equation (2) by the lowest common denominator = 12 to clear the fractions.

$$x + 3y = 36 \qquad (3)$$
$$x + y = 20 \qquad (1)$$

Subtract equation (1) from equation (3) to eliminate the terms in x.

$$2y = 16$$
$$y = 8$$

From equation (1), if $y = 8$ then $x = 12$, so the first part is 12 km and the second part is 8 km.

Check: These values work in equations (1) and (2).

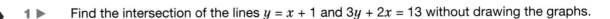

EXERCISE 8*

1 ▶ Find the intersection of the lines $y = x + 1$ and $3y + 2x = 13$ without drawing the graphs.

2 ▶ The line $y = mx + c$ passes through the points (1, 1) and (2, 3). Find m and c.

3 ▶ The denominator of a fraction is 5 more than the **numerator**. If both the denominator and the numerator are increased by 3, the fraction becomes $\frac{3}{4}$. Find the original fraction.

4 ▶ Aidan is rowing along a river in Canada. He can row at 3 m/s against the current and at 6 m/s with the current. Find the speed of the current.

5 ▶ One year ago, Gill was five times as old as her horse. One year from now the sum of their ages will be 22. How old is Gill now?

6 ▶ To cover a distance of 10 km, Jacob runs some of the way at 15 km/h, and walks the rest of the way at 5 km/h. His total journey time is 1 hour. How far did Jacob run?

7 ▶ On a journey of 240 km, Archita travels some of the way on a motorway at 100 km/h and the rest of the way on minor roads at 60 km/h. The journey takes 3 hours. How far did she travel on the motorway?

8 ▶ A 2-digit number is increased by 36 when the digits are reversed. The sum of the digits is 10. Find the original number.

9 ▶ A 2-digit number is equal to seven times the sum of its digits. If the digits are reversed, the new number formed is 36 less than the original number. What is the number?

10 ▶ When visiting his parents, Tyler drives at an average speed of 42 km/h through urban areas and at an average speed of 105 km/h on the motorway. His journey usually takes him 2.5 hours. One day when there is fog, he sets off 1 hour early and only manages to drive at an average speed of 28 km/h in the urban areas and 60 km/h on the motorway. He arrives 30 minutes late. What was the total distance that Tyler travelled?

EXERCISE 9   **REVISION**

Factorise these.

1 ▶ $x^2 - 8x$ **2 ▶** $3x^2 + 12x$ **3 ▶** $6xy^2 - 30x^2y$ **4 ▶** $12x^3 + 9x^2 - 15x$

Simplify these.

5 ▶ $\dfrac{x^2 - x}{x}$ **6 ▶** $\dfrac{x^2 + xy}{x^2 - xy}$

Solve these equations.

7 ▶ $\dfrac{3x - 4}{4} = 2$ **9 ▶** $\dfrac{2x + 7}{4} - \dfrac{x + 1}{3} = \dfrac{3}{4}$

8 ▶ $\dfrac{1}{4}(x - 2) = \dfrac{1}{7}(x + 1)$ **10 ▶** $\dfrac{4}{n} - 1 = \dfrac{2}{n}$

11 ▶ Sarah shares some sweets with her friends. She gives one-eighth of the sweets to Ann, one-sixth to Nikita and one-third to Ruth. She then has nine sweets remaining for herself. How many sweets did she have at the beginning?

Solve these pairs of simultaneous equations.

12 ▶ $y - x = 4$
$y + 2x = 1$

14 ▶ $3x + 2y = 10$
$5x - 4y = 2$

13 ▶ $y + x = 3$
$y - 2x = 3$

15 ▶ $5x - 2y = -1$
$10x - 3y = 1$

16 ▶ At a sale, Andy buys two books and three USB sticks for £25.50. His friend Charlie buys four books and five USB sticks for £47.50. What is the cost of each item if all the books cost the same and all the USB sticks cost the same?

17 ▶ Rana is collecting 10p and 20p pieces. When she has 30 coins, the value of them is £4.10. How many of each coin does she have?

EXERCISE 9*   **REVISION**

Factorise these.

1 ▶ $3x^4 - 12x^3$

3 ▶ $24x^3y^2 - 18x^2y$

2 ▶ $\frac{4}{3}pr^3 + \frac{2}{3}pr^2$

4 ▶ $15a^2b^3c^2 - 9a^3b^2c^2 + 21a^2b^2c^3$

Simplify these.

5 ▶ $\dfrac{x^2 - xy}{xy - y^2}$

6 ▶ $\dfrac{ax - bx}{x^2 + xy} \div \dfrac{2a - 2b}{2x^2 + 2xy}$

Solve these equations.

7 ▶ $\frac{2}{7}(3x - 1) = 0$

9 ▶ $1\frac{2}{3}(x + 1) = x + 5\frac{2}{3}$

8 ▶ $\dfrac{3x + 2}{5} - \dfrac{2x + 5}{3} = x + 3$

10 ▶ $\dfrac{1}{x} + \dfrac{1}{2x} - \dfrac{1}{3x} = 2\frac{1}{3}$

11 ▶ Mrs Taylor has lived in many countries. She spent the first third of her life in England, the next sixth in France, one-quarter in Spain, $3\frac{1}{2}$ years in Italy, and one-fifth in Germany, where she is now living. How old is Mrs Taylor?

Solve these pairs of simultaneous equations.

12 ▶ $5x + 4y = 22$
$3x + 5y = 21$

14 ▶ $3x + 8y = 24$
$x - 2y = 1$

13 ▶ $5x + 3y = 23$
$x + 2y = 6$

15 ▶ $6x + 5y = 30$
$3x + 4y = 18$

16 ▶ The straight line $ax + by = 1$ passes through the points (1, 4) and (3, 1). Find the values of a and b.

17 ▶ Ten years from now, Abdul will be twice as old as his son Pavel. Ten years ago, Abdul was seven times as old as Pavel. How old are Abdul and Pavel now?

EXAM PRACTICE: ALGEBRA 3

1   Factorise these completely

    a $3x^2 + 6x$
    b $28ab^2 - 21a^2b$ **[2]**

2   Simplify these.

    a $\dfrac{x^2 - 2x}{2x}$

    b $\dfrac{x - xy}{y - y^2}$ **[4]**

3   Solve these equations.

    a $\dfrac{3(x - 7)}{4} = -9$ **c** $\dfrac{x}{3} - \dfrac{x}{5} = 2$

    b $\dfrac{x - 1}{3} = \dfrac{x + 1}{4}$ **d** $\dfrac{5}{x} = -\dfrac{1}{3}$ **[8]**

4   Solve these simultaneous equations.

    a $x = 3y - 7$
           $x + 2y = 3$

    b $2x + y = 4$
           $3x + 2y = 5$ **[6]**

5   At the market, Malik buys 2 oranges and 5 mangoes at a cost of \$4.50 while his friend Seb buys 4 oranges and 3 mangoes at a cost of \$4.10. What is the cost of each item? (All the oranges cost the same, and all the mangoes cost the same.)   **[5]**

[Total 25 marks]

CHAPTER SUMMARY: ALGEBRA 3

SIMPLE FACTORISING

Take out the common factors. Check your answer by multiplying out.

$2x^3 + 6x^5 = 2x^3(1 + 3x^2)$

$9xy^3 - 12x^2y^2 = 3xy^2(3y - 4x)$

SIMPLIFYING FRACTIONS

Factorise first, then simplify

$$\frac{x^2y - xy^2}{xy} = \frac{^1\cancel{xy}(x - y)}{_1\cancel{xy}} = x - y$$

EQUATIONS WITH FRACTIONS

Clear the fractions by multiplying both sides by the lowest common denominator.

$\dfrac{2(x - 3)}{3} = \dfrac{x - 1}{2}$ (Multiply both sides by $3 \times 2 = 6$)

$4(x - 3) = 3(x - 1)$ (Multiply out brackets)

$4x - 12 = 3x - 3$ (Subtract $3x$ from both sides and add 12 to both sides)

$x = 9$

$\dfrac{2}{x} = \dfrac{1}{3}$ (Multiply both sides by $3 \times x = 3x$)

$\dfrac{2}{x} \times 3x = \dfrac{1}{3} \times 3x$ (Simplify)

$6 = x$

SIMULTANEOUS EQUATIONS

SUBSTITUTION METHOD

$x = y + 1$ (1)

$x + 2y = 4$ (2)   (Substitute (1) into (2) to give equation (3))

$y + 1 + 2y = 4$ (3)

$3y = 3 \Rightarrow y = 1$ (Substitute into equation (1) to find x)

$x = 2$ (Check by substituting into equation (2))

$2 + 2 = 4$ (Correct)

ELIMINATION METHOD

$x + 2y = 5$ (1)

$3x - 4y = 25$ (2)   (Multiply equation (1) by 2 to give equation (3))

$2x + 4y = 10$ (3)   (Add equations (2) and (3))

$5x = 35 \Rightarrow x = 7$ (Substitute into equation (1))

$7 + 2y = 5 \Rightarrow y = -1$ (Check in equation (2))

$21 - (-4) = 25$ (Correct)

GRAPHS 3

Travel graphs represent motion in the form of a graph.

These graphs help us to understand the relationship between movement and time.

There are many applications in science and everyday life for these graphs.

Scientists working on the Mars Rover mission used them to illustrate motion over vast distances in space.

▲ Mars Rover

LEARNING OBJECTIVES

■ Draw and interpret distance–time graphs ■ Draw and interpret speed–time graphs

BASIC PRINCIPLES

The motion of an object can be simply described by a graph of distance travelled against the time taken. The examples shown illustrate how the shape of the graph can describe the speed of the object.

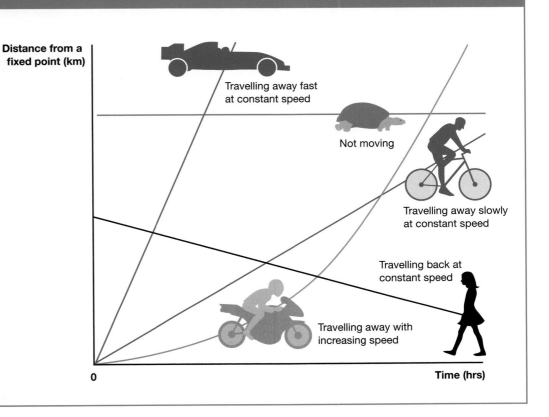

Distance from a fixed point (km)

Travelling away fast at constant speed

Not moving

Travelling away slowly at constant speed

Travelling back at constant speed

Travelling away with increasing speed

0   Time (hrs)

DISTANCE–TIME GRAPHS

Travel graphs show motion. They make understanding how things move when compared to time much clearer by using diagrams.

EXAMPLE 1

SKILLS

INTERPRETATION

A vintage car goes from London to Brighton for a car show, and then returns to London. Here is a graph representing the distance in relation to the time of the journey.

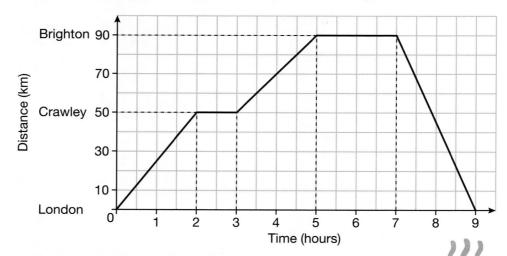

a What is the speed of the car from London to Crawley?

b The car breaks down at Crawley. For how long does the car break down?

c What is the speed of the car from Crawley to Brighton?

d The car is transported by a recovery vehicle back to London from Brighton. At what speed is the car transported?

a The speed from London to Crawley is $\dfrac{50 \text{ km}}{2 \text{ h}} = 25 \text{ km/h}$.

b The car is at Crawley for 1 hour.

c The speed from Crawley to Brighton is $\dfrac{40 \text{ km}}{2 \text{ h}} = 20 \text{ km/h}$.

d The speed from Brighton to London is $\dfrac{90 \text{ km}}{2 \text{ h}} = 45 \text{ km/h}$.

KEY POINTS

On a distance–time graph:

- The vertical axis represents the distance from the starting point.
- The horizontal axis represents the time taken.
- A horizontal line represents no movement.
- The **gradient** of the slope gives the speed (a straight line implies a constant speed).
- A positive gradient represents the outbound journey.
- A negative gradient represents the return journey.

EXERCISE 1

1 ▶ Ingar travels south on a motorway from Hamburg, while Franz travels north on the same road from Hannover. This distance–time graph (showing the distance from Hannover) shows the journeys of both travellers.

a What is Ingar's speed in kilometres per hour?

b What is Franz's speed in kilometres per hour?

c At what time does Ingar reach Hannover?

d What is the distance between Ingar and Franz at 10:30?

e At what time do Ingar and Franz pass each other?

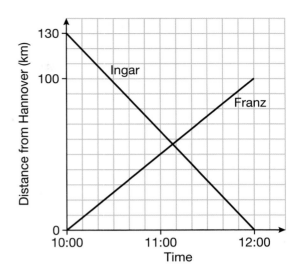

2 ▶ This distance–time graph shows the journeys of a car and a motorcycle between Mandalay (M) and Pyawbwe (P).

a When did the car stop, and for how long?

b When did the car and the motorcycle pass each other?

c What is the distance between the car and the motorcycle at 09:30?

d After the motorcycle's first stop, it increased its speed until it arrived in Pyawbwe. The speed limit on the road was 70 miles/hour. Did the motorcyclist go over the speed limit?

e Over the whole journey (excluding stops), what was the average speed of the car?

f What was the average speed of the motorcycle (excluding stops)?

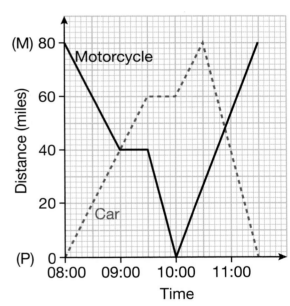

3 ▶ Naseem leaves home at 09:00, and drives to Clare's house at a speed of 60 km/h for 1 hour. Then she stops at a petrol station for 15 minutes. She continues on her journey at 40 km/h for 30 minutes, and then arrives at her destination. At 13:00, she starts her return journey, and drives at a constant speed of 80 km/h without stopping.

a Draw a distance–time graph to illustrate Naseem's journey.

b Use this graph to estimate at what time Naseem returns home.

4 ▶ Li and Jacki train for a triathlon by swimming 1 km along the coast, cycling 9 km in the same direction along the straight coast road, and then running directly back to their starting point along the same road. The times of this training session are shown in the table.

ACTIVITY	LI'S TIME (MINUTES)	JACKI'S TIME (MINUTES)
Swimming	20	15
Rest	5	5
Cycling	10	15
Rest	10	5
Running	35	50

a Draw a distance–time graph (in kilometres and hours) to illustrate this information, given that Li and Jacki both start at 09:00. Let the time axis range from 09:00 to 10:30.

b Use your graph to estimate when Li and Jacki finish.

c Use your graph to estimate when Li and Jacki are at the same point.

d Calculate the average speed of both athletes over the whole session, excluding stops, in km/h.

EXERCISE 1*

1 ▶ A goat is tied to a pole at A in the corner of a square field ABCD. The rope is the same length as the side of the field. The goat starts at B and runs slowly at a constant speed to corner D, keeping the rope tight. **Sketch** the following graphs for this journey:

a Distance from A against time

b Distance from B against time

c Distance from C against time

d Distance from D against time.

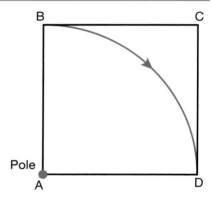

2 ▶ Harry and Jack are two footballers who do an extra training session of running at *identical constant speeds*. For all three exercises Harry always starts from A, and Jack always starts from C.

Exercise 1 is that Harry and Jack both run one clockwise circuit.

Exercise 2 is that Harry runs a circuit clockwise, and Jack runs a circuit anticlockwise.

Exercise 3 is that Harry runs to D and Jack runs to F.

Sketch three graphs to illustrate the distances between Harry and Jack over time.

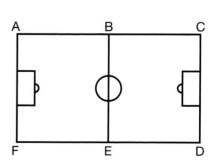

3 ▶ Three motorcyclists, A, B and C, go on a journey along the same road. Part of their journey is shown in the travel graph.

a Place the riders in order (first, second and third) after
(i) 0 s   **(ii)** 15 s   **(iii)** 30 s

b When are all the riders the same distance along the road?

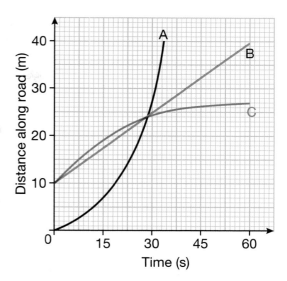

c Which rider travels at a constant speed?

d Which rider's speed is gradually

(i) increasing

(ii) decreasing?

4 ▶ The diagram shows the distances, in kilometres, between some junctions on a motorway.

The junctions are numbered as 1, 2 … and Ⓟ is the Petrol Station.

Driver A (going north) joins 5 at 08:00, arrives at Ⓟ at 09:00, rests for half an hour, and then continues his journey, passing 1 at 12:00.

Driver B (going south) joins 1 at 08:00, arrives at Ⓟ at 10:00, rests for 1 hour, and then continues her journey, passing 5 at 12:00.

a Draw a graph of the distance in kilometres from 1 against time in hours to show both journeys.

b When does driver A pass driver B?

c What are A and B's final speeds in km/h?

d Find their average speeds, excluding stops, in km/h.

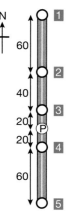

SPEED–TIME GRAPHS

Travel graphs of speed against time can be used to find out more about speed changes and distances travelled.

EXAMPLE 2

SKILLS

INTERPRETATION

A train changes speed as shown in the speed–time graph.

The train's speed is increasing between A and B, so it is accelerating.

The train's speed is decreasing between C and D, so it is decelerating (retarding).

The train's speed is constant at 20 m/s (and therefore the acceleration is zero) between B and C for 30 s. It has travelled 600 m (20 × 30 m).

This is the area under the graph between B and C.

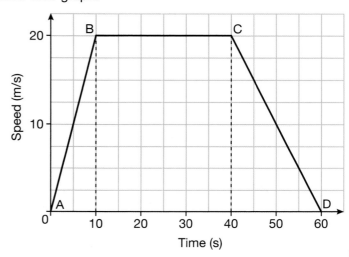

a Find the total distance travelled by the train, and therefore find the average speed for the whole journey.

b Find the train's acceleration between A and B, B and C, and C and D.

a Total distance travelled   = area under graph

$$= \left(\frac{1}{2} \times 10 \times 20\right) + (30 \times 20) + \left(\frac{1}{2} \times 20 \times 20\right) = 900$$

Therefore, average speed $= \dfrac{900 \text{ m}}{60 \text{ s}} = 15 \text{ m/s}$

b Acceleration between A and B = gradient of line AB

$$= \frac{20 \text{ m/s}}{10 \text{ s}} = 2 \text{ m/s}^2$$

Between B and C the speed is constant, so the acceleration is zero.

Acceleration between C and D = gradient of line CD

$$= \frac{-20 \text{ m/s}}{20 \text{ s}} = -1 \text{ m/s}^2$$

(The − sign indicates retardation or deceleration.)

KEY POINTS

On a speed–time graph:

- The vertical axis represents speed.

- The horizontal axis represents time.

- The gradient of the slope gives the acceleration.

- Acceleration = $\dfrac{\text{change in speed}}{\text{time}}$

- A positive gradient represents acceleration.

- A negative gradient represents deceleration or **retardation**.

- The area under the graph gives the distance travelled.

EXERCISE 2

1 ▶ A speed–time graph for a journey of 15 s is shown.

a Find the acceleration over the first 10 s in m/s².

b Find the retardation over the last 5 s in m/s².

c Find the total distance travelled in m.

d Find the average speed for the journey in m/s.

2 ▶ A speed–time graph for a journey of 3 hours is shown.

a Find the acceleration over the first 2 hours in km/h².

b Find the retardation over the last hour in km/h².

c Find the total distance travelled in km.

d Find the **mean** speed for the journey in kilometres per hour.

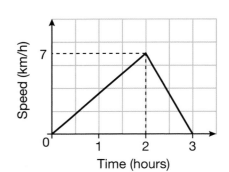

3 ▶ A speed–time graph is shown for the journey of a train between two stations.

  a Find the acceleration over the first 40 s in m/s².

  b Find the retardation over the final 80 s in m/s².

  c Find the total distance travelled in m.

  d Find the average speed for the journey in metres per second.

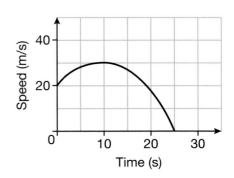

4 ▶ The speed–time graph for a firework is shown.

  a Find the firework's maximum speed in m/s.

  b When does the firework have zero acceleration?

  c Estimate the total distance travelled by the firework in m.

  d By calculation, estimate the average speed of the firework during its journey in m/s.

EXERCISE 2*

1 ▶ A cycle-taxi accelerates from rest to 6 m/s in 10 s, remains at that speed for 20 s, and then slows steadily to rest in 12 s.

  a Draw the graph of speed, in metres per second, against time in seconds for this journey.

  b Use your graph to find the cycle-taxi's initial acceleration in m/s².

  c What was the final acceleration in m/s²?

  d What was the average speed over the whole journey in m/s?

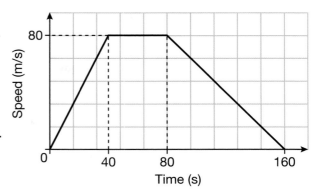

2 ▶ The acceleration of the first part of the journey shown is 3 m/s².

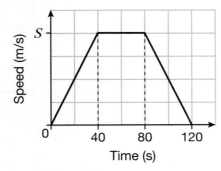

  a Find the maximum speed, S metres per second.

  b Find the total distance travelled.

  c Find the average speed of the whole journey in m/s.

3 ▶ The speed–time graph shows an initial constant retardation of 2 m/s² for t seconds.

  a Find the total distance travelled in m.

  b Find the deceleration at $3t$ seconds in m/s²

  c Find the average speed of the whole journey, including stops, in m/s.

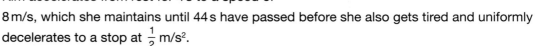

4 ▶ Sasha and Kim race over d metres. Sasha accelerates from rest for 6 s to a speed of 8 m/s, which she maintains for the next 40 s before she gets tired and uniformly decelerates at $\frac{4}{7}$ m/s² until she stops. Kim accelerates from rest for 4 s to a speed of 8 m/s, which she maintains until 44 s have passed before she also gets tired and uniformly decelerates to a stop at $\frac{1}{2}$ m/s².

  a Draw the speed–time graph in metres per second and seconds for both girls on the same axes.

  b Use your graph to find who wins the race.

  c What was the average speed for each runner in m/s?

  d Over what distance, in m, do the girls race?

  e Who is first in the race after **(i)** 100 m **(ii)** 300 m?

5 ▶ Explain carefully why this graph could never represent the speed–time graph for a bee's journey in one day.

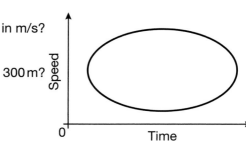

---

1 ▶ The graph shows the journeys of Cheri and Felix, who went on a cycling trip.

  a How much time did Cheri stop for?

  b At what time did Felix start?

  c Find Cheri's average speed in km/h.

  d How far apart were they at 10:20?

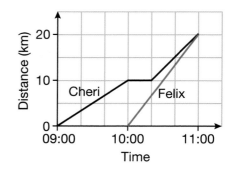

2 ▶ A bee flies out from its hive to some flowers, and returns to its hive some time later. Its journey is shown on the distance–time graph.

  a Find the bee's outward journey speed in metres per second.

  b How long does the bee stay at the flowers?

  c Find the bee's return journey speed in metres per second.

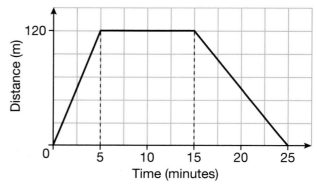

3 ▶ Robin sails from a resting position in his boat to a constant speed of 4 m/s in 30 s. He then remains at this speed for a further 60 s, before he slows down at a constant retardation until he stops 15 s later.

     a Draw a speed–time graph showing this journey, and use it to find Robin's

     b initial acceleration in m/s²

     c acceleration at 60 s in m/s²

     d retardation in m/s²

     e average speed for the whole journey in m/s.

4 ▶ The speed–time graph illustrates the journey of a cyclist.

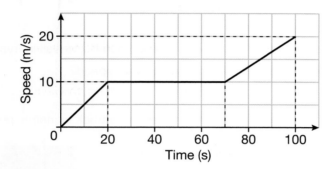

     a Find the distance travelled in the first 50 s in m.

     b Find the total distance travelled in m.

     c Find the average speed of the cyclist in m/s.

     d Find the acceleration when $t = 80$ s in m/s².

EXERCISE 3*   **REVISION**

1 ▶ This distance–time graph shows the journeys of Daniela and Alberto, who cycle from their houses to meet at a lake. After staying at the lake for 90 minutes, Daniela cycles back home at 8 km/hour and Alberto returns home at 12 km/hour.

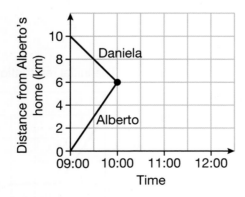

     a Copy the graph and represent these facts on your graph.

     b When did each person arrive home?

     c What is the average speed, excluding stops, in m/s for each cyclist?

2 ▶ A squash ball is hit against a wall by Thom. He remains stationary throughout the ball's flight, which is shown in the distance–time graph.

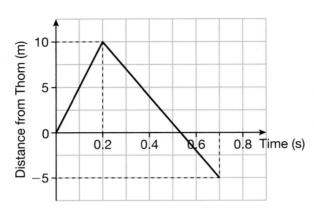

a What is the speed of the ball when it approaches the wall in m/s?

b When does the ball pass Thom, and at what speed?

3 ▶ This speed–time graph illustrates the speed of a truck in metres per second.

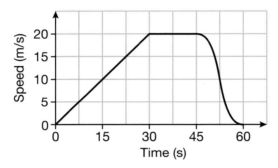

Which of these statements are true? Which are false? Show **working** to justify your answers.

a The initial acceleration over the first 30 s changes.

b The braking distance is 150 m.

c The average speed for the whole journey is 12.5 m/s.

d The maximum speed is 60 km/hour.

Q4c HINT
Find the value of
***t* first.**

4 ▶ This speed–time graph is for a toy racing car. The initial retardation is 2 m/s².

a Find the total distance travelled in m.

b Find the deceleration at $6t$ seconds in m/s².

c Find the average speed of the whole journey in m/s.

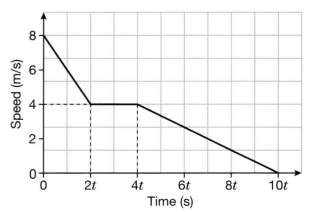

EXAM PRACTICE: GRAPHS 3

1 The travel graph shows the outward and return journey when Anjola drives to her friend's house. Use the graph to calculate Anjola's:

a outward speed in km/min
b visiting time
c return speed in km/hr. **[6]**

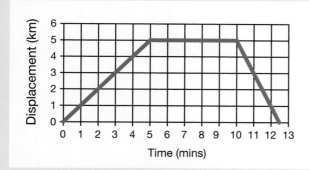

2 A drone accelerates constantly from rest to 12 m/s in 20 s, remains at that speed for 20 s and then slows steadily to rest in 60 s.

a Draw the speed–time graph for the drone's journey.
b Use this graph to find the drone's:
  (i) initial acceleration in m/s^2
  (ii) final acceleration in m/s^2
  (iii) average speed over the whole 100 s journey in m/s. **[10]**

3 In the College Games, the winner ran the 200 metres race in a time of 20.32 seconds.

a Calculate his average speed in metres per second. Give your answer correct to 1 decimal place.
b Change your answer to part **a** to kilometres per hour. Give your answer correct to 1 decimal place.

The diagram shows a sketch of the speed–time graph for the winner's race.

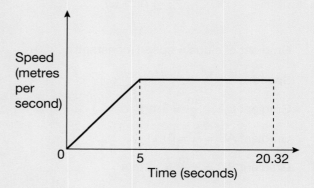

c Calculate his maximum speed in metres per second. Give your answer correct to 1 decimal place.
d Calculate his acceleration over the first 5 seconds. State the units in your answer. Give your answer correct to 2 significant figures. **[9]**

[Total 25 marks]

CHAPTER SUMMARY: GRAPHS 3

DISTANCE–TIME GRAPHS

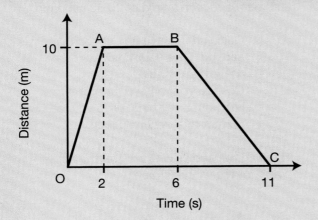

Gradient of slope = speed (constant)

Speed:

Gradient OA = $\frac{10}{2}$ = 5 m/s

Gradient AB = $\frac{0}{4}$ = 0 m/s

Gradient BC = $-\frac{10}{5}$ = –2 m/s

(negative implies returning)

SPEED–TIME GRAPHS

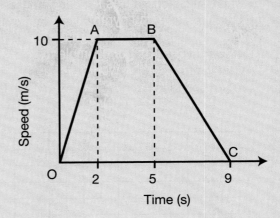

Gradient of slope = acceleration (constant)

Area under graph = distance travelled

Acceleration:

Gradient OA = $\frac{10}{2}$ = 5 m/s² (speeding up)

Gradient AB = $\frac{0}{3}$ = 0 m/s² (constant speed)

Gradient BC = $-\frac{10}{4}$ = –2.5 m/s² (slowing down)

Average speed:

Average speed = $\dfrac{\text{distance travelled}}{\text{time}} = \dfrac{\frac{1}{2} \times (3+9) \times 10}{9} = 6\frac{2}{3}$ m/s

SHAPE AND SPACE 3

The history of mankind is full of examples of how we used features of similar triangles to build structures (for example Egyptian pyramids), examine the sky (as Greek astronomers did), and make a record of geographical features (for example to produce Eratosthenes' map of the world).

Trigonometry (triangle measurement) is used today by architects, engineers, town-planners and scientists. It allows us to solve right-angled triangles without the use of scale drawings. The sides of a right-angled triangle are given special names which must be easily recognised.

LEARNING OBJECTIVES

■ Use the tangent ratio to find a length and an angle in a right-angled triangle

■ Use angles of elevation and depression

■ Use the tangent ratio to solve problems

BASIC PRINCIPLES

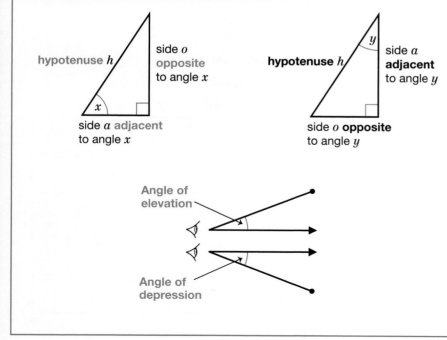

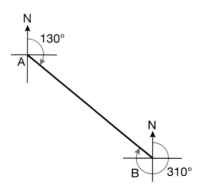

Bearings are measured
• clockwise
• from north.

A is 310° from B. B is 130° from A.

TANGENT RATIO

ACTIVITY 1

SKILLS

REASONING

Triangles X, Y and Z are **similar**. For each triangle, measure the sides opposite (o) and adjacent (a) to the 30° angle in millimetres.

Calculate the **ratio** of $\dfrac{o}{a}$ to 2 **decimal places** for X, Y and Z.

What do you notice?

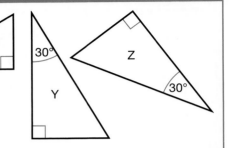

In Activity 1, you should have found that the ratio $o : a$ for the 30° angle is the same for all three triangles. This is the case for any similar right-angled triangle with a 30° angle; this should not surprise you because you were calculating the **gradient** of the same slope each time.

The actual value of $\dfrac{\text{opposite}}{\text{adjacent}}$ for 30° is 0.577 350 (to 6 d.p.).

The ratio $\dfrac{\text{opposite}}{\text{adjacent}}$ for a given angle θ is a fixed number. It is called the **tangent** of θ, or **tan θ**.

KEY POINT

- $\tan \theta = \dfrac{\text{opposite side}}{\text{adjacent side}} = \dfrac{o}{a}$

ACTIVITY 2

SKILLS

ANALYSIS

You can find the tangent ratio on your calculator.

Make sure your calculator is in **degree mode**.

Press the [tan] button followed by the value of the angle. Then press [=].

Copy and complete the table, **correct to 3 significant figures**.

θ (°)	0°	15°	30°	45°	60°	75°	89°	90°
$\tan \theta$			0.577			3.73		

Why is tan 89° so large?

Why can tan 90° not be found?

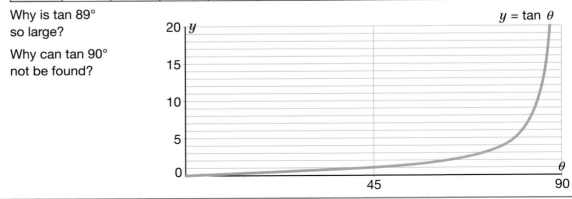

CALCULATING SIDES

EXAMPLE 1

SKILLS

PROBLEM
SOLVING

Find the length of the side p correct
to 3 significant figures.

$$\tan 30° = \frac{p}{12}$$

$$12 \times \tan 30° = p$$

$$p = 6.93\,\text{cm (to 3 s.f.)}$$

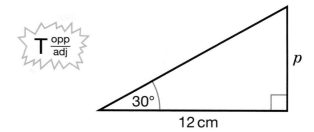

1 2 × tan 3 0 = 6.92820 (to 6 s.f.)

EXAMPLE 2

SKILLS

PROBLEM
SOLVING

PQ represents a 25 m tower, and R is an engineer's
mark p m away from Q. The angle of elevation of
the top of the tower from the engineer's mark R
on level ground is 60°.

Find the distance RQ correct to
3 significant figures.

$$\tan 60° = \frac{25}{p}$$

$$p \times \tan 60° = 25$$

$$p = \frac{25}{\tan 60°}$$

$$p = 14.4\,\text{m (to 3 s.f.)}$$

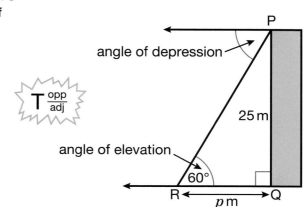

2 5 ÷ tan 6 0 = 14.4338 (to 6 s.f.)

EXERCISE 1

Which sides are the hypotenuse, opposite and adjacent to the given angle a?

1 ▶

2 ▶
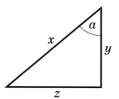

3 ▶
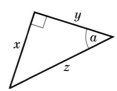

What is the value of tan b for each of these triangles?

4 ▶
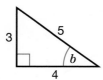

5 ▶
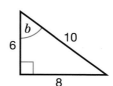

6 ▶
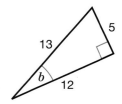

Find the length of side x. Give your answers correct to 3 significant figures.

7 ▶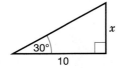

8 ▶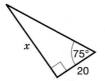

9 ▶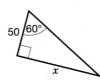

10 ▶

11 ▶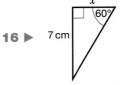

12 ▶

13 ▶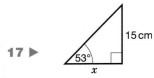

14 ▶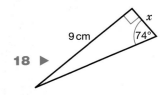

15 ▶

16 ▶

17 ▶

18 ▶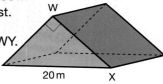

19 ▶ The angle of elevation of the top of a cliff from a boat 125 m away from the bottom of the cliff is 35°. Find the height of the cliff.

20 ▶ The angle of elevation of a radio mast from Remi is 60°. Remi is 50 m away from the base of the mast. Find the height of the radio mast.

21 ▶ Find the **cross-sectional** area of the sloped roof WXY if WX = WY.

Give your answers correct to 3 significant figures.

Find the length of the side marked x.

1 ▶

2 ▶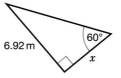

3 ▶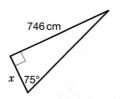

4 ▶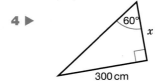

5 ▶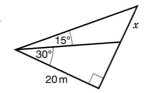

6 ▶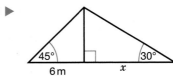

7 ▶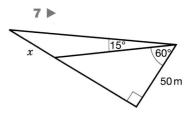

8 ▶ The angle of depression from a window 10 m above the ground to a coin on the ground is 15°. Find the distance of the coin from the base of the building.

9 ▶ The gnomon (central pin) of the giant equatorial sundial in Jaipur, India, is an enormous right-angled triangle. The angle the hypotenuse makes with the base is 27°. The base is 44 m long. Find the height of the gnomon.

10 ▶ In a triangle ABC, the angle at B is 62°, the angle at C is 75°. AX is perpendicular to BC and the length AX = 5 m. Calculate BX and BC.

Find the lengths of x and y.

11 ▶
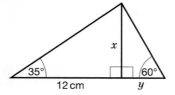

13 ▶
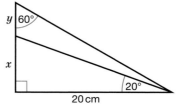

12 ▶
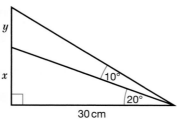

14 ▶
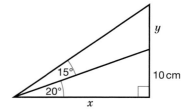

15 ▶ From the top of a 25 m high cliff, the angle of depression of a jet ski at point A is 20°. The jet ski moves in a straight line towards the base of the cliff so that its angle of depression 5 seconds later at point B is 30°.

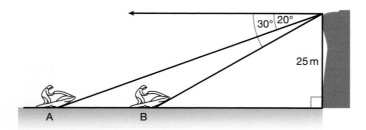

a Calculate the distance AB.

b Find the average speed of the jet ski in kilometres/hour.

16 ▶ A regular pentagon has sides of 10 cm. Find the **radius** of the largest circle which can be drawn inside the pentagon.

CALCULATING ANGLES

If you know the adjacent and opposite sides of a right-angled triangle, you can find the angles in the triangle. For this 'inverse' operation, you need to use the INV tan buttons on your calculator.

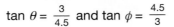

SKILLS

PROBLEM SOLVING

The diagram shows a child on a slide in a playground. Find angles θ and ϕ to the nearest degree.

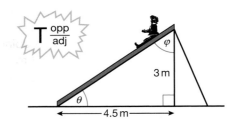

$\tan \theta = \dfrac{3}{4.5}$ and $\tan \phi = \dfrac{4.5}{3}$

INV tan (3 ÷ 4 . 5) = **33.6901** (to 6 s.f.)

INV tan (4 . 5 ÷ 3) = **56.3099** (to 6 s.f.)

So $\theta = 34°$ and $\phi = 56°$ (to the nearest degree).

Finding one angle in a right-angled triangle allows the third angle to be found as the sum of the angles in a triangle is 180°.

KEY POINT

• To calculate an angle from a tangent ratio, use the INV tan or SHIFT tan buttons.

EXERCISE 2

Find the angles that have these tangents, giving your answers correct to 2 significant figures.

1 ▶   1.000   **2 ▶**   0.577   **3 ▶**   0.268

Find the angles that have these tangents, giving your answers correct to 3 significant figures.

4 ▶   1.732   **5 ▶**   2.747   **6 ▶**   3.732

Find the angle a correct to 1 decimal place.

7 ▶ 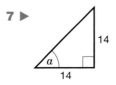   **8 ▶** 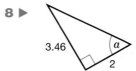   **9 ▶**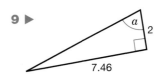

Find the angle θ correct to 1 decimal place.

10 ▶   **12 ▶** 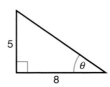   **14 ▶**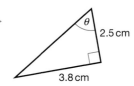

11 ▶   **13 ▶**    **15 ▶**

16 ▶ Calculate the angles a and b of this dry ski slope correct to 1 decimal place.

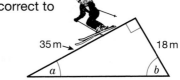

17 ▶ A bell tower is 65 m high. Find the angle of elevation, to 1 decimal place, of its top from a point 150 m away on horizontal ground.

18 ▶ Ollie is going to walk in the rainforest. He plans to go up a slope along a straight path from point P to point Q. The hill is 134 m high, and distance PQ on the map is 500 m. Find the angle of elevation of the hill.

EXERCISE 2*

1 ▶ ABCD is a rectangle. Find angles a and b to the nearest degree.

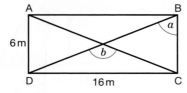

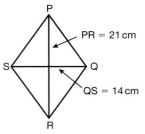

2 ▶ The **rhombus** PQRS has diagonals 14 cm and 21 cm long. Find the angle PQR to 3 significant figures.

Find angle a.

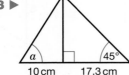

3 ▶

4 ▶

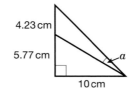

5 ▶ Rectangle

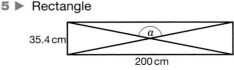

6 ▶ A bank B is 8.6 km north and 12.5 km west of a school S. Calculate correct to 3 significant figures:

a the bearing of S from B

b the bearing of B from S.

7 ▶ The grid represents a map on which villages X, Y and Z are shown. Each side of the grid squares represent 5 km.

Find, to 1 decimal place, the bearing of:
a Y from X
b X from Y
c Z from X
d Z from Y.

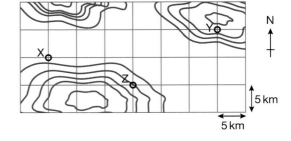

8 ▶ A 5 m flagpole is secured by two ropes PQ and PR.
Point R is the **mid-point** of SQ. Find angle a to 1 decimal place.

9 ▶ In a **quadrilateral** ABCD, AB = 3 cm, BC = 5.7 cm, CD = 4 cm
and AD = 5 cm. Angle B = angle D = 90°. Calculate the angle
at A to 1 decimal place.

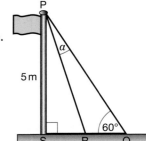

10 ▶ Draw an **equilateral triangle** and **bisect** it.

Prove that the exact values of the
tangent ratios of 30° and 60° are

$\dfrac{1}{\sqrt{3}}$ and $\sqrt{3}$ respectively.

11 ▶ Given that $\tan 30° = \dfrac{1}{\sqrt{3}}$ and $\tan 60° = \sqrt{3}$,
show that the exact value of the height of
the tree in metres is given by $25\sqrt{3}$.

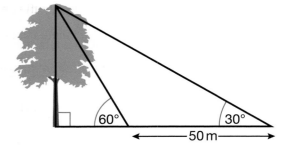

EXERCISE 3   **REVISION**

Find angle x. Give your answers correct to 3 significant figures.

1 ▶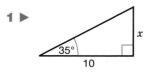

3 ▶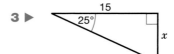

5 ▶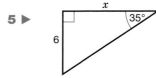

2 ▶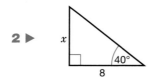

4 ▶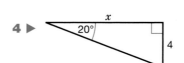

6 ▶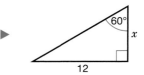

Find angle a.

7 ▶

8 ▶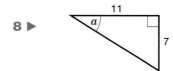

9 ▶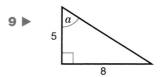

10 ▶ Find the area of the **isosceles triangle** ABC, given that $\tan 30° = 0.577$.

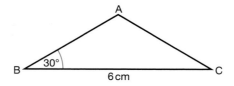

11 ▶ Calculate the angle between the longest side and the diagonal of
a 577 mm by 1000 mm rectangle.

EXERCISE 3*

REVISION

Give your answers to 3 significant figures.

1 ▶ The angle of elevation to the top of the CN Tower (Toronto, Canada) from a point on the ground 50 m away from the tower is 84.8°. Find the height of the CN Tower.

2 ▶ A harbour H is 25 km due (directly) north of an airport A. A town T is 50 km due east of H.

    a Calculate the bearing of T from A.

    b Calculate the bearing of A from T.

3 ▶ The diagram shows the lines of sight of a car driver.

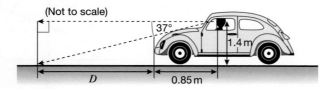

(Not to scale)

37°

1.4 m

D 0.85 m

    a Calculate the driver's 'blind' distance D in metres.

    b Why is this distance important in the car design?

4 ▶ Show that the area of an equilateral triangle of side $2x$ is $x^2\sqrt{3}$, given that $\tan 60° = \sqrt{3}$.

5 ▶ A lighthouse is 25 m high. From the top of the lighthouse, the angles of depression of two buoys due (directly) north of it are 45° and 30°. Given than $\tan 30° = \dfrac{1}{\sqrt{3}}$, show that the distance x, in metres, between the buoys is $25\left(\sqrt{3}-1\right)$.

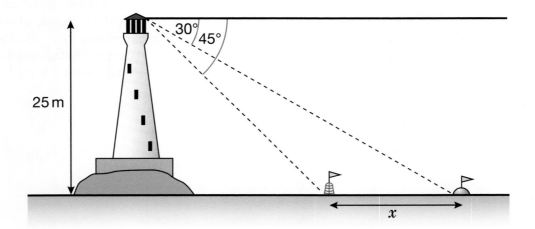

30°

45°

25 m

x

EXAM PRACTICE: SHAPE AND SPACE 3

Give your answers correct to
3 significant figures.

1 ▶ Find the length of side a. **[3]**

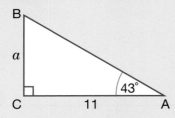

2 ▶ An aeroplane takes off from point A at angle of
elevation $\theta°$. Calculate θ. **[3]**

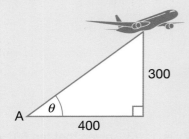

3 ▶ A hawk sits on top of a tree and sees a mouse on
the ground at an angle of depression of 25°. The
mouse is 25 m away from the base of the tree.
Find the height of the tree. **[4]**

4 ▶ A hot-air balloon rises vertically from the ground,
stopping h_1 m above the ground before rising
h_2 m further.

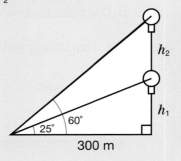

a Find the heights h_1 and h_2.
b The balloon takes 1 minute to rise from the
ground to h_1 m. It takes a further 5 mins to
rise to its highest point. Calculate the average
speed of the total ascent in m/s. **[7]**

5 ▶ Zeno sails his boat 20 km from Port A on a
bearing of 030° to point B. He then sails 10 km
on a bearing of 120° to point C arriving at 3pm. A
storm warning tells him to return directly to Port A
before 5:15pm.

a Draw a diagram of Zeno's route and use it
to find the bearing of his return journey.
b If distance CA = $10\sqrt{5}$ km and he returns at
10 km/h, find out whether Zeno returns to
Port A before 5.15pm. **[8]**

[Total 25 marks]

CHAPTER SUMMARY: SHAPE AND SPACE 3

TANGENT RATIO

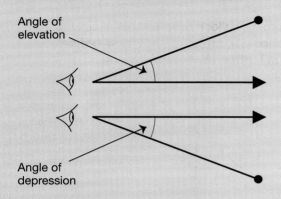

Angle of elevation

Angle of depression

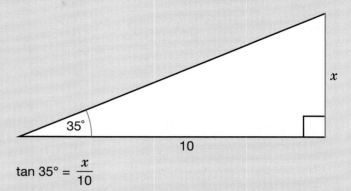

$$\tan 35° = \frac{x}{10}$$

$$x = 10 \tan 35° = 7.00 \text{ (3 s.f.)}$$

Bearings are measured from north and clockwise.

240°

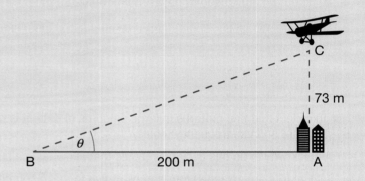

$$\tan \theta = \frac{73}{200}$$

Using the INV and tan buttons, $\theta = 20.1°$ (3 s.f.)

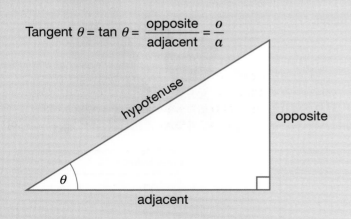

$$\text{Tangent } \theta = \tan \theta = \frac{\text{opposite}}{\text{adjacent}} = \frac{o}{a}$$

hypotenuse

opposite

θ

adjacent

HANDLING DATA 2

One of the largest collections of numerical data in the 1940s was gathered to decode secret radio messages. This took place under the guidance of the code-breaker Alan Turing (1912–1954) who used early computers to find patterns in data that at first appeared to be random.

Frequency tables allowed his team to see these patterns more efficiently.

▲ Alan Turing

LEARNING OBJECTIVES

- Estimate the mean and range from a grouped frequency table
- Find the modal class and the group containing the median

BASIC PRINCIPLES

- To collect and find patterns in large amounts of data, it is necessary to group the information together and use frequency tables.

  A quick way to do this is by tally tables that allow fast calculation of frequency.

  Tally marks are arranged into groups of five to make counting faster, allowing frequencies to be displayed.

  Note: ⪼ represents 5, |||| represents 4, ||| represents 3 etc.

TYPE OF PET	TALLY	FREQUENCY
Dog	⪼ ⪼		11
Cat	⪼ ||	7
Goldfish	⪼		6
Guinea pig	|||	3
Hamster	||	2
Lizard			1
Tortoise			1
Rabbit	|||	3

- Mean = $\dfrac{\text{total of all values}}{\text{total number of values}}$

- Median = value of the middle number when data is ordered in ascending or descending order
- Mode = number that occurs most frequently
- Discrete data can only be integer values (number of people, goals, boats…).
- Continuous data can have any value in a particular range (time, speed, weight…).
- The symbol sigma $\sum$ is used many times in statistics as a quick way to write 'adding up' of a particular quantity.

FREQUENCY TABLES

Data can be summarised efficiently in a frequency table.

DISCRETE DATA

EXAMPLE 1

SKILLS

ANALYSIS

A teacher records how many times 20 pupils are late to class in a school year.

| 1 | 5 | 3 | 4 | 2 | 0 | 0 | 4 | 5 | 5 |
| 3 | 4 | 4 | 5 | 1 | 3 | 3 | 4 | 5 | 5 |

a Work out the mean number of late arrivals.

b Work out the median number of late arrivals.

c Write down the mode of the data.

d Draw a bar chart for the data.

x represents the recorded number of late arrivals.

x	TALLY	FREQUENCY f	$f \times x$
0	||	2	$2 \times 0 = 0$
1	||	2	$2 \times 1 = 2$
2	|	1	$1 \times 2 = 2$
3	||||	4	$4 \times 3 = 12$
4	卌	5	$5 \times 4 = 20$
5	卌 |	6	$6 \times 5 = 30$
		$\sum f = 20$	$\sum fx = 66$

The fourth column ($f \times x$) produces a value for the 0's and the 1's and the 2's etc.

Therefore the sum of the fx column, $\sum fx$ = the total of all the values.

a Mean = $\dfrac{\text{sum of all values}}{\text{number of values}} = \dfrac{\sum fx}{\sum f} = \dfrac{66}{20} = 3.3$ days per pupil.

b Median = 4 days per pupil (10th value = 4 and 11th value = 4).

c Mode = 5 days per pupil (5 is the value with the highest frequency of 6).

d The bar chart for this data is shown.

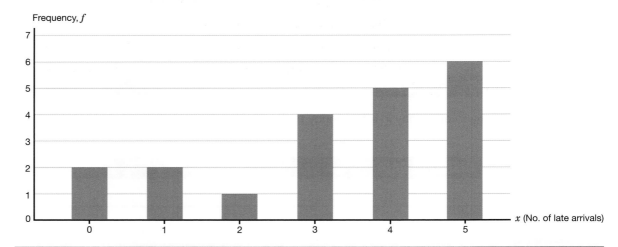

CONTINUOUS DATA

EXAMPLE 2

SKILLS

PROBLEM
SOLVING

The national flower of Malaysia is the Chinese Hibiscus. A botanist takes a **sample** of 50 of these plants and produces a frequency table of their heights, h m. The exact heights are not recorded, but the values are grouped in **classes** with exact boundaries.

a Work out an estimate of the mean height.
b Work out which class contains the median height.
c Write down which class contains the mode of the data.
d Draw a **frequency polygon** for the data.

To calculate useful values (mean, median and mode) it is necessary to add to the two columns of height and frequencies as shown below.

Let the value of the Chinese Hibiscus height be h m.

h	FREQUENCY f	MID-POINT x	$f \times x$
$0 \leq h < 0.5$	3	0.25	$3 \times 0.25 = 0.75$
$0.5 \leq h < 1$	5	0.75	$5 \times 0.75 = 3.75$
$1 \leq h < 1.5$	7	1.25	$7 \times 1.25 = 8.75$
$1.5 \leq h < 2$	15	1.75	$15 \quad 1.75 = 26.25$
$2 \leq h < 2.5$	11	2.25	$11 \times 2.25 = 24.75$
$2.5 \leq h \leq 3$	9	2.75	$9 \times 2.75 = 24.75$
	$\sum f = 50$		$\sum fx = 89$

The **mid-point**, x, is used for each group since it is the best estimate for the mean of all the heights in each group.

The value of $f \times x$ is the best estimate for all the heights in each class.

So, the sum of the fx column , $\sum fx$ = the best estimate total of all the heights.

a Estimate of mean = $\dfrac{\text{sum of all values}}{\text{number of values}} = \dfrac{\sum fx}{\sum f} = \dfrac{89}{50} = 1.78\,\text{m}.$

b Median is in the $1.5 \leq h < 2$ class (as this contains the 25th value).

c **Modal class** is $1.5 \leq h < 2$ as these values have the highest frequency of 15.

d The frequency polygon for this data is shown using the mid-points of each class.

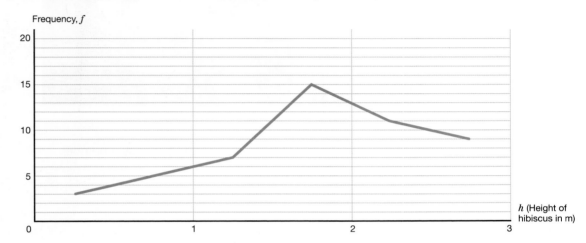

KEY POINT

• If data is distributed with a frequency distribution table, the mean is given by

$$\text{Mean} = \dfrac{\sum fx}{\sum f}$$

Discrete data: x values are the exact scores.

Continuous data: x values are the mid-points of each class.

$\sum$ is a Greek letter 'sigma' which means add up all the values.

EXERCISE 1

1 ▶ A spinner with ten sides is spun 30 times with the following results.

4	5	8	10	3	3	1	4	9	2
10	7	3	2	6	6	9	2	1	8
9	4	5	5	6	7	4	8	1	10

a Construct a table with four columns:
score, tally, frequency and frequency × score.

b Calculate the mean score.

c Find the median and modal scores.

2 ▶ The number of pupils who went to a 'Mandarin for Beginners' club for 20 lessons is shown.

4	5	6	10	12	8	5	7	7	4
7	8	9	12	12	8	7	9	9	11

a Construct a table with four columns:
number of pupils, tally, frequency and frequency × number.

b Calculate the mean number.

c Find the median and modal numbers.

3 ▶ The table shows information about the number of presents, x, received by 50 teenagers on their 16th birthdays.

a Copy this table and use it to calculate the mean number of presents received.

b Find the median and modal number of presents.

NUMBER OF PRESENTS x	FREQUENCY f
1	5
2	21
3	17
4	7

4 ▶ The table shows Winnie's scores in her weekly Spanish vocabulary tests.

a Copy this table and use it to calculate her mean score.

b Find the median and modal score.

TEST SCORE x	FREQUENCY f
5	4
6	6
7	3
8	12
9	3
10	2

1 ▶ The times (t secs) to swim a 50 m butterfly stroke for 20 pupils are shown below.

| 45.7 | 38.9 | 34.7 | 49.2 | 55.7 | 59.5 | 43.2 | 32.9 | 35.0 | 59.8 |
| 55.5 | 35.9 | 43.5 | 44.1 | 47.0 | 37.5 | 43.4 | 48.7 | 32.4 | 48.1 |

Q1a HINT
Be careful where you place times close to the class boundaries.

a Construct a tally chart using classes of $30 \leq t < 35$, $35 \leq t < 40$ with equal class widths up to $55 \leq t \leq 60$.

b Use this table to calculate an estimate of the mean butterfly time.

c Find the median class and the modal class times.

2 ▶ The table shows the weights, w kg, of the Giant Grouper fish caught by a Hong Kong fishing boat.

a Copy and complete the table and use it to calculate an estimate of the mean Giant Grouper weight caught by the fishing boat.

b Find the median class and the modal class weight for the Giant Groupers.

WEIGHT w kg	TALLY	FREQUENCY f
$100 \leq w < 150$	||||	
$150 \leq w < 200$	⨫ ⨫ ||	
$200 \leq w < 250$	⨫ |	
$250 \leq w \leq 300$	|||	

3 ▶ The incomplete frequency table shows the time, t hrs per week, spent by 100 teenagers revising for an examination.

a Copy and complete the table and use it to calculate an estimate of the mean revision time.

b Find the median class and the modal class revision time.

TIME t HRS	FREQUENCY f
$0 \leq t < 2$	14
$2 \leq t < 4$	
$4 \leq t < 6$	37
$6 \leq t < 8$	18
$8 \leq t \leq 10$	13

4 ▶ The frequency table shows the height, h m, of 30 teenagers in a class at school.

a Find the value of t.

b Copy and complete the table and use it to calculate an estimate of the mean pupil height.

c Find the median class and the modal class heights of the pupils

HEIGHT h m	FREQUENCY f
$0 \leq h < 1.2$	1
$1.2 \leq h < 1.4$	9
$1.4 \leq h < 1.6$	12
$1.6 \leq h < 1.8$	$3t$
$1.8 \leq h \leq 2$	t

EXERCISE 2

REVISION

1 ▶ Twenty people record the time, t hours, they spend on the internet during a day.

TIME (t HOURS)	$0 \leq t < 2$	$2 \leq t < 4$	$4 \leq t < 6$	$6 \leq t < 8$	$8 \leq t < 10$
FREQUENCY	1	3	9	5	2
MID-POINT	1	3			

a Copy and complete the table to show the mid-points.

b Copy and complete the frequency polygon.

Plot the mid-points on the horizontal axis and frequency on the vertical axis.

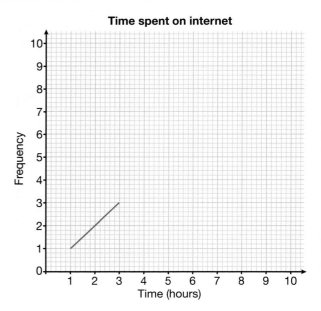

Time spent on internet

2 ▶   Draw a frequency polygon for this data.

TIME	$0 \leq t < 20$	$20 \leq t < 40$	$40 \leq t < 60$	$60 \leq t < 80$	$80 \leq t < 100$
FREQUENCY	6	5	1	2	5

3 ▶   For this grouped frequency table:

a Estimate the mean.

b State the group containing the median.

c Estimate the range.

d State the modal class.

CLASS	FREQUENCY
$0 \leq x < 5$	7
$5 \leq x < 10$	15
$10 \leq x < 15$	13
$15 \leq x < 20$	4
$20 \leq x < 25$	1

4 ▶   A social scientist is studying urban life in Costa Rica.
She uses a data collection sheet to record information about the size of families living in a city.

NUMBER OF CHILDREN	FREQUENCY
0	IIII
1	JHT JHT
2	JHT III
3	JHT I
4	JHT
5	II

a Work out the range of the number of children per family in the city.

b Work out the total number of families in the survey.

c Calculate the mean. **Round** your answer to 1 **decimal place** (1 d.p.).

d The mean number of children per family in a rural community is 3.1. Compare this with the mean for city families.

EXERCISE 2*

1 ▶ The heights, in centimetres, of 12 students in Year 10 are

162, 154, 174, 165, 175, 149, 160, 167, 171, 159, 170, 163

a Is the data discrete or continuous?

b Work out the missing numbers, x and y, in the grouped frequency table.

c Draw a frequency polygon.

HEIGHT (h cm)	FREQUENCY
$140 \leq h < 150$	1
$150 \leq h < 160$	2
$160 \leq h < 170$	x
$170 \leq h < 180$	y

2 ▶ The table shows the distances jumped by two athletes training for a long jump event.

a How many jumps did Ben do in training?

b Explain why Ben's median distance is halfway between the 18th and 19th items in the data set.

c In which class interval is Ben's median?

d Work out which class interval contains Jamie's median distance.

e On average, which athlete jumps the furthest in training?

f State the modal class for Ben and Jamie.

g At the long jump event, both athletes must compete against the current champion, who jumped 8.31 m. Who has the better chance of beating him? Explain your answer.

DISTANCE (d m)	BEN'S FREQUENCY	JAMIE'S FREQUENCY
$6.5 \leq d < 7.0$	3	8
$7.0 \leq d < 7.5$	7	18
$7.5 \leq d < 8.0$	25	21
$8.0 \leq d < 8.5$	1	3
$8.5 \leq d < 9.0$	0	1

3 ▶ The table shows the age distribution of male and female teachers in a school.

a Draw frequency polygons for these two sets of data on the same diagram.

b By calculating the mean of each data set, compare the age distributions of male and female teachers.

c What feature of your diagram confirms that your comparison is correct?

AGE (x YEARS)	MALE	FEMALE
20 ≤ x < 25	1	0
25 ≤ x < 30	2	9
30 ≤ x < 35	3	10
35 ≤ x < 40	7	12
40 ≤ x < 45	10	8
45 ≤ x < 50	10	7
50 ≤ x < 55	12	4
55 ≤ x < 60	4	0
60 ≤ x < 65	1	0

4 ▶ A biologist measures the lengths of 40 fish and records the results in a grouped frequency table.

LENGTH (L cm)	$0 \le L < 10$	$10 \le L < x$	$x \le L < 3x$
FREQUENCY	6	24	10

Find x if the mean length is 15.75 cm.

EXAM PRACTICE: HANDLING DATA 2

1 Chica records the number of baskets per game (x) that she scores for her basketball team over a season of 20 games.

x	0	1	2	3	4	5	6	7
FREQUENCY	2	3	5	4	3	2	0	1

Last season Chica's mean baskets per game was 2.
Show that she has improved her basket-scoring skills in the current season. **[5]**

2 The exact times (t mins) for 20 children to complete the highest level in a new computer game 'Tower of Hanoi' are given below.

2   17   4   20   5   6   9   8   14   11
8   6   9   12   11   14   14   13   9   6

a Construct a tally chart using groups $0 \leq t < 5$, $5 \leq t < 10$, $10 \leq t < 15$ and $15 \leq t \leq 20$ to create a frequency table and use this table to
   (i) draw a frequency polygon
   (ii) estimate the mean time of all the pupils and state the modal class.

b Calculate the exact mean time and compare this to the estimated value.

c Explain why there is a difference. **[10]**

3 The frequency table shows the results in a survey of the hours of sleep of 100 teenagers in Rome on New Year's Day.

TIME t HOURS	$0 \leq t < 4$	$4 \leq t < 6$	$6 \leq t < 8$	$8 \leq t \leq 12$
FREQUENCY f	p	24	$3p$	16

a Find p and use it to copy and complete the frequency table.

b Use this table to

   (i) draw a frequency polygon

   (ii) estimate the mean and modal class of these sleep times

   (iii) estimate the percentage of teenagers who had at least 7 hours sleep. **[10]**

[Total 25 marks]

CHAPTER SUMMARY: HANDLING DATA 2

FREQUENCY TABLES

DISCRETE DATA

Mean = $\dfrac{\text{sum of (frequency} \times \text{value)}}{\text{sum of frequencies}} = \dfrac{\sum fx}{\sum f}$ ($\sum$ means 'the sum of')

SCORE x	FREQUENCY f	$f \times x$
2	4	8
3	10	30
5	6	30
	$\sum f = 20$	$\sum fx = 68$

Mean = $\dfrac{68}{20}$ = 3.4

Median = 3

Mode = 3 as it has the highest frequency of 10.

CONTINUOUS DATA

For a grouped frequency table:

To estimate a mean, add the products of the frequency (f) and class mid-points (x) and divide by the total frequency.

Estimated mean = $\dfrac{\sum f \times x}{\sum f}$.

The modal class has the highest frequency.

If the total frequency is n, the median lies in the class containing the $\dfrac{n+1}{2}$ th item of data.

WEIGHT (g)	MID-POINT x	FREQUENCY f	$f \times x$
$8 \leq w < 10$	9	6	54
$10 \leq w < 16$	13	9	117
$16 \leq w \leq 20$	18	5	90
		$\sum f = 20$	$\sum fx = 261$

Estimate of mean = $\dfrac{261}{20}$ = 13.1 g (3 s.f.)

Median class is $10 \leq w < 16$

Modal class is $10 \leq w < 16$ as it has the highest frequency of 9.

UNIT 4

4 is the lowest square of a prime number. It is the smallest number of colours needed to shade a map so that no neighbouring countries are the same colour. Also if x and y are integers, $x^2 - y^2$ is divisible by 4 only when $(x - y)$ is an even number.

4 is the lowest honest number. These are numbers n that can be described using exactly n letters in English.

4-leaf clovers are rare and are considered to be lucky plants!

NUMBER 4

In Ancient Rome, calculations were often made in fractions which were multiples of $\frac{1}{100}$. 'Percent' literally means 'per one hundred' in Latin. It is a number without dimension that helps us to make quick numerical judgements. As currencies of money grew across the world, calculations with a denominator of 100 became common, and profit and loss became easy to compare.

LEARNING OBJECTIVES

■ Find an amount after a repeated percentage change, including compound interest

■ Find an original amount after a percentage increase or decrease

• Solve real-life problems involving percentages

BASIC PRINCIPLES

■ To calculate x as a percentage of y: $\dfrac{x}{y} \times 100$

■ To calculate x percent of y: 1% of $y = \dfrac{y}{100}$ so x % of $y = x \times \dfrac{y}{100}$ $= y \times \left(\dfrac{x}{100}\right)$

■ The $\left(\dfrac{x}{100}\right)$ part of the last expression is the **multiplying factor**.

■ 5% of a quantity can be found by using a multiplying factor of 0.05.

■ 95% of a quantity can be found by using a multiplying factor of 0.95 and so on.

■ 'Per annum' (p.a.) is frequently used and means 'per year'.

■ To increase a quantity by R%, multiply it by $1 + \dfrac{R}{100}$

■ To decrease a quantity by R%, multiply it by $1 - \dfrac{R}{100}$

PERCENTAGE CHANGE	MULTIPLYING FACTOR
+15%	1.15
+85%	1.85
−15%	0.85
−85%	0.15

COMPOUND PERCENTAGES

The interest (money gained) on savings accounts in banks and building societies is often **compound interest**. In the words of Albert Einstein, a Nobel Prize winning scientist:

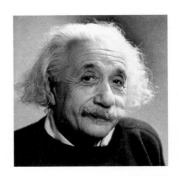

'Compound interest is the eighth wonder of the world.
He who understands it, earns it ... he who does not ... pays it.'

Compound percentages are used when one percentage change is followed by another in a calculation.

EXAMPLE 1

SKILLS

ADAPTIVE
LEARNING

Stanislav makes an investment of $500 which pays him 8% p.a. compound interest for three years. Find the value of his investment at the end of this period.

The multiplying factor for an 8% increase is $1 + \dfrac{8}{100} = 1.08$

Let the value of the investment be v.

$v = \$500 \times 1.08$ After 1 yr

$v = \$500 \times 1.08 \times 1.08 = \$500 \times 1.08^2$ After 2 yrs

$v = \$500 \times 1.08 \times 1.08 \times 1.08 = \$500 \times 1.08^3$ After 3 yrs

Stanislav's investment is worth $629.86

Note: in the period of the investment, the interest earned has not been removed so that it also earns interest in the next year and the following years.

KEY POINTS

- To increase a quantity by $R\%$ p.a. for n years, multiply it by $\left(1 + \dfrac{R}{100}\right)^n$

- To decrease a quantity by $R\%$ p.a. for n years, multiply it by $\left(1 - \dfrac{R}{100}\right)^n$

PERCENTAGE CHANGE p.a.	n YEARS	MULTIPLYING FACTOR
+15% (appreciation)	5	$(1.15)^5$
−15% (depreciation)	10	$(0.85)^{10}$

EXAMPLE 2

SKILLS

REASONING

When a cup of coffee at 100°C cools down, it loses 12% of its current temperature per minute.

What will the temperature be after 10 mins?

Let the temperature of the cup of coffee after 10 mins be t.

$t = 100 \times (1 - 0.12)^{10} = 100 \times (0.88)^{10}$

$t = 27.9°C$

EXERCISE 1

1 ▶ Copy and complete the following table.

ORIGINAL VALUE	COMPOUND PERCENTAGE p.a.	TIME (yrs)	NEW VALUE
100	+2	3	
500	+4	5	
360	+6	7	
1250	+8	9	

2 ▶ Copy and complete the following table.

ORIGINAL VALUE	COMPOUND PERCENTAGE p.a.	TIME (yrs)	NEW VALUE
100	−2	3	
500	−4	5	
360	−6	7	
1250	−8	9	

3 ▶ Alec invests £12 000 at 3% compound interest p.a. Find how much he will have after
  a 3 years   **b** 5 years   **c** 10 years

4 ▶ Honor invests $2000 at 5% compound interest p.a. Find how much she will have after
  a 2 years   **b** 4 years   **c** 10 years

5 ▶ Mhairi invests €1000 for 5 years at 4% compound interest p.a. Calculate how much interest she has gained over the 5 years.

6 ▶ Stonebank Town has a population of 7500. The population is expected to increase at 2% each year for the next 5 years. Work out an estimate for the population of Stonebank Town after 5 years.

7 ▶ An ancient Egyptian jewel is valued at $1 million. Its value increases by 7% each year. What is its value after 4 years?

8 ▶ A car is bought for €50 000. The value of the car **depreciates** by 5% each year. What is the value of the car after 5 years?

EXERCISE 1*

1 ▶ Copy and complete the following table.

ORIGINAL VALUE (€)	COMPOUND PERCENTAGE p.a.	TIME (yrs)	NEW VALUE (€)
	+12	3	180
	+8	12	5000
	−15	5	6000
	−5	10	1000

2 ▶ A computer touchpad is bought for £1800. Its value depreciates by 6% each year. What is the value of the touchpad after 3 years?

3 ▶　An ancient Roman Mosaic is valued at €2 million.
Its value increases by 8% each year.
What is its value after 10 years?

4 ▶　Hyperland has a **rate** of inflation of 12% p.a.
compound interest. If a cup of coffee costs €5, find
how much a cup of coffee will cost in Hyperland in
20 years' time.

5 ▶　Sealand has a rate of deflation of 12% p.a.
compound interest. If a luxury yacht is purchased for
$40 million, find how much this yacht will be worth in
20 years' time.

6 ▶　If Emperor Nero had invested 1 cent (in euros) at 1% p.a. compound interest in the year
0 AD, what would it be worth in € after 2016 years?

7 ▶　Shakira invests $500 000 at 5% compound interest p.a.
Calculate how many years it takes for her investment to double in value.

8 ▶　A helicopter is bought for £5 million. Its value depreciates by 7% each year.
How many years will it take for the value to halve?

ACTIVITY 1

Heinz makes two investments each of €100 value for five years.

Investment I:　　€100 at 5% p.a. compound interest

Investment II:　　€100 at 10% p.a. compound interest

Copy and complete the table to the nearest euro.

NUMBER OF YEARS n	0	1	2	3	4	5
INVESTMENT I (€)	100			109		116
INVESTMENT II (€)	100			123		140

Draw a graph of the value of the investments v (€) against number of years n (years) for
$90 \leq v \leq 170$ and $0 \leq n \leq 5$. (Draw two lines of each investment on the same graph.)

Are these graphs curves or straight lines?

Use your graph to estimate when each
investment has increased by 25%.

HINT

**See the shape of
the graphs drawn
and the numbers
in the table.**

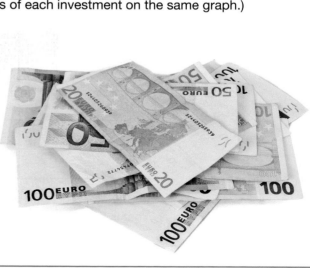

INVERSE PERCENTAGES

Inverse operations can be used to find an original amount after a percentage increase or decrease. If a distance of x km is increased by 10% and its new value is 495 km, finding the original value is simple.

EXAMPLE 3

SKILLS

REASONING

A house in Portugal is sold for €138 000, giving a profit of 15%.

Find the original price that the owner paid for the house.

Let €x be the original price.

$x \times 1.15 = 138\,000$ [Selling price after a 15% increase]

$x = \dfrac{138\,000}{1.15}$

$x = €120\,000$

EXAMPLE 4

An ancient Japanese book is sold for ¥34 000 (yen), giving a loss of 15%.

Find the original price that the owner paid for the book.

Let ¥x be the original price.

$x \times 0.85 = 34\,000$ [Selling price after a 15% decrease]

$x = \dfrac{34\,000}{0.85}$

$x = ¥40\,000$

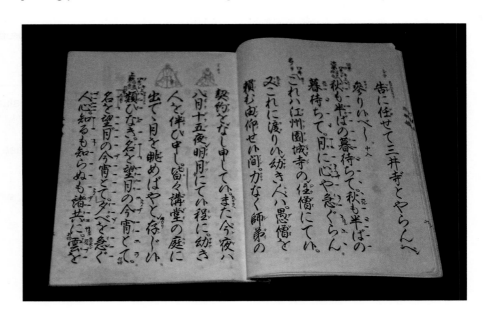

EXERCISE 2

1 ▶ A pair of shoes is sold for $48 at a profit of 20%. Find the original price of the shoes.

2 ▶ A shirt is sold for $33 at a profit of 10%. Find the original price of the shirt.

3 ▶ Find the price of this set of drawers before the reduction.

SALE PRICE $54 10% OFF!

4 ▶ A picture is sold for $32, making a loss of 20%. Find the original price of the picture.

5 ▶ The value of a bracelet increases by 6% to €78.56. Find the original value.

6 ▶ A house is sold for €234 000, which gives a profit of 12%. Find the actual profit.

7 ▶ A computer loses 32% of its value in the first year. It is worth $1650 after one year. How much was it bought for, to the nearest $?

8 ▶ A garden chair is sold for $25.30 at a profit of 10%. Find the original price of the chair.

9 ▶ The price of a house is reduced by 15% to $153 000.
What was the original price of the house?

10 ▶ A vase is bought for $23.50, which includes a profit of 17.5%.
Calculate the amount of profit.

EXERCISE 2*

1 ▶ A rare stamp is worth $81 after an increase in value of 35%. What was its value before the increase?

2 ▶ A mobile phone is valued at $220 after a decrease in value of 45%. What was its value before the decrease?

3 ▶ A seed is planted. It grows to a height of 45 cm, which is 72% of its maximum height. Find its maximum height.

4 ▶ A farm is sold for €457 000, which gives a profit of 19%. Find the profit.

5 ▶ A valuable watch has an original price of $x. It is sold for $5304 after its original price has been increased by 2% and then by 4%. Find x.

6 ▶ A Giant Redwood Tree is x m tall. It grows by 5% and then by 8% to reach a height of 22.68 m. Find x.

7 ▶ Zara's Physics test **mean** was x%. It is now 78.2% after an increase of 15% and a decrease of 15%. Find x.

8 ▶ A room in an exclusive Dubai Hotel cost $x per night. The price then changes to $4370 per night after a decrease of 5% and an increase of 15%. Find x.

9 ▶ Baseball star Babe Ruth's shirt sold for $4 338 500 at auction. Its value three years before the sale, $x, had **appreciated** by 5% p.a. compound interest. Find x.

10 ▶ The violin that was played while the Titanic sank was sold for £900 000. Its value, £y, five years before the **sale** depreciated by 2% p.a. compound interest for five years. Find y.

EXERCISE 3   REVISION

1 ▶ Increase 2500 RM (Malaysian Ringgit) by 12%.

2 ▶ Decrease 5000 ₹ (Indian Rupee) by 12%.

3 ▶ A rare book is worth £1.5 million (Egyptian pounds) and appreciates by 12.5%. Find its new value.

4 ▶ A cost of petrol depreciates by 6% from $2 (Singapore dollar) per litre. Find its new value.

5 ▶ Ian invests £12 000 for 5 years with a compound interest of 5% p.a.. Find the value of his investment after 5 years.

6 ▶ David buys a new racing bike for £x. He then sells it for £1584 making a loss of 12%. Find x.

EXERCISE 3*   **REVISION**

1 ▶ Ryan has an investment of 10 000 ¥ (Chinese Yen) which increases by 15% then decreases by 15%. What is it worth now after both changes?

2 ▶ Charlotte has an investment of €1 million which decreases by 8% then increases by 10%. What is it worth now after both changes?

3 ▶ Rufus buys a diamond ring for 60 000 ₦ (Nigerian Naira). After one year its value is inflated by 7%. Find its new value.

4 ▶ Riko buys a new jet-ski for $12 500 (Australian dollars). After one year its value is deflated by 9%. Find its new value.

5 ▶ Nicola invests £8000 for 3 years at 5% per annum compound interest.

    a Calculate the value of her investment at the end of 3 years.

Jim invests a sum of money for 30 years at 4% per annum compound interest.

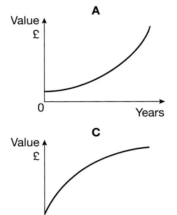

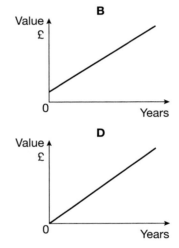

    b Write down the letter of the graph which best shows how the value of Jim's investment changes over the 30 years.

Hannah invested an amount of money in an account paying 5% per annum compound interest. After 1 year the value of her investment was £3885.

    c Work out the amount of money that Hannah invested.

6 ▶ Axel buys a ski-chalet for 950 000 kr (Swedish Krona). Its value 10 years before the sale was x kr and this appreciated by 5% p.a. compound interest for 10 years before Axel bought it. Find x.

EXAM PRACTICE: NUMBER 4

1
  a Increase $1200 by 12%.
  b Decrease $1200 by 12%.   **[4]**

2
A valuable painting has an original price of €25 000. It gains in value by 8% and a year later by a further 5%. Find the value of the painting after both price increases.   **[3]**

3
An exclusive apartment in San Francisco has an original price of $1 million. It loses value by 15% and one year later by a further 3%. Find the value of the apartment after both price decreases.   **[3]**

4
A Premier League footballer is valued at £30 million and after a bad season his transfer value depreciates by 20%. His next season is a good one and his transfer value now appreciates by 20%.

Find the value of the footballer after his good season.   **[3]**

5
The Graff Pink is the most expensive diamond in the world. In 2010 it was sold in Switzerland for $46 158 674. If it appreciated for the next 5 years at 7% p.a. what was the value of the diamond after 5 years?   **[4]**

6
A cheetah can run at a maximum speed of 113 km/h. The cheetah loses 7% of its maximum speed each year. Find the cheetah's maximum speed after 5 years.   **[4]**

7
An ancient sculpture is valued at €x. It appreciates by 2% p.a. for 2 years, then depreciates by 3% p.a. for 3 years and is then sold for €5 million. Find x.   **[4]**

[Total 25 marks]

CHAPTER SUMMARY: NUMBER 4

COMPOUND PERCENTAGES

'Per annum' (p.a.) is frequently used and means 'per year'.

'Appreciation' (inflation: prices increase) means a gain in value while 'depreciation' (deflation: prices decrease) means a loss in value over a period of time.

To increase a quantity by R% p.a. for n years, multiply it by $\left(1+\dfrac{R}{100}\right)^n$

To decrease a quantity by R% p.a. for n years, multiply it by $\left(1-\dfrac{R}{100}\right)^n$

PERCENTAGE CHANGE p.a.	n YEARS	MULTIPLYING FACTOR
+5% (appreciation)	3	$(1.05)^3$
–5% (depreciation)	7	$(0.95)^7$

INVERSE PERCENTAGES

To calculate the original amount, divide by the multiplying factor.

- A sun-hat is sold at a discount of 25% for €15.

  Find the original price of the sun-hat.

  Let €p be the original price. $p \times 0.75 = 15$ $p = \dfrac{15}{0.75} = 20$

  Original price = €20

- A drone is sold for €1750 making a profit of 25%.

  Find the original price of the drone.

  Let €p be the original price. $p \times 1.25 = 1750$ $p = \dfrac{1750}{1.25} = 1400$

  Original price = €1400

ALGEBRA 4

Al'Khwarizmi was an Islamic mathematician and astronomer who lived in Baghdad during the ninth century. He wrote the first algebra book called *Al-jabr wa'l Muqabalah*; this is where the word 'algebra' comes from. The title translates as 'restoring and balancing' which refers to the way equations are solved in algebra. He was one of the first people to use the symbol zero. The word 'algorithm' comes from his name.

▲ Statue of Al'Khwarizmi in Uzbekistan

LEARNING OBJECTIVES

■ Substitute numbers into formulae   ■ Change the subject of a formula

BASIC PRINCIPLES

■ When solving equations, isolate the unknown letter by systematically doing the same operation to both sides.

■ Use your calculator to evaluate expressions to a certain number of **significant figures** or decimal places.

USING FORMULAE

A formula is a way of describing a relationship using algebra.

The formula to calculate the volume of a cylindrical can is $V = \pi r^2 h$ where V is the volume, r is the radius and h is the height.

| EXAMPLE 1 | Find the volume of a cola can that has a radius of 3 cm and a height of 11 cm. |

SKILLS

PROBLEM SOLVING

Facts: $r = 3$ cm, $h = 11$ cm, $V = ?$ cm^3

Equation: $V = \pi r^2 h$

Substitution: $V = \pi \times 3^2 \times 11$

Working: $\pi \times 3^2 \times 11 = \pi \times 9 \times 11 = 311$ cm^3 (3 s.f.)

Volume = 311 cm^3 (3 s.f.)

KEY POINTS

When using any formula:

• Write down the facts with the correct units.

• Write down the equation.

• Substitute the facts.

• Do the working.

SOME COMMONLY-USED FORMULAE

You will need these formulae to complete the following exercises.

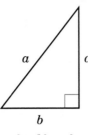

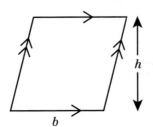

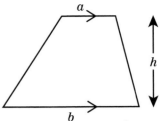

$a^2 = b^2 + c^2$ Area of **parallelogram** $= bh$ Area of **trapezium** $= \dfrac{h}{2}(a+b)$

Area of a triangle $= \dfrac{1}{2} \times$ base $\times$ height   Speed $= \dfrac{\text{distance}}{\text{time}}$

For a circle of **radius** r: **Circumference** $= 2\pi r$ Area $= \pi r^2$

ACTIVITY 1

SKILLS

REASONING

Prove the formulae for the area of a parallelogram and the area of a trapezium.

EXERCISE 1

1 ▶ The area of a parallelogram is 31.5 cm² and its base is 7 cm long. Find its height.

2 ▶ The radius of a circle is 7 cm. Find the circumference of the circle and its area.

3 ▶ The area of this triangle is 72 cm². Find its height h.

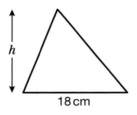

4 ▶ Find YZ.

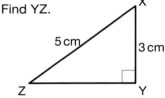

5 ▶ The area of this trapezium is 21.62 cm². Find its height h.

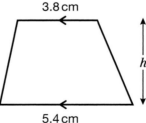

6 ▶ A ship travels 6 km north-west and then 10 km north-east. How far is the ship from its starting point?

7 ▶ It takes light $8\frac{1}{3}$ minutes to reach the Earth from the Sun. Calculate the distance between the Sun and the Earth if light travels at 300 000 km/s.

8 ▶ The Earth, which is 150 million km from the Sun, takes 365 days to complete one orbit. (Assume the orbit to be a circle.)

　a Find the length of one orbit, giving your answer in **standard form correct to 3 significant figures**.

　b Find the speed of the Earth around the Sun in km per hour correct to 2 significant figures.

EXERCISE 1*

1 ▶ The circumference of a circle is 88 cm. Find its radius.

2 ▶ This arrowhead has an area of 35 cm². Find the length x.

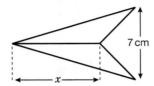

7 cm

x

3 ▶ The area of this trapezium is 30.8 cm². Find its height h.

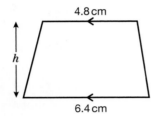

4.8 cm

h

6.4 cm

4 ▶ The diagram shows the **cross-section** of a metal pipe. Find the area of the shaded part correct to 3 significant figures.

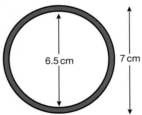

6.5 cm   7 cm

5 ▶ Calculate the distance between the points (3, 2) and (−2, −1). Give your answer correct to 3 significant figures.

6 ▶ Find the area of the shaded region in each of the diagrams correct to 3 significant figures. Use your answers to work out the shaded region of a similar figure with 100 identical circles.

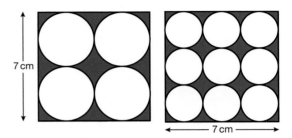

7 cm

7 cm

7 ▶ Because the Earth rotates, a point on the equator is moving at 1660 km/hour. Find the circumference of the Earth at the equator, correct to 3 significant figures.

8 ▶ A triangle has sides of 5 cm, 3.3 cm and 6 cm. What type of triangle is it: **obtuse**, **acute** or right-angled?

9 ▶ Calculate the height of an **equilateral triangle** which has the same area as a circle with a circumference of 10 cm. Give your answer correct to 3 significant figures.

10 ▶ The area of the shaded region is 20 cm². Find the value of x, correct to 3 significant figures.

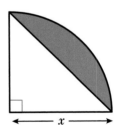

x

CHANGE OF SUBJECT

SUBJECT OCCURS ONCE

It is sometimes helpful to write an equation or formula in a different way. To draw the graph of $2y - 4 = 3x$ it is easier to make a table of values if y is the subject, meaning if $y = \ldots$

Example 2 shows how to do this. Example 3 shows how a similar equation is solved.

EXAMPLE 2 Make y the subject of the equation $2y - 4 = 3x$.

$2y - 4 = 3x$ (Add 4 to both sides)

$\quad 2y = 3x + 4$ (Divide both sides by 2)

$\quad y = \dfrac{3x + 4}{2}$ (**Simplify**)

$\quad y = \dfrac{3}{2}x + 2$ (y is now the subject of the equation)

EXAMPLE 3 Solve $2y - 4 = 2$.

$2y - 4 = 2$ (Add 4 to both sides)

$\quad 2y = 6$ (Divide both sides by 2)

$\quad y = 3$

KEY POINT

- To rearrange an equation or formula, apply the same rules that are used to solve equations.

EXERCISE 2 Make x the subject of these equations.

1 ▶ $x + 2 = a$ **5** ▶ $3x + a = b$ **9** ▶ $x(a + b) = c$

2 ▶ $x - p = 5$ **6** ▶ $t - 2x = s$ **10** ▶ $8b + cx = d$

3 ▶ $c = x + a$ **7** ▶ $ax + b = 4$ **11** ▶ $3(x + b) = a$

4 ▶ $5x = b$ **8** ▶ $f = ex - g$ **12** ▶ $a(x + b) = c$

13 ▶ $a = \dfrac{x}{b}$ **15** ▶ $p + q = \dfrac{x}{r}$

14 ▶ $\dfrac{px}{q} = r$ **16** ▶ $\dfrac{x + p}{q} = r$

EXERCISE 2* Make x the subject of these equations.

1 ▶ $ax + b = c$ **5** ▶ $P = \pi x + b^2$ **9** ▶ $\dfrac{a}{x} = b$

2 ▶ $d = \dfrac{x - b}{c}$ **6** ▶ $\dfrac{bx}{d^2} = T$ **10** ▶ $\dfrac{a + b}{x} = c$

3 ▶ $c = \dfrac{bx}{d}$ **7** ▶ $\pi - x = b$ **11** ▶ $p = q + \dfrac{s}{x}$

4 ▶ $a(x + c) = e$ **8** ▶ $ab - dx = c$

Change the subject of each formula to the letter given in brackets.

12 ▶ $A = 2\pi r$ (r) **15** ▶ $v^2 = u^2 + 2as$ (s) **18** ▶ $S = \dfrac{a(1-r^n)}{1-r}$ (a)

13 ▶ $V = \dfrac{1}{3}\pi r^2 h$ (h) **16** ▶ $m = \dfrac{1}{2}(a+b)$ (a)

14 ▶ $y = mx + c$ (x) **17** ▶ $S = \dfrac{n}{2}\{2a+(n-1)d\}$ (a)

POWER OF SUBJECT OCCURS OR SUBJECT OCCURS TWICE

EXAMPLE 4

Make x the subject of the equation $ax^2 + b = c$.

$ax^2 + b = c$ (Subtract b from both sides)

$\quad ax^2 = c - b$ (Divide both sides by a)

$\quad x^2 = \dfrac{c-b}{a}$ (Square root both sides)

$\quad x = \pm\sqrt{\dfrac{c-b}{a}}$

EXAMPLE 5

Make x the subject of the equation $ax + bx = c$.

$ax + bx = c$

x appears twice in the equation. **Factorise** the left-hand side so x appears only once.

$x(a+b) = c$ (Divide both sides by $(a+b)$)

$\quad x = \dfrac{c}{(a+b)}$

KEY POINT

• When the letter that will become the subject appears twice in the formula, one of the steps will involve factorising.

EXERCISE 3

Make x the subject of these equations.

1 ▶ $ax^2 = b$ **4** ▶ $\dfrac{x^2}{a} + b = c$ **7** ▶ $a(x-b) = x$

2 ▶ $\dfrac{x^2}{a} = b$ **5** ▶ $ax^2 + 2b = c$ **8** ▶ $a(x+1) = b(x+2)$

3 ▶ $x^2 + C = 2D$ **6** ▶ $ax + dx = t$

Change the subject of each formula to the letter given in brackets.

9 ▶ $A = 4\pi r^2$ (r) **11** ▶ $V = \dfrac{4}{3}\pi r^3$ (r)

10 ▶ $a = \dfrac{v^2}{r}$ (v) **12** ▶ $T = 2\pi\sqrt{l}$ (l)

EXERCISE 3*

Make x the subject of these equations.

1 ▶ $Rx^2 = S$ **5 ▶** $\tan b + a(x + c) = x$

2 ▶ $g = cx^2 + a$ **6 ▶** $p = \sqrt{s + \dfrac{x}{t}}$

3 ▶ $ax = bx - c$

7 ▶ $\dfrac{Ab - x^2}{D} = a$

4 ▶ $c - dx = ex + f$

Change the subject of each formula to the letter given in brackets.

8 ▶ $V = \dfrac{1}{3}\pi r^2 h$ (r) **13 ▶** $F = \dfrac{k}{\sqrt[3]{d}}$ (d)

9 ▶ $mgh = \dfrac{1}{2}mv^2$ (v) **14 ▶** $y = \dfrac{1}{\sqrt{1 - x^2}}$ (x)

10 ▶ $y = \dfrac{1}{a^2 + x^2}$ (x) **15 ▶** $x = \dfrac{-b + \sqrt{b^2 - 4ac}}{2a}$ (c)

11 ▶ $s = \dfrac{1}{12}(b - a)^2$ (a) **16 ▶** $y = \dfrac{x + p}{x - p}$ (x)

12 ▶ $r = \dfrac{S}{\sqrt{PQ}}$ (Q)

FURTHER FORMULAE

EXAMPLE 6

SKILLS

PROBLEM SOLVING

The volume V m³ of a pyramid with a square base of length a m and a height of h m is given by $V = \dfrac{1}{3}a^2 h$.

a Find the volume of the Great Pyramid of Cheops, where $a = 232$ m and $h = 147$ m.

b Another square-based pyramid has a volume of 853 000 m³ and a height of 100 m. Find the length of the side of the base.

---

a $V = \dfrac{1}{3} \times 232^2 \times 147 = 2\,640\,000$ m³ to 3 s.f.

b   Make a the subject of the formula: $a^2 = 3\dfrac{V}{h} \Rightarrow a = \sqrt{\dfrac{3V}{h}}$

    $a = \sqrt{\dfrac{3 \times 853000}{100}} \Rightarrow a = 160$ m to 3 s.f.

KEY POINT

• When using a formula, rearrange the formula if necessary.

ACTIVITY 2

SKILLS

INTERPRETATION

The period, T seconds, for a pendulum of length L metres to swing backwards and forwards is given by the formula

$$T = 2\pi\sqrt{\frac{L}{g}}$$

where g is the acceleration due to gravity = 9.81 m/s².

What is the period of a pendulum 1 km long? (Give your answer correct to 1 **decimal place**.)

Show that, when L is made the subject, the formula becomes

$$L = g\left(\frac{T}{2\pi}\right)^2$$

Use the rearranged formula to complete this table, giving your answers correct to 2 significant figures.

Period	1 s	10 s	1 minute	1 hour	1 day
Length					

EXERCISE 4

1 ▶ The area A cm² of a triangle with base b cm and height h cm is given by

$$A = \frac{bh}{2}$$

  a Find A when $b = 12$ and $h = 3$.

  b Find h when $A = 25$ and $b = 5$.

2 ▶ The increase in length e cm of an aluminium bar of length l cm when heated by T degrees Celsius is $e = 0.00003lT$.

  a Find e when $l = 100$ and $T = 50$.

  b Find T when $l = 150$ and $e = 0.9$.

3 ▶ The time, T minutes, to cook a piece of meat weighing w kg is $T = 45w + 20$.

  a Find the time to cook a piece weighing 3 kg.

  b Find the weight of a piece of meat that took 110 minutes to cook.

4 ▶ A formula to calculate income tax I in $ for a salary of $$S$ is $I = 0.2(S - 8250)$.

  a Find I when $S = 20000$.

  b Find S when $I = 3500$.

5 ▶ **a** Find the formulae for the area A and the **perimeter** P of the shape shown.

  b Find the area and perimeter when $r = 5$ cm.

  c Find r when $A = 100$ cm².

  d Find r when $P = 50$ cm.

  e Find the value of r that makes $A = P$ numerically.

EXERCISE 4*

1 ▶ The area A cm² of a ring with outer radius R cm and inner radius r cm is given by

$A = \pi(R^2 - r^2)$.

a Find A when $R = 12$ and $r = 6$.

b Find R when $A = 37.7$ and $r = 2$.

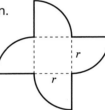

2 ▶ The stopping distance d m of a car travelling at v km/h is given by $d = 0.0065v^2 + 0.75v$.

a Find the stopping distance of a car travelling at 50 km/h.

b Estimate the speed of a car which takes 100 m to stop.

3 ▶ The distance d km that a person can see when at a height of h metres above the surface of the sea is given by

$d = \sqrt{12.8h}$

a Find how far a person can see when $h = 20$ m.

b How many metres up does a person have to be to see 50 km?

4 ▶ $\dfrac{1}{f} = \dfrac{1}{u} + \dfrac{1}{v}$ is a formula used in the science of optics.

a Find f when $u = 10$ and $v = 20$.

b Find u when $v = 30$ and $f = 12$.

5 ▶ **a** Find the formulae for the area and the perimeter of the shape shown.

b Find the area and perimeter when $r = 8$ cm.

c Find r when $A = 100$ cm².

d Find r when $P = 40$ cm.

e Find the value of r that makes $A = P$ numerically.

EXERCISE 5

REVISION

Make x the subject of these equations.

1 ▶ $ax = b$

2 ▶ $\dfrac{x}{c} = a$

3 ▶ $bx + c = a$

Make y the subject of these equations.

4 ▶ $by^2 = d$

5 ▶ $\sqrt{ay} = b$

6 ▶ $ay - cy = d$

7 ▶ $c(y - b) = y$

8 ▶ From a height h metres above sea level, the horizon appears to be $1.6\sqrt{4.9h}$ kilometres away.

a What is the distance, correct to 2 significant figures, to the horizon from the top of a 100 m high cliff?

b How high must you be to see 50 km to the horizon? Give your answer correct to 2 significant figures.

c You are sitting on the beach with your eye 1.8 m above sea level, and you can just see the top of a cruise ship. The cruise ship is 40 m high. How far out to sea is the cruise ship? Give your answer to the nearest kilometre.

9 ▶ Elise is organising a party. The caterer tells her that the cost C dollars of each meal when n meals are supplied is given by

$$C = 20 + \frac{300}{n} \, .$$

a Find the cost of each meal if 50 people come to the party.

b How many people must come if the cost of each meal is to be less than $23?

c What must Elise pay the caterer if 75 meals are provided?

10 ▶ The shape shown is two quarter-circles of radius r cm.

a Find the formulae for the area A cm² and the perimeter P cm of the shape.

b Find the area and perimeter when $r = 5$ cm.

c Find r when $A = 20$ cm².

d Find r when $P = 60$ cm.

e Find the value of r that makes $A = P$ numerically.

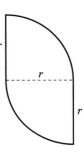

EXERCISE 5*

REVISION

Make x the subject of these equations.

1 ▶ $c - ax = b$

2 ▶ $\dfrac{b}{x} + d = a$

3 ▶ $a(b - x) = \tan c$

Make y the subject of these equations.

4 ▶ $\dfrac{a}{y^2} + c = b$

5 ▶ $a(y - c) + d = by$

6 ▶ $c = a + \sqrt{\dfrac{b - y}{d}}$

7 ▶ The shape shown is a right-angled triangle together with two quarter-circles of radius r cm.

a Find the formulae for the area A and the perimeter P of the shape.

b Find the area and perimeter when $r = 3$ cm.

c Find r when $A = 12$ cm².

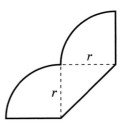

d Find r when $P = 34\,$cm.

e Find the value of r that makes $A = P$ numerically.

8 ▶ A rubber ball is dropped onto the floor from a height of h metres. The time taken for it to stop bouncing is t seconds. This is given by the formula

$$t = \left(\frac{1+e}{1-e}\right)\sqrt{\frac{h}{5}}$$

where e is a number that measures the 'bounciness' of the rubber ball.

When dropped from a height of 1.25 m, it bounces for 2.5 s.

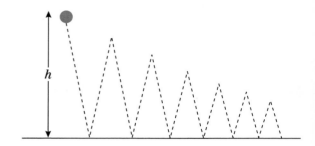

a Find the value of e.

b For how long would the rubber ball bounce if it was dropped from a height of 1.8 m?

c The same rubber ball is dropped again, and this time it bounces for 3.5 s. Find the height that it was dropped from.

Q9 HINT

Volume of cone is $\frac{1}{3}$ shaded area × height.

Volume of cylinder is shaded area × length.

9 ▶ The cone and the cylinder have the same volume. Find the **ratio** $x : y$.

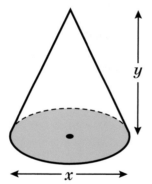

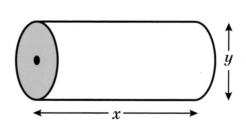

10 ▶ The **tangent** t of the angle between two straight lines with **gradients** m_1 and m_2 is given by

$$t = \frac{m_1 - m_2}{1 + m_1 m_2}$$

a Find t when $m_1 = 2$ and $m_2 = \frac{1}{2}$.

b Make m_2 the subject of the formula.

c If $t = 0.5$ and $m_1 = 3$, find m_2.

EXAM PRACTICE: ALGEBRA 4

1 Make x the subject of the equations.

   a $d - 3x = f$

   b $p = 2(q + x)$

   c $\dfrac{x + a}{b} = c$ **[6]**

2 Make x the subject of the formulae.

   a $x^2 - B = 3C$

   b $\dfrac{x^2}{y} - z = a$

   c $p(x - q) = x$ **[9]**

3 The formula connecting distance travelled (s), initial speed (u), time (t) and acceleration (a) is

$$s = ut + \frac{1}{2}at^2$$

   a Make a the subject of the formula.

   b Calculate a if $s = 100\,\text{m}$, $u = 2\,\text{m/s}$ and $t = 5$ secs.   **[4]**

4 The shape shown is a semicircle of radius r.

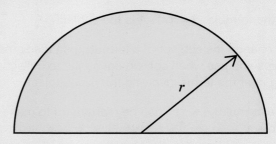

   a Find the formula for the perimeter P.

   b Find the formula for the area A.

   c Find the value of r that makes $A = P$ numerically.   **[6]**

Q4 HINT
For a circle of radius r, $C = 2\pi r$ and $A = \pi r^2$.

[Total 25 marks]

CHAPTER SUMMARY: ALGEBRA 4

CHANGE OF SUBJECT

A formula is a way of describing a relationship between two or more different quantities.

A formula has an equals sign and letters to represent the different quantities.

The subject of a formula is the letter on its own on one side of the equals sign.

In the formula $A = \pi r^2$, A is the subject.

To change the subject of a formula, use the same steps you use when solving equations to collect together the terms involving the new subject.

The formula $A = \pi r^2$ can be rearranged to make r the subject:

$$r^2 = \frac{A}{\pi} \Rightarrow r = \sqrt{\frac{A}{\pi}}$$

USING FORMULAE

The volume of a cylinder is given by $V = \pi r^2 h$.

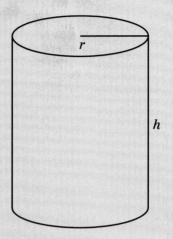

Find r when $V = 600 \, \text{cm}^3$ and $h = 12 \, \text{cm}$.

Facts: $V = 600 \, \text{cm}^3$, $h = 12 \, \text{cm}$, $r = ?$

Equation: $V = \pi r^2 h$

Rearrange: $r^2 = \dfrac{V}{\pi h} \Rightarrow r = \sqrt{\dfrac{V}{\pi h}}$

Substitute: $r = \sqrt{\dfrac{600}{\pi \times 12}}$

Working: $r = 3.99 \, \text{cm}$ (3 s.f.)

GRAPHS 4

Quadratic curves are natural, beautiful shapes that appear in many places.

They can be used to represent the path of objects moving through the air, such as an arrow or the path of a basketball when someone is shooting hoops.

The early Babylonian mathematicians (2000 years BC) wrote equations on stone tablets for areas of squares that are related to quadratic graphs.

LEARNING OBJECTIVES

- Recognise and draw graphs of quadratic functions
- Interpret quadratic graphs relating to real-life situations
- Use graphs to solve quadratic equations

BASIC PRINCIPLES

- You have seen how to plot straight lines of type $y = mx + c$; but, in reality, many graphs are curved.

- Quadratic curves are those in which the highest power of x is x^2, and they produce curves called parabolas.

- Quadratic graphs are those of type $y = ax^2 + bx + c$, where a, b and c are constants.

- They are simple to draw either manually or with the use of a calculator.

QUADRATIC GRAPHS $y = ax^2 + bx + c$

ACTIVITY 1

SKILL: ANALYSIS

Mathematicians and scientists often try to find a formula to connect two quantities. The first step is usually to plot the graph. For these three graphs, which are parts of quadratic curves, suggest two quantities from real life that might be plotted as x and y to produce the shapes of graphs shown here.

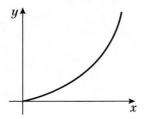
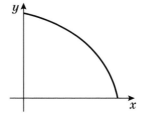
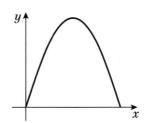

EXAMPLE 1

SKILLS

REASONING

Plot the curve $y = 2x^2 - 3x - 2$ in the **range** $-2 \leq x \leq 4$.

Construct a table of values and plot a graph from it.

x	−2	−1	0	1	2	3	4
$2x^2$	8	2	0	2	8	18	32
$-3x$	6	3	0	−3	−6	−9	−12
-2	−2	−2	−2	−2	−2	−2	−2
y	12	3	−2	−3	0	7	18

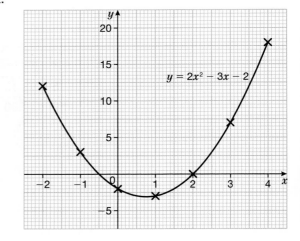

EXAMPLE 2

SKILLS

REASONING

Plot the curve $y = -3x^2 + 3x + 6$ in the range $-2 \leq x \leq 3$.

Construct a table of values and plot a graph from it.

x	−2	−1	0	1	2	3
$-3x^2$	−12	−3	0	−3	−12	−27
$+3x$	−6	−3	0	3	6	9
$+6$	6	6	6	6	6	6
y	−12	0	6	6	0	−12

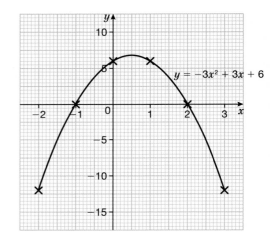

Some calculators have functions that enable fast and accurate plotting of points. It is worth checking whether or not your calculator has this facility.

A number of quadratic graphs will have real-life applications.

EXAMPLE 3

SKILLS

MODELLING

Adiel keeps goats, and she wants to use a piece of land beside a straight stone wall for the goats. The area of this land must be rectangular in shape, and it will be surrounded by a fence of total length 50 m.

a What dimensions of this rectangle will provide the goats with the largest area of land?

b What range of values can the rectangle width (x m) take in order for the enclosed area to be at least 250 m²?

If the total fence length is 50 m, the dimensions of the rectangle are x by $(50 - 2x)$. Let the area enclosed be A m².

$$A = x(50 - 2x)$$
$$\Rightarrow \quad A = 50x - 2x^2$$

Construct a table of values and plot a graph from it.

x	0	5	10	15	20	25
$50x$	0	250	500	750	1000	1250
$-2x^2$	0	−50	−200	−450	−800	−1250
A	0	200	300	300	200	0

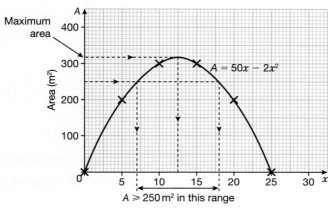

Rectangle width (m)

The solutions can be read from the graph.

a The maximum enclosed area is when $x = 12.5$ m, giving dimensions of 12.5 m by 25 m, and an area of 313 m² (to 3 s.f.).

b If $A \geq 250$ m², x must be in the range $7 \leq x \leq 18$ approximately.

- Expressions of the type $y = ax^2 + bx + c$ are called quadratics. When they are plotted, they produce parabolas.

- If $a > 0$, the curve is U-shaped.   • If $a < 0$, the curve is an **inverted** U shape.

- Plot enough points in order to draw a smooth curve, especially where the curve turns.

- Do not connect the points with straight lines. Plotting intermediate points will show you that this is incorrect.

EXERCISE 1

Draw a graph for each equation after completing a suitable table between the stated x values.

1 ▶ $y = x^2 + 2$ for $-3 \le x \le 3$

2 ▶ $y = x^2 + 2x$ for $-3 \le x \le 3$

Draw a graph for each equation between the stated x values after copying and completing these tables.

3 ▶ $y = x^2 + x + 2$ for $-3 \le x \le 2$

x	−3	−2	−1	0	1	2
x^2	9			0		4
x	−3			0		2
2	2			2		2
y	8			2		8

4 ▶ $y = 2x^2 + 3x + 2$ for $-3 \le x \le 2$

x	−3	−2	−1	0	1	2
y	11			2		16

5 ▶ A water container has a square base of side length x metres and a height of 2 m.

a Show that the volume V, in cubic metres, of water in a full container is given by the formula $V = 2x^2$.

b Copy and complete this table, and use it to draw the graph of V against x.

x (m)	0	0.4	0.8	1.2	1.6	2.0
V (m³)	0					8

c Use your graph to estimate the dimensions of the base that give a volume of 4 m³.

d What volume of water could be held by the container if its base area is 0.36 m²?

e A hotel needs a water container to hold at least 3 m³. For the container to fit into the storage room its side length cannot be more than 1.8 m. What range of x values enables the container to fit into the storage room?

6 ▶ On a Big-Dipper ride at a funfair, the height y metres of a carriage above the ground t seconds after the start is given by the formula $y = 0.5t^2 - 3t + 5$ for $0 \le t \le 6$.

a Copy and complete this table, and use it to draw the graph of y against t.

Start

t (s)	0	1	2	3	4	5	6
y (m)		2.5		0.5		2.5	

b Use your graph to find the height above the ground at the start of the ride.

c What is the minimum height above the ground and at what time does this happen?

d What is the height above the starting point after 6 s?

e Between what times is the carriage at least 3 m above the ground?

EXERCISE 1*

Draw a graph for each equation after completing a suitable table between the stated x values.

7th

1 ▶ $y = -x^2 + 2$ for $-3 \le x \le 3$

2 ▶ $y = -x^2 + 4x$ for $-1 \le x \le 5$

8th

3 ▶   Draw the graph of $y = -2x^2 + 2x + 5$ for $-2 \le x \le 3$ after completing the table.

x	−2	−1	0	1	2	3
y	−7					−7

9th

Q4a HINT

$t = 2$, $P = 10$
satisfies equation
$P = kt^2 + t + 1$.

4 ▶   The population P (in millions) of bacteria on a piece of cheese after t days is given by the equation $P = kt^2 + t + 1$, where k is a constant that is valid for $2 \le t \le 12$.

   a Use this table to calculate the value of k, and then copy and complete the table.

t (days)	2	4	6	8	10	12
P (millions)	10					265

   b Draw a graph of P against t.
   c Use your graph to estimate the bacteria population after 5 days.
   d How many days does it take for the bacteria population to be more than 10^8?

5 ▶   The depth of water, y m, at the entrance of a tidal harbour (where the depth of water changes) t hours after midday is given by the formula $y = 4 + 3t - t^2$ where $0 \le t \le 4$.

   a Copy and complete this table, and use it to draw a graph of y against t.

t (hours after 12:00)	0	1	1.5	2	3	4
y (m)		6			4	

   b Use your graph to find the depth of water at the harbour entrance at midday.
   c At what time is the harbour entrance dry?
   d What is the maximum depth of water at the entrance and at what time does this occur?
   e A large ferry requires at least 5 m of water if it is to be able to enter a harbour. Between what times of the day can it safely enter the harbour? Give your answers to the nearest minute.

6 ▶   An open box is made from a thin square metal sheet measuring 10 cm by 10 cm. Four squares of side x centimetres are cut away, and the remaining sides are folded upwards to make a box of depth x centimetres.

   a Show that the external surface area A cm^2 is given by the formula $A = 100 - 4x^2$ where $0 \le x \le 5$.
   b Draw the graph of A against x by first constructing a table of values.
   c Use your graph to find values of x which will produce a box with an external surface area of between 50 cm^2 and 75 cm^2 inclusive.

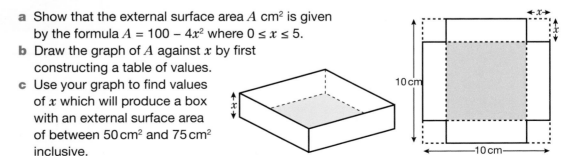

7 ▶ The total stopping distance y metres of a car in dry weather travelling at a speed of x mph is given by the formula $y = 0.015x^2 + 0.3x$ where $20 \leq x \leq 80$.

a Copy and complete this table and use it to draw a graph of y against x.

x (miles/hour)	20	30	40	50	60	70	80
y (m)		22.5		52.5		94.5	

b Use your graph to find the stopping distance for a car travelling at 55 mph.
c At what speed does a car have a stopping distance of 50 m?
d The stopping distance is measured from when an obstacle is observed to when the car is stationary. Therefore, a driver's reaction time before applying the brakes is an important factor.

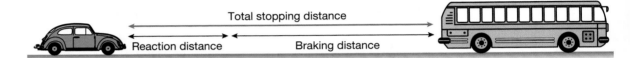

Total stopping distance

Reaction distance   Braking distance

Sam is driving at 75 mph when she sees a stationary school bus ahead of her. She manages to avoid hitting the bus by stopping just in time. Her braking distance is 83.5 m. Calculate her reaction time. (1 mile ≈ 1600 m)

ACTIVITY 2

SKILLS

ADAPTIVE
LEARNING

A rescue helicopter has a searchlight.

Find the **radius** of the illuminated circle when the light is 50 m above the ground.

What is the radius when the light is 100 m above the ground?

Calculate the illuminated area for heights of both 50 m and 100 m.

Show that the relationship of the illuminated area A and the vertical height of the beam H is given by $A = \pi(H \tan 25°)^2$.

Investigate their relationship by drawing a suitable graph of A against H.

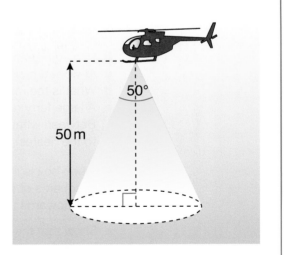

SOLUTION OF $0 = ax^2 + bx + c$

Solving **linear simultaneous equations** by graphs is a useful technique. Their solution is the intersection point of two straight lines.

The **quadratic equation** $ax^2 + bx + c = 0$ can be solved by identifying where the curve $y = ax^2 + bx + c$ **intersects** the x-axis ($y = 0$). The solutions (roots) are the x-**intercepts**.

EXAMPLE 4

SKILLS

PROBLEM SOLVING

Use the graph of $y = x^2 - 5x + 4$ to solve the equation $0 = x^2 - 5x + 4$.

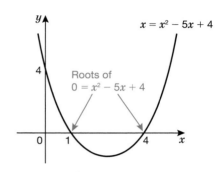

The curve $y = x^2 - 5x + 4$ cuts the x-axis ($y = 0$) at $x = 1$ and $x = 4$.
Therefore at these points, $0 = x^2 - 5x + 4$, and the solutions are $x = 1$ or $x = 4$.

Check: If $x = 1$, $y = 1^2 - 5 \times 1 + 4 = 0$
       If $x = 4$, $y = 4^2 - 5 \times 4 + 4 = 0$

EXERCISE 2

7th

1 ▶ The graph of $y = x^2 - x - 6$ is shown. Use it to find the solutions to $x^2 - x - 6 = 0$.

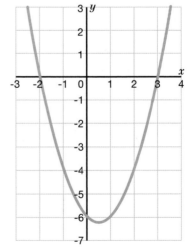

Draw the graphs of these equations between the suggested x-values, and use them to solve the equations. Check your solutions.

	GRAPH	x-VALUES	EQUATION
2 ▶	$y = x^2 - 5x + 6$	$0 \leq x \leq 5$	$0 = x^2 - 5x + 6$
3 ▶	$y = x^2 - 2x - 3$	$-2 \leq x \leq 4$	$0 = x^2 - 2x - 3$
4 ▶	$y = x^2 - 7x + 10$	$0 \leq x \leq 6$	$0 = x^2 - 7x + 10$
5 ▶	$y = x^2 - 5x$	$-1 \leq x \leq 6$	$0 = x^2 - 5x$

EXERCISE 2*

1 ▶ The graph of $y = 2x^2 + x - 1$ is shown. Use it to find the solutions to $2x^2 + x - 1 = 0$.

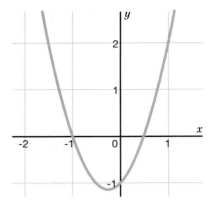

Draw the graphs between the suggested x-values, and use them to solve the equations. Check your solutions.

GRAPH	x-VALUES	EQUATION
2 ▶ $y = 2x^2 - 5x + 2$	$0 \le x \le 4$	$0 = 2x^2 - 5x + 2$
3 ▶ $y = 4x^2 - 1$	$-2 \le x \le 2$	$0 = 4x^2 - 1$

Find the equations of these curves in the form $y = ax^2 + bx + c$.

4 ▶

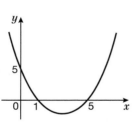

6 ▶

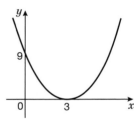

5 ▶

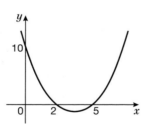

7 ▶

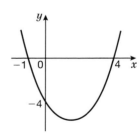

8 ▶ **Sketch** the graphs of $y = ax^2 + bx + c$ (for $a > 0$) when the equation $0 = ax^2 + bx + c$ has two solutions, one solution, and no solutions.

EXERCISE 3

REVISION

1 ▶ Draw the graph of $y = x^2 + x - 2$ for $-3 \le x \le 3$ by first completing a table of values.

2 ▶ Draw the graph of $y = x^2 - 4x + 2$ for $-1 \le x \le 5$ and use this graph to find approximate solutions to the equation $x^2 - 4x + 2 = 0$. Check your answers.

3 ▶   **a**   Copy and complete the table and use it to draw the graph of
$y = x^2 - 2x - 5$ for $-2 \le x \le 4$.

x	-2	-1	0	1	2	3	4
x^2			0		4		
$-2x$			0		-4		
-5			-5		-5		
y			-5		-5		

b   Use this graph to find approximate solutions to the equation $x^2 - 2x - 5 = 0$.
Check your answers.

4 ▶   The area A cm^2 of a semicircle formed from a circle
of **diameter** d cm is given by the approximate
formula $A \approx 0.4d^2$.

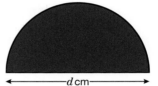

$\longleftarrow$ d cm $\longrightarrow$

Draw a graph of A against d for $0 \le d \le 6$ and use this graph to find

a   the area of a semicircle of diameter 3.5 cm

b   the diameter of a semicircle of area 8 cm^2

c   the **perimeter** of the semicircle whose area is 10 cm^2

5 ▶   The distance s m fallen by a small stone from a clifftop after t seconds is given by the
equation $s = 4.9t^2$, for $0 \le t \le 4$.

a   Draw a graph of s against t.

b   Use your graph to estimate the distance fallen by the small stone after 2.5 s.

c   At what time has the small stone fallen 50 m?

EXERCISE 3*   **REVISION**

1 ▶   Draw the graph of $y = 2x^2 + 3x - 4$ for $-3 \le x \le 3$ by first completing a table of values.

2 ▶   Draw the graph of $y = 2x^2 + 3x - 6$ for $-3 \le x \le 3$ and use this graph to find approximate
solutions to the equation $2x^2 + 3x - 6 = 0$. Check your answers.

3 ▶   **a**   Copy and complete the table below and use it to draw the graph of $y = -2x^2 - 3x + 6$ for
$-3 \le x \le 3$.

x	-3	-2	-1	0	1	2	3
$-2x^2$				0		-8	
$-3x$				0		-6	
$+6$				6		6	
y				6		-8	

b   Use this graph to find approximate solutions to the equation $-2x^2 - 3x + 6 = 0$.
Check your answers.

4 ▶ Lee is designing a bridge to cross a jungle river. She decides that it will be supported by a parabolic arch. The equation $y = -\frac{1}{2}x^2$ is used as the mathematical model to design the arch, where the axes are as shown in the diagram.

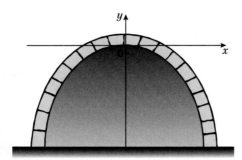

a Draw the graph of the arch for $-4 \le x \le 4$.

b Draw the line $y = -6$ to represent the water level of the river, and use your graph to estimate the width of the arch 10 m above the river, if the **scale** of the graph is 1 unit to 5 m.

5 ▶ The equation for the flight path of a golf ball is $y = 0.2x - 0.001x^2$, for $0 \le x \le 200$, where y m is the ball's height, and x m is the horizontal distance moved by the ball.

a Draw a graph of y against x by first completing a suitable table of values between the stated x-values.

b Use your graph to estimate the maximum height of the ball.

c Between what distances is the ball at least 5 m above the ground?

EXAM PRACTICE: GRAPHS 4

1 Copy and complete the table, then draw the graph of $y = x^2 + x - 6$ for $-4 \leq x \leq 4$.   **[6]**

x	−4	−3	−2	−1	0	1	2	3	4
y		0			−6	−4	0		14

2 **a** Copy and complete the table, then draw the graph of $y = 2x^2 - 3x - 2$ for $-3 \leq x \leq 3$.

x	−3	−2	−1	0	1	2	3
$2x^2$		8		0	2	8	
$-3x$		6		0	−3	−6	
-2		−2		−2	−2	−2	
y		12		−2	−3	0	

  b Use your graph to solve the equation $2x^2 - 3x - 2 = 0$.   **[8]**

3 The profit p ($ millions) made by an African Oil and Natural Gas exploration company, Lag-Oil, t years after opening, is given by the equation $p = 4t - kt^2$, valid for $0 \leq t \leq 8$, where k is a constant.

  a Use the equation and the information in the table to show that $k = 0.5$, and then copy and complete the table.

t	0	2	4	6	8
p	0		8		0

  b Draw the graph of p against t for $0 \leq t \leq 8$.

  c Use this graph to estimate for Lag-Oil

   (i) the greatest profit made and when this happened

   (ii) when the profit is at least $6 million.   **[11]**

[Total 25 marks]

CHAPTER SUMMARY: GRAPHS 4

QUADRATIC GRAPHS $y = ax^2 + bx + c$

Parabolas

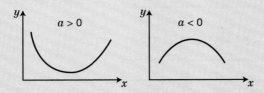

SOLUTION OF $0 = ax^2 + bx + c$

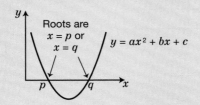

Quadratic graphs can be drawn by producing two types of table.

You need to be able to understand and use both types; these are shown below.

Draw the graph of $y = x^2 + 2x - 1$ for $-2 \le x \le 2$.

All cells shown:

x	-2	-1	0	1	2
x^2	4	1	0	1	4
$+2x$	-4	-2	0	2	4
-1	-1	-1	-1	-1	-1
y	-1	-2	-1	2	7

x and y values only shown:

x	-2	-1	0	1	2
y	-1	-2	-1	2	7

Some calculators have functions that enable the y-values to be found quickly and accurately by producing a simple table.

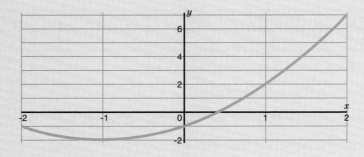

REAL-LIFE GRAPHS

The variables y and x can be changed to represent real-life values such as time, weight, money etc. and these graphs can be used to understand situations from everyday life.

SHAPE AND SPACE 4

All three trigonometry functions (tangent, sine and cosine) are used in the process of studying real-life situations, especially those involving waves. One of the applications is in the study of music.

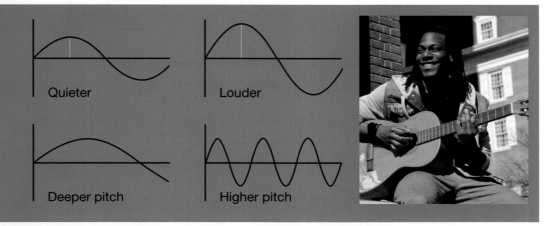

Quieter   Louder

Deeper pitch   Higher pitch

LEARNING OBJECTIVES

- Use the trigonometric ratios to find a length and an angle in a right-angled triangle
- Use angles of elevation and depression
- Use the trigonometric ratios to solve problems

BASIC PRINCIPLES

$$\tan x = \frac{\text{opposite side}}{\text{adjacent side}} = \frac{o}{a}$$

hyp o opp to x

x

a adj to x

SINE AND COSINE RATIOS

The tangent **ratio** reveals that for a right-angled triangle, the ratio of the opposite side: **adjacent** side is the same for a given angle.

We now investigate the relationship between other sides of a right-angled triangle for a fixed angle.

ACTIVITY 1

SKILLS

REASONING

Triangles X, Y and Z are all **similar**.

For each triangle, measure the three sides in millimetres, and then copy and complete the table.

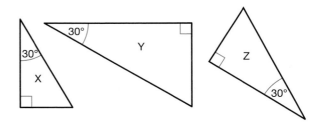

Triangle	Side length (mm)		
	o Opposite to 30°	a Adjacent to 30°	h Hypotenuse
X			
Y			
Z			

Calculate the $o : h$ ratio for each of the three triangles X, Y and Z.

Use a calculator to complete this table **correct to 3 significant figures**.

θ	0°	15°	30°	45°	60°	75°	90°
sin θ			0.500		0.866		

Calculate the $a : h$ ratio for each of the three triangles X, Y and Z.

Use a calculator to complete this table correct to 3 significant figures.

θ	0°	15°	30°	45°	60°	75°	90°
cos θ			0.866		0.500		

In Activity 1 you should have found that:

- the ratio $o : h$ is the same. For 30°, the actual value of $\dfrac{\text{opposite}}{\text{hypotenuse}}$ is 0.5.

  The ratio $\dfrac{\text{opposite}}{\text{hypotenuse}}$ for a given angle θ is a fixed number. It is called the sine of θ, or **sin θ**.

- the ratio $a : h$ is the same. For 30°, the actual value of $\dfrac{\text{adjacent}}{\text{hypotenuse}}$ is 0.866 (to 3 d.p.).

  The ratio $\dfrac{\text{adjacent}}{\text{hypotenuse}}$ for a given angle θ is a fixed number. It is called the cosine of θ, or **cos θ**.

KEY POINTS

- $\sin\theta = \dfrac{\text{opposite side}}{\text{hypotenuse}} = \dfrac{o}{h}$ $S \dfrac{\text{opp}}{\text{hyp}}$

- $\cos\theta = \dfrac{\text{adjacent side}}{\text{hypotenuse}} = \dfrac{a}{h}$ $C \dfrac{\text{adj}}{\text{hyp}}$

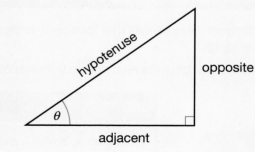

CALCULATING SIDES

EXAMPLE 1

SKILLS

PROBLEM SOLVING

A boy is flying a kite at the end of a 10 m string. The **angle of elevation** of the kite from the boy is 32°. Find the height p m of the kite.

$\sin 32° = \dfrac{p}{10}$

$10 \times \sin 32° = p$

$p = 5.30$ (to 3 s.f.)

[1][0][×][sin][3][2][=] 5.29919 (to 6 s.f.)

So the height of the kite is 5.30 metres.

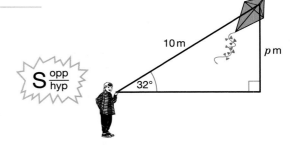

EXAMPLE 2

SKILLS

PROBLEM SOLVING

Find the length of side q correct to 3 significant figures.

$\cos 26° = \dfrac{q}{35}$

$35 \times \cos 26° = q$

$q = 31.5$ (to 3 s.f.)

[3][5][×][cos][2][6][=] 31.4578 (to 6 s.f.)

So the length of the side is 31.5 m.

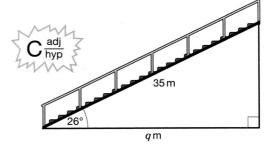

KEY POINTS

When using trigonometrical ratios in a right-angled triangle, it is important to choose the correct one.

- Identify the sides of the triangle as opposite, adjacent or **hypotenuse** to the angle you are looking at.

- Write down the sine, cosine and tangent ratios as:

$S \dfrac{\text{opp}}{\text{hyp}}$ $C \dfrac{\text{adj}}{\text{hyp}}$ $T \dfrac{\text{opp}}{\text{adj}}$

- Mark off the side you have to find and the side you have been given in the question.
The ratio with the two marks is the correct one to use.

EXAMPLE 3

SKILLS

PROBLEM SOLVING

Find the length y cm of the minute hand of a clock correct to 3 significant figures.

$\cos 43° = \dfrac{75}{y}$

$y \times \cos 43° = 75$

$y = \dfrac{75}{\cos 43°}$

$y = 103$ (to 3 s.f.)

[7][5][÷][cos][4][3][=] 102.550 (to 6 s.f.)

So the length of the minute hand is 103 cm.

EXERCISE 1

Give your answers correct to 3 significant figures.

Find x.

1 ▶

2 ▶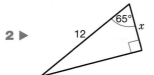

3 ▶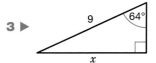

Find y.

4 ▶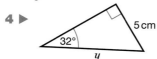

5 ▶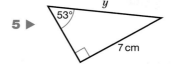

6 ▶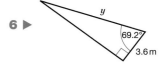

7 ▶ A 3.8 m ladder making a 65° angle with the ground rests against a vertical wall. Find the distance of the base of the ladder from the wall.

8 ▶ A kite is at the end of a 70 m string. The other end of the string is attached to a point on horizontal ground. The string makes an angle of elevation of 75° with the ground. At what height above the ground is the kite flying?

EXERCISE 1*

Give your answers correct to 3 significant figures.

1 ▶ Find BC in this **isosceles triangle**.   **2** ▶ Find LM in this isosceles triangle.

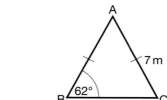   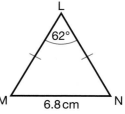

3 ▶ Calculate

  a AD
  b BD
  c the area ABC
  d the angle C.

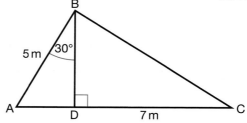

4 ▶ Find the area of an **equilateral triangle** of **perimeter** 12 m.

5 ▶ The cable car climbs at 48° to the horizontal up the mountainside.
BC = 520 m and DE = 370 m.

Calculate

  a the total length of the cable AC
  b the vertical height gained from C to A.

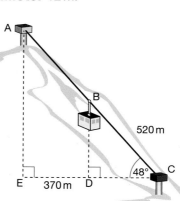

6 ▶ A submarine dives at a constant speed of 10 m/s at a diving angle measured from the vertical of 75°. If the submarine starts its dive from the surface, how deep is the front end of the submarine at the end of a 1-minute dive?

7 ▶ A regular pentagon is **inscribed** inside a circle of **radius** 5 cm. Find the length of one side.

8 ▶ The Petronas Tower II in Kuala Lumpur, Malaysia, is one of the tallest buildings in the world. From a position X on level ground, the angle of elevation to the top is 80°. Position Y lies 84.81 m further back from X in a direct line with the building.

The angle of elevation from Y to the top is 70°.

How high is the Petronas Tower II?

CALCULATING ANGLES

If you know the lengths of two sides in a right-angled triangle, you can find a missing angle using the **inverse** trigonometric functions.

ACTIVITY 2

SKILLS

REASONING

If you are given the opposite side to angle θ and the hypotenuse in a triangle, you can find $\sin \theta$.

You can use the [INV] [sin] buttons on a calculator to find the angle θ.

If you are given the adjacent side to angle θ and the hypotenuse, you can find $\cos \theta$.

You can use the [INV] [cos] buttons on a calculator to find the angle θ.

Check that the calculator is in **degree mode**.

Copy and complete the table to the nearest degree.

$\sin \theta$	0	0.259	0.500	0.866	0.966	1
θ			30°			
$\cos \theta$	1	0.966	0.866	0.500	0.259	0
θ				60°		

EXAMPLE 4

SKILLS

PROBLEM
SOLVING

Find the angle of the tent roof to the ground, θ, correct to 3 significant figures.

$$\cos \theta = \frac{1.5}{2}$$

$\theta = 41.4°$ (to 3 s.f.)

[INV] [COS] [(] [1] [.] [5] [÷] [2] [)] [=] [41.4096] (to 6 s.f.)

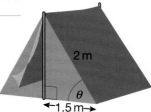
2 m

θ

←1.5 m→

EXAMPLE 5

SKILLS

PROBLEM
SOLVING

Find angle of the crane jib (arm) with the cable, θ, correct to 3 significant figures.

$$\sin \theta = \frac{3.5}{4.3}$$

$\theta = 54.5°$ (to 3 s.f.)

[INV] [sin] [(] [3] [.] [5] [÷] [4] [.] [3] [)] [=] [54.4840] (to 6 s.f.)

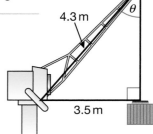
4.3 m

θ

3.5 m

KEY POINTS

To find an angle in a right-angled triangle:

• Write down the sine, cosine and tangent ratios as

$$S \frac{opp}{hyp} \qquad C \frac{adj}{hyp} \qquad T \frac{opp}{adj}$$

• Mark off the sides of the triangle you have
been given in the question.

• The correct ratio to use is the one with two marks.

• Use the [INV] and [sin], [cos] or [tan] buttons on a calculator to find the angle, making sure
that the calculator is in degree mode.

hypotenuse   opposite

θ

adjacent

EXERCISE 2

Give your answers correct to 3 significant figures.

Find each angle marked θ.

1 ▶
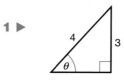
4
3
θ

3 ▶
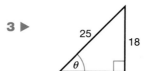
25
18
θ

5 ▶
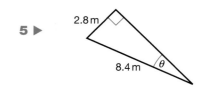
2.8 m
8.4 m
θ

2 ▶
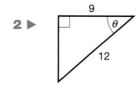
9
θ
12

4 ▶
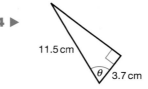
11.5 cm
θ 3.7 cm

6 ▶
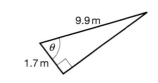
9.9 m
θ
1.7 m

7 ▶ A small coin is thrown off the Eiffel Tower in Paris. It lands 62.5 m away from the centre of the base of the 320 m-high structure. Find the angle of elevation from the coin to the top of the tower.

8 ▶ A rectangle has a side of 10 m and diagonals of 25 m.
Find the angle between the longer side and the diagonal.

9 ▶ A train travels at 20 km/h for 15 minutes along a straight track inclined at $\theta°$ to the horizontal. During this time it has risen vertically by 150 m. Calculate the angle $\theta°$.

10 ▶ A toy plane attached to a 15 m wire is flying in a horizontal circle of radius 5 m.
What angle does the wire make with the ground?

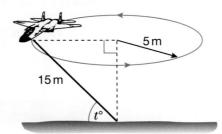

EXERCISE 2*

Give your answers correct to 3 significant figures.

Find each angle marked θ.

1 ▶

3 ▶
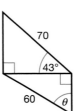

5 ▶
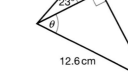

2 ▶
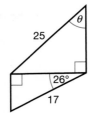

4 ▶
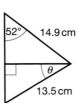

6 ▶
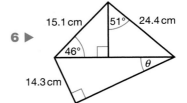

7 ▶ Martina starts from point M. She cycles 15 km north, and then 4 km east. She finally stops at point P. Find the **bearing** of P from M, and then the bearing of M from P.

8 ▶ A camera tripod has three equally spaced legs, each of length 1.75 m, around a circle of radius 52 cm on horizontal ground. Find the angle that the legs make with the horizontal.

9 ▶ An isosceles triangle of sides 100 cm, 60 cm and 60 cm has a base angle θ. Find θ.

10 ▶ ABCD is a **quadrilateral**. Angles BAD and DCB are both 90°. AB = 8 m, DB = 9 m and DC = 4.5 m. Calculate angle ABC.

ACTIVITY 3

Investigate the value of $(\sin x)^2 + (\cos x)^2$ for $0° \le x \le 90°$.

Prove this result.

HINT Use Pythagoras' Theorem.

Investigate the value of $\dfrac{\sin x}{\cos x}$ compared to $\tan x$ for $0° \le x \le 90°$.

Prove this result.

HINT $\dfrac{a}{b} \div \dfrac{c}{d} = \dfrac{a}{b} \times \dfrac{d}{c}$

For an equilateral triangle with sides of 2 units, express the sine, cosine and tangent ratios of angles of 30° and 60° as exact fractions.

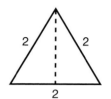

MIXED QUESTIONS

The real skill in trigonometry is deciding which ratio to use. The next exercise has a variety of situations involving the sine, cosine and tangent ratios.

EXERCISE 3

Give your answers correct to 3 significant figures.

Find each side marked x.

1 ▶
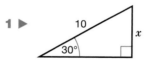

2 ▶

3 ▶
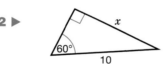

Find each angle marked a.

4 ▶
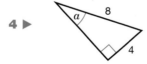

5 ▶

Find each marked side or angle.

6 ▶
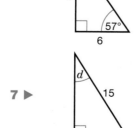

8 ▶
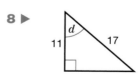

10 ▶
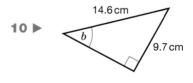

7 ▶

9 ▶
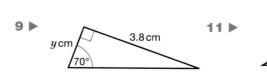

11 ▶

12 ▶ Jake runs from position A on a constant bearing of 060° for 500 m.
How far north of A is he at the end of his run?

13 ▶ A straight 20 m wheelchair ramp (straight slope) rises 348 cm.
Find the angle that the slope makes with the horizontal.

The triangle ABC has a right angle at B.

14 ▶ In triangle ABC, angle BCA = 23° and AC = 14 km. Calculate AB.

15 ▶ In triangle ABC, AC = 9 m and AB = 4 m. Calculate angle BAC.

EXERCISE 3*

Give your answers to Questions 1–10 correct to 2 significant figures.
Find x.

1 ▶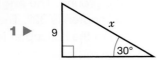

3 ▶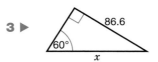

5 ▶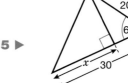

2 ▶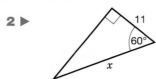

4 ▶

6 ▶ Regular hexagon
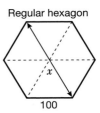

Find the angles marked a.

7 ▶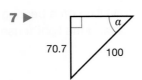

8 ▶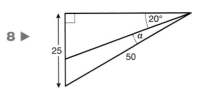

9 ▶ The area of the triangle is 1500 cm². Find the angle a.

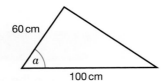

10 ▶ Find the angle a and sides x and y.

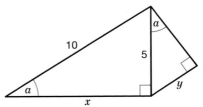

Give your answers to Questions 11–15 correct to 3 significant figures.

11 ▶ A hot-air balloon flies for 90 minutes at a constant height on a bearing of 285° at a steady speed of 12 km/h. After 90 mins, how far is it from its starting position

a north
b west?

12 ▶ For this **cross-section** of a railway bridge, calculate the depth of the valley and the length of the bridge.

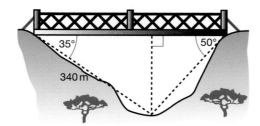

13 ▶ Calculate the height H of these stairs.

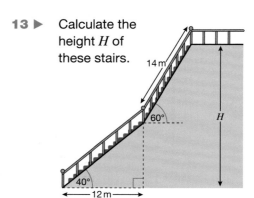

14 ▶ A helicopter hovers in a fixed position 150 m above the ground. The **angle of depression** from the helicopter to house A (directly west of the helicopter) is 32°. The angle of elevation from house B (directly east of the helicopter) to the helicopter is 22°. Calculate the distance d between the two houses.

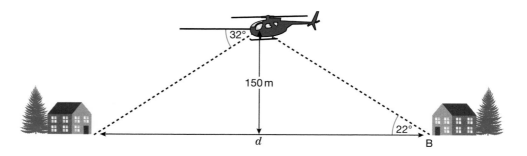

15 ▶ A motorboat is 10 km south of a lighthouse and is travelling on a bearing of 053°. What is the shortest distance between the motorboat and the lighthouse?

16 ▶ Gita sits on her garden swing, and swings. At the highest point, the angle that the 3 m chain makes with the vertical is 60°. Find the difference in height between the highest and lowest points of her ride. Give your answer correct to 2 s.f.

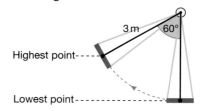

ACTIVITY 4

SKILLS

ANALYSIS

Use your calculator to draw the graphs of $y = \sin \theta$, $y = \cos \theta$ on the same axes for $0° \leq \theta \leq 90°$.

What do you notice?

HINT
Draw a table first in steps of 10° for both graphs.

EXERCISE 4

REVISION

Give your answers correct to 3 significant figures.

Find the length of the side marked x and the size of angle θ.

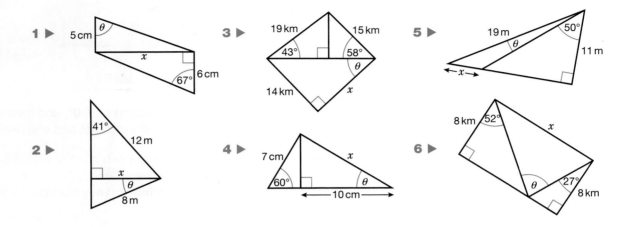

1 ▶

3 ▶

5 ▶

2 ▶

4 ▶

6 ▶

7 ▶   Calculate the area of an equilateral triangle with sides of 10 cm.

8 ▶   The coordinates of triangle ABC are A(1, 1), B(7, 1) and C(7, 5).
Calculate the size of angle CAB.

EXERCISE 4*

REVISION

1 ▶   The area of triangle ABC is 50 cm².

    a Find the value of sin θ.
    b What is the size of angle θ?

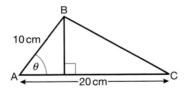

2 ▶   The centre of the clock face in a tower is
20 m above the ground. The hour hand is
1 m long. How far above the ground is the
end of the hour hand at

    a 2am (h in the diagram)
    b 7am
    c 10.30am?

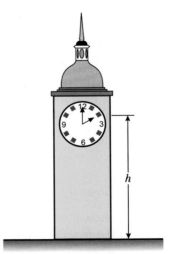

3 ▶ A scuba diver dives directly from A to B, and then to C, and then to the bottom of the sea at D. She then realises that she has only 4 minutes' worth of oxygen left in her tank. She can ascend vertically at 10 cm/s. AB = 8 m, BC = 12 m and CD = 16 m. Can she reach the surface before her oxygen supply runs out?

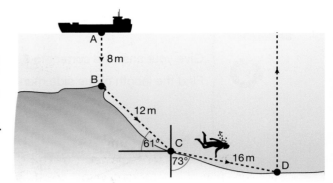

4 ▶ A hiker walks from her base camp for 10 km on a bearing of 050°, and then walks a further 14 km on a new bearing of 140°. At that moment a storm starts and she decides to return directly back to base camp.

    a Find the distance and bearing of the return journey.
    b The hiker's speed is a constant 1.5 m/s. If her return journey starts at 15:00, at what time will she arrive back?

5 ▶ A rectangular box ABCD is leaning against a vertical wall XY. AB = 2 m, AD = 3 m and angle DCZ = 25°. Calculate the height of A above the floor YZ.

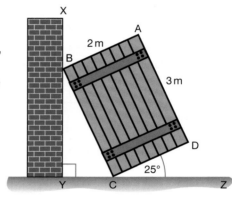

6 ▶ A rabbit wants to cross a busy road. He measures the angle of elevation from the edge of the road to the top of a lamp-post directly on the other side as 25°. From a position 12 m further back from the road, the angle is 15°.

    a Calculate the width of the road.
    b The rabbit can run across the road at 1 m/s.
       Find the time he could take to cross the road.
    c The traffic on the road travels at 60 miles/hour. Find how far apart the vehicles must be for him to cross safely. (1 mile ≈ 1600 m)

7 ▶ Given that $\sin 60° = \dfrac{\sqrt{3}}{2}$, show that side x of the triangle is given by $p\sqrt{3}$, where p is a whole number. Find the value of p.

8 ▶ Given that $\sin 60° = \dfrac{\sqrt{3}}{2}$ and $\cos 45° = \dfrac{1}{\sqrt{2}}$, show that side x of the triangle is given by $q\sqrt{6}$, where q is a whole number. Find the value of q.

EXAM PRACTICE: SHAPE AND SPACE 4

Give your answers correct to 3 significant figures.

1 A window cleaner uses a 5 m ladder. The ladder leans against the vertical wall of a building with the base of the ladder on level ground.

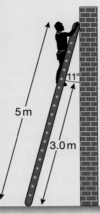

  a Calculate the height of the top of the ladder above the ground.

  b The window cleaner climbs 3 m up the ladder (see diagram). How far is his lower foot from the wall?

                                   [4]

2 The diagram shows the positions of three telephone masts A, B and C. Mast C is 5 kilometres due east of Mast B. Mast A is due north of Mast B, and 8 kilometres from Mast C.

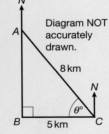

  a Calculate to 1 **decimal place**

    (i) the size of the angle marked $\theta°$

    (ii) the bearing of A from C

    (iii) the bearing of C from A.

  b Calculate the distance of A from B. Give your answer in kilometres.　　　**[8]**

3 In the diagram, the circle, centre O, represents the Earth. The point S represents a communications satellite used to pass radio messages between Washington (W) and Delhi (D). The line OS **intersects** the line WD at right angles at N. $OW = 6370$ km. $OS = 42\,300$ km. Angle $WOD = 100°$.

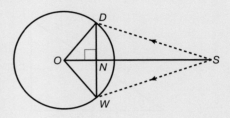

  a Calculate, correct to 3 significant figures or to the nearest degree:

    (i) WN　**(ii)** ON　**(iii)** NS　**(iv)** angle ODS.

  b Explain briefly why, if angle ODS were less than 90°, a signal from the satellite would not be able to reach Delhi.

  c A radio signal is sent from W to D via S. Calculate the distance it will have to travel.

  d Radio signals travel at 300 000 km/s. How long does the signal take to travel from W to D?　**[13]**

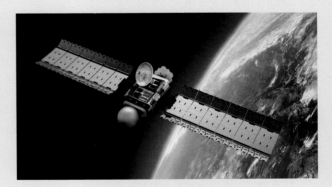

[Total 25 marks]

CHAPTER SUMMARY: SHAPE AND SPACE 4

RIGHT-ANGLED TRIANGLES

Trigonometry is the study of triangles.

The side opposite the right angle is called the hypotenuse. It is the longest side.

The side opposite the angle θ is called the opposite.

The side next to the angle θ is called the adjacent.

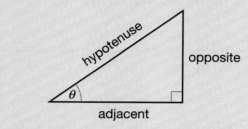

If you know an angle and a side, you can find another length using the trigonometric ratios.

The sine of angle θ is the ratio of the opposite side to the hypotenuse:

$$\sin\theta = \frac{o}{h}$$

The cosine of angle θ is the ratio of the adjacent side to the hypotenuse:

$$\cos\theta = \frac{a}{h}$$

The tangent of angle θ is the ratio of the opposite side to the adjacent side:

$$\tan\theta = \frac{o}{a}$$

You can use SOHCAHTOA to remember the ratios.

If you know two sides you can use the inverse trigonometric functions $\sin^{-1}$, $\cos^{-1}$, $\tan^{-1}$ on your calculator to find the angle θ.

The angle of elevation is the angle measured upwards from the horizontal.

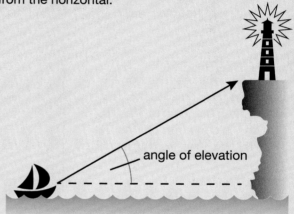

The angle of depression is the angle measured downwards from the horizontal.

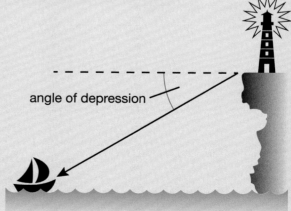

HANDLING DATA 3

Florence Nightingale is best known for her work as a nurse during the Crimean War. However, what is less well known is her love of statistics. It was her contribution to the analysis of a vast amount of army data in 1856 that led to the finding that of 18 000 army deaths, 16 000 were due not to battle wounds but to preventable diseases spread by poor sanitation (dirty conditions). Her work led directly to changes in sanitary science – she saved lives with statistics.

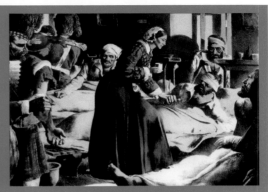

LEARNING OBJECTIVES

■ Find the inter-quartile range of discrete data

■ Draw and interpret cumulative frequency tables and diagrams

■ Estimate the median and inter-quartile range from a cumulative frequency diagram

BASIC PRINCIPLES

It is often useful to know more about data than just the **mean** value.

Consider two social events:

	Guests	Mean age (yrs)	Ages of guests	Age range
Party A	5	16	2, 2, 2, 2, 72	72 − 2 = 70
Party B	5	16	16,16,16,16,16	16 − 16 = 0

It is probable that the additional information about the **dispersion** (spread) of ages in the final column will determine which party you would prefer to attend. The mean does not tell you everything.

MEASURES OF DISPERSION

ACTIVITY 1

a 'The average family in the Caribbean has 2.3 children.'

Does this statement make sense?

What information does this sentence give about families?

Can you say how many families have 4 children?

Who might like to know this information?

b A restaurant uses on average 210 mangoes a day, but how does the restaurant decide how many mangoes to buy each day?

c In a game of cricket, two batsmen have the same mean (average) of 50.

One scored 49, 51, 48, 50, 52 and the other scored 0, 101, 98, 4, 47.

Comment on the difference between the batsmen.

Which batsman would you prefer to be in your team?

QUARTILES

The **median** is the middle of a set of data, dividing it into two equal halves. Half the data is smaller than the median and half is bigger. If the middle falls exactly on a number, that number is the median, if it falls in the space between two numbers then the median is the mean of the two numbers either side of the middle.

Quartiles divide the data into four equal quarters.

To find the lower quartile, take the data smaller than the median and find the middle. Similarly, to find the upper quartile, take the data larger than the median and find the middle.

Follow the same rule if the middle falls on a number or between two numbers.

EXAMPLE 1

SKILLS

ANALYSIS

15 children were asked how many pieces of fruit they had eaten during the last week, with the following results.

| 17 | 7 | 3 | 12 | 20 | 6 | 0 | 9 | 1 | 15 | 0 | 4 | 11 | 18 | 6 |

Find the quartiles.

First, sort the data into ascending order and find the middle number (the median):

| 0 | 0 | 1 | 3 | 4 | 6 | 6 | <u>7</u> | 9 | 11 | 12 | 15 | 17 | 18 | 20 |

So 7 is the median.

Now find the middle of the left-hand side and of the right-hand side:

L: 0   0   1   <u>3</u>   4   6   6   R: 9   11   12   <u>15</u>   17   18   20

So 3 is the lower quartile and 15 is the upper quartile.

The first quartile is known as the lower quartile or Q_1. So $Q_1 = 3$.

The second quartile is the median m or Q_2. So $Q_2 = 7$.

The third quartile is known as the upper quartile or Q_3. So $Q_3 = 15$.

In Example 1, the three quartiles fell exactly on numbers. This will not always happen, and the mean of two **consecutive** numbers may have to be used.

EXAMPLE 2

SKILLS

ANALYSIS

16 children were asked how much pocket money they received. The results, in dollars, are shown in increasing order. Find the quartiles.

| 9 | 10 | 12 | 13 | 15 | 15 | 17 | 19 | 20 | 22 | 22 | 25 | 25 | 25 | 27 | 35 |
| | | | | | | | ↑ | | | | | | | | |

The arrow in the middle falls between 19 and 20, so the median is 19.5 (the mean of 19 and 20).

| 9 | 10 | 12 | 13 | 15 | 15 | 17 | 19 | 20 | 22 | 22 | 25 | 25 | 25 | 27 | 35 |
| | | | ↑ | | | | | | | | | ↑ | | | |

The two arrows show the middle of the left-hand side and of the right-hand side.

The first arrow lies between 13 and 15, so $Q_1 = 14$ (the mean of 13 and 15).

The second arrow lies between 25 and 25, so $Q_3 = 25$ (the mean of 25 and 25).

The **range** is largest data value – smallest data value.

It is possible to have unusual values (also called alien points or **anomalies**) which can give a false picture of the true data set.

The lower quartile (Q_1) is the first quartile or the 25th **percentile**.

The median (Q_2) is the second quartile or the 50th percentile, splitting the data in halves.

The upper quartile (Q_3) is the third quartile or the 75th percentile.

The **inter-quartile range** = upper quartile – lower quartile = $Q_3 - Q_1$.

This is a measure of the range of the middle half of the data. It is not skewed (affected) by outlier points.

Care must be taken when finding these values.

The first step is to arrange the data in increasing order.

KEY POINTS

- Lower quartile (Q_1) = $\frac{1}{4}(n + 1)$th value   (25th percentile)
- Median (Q_2) = $\frac{1}{2}(n + 1)$th value   (50th percentile)
- Upper quartile (Q_3) = $\frac{3}{4}(n + 1)$th value   (75th percentile)
- Range = highest value – lowest value
- Inter-quartile range (IQR) = upper quartile – lower quartile = $Q_3 - Q_1$

  IQR is the range of the middle 50% of the data.

  If the value lies between two numbers, the mean of these values is used.

EXAMPLE 3

SKILLS

PROBLEM
SOLVING

Seven children were asked how much pocket money they received each week from their parents.

$10 $4 $12 $6 $6 $7 $15

Find the median and inter-quartile range of their pocket money.

Arrange the data into increasing order.

$4 $6 $6 $7 $10 $12 $15
        Q_1 Q_2 Q_3

The number of values, $n = 7$.

Q_1 is at $\frac{1}{4}(n + 1)$th value = 2nd value = $6.

Q_2 is at $\frac{1}{2}(n + 1)$th value = 4th value = $7.

Q_3 is at $\frac{3}{4}(n + 1)$th value = 6th value = $12.

Median = $7 and IQR = $12 – $6 = $6.

EXAMPLE 4

SKILLS

PROBLEM
SOLVING

The tail lengths of five baby lizards were measured in cm to study their growth **rates**.

3   7   2   10   8

Find the median and inter-quartile range of these tail lengths.

Arrange the data into increasing order.

2   3   7   8   10
     Q_1 Q_2 Q_3

The number of values, $n = 5$.

Q_1 is at $\frac{1}{4}(n + 1)$th value = 1.5th value = mean of 2 and 3 = 2.5 cm.

Q_2 is at $\frac{1}{2}(n + 1)$th value = 3rd value = 7 cm.

Q_3 is at $\frac{3}{4}(n + 1)$th value = 4.5th value = mean of 8 and 10 = 9 cm.

Median = 7 cm and IQR = 9 cm – 2.5 cm = 6.5 cm.

EXERCISE 1

Find the median, lower-quartile, upper-quartile and inter-quartile range of the following sets of discrete data.

1 ▶   9   0   1   14   6   8   1

2 ▶   5   11   9   1   3   13

3 ▶   5   5   0   1   1   1   −3   −7   5   6

4 ▶ $\frac{1}{2}$ $\frac{1}{2}$ $\frac{3}{4}$ $\frac{3}{4}$ $\frac{1}{4}$

Q5 HINT
Answer in cm.

5 ▶   0.2 m   50 cm   30 cm   0.1 m   1.5 m   0.4 m

6 ▶   The numbers of typing errors made in a day on a typing training course:

2,   24,   8,   5,   1,   3,   0,   6,   4

7 ▶   The numbers of text messages sent by a group of friends one day:

4,   6,   5,   1,   7,   0,   28,   0,   3

8 ▶   The numbers of beetles found on one plant on consecutive days:

6,   9,   4,   3,   8,   0,   2,   1

EXERCISE 1*

1 ▶   Malik records the number of minutes he spent revising for his exams each day in June. Find the median, inter-quartile range and range of these times.

20	15	25	30	70	90	20	25	0	10
72	84	80	25	90	90	90	10	45	0
25	56	76	34	80	120	120	120	30	60

2 ▶   The training times (in seconds) of Zola to run ten 100 m sprints are shown in the table. Find the median, inter-quartile range and range of these times.

14.1	14.1	15.2	13.9	13.1	12.7	14.3	15.2	16.0	16.2

3 ▶   The scores when a die is rolled 30 times are shown in the frequency table. Find the mean, median, inter-quartile range and range of these scores.

SCORE	1	2	3	4	5	6
FREQUENCY	6	5	2	10	4	3

4 ▶ Find the median, inter-quartile range and range of the first ten **prime numbers**.

5 ▶ A small factory has a managing director and seven workers.
The weekly wages are $700, $700, $700, $750, $750, $800, $800 and $4000.

    a Find the mean, **mode** and median of these wages. Which average best describes these wages?

    b Find the range and inter-quartile range. Which figure best describes the dispersion of these wages?

6 ▶ For two weeks Corine records the number of emails she receives each day.
The results were: 39, 57, 70, 45, 70, 32, 0, 51, 56, 44, 65, 31, 50, 48.

    a Find the mean, mode and median of these numbers. Which average best describes the number of emails received each day?

    b Find the range and inter-quartile range. Which average best describes the dispersion of the number of emails received each day?

7 ▶ For the data 4, 2, 5, x, 8, 2, 9, 9, 8, find x if

    a $Q_2 = 6$ **b** $Q_1 = 2$ **c** $Q_1 = 2.5$ **d** $Q_1 = 3$

8 ▶ For the data 1, 5, x, 1, 0, 8, 9, 2, 5, 5, 3, 2, 9, find x if

    a $Q_2 = 5$ **b** $Q_3 = 8$ **c** $Q_3 = 7.5$ **d** $Q_3 = 7$

CUMULATIVE FREQUENCY

Cumulative frequency is the running total of the frequencies.

A cumulative frequency table shows how many data points are less than or equal to the highest possible value in each **class**.

Cumulative frequency graphs provide a fast way of displaying data and estimating dispersion values as the data is grouped in increasing order. If the number of data points is large the quartile values of $n + 1$ can be changed to n.

It is acceptable to find the quartiles: Q_1 at $\frac{1}{4}n$, Q_2 at $\frac{1}{2}n$, Q_3 at $\frac{3}{4}n$ for large n.

The cumulative frequency (F) is on the vertical axis and the **end-points** are plotted on the horizontal axis. The points are then joined by a smooth curve.

EXAMPLE 5

SKILLS

REASONING

A large Indian coconut tree drops its fruit over the first 30 days of December.

The weight of the coconuts that fall each day is recorded in the frequency table.

a Draw a cumulative frequency graph.

b Use the cumulative frequency graph to find an estimate for the median weight.

c Estimate the lower quartile and the upper quartile of the weight.

d Work out an estimate for the inter-quartile range.

a

WEIGHT w (kg)	FREQUENCY	CUMULATIVE FREQUENCY (F)
$0 < w \leq 4$	3	3 total weight was ≤ 4 kg on ≤ 3 days
$4 < w \leq 8$	5	$3 + 5 = 8$ total weight was ≤ 8 kg on ≤ 8 days
$8 < w \leq 12$	9	$3 + 5 + 9 = 17$ total weight was ≤ 12 kg on ≤ 17 days
$12 < w \leq 16$	10	$3 + 5 + 9 + 10 = 27$ total weight was ≤ 16 kg on ≤ 27 days
$16 < w \leq 20$	3	$3 + 5 + 9 + 10 + 3 = 30$ total weight was ≤ 20 kg on ≤ 30 days

The points plotted are (4, 3), (8, 8), (12, 17), (16, 27) and (20, 30).

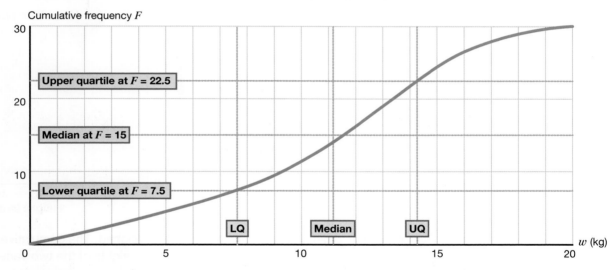

The results are estimated by drawing lines on the graph as:

b Median = 11.1 kg   (at 15th value)

c Q_1 = 7.6 kg   (at 7.5th value)

  Q_3 = 14.2 kg   (at 22.5th value)

d IQR = 14.2 − 7.6 = 6.6 kg

KEY POINTS

For a set of n values on a cumulative frequency diagram, the estimate for

- the lower quartile (Q_1) is the $\frac{n}{4}$th value
- the median (Q_2) is the $\frac{n}{2}$th value
- the upper quartile (Q_3) is the $\frac{3n}{4}$th value.

EXERCISE 2

1 ▶ 120 people were timed on how long they took to complete a puzzle.

The cumulative frequency diagram shows the results.

Estimate
a the median time
b the IQR.

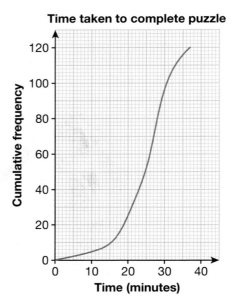

2 ▶ The cumulative frequency graph shows the heights of 80 plants at a garden centre.

a What is the range of heights?
b What percentage of the plants were taller than 45 cm?

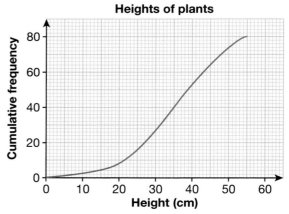

3 ▶ Tomatoes of two different varieties, X and Y, are weighed. The cumulative frequency diagram shows the frequency distributions of the weights of the two varieties.

a How many tomatoes of variety X were weighed?
b Estimate the minimum and maximum weights of tomatoes from variety X.
c Work out the median and the inter-quartile range for tomatoes from variety X.
d How many tomatoes of variety Y were weighed?
e Estimate the minimum and maximum weights of tomatoes from variety Y.
f Work out the median and the inter-quartile range for tomatoes from variety Y.
g Compare the two varieties, giving reasons for any statements you make.

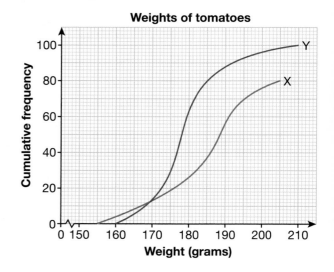

4 ▶ The cumulative frequency graph gives information about how long the batteries last in two different types of mobile phones.

    a Use the graph to find the median and quartiles for each type of phone.
    b Compare the two phones.

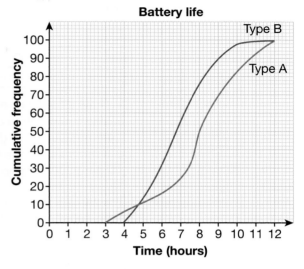

Battery life

EXERCISE 2*

1 ▶ The times taken by 50 students to complete their maths homework are shown in the table.

TIME, m (MINUTES)	FREQUENCY
$10 < m \leq 15$	1
$15 < m \leq 20$	7
$20 < m \leq 25$	11
$25 < m \leq 30$	12
$30 < m \leq 35$	12
$35 < m \leq 40$	7

    a Draw a cumulative frequency diagram.
    b Estimate the median time taken.
    c Estimate the lower quartile of the time taken.
    d Estimate the upper quartile.
    e Use your answers to parts **c** and **d** to work out an estimate for the inter-quartile range.

2 ▶ The table shows the weights of 100 cakes in grams.

WEIGHT, m (GRAMS)	FREQUENCY
$900 < m \leq 950$	2
$950 < m \leq 1000$	37
$1000 < m \leq 1050$	32
$1050 < m \leq 1100$	22
$1100 < m \leq 1150$	5
$1150 < m \leq 1200$	2

    a Draw a cumulative frequency graph.
    b Estimate the median, quartiles and inter-quartile range.
    c Estimate how many cakes weigh less than 1075 g.
    d Copy and complete.

       90 cakes are estimated to weigh less than ___ grams.

3 ▶ The table shows the marks obtained by 50 pupils in a violin exam.

MARKS, x	FREQUENCY
$0 < x \le 30$	5
$30 < x \le 60$	8
$60 < x \le 90$	14
$90 < x \le 120$	13
$120 < x \le 150$	10

a Draw a cumulative frequency table and use it to draw a cumulative frequency graph.
b Use this graph to estimate the
  (i) median   (ii) lower quartile   (iii) upper quartile   (iv) inter-quartile range.
c If the mark for the highest grade pass (merit) in this exam was 130 marks, calculate the percentage of pupils who gained this merit.

4 ▶ The weights (in kilograms) of the waste produced by Zara the elephant on a daily basis are shown in the table. The data is produced to check on the elephant's health over a 50-day period.

WEIGHT, x (kg)	FREQUENCY
$50 < x \le 70$	8
$70 < x \le 90$	15
$90 < x \le 110$	14
$110 < x \le 130$	9
$130 < x \le 150$	4

a Draw a cumulative frequency table and use it to draw a cumulative frequency graph.
b Use this graph to estimate the
  (i) median   (ii) lower quartile   (iii) upper quartile   (iv) inter-quartile range.
c The park vet decides that her elephants are healthy if their daily production of waste is more than 100 kg for at least 50% of this period. Having this information, is Zara healthy?

EXERCISE 3

REVISION

1 ▶ Find the median, lower quartile, upper quartile, inter-quartile range and range of the following numbers.

a	2	5	11	2	7	4	
b	5	12	9	17	19	3	3

Q2 HINT
0 is the first even number.

2 ▶ Find the median, lower quartile, upper quartile, inter-quartile range and range of the first ten even numbers.

3 ▶ The times (t secs) taken by eight pupils to solve a puzzle are given below.

PUPIL	A	B	C	D	E	F	G	H
TIME, t (secs)	22	32	17	17	35	54	25	30

a Find the median, inter-quartile range and range of these times.
b Which pupils are outside the middle 50%?

4 ▶ The table shows the weights of bags of rice in kilograms.

WEIGHT, w (kg)	$0 < w \leq 2$	$2 < w \leq 4$	$4 < w \leq 6$	$6 < w \leq 8$	$8 < w \leq 10$
FREQUENCY	4	8	12	10	6

a Draw a cumulative frequency table and use it to draw a cumulative frequency graph.

b Use this graph to estimate the
    (i) median   **(ii)** lower quartile   **(iii)** upper quartile   **(iv)** inter-quartile range.

EXERCISE 3*   **REVISION**

Q1 HINT

0 is the first square number.

1 ▶ Find the median, lower quartile, upper quartile, inter-quartile range and range of the first ten square numbers.

2 ▶ A survey of the number of eggs in humming birds' nests gave the following results.

NUMBER OF EGGS	0	1	2	3	4	5
FREQUENCY	3	5	4	9	0	2

Make a cumulative frequency table and use it to find the median and the range of the number of eggs.

3 ▶ Eight swimmers have a timed race. Their times, t secs, are shown in the table.

SWIMMER	A	B	C	D	E	F	G	H
TIME, t (secs)	42	39	47	32	29	49	50	42

a Find the median, inter-quartile range and range of these times.

b Find the swimmers that are inside the
    (i) top 25%   **(ii)** bottom 25%.

4 ▶ The table shows the heights (in metres) of 30 Norwegian spruce trees.

HEIGHT, h (m)	$0.5 < h \leq 1.0$	$1.0 < h \leq 1.5$	$1.5 < h \leq 2.0$	$2.0 < h \leq 2.5$
FREQUENCY	6	9	$2x$	x

a Find the value of x.

b Copy and complete a cumulative frequency table and draw a cumulative frequency graph.

c Use this graph to estimate the
    (i) median
    (ii) inter-quartile range of the heights of these trees.

d Calculate an estimate for the mean height of the trees.

EXAM PRACTICE: HANDLING DATA 3

1 The data shows the average number of days of rainfall in Rangoon for each month of the year.

MONTH	Jan	Feb	Mar	Apr	May	Jun	Jul	Aug	Sept	Oct	Nov	Dec
DAYS OF RAIN	1	1	2	2	17	26	28	28	22	13	6	1

Calculate for this rainfall data the
a range
b median
c inter-quartile range.

[6]

2 Mira divides her garden up into nine equal squares so that she can count white flowers in each section.

Her garden is shown with the grid.

**	*	***
*	**	
**	*	***

Key: * = 5 white flowers

For the number of white flowers per square in Mira's garden calculate the

a range   b median   c inter-quartile range.   [6]

3 The results of a Chinese examination are shown.

MARKS, x %	BOYS' FREQUENCY	GIRLS' FREQUENCY
$0 < x \le 20$	2	1
$20 < x \le 40$	8	2
$40 < x \le 60$	9	8
$60 < x \le 80$	6	10
$80 < x \le 100$	5	9

a Draw a cumulative frequency graph for both sets of data on the same axes and use it to find the
(i) median   (ii) inter-quartile range.

b Compare the performance of the boys and girls.   [13]

[Total 25 marks]

CHAPTER SUMMARY: HANDLING DATA 3

MEASURES OF DISPERSION

The dispersion of data gives additional information on how the information is spread.

If the data consists of n values it is arranged in increasing order.

QUARTILES

Lower quartile $(Q_1) = \frac{1}{4}(n + 1)$th value   (25th percentile)

Median $(Q_2) = \frac{1}{2}(n + 1)$th value   (50th percentile)

Upper quartile $(Q_3) = \frac{3}{4}(n + 1)$th value   (75th percentile)

Range = highest value – lowest value

Inter-quartile range (IQR) = upper quartile – lower quartile = $Q_3 - Q_1$

IQR is the range of the middle 50% of the data.

If the value lies between two numbers, the mean of these values is used.

CUMULATIVE FREQUENCY

Cumulative frequency graphs are used when there are a larger number of data values to consider (> 25 approximately).

The cumulative frequency (F) is on the vertical axis and the end-points are plotted on the horizontal axis.

When n is 'large' it is acceptable to find the quartiles at: Q_1 at $\frac{1}{4}n$, Q_2 at $\frac{1}{2}n$, Q_3 at $\frac{3}{4}n$.

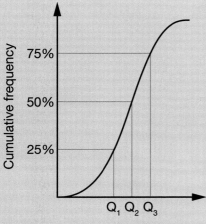

$Q_3 - Q_3$ = inter-quartile range

UNIT 5

5 is the only prime number ending in 5. A 5-sided polygon is called a pentagon and is the only polygon with the same number of diagonals as sides.

5^n always ends in a 5 except when $n = 0$.

Human beings have 5 senses!

NUMBER 5

The world's first all-electronic desktop calculator was produced in 1961. The ANITA (A New Inspiration To Arithmetic) was made in the UK. The push-button keys were the only moving parts. It weighed 15 kg compared with present-day devices which weigh about 100 g.

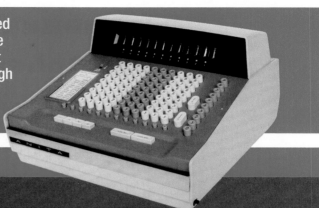

LEARNING OBJECTIVES

- Use a calculator
- Estimate an answer
- Identify the upper and lower bound of a number given the accuracy to which it has been written
- Solve problems using upper and lower bounds

BASIC PRINCIPLES

The word **BIDMAS** will help you perform the operations in the right order.

B Brackets　　**I** Indices　　**D** Division　　**M** Multiplication　　**A** Addition　　**S** Subtraction

CALCULATORS

√ ② ③ ☰ *4.79583152*

The answer can be **rounded** to various degrees of accuracy as shown in the table.

DEGREE OF ACCURACY	SIGNIFICANT FIGURES	DECIMAL PLACES
5	4.7958	4.79583
3	4.80	4.796
1	5	4.8

BIDMAS is helpful with the order of calculations. More complex calculations will require the use of brackets. Be familiar with your calculator and use the instructions that came with it when you bought it.

CALCULATOR FUNCTIONS

- To calculate 6^7, press ⑥ $x^\blacksquare$ ⑦ ☰ *279936*
- To enter 2.5×10^{-3} (written in standard form), press ② · ⑤ ×10ˣ (-) ③ ☰
- To enter $\frac{8}{9}$, press ⑧ a% ⑨ ☰
- To enter $3\frac{1}{5}$, press ③ a% ① a% ⑤ ☰

EXAMPLE 1

SKILLS

REASONING

Calculate these **correct to** 3 **significant figures**.

a $\sqrt{12.5^2 - 2.5^2}$ **b** $3\frac{4}{5} - 2.5 \times 10^{-2}$ **c** $\sqrt{\dfrac{7.75^4}{11.3 + 27.7}}$

a [√] [(] [1] [2] [.] [5] [x²] [−] [2] [.] [5] [x²] [)] [=] The answer is 12.2 (to 3 s.f.)

b [3] [aᵇ/꜀] [4] [aᵇ/꜀] [5] [−] [2] [.] [5] [×10ˣ] [(−)] [2] [=] The answer is 3.78 (to 3 s.f.)

c This is a long calculation, so write it out first: $\sqrt{7.75^4 \div (11.3 + 27.7)} =$

[√] [(] [7] [.] [7] [5] [xⁿ] [4] [÷] [(] [1] [1] [.] [3] [+] [2] [7] [.] [7] [)] [)] [=]

The answer is 9.62 (to 3 s.f.)

EXERCISE 1

Calculate, giving your answers correct to 3 s.f.

1 ▶ $5.3 + 11.2 \div 1.7$

2 ▶ $(7.8 + 17.3) \div 3.1$

3 ▶ $6.3 + \dfrac{12.5}{8.3}$

4 ▶ $\dfrac{5.6 + 18.7}{3.7}$

5 ▶ $(3.7 + 2.9)^2 + 6.3$

6 ▶ $\dfrac{1}{7} + \dfrac{7}{11}$

7 ▶ $5\frac{4}{7} + 11.4$

8 ▶ $7.5 + 5.7^2$

9 ▶ $\dfrac{8.3 - 3.8}{0.83^2}$

10 ▶ $\sqrt{11.1^2 + 2.2^2}$

11 ▶ $\sqrt{\dfrac{25.1}{3.5} + 7.5}$

12 ▶ $\dfrac{2.5^3 + 2.5^2}{2.5}$

13 ▶ $52.1 \div (3.25 - 0.71)$

14 ▶ $\dfrac{5.75}{1.35 \times \pi}$

15 ▶ 11^5

16 ▶ π^5

17 ▶ $\pi^3 \times 1.5^7$

18 ▶ $5750^2 + 3.5 \times 10^7$

19 ▶ $7.8 \times 10^5 - 87\,500$

20 ▶ $\dfrac{3.7 \times 10^7}{1.7 \times 10^3}$

EXERCISE 1*

Calculate, giving your answers correct to 3 s.f.

1 ▶ $\dfrac{75.8}{1.2 \times 2.1}$

2 ▶ $\dfrac{32.1}{\sqrt{\pi}}$

3 ▶ $\dfrac{0.075}{15.1 - 2.1}$

4 ▶ $\dfrac{0.075}{(15.1 + 3.5)^2}$

5 ▶ $\dfrac{22.1 - 17.3}{22.1 + 17.3}$

6 ▶ $\dfrac{56.3 + 45.1}{56.3 - 45.1}$

7 ▶ $5\frac{3}{11} - \frac{3}{7}$

8 ▶ $5\frac{3}{11} \times \frac{3}{7}$

9 ▶ $\dfrac{\pi}{0.75^{11}}$

10 ▶ $1.2^3 + 3.4^5$

11 ▶ $\dfrac{1.2^3}{3.4^5}$

12 ▶ $\dfrac{4.5 \times 10^{-3}}{6.3 \times 10^{-7}}$

13 ▶ $\left(\dfrac{1}{0.45} + \dfrac{1}{0.67}\right)^5$

14 ▶ $\left(\dfrac{1}{0.45^2} + \dfrac{1}{0.67^2}\right)^5$

15 ▶ $\left(\dfrac{9.3 \times 10^2}{7.3 \times 10^{-2}}\right)^2$

16 ▶ $(1^2 + 3^4 + 5^6)^7$

17 ▶ $\sqrt[3]{7.5 \times 10^2 \times \cos 60°}$

18 ▶ $\dfrac{1}{\sqrt{\pi^5} \times 10^{-5}}$

19 ▶ $\sqrt{\pi + \sqrt{\pi + \sqrt{\pi + \sqrt{\pi}}}}$

20 ▶ $\sqrt{\pi + \sqrt{\pi^2 + \sqrt{\pi^3 + \sqrt{\pi^4}}}}$

ESTIMATING

On many occasions it is acceptable and desirable not to calculate an exact answer, but to make a sensible estimate.

You have already been approximating numbers to a certain number of **decimal places** (2.47 = 2.5 to 1 d.p.), significant figures (34.683 = 34.7 to 3 s.f.) and rounding to a fixed suitable value (12 752 = 13 000 to the nearest 1000). Estimation is usually done without a calculator and is performed in a way that makes the **working** simple.

EXAMPLE 2

SKILLS

REASONING

Estimate the answers to these calculations.

a 19.7 × 3.1

b 121.3 × 98.6

c 252.03 ÷ 81.3

d (11.1 × (7.8 − 5.1))²

a 19.7 × 3.1   ≈ 20 × 3
                     = 60   (exact answer is 61.07)

b 121.3 × 98.6   ≈ 120 × 100
                     = 12 000   (exact answer is 11 960.18)

c 252.03 ÷ 81.3   ≈ 240 ÷ 80
                     = 3   (exact answer is 3.1)

d (11.1 × (7.8 − 5.1))²   ≈ (10 × (8 − 5))²
                           = (30)²
                           = 900   (exact answer is 898.2009)

ESTIMATING USING STANDARD FORM

It is often useful to use **standard form** to work out an estimate. Make sure you can write a number in standard form.

EXAMPLE 3

SKILLS
REASONING

Use standard form to calculate an estimate for 0.06768×38750.

     Change to 1 s.f.   Write in standard form   Use rules of indices
       ↓   ↓   ↙   ↘   ↓

$0.06768 \times 38750 \approx 0.07 \times 40000 = 7 \times 10^{-2} \times 4 \times 10^{4} \approx 30 \times 10^{-2\,+\,4} = 30 \times 10^{2} = 3000$

EXAMPLE 4

SKILLS
REASONING

Use standard form to calculate an estimate for $\sqrt{3.3 \times 10^{7}}$.

$\sqrt{3.3 \times 10^{7}} = \sqrt{33 \times 10^{6}}$ (Change 33 to the nearest square whole number)

$\approx \sqrt{36 \times 10^{6}}$

$\approx \sqrt{36} \times \sqrt{10^{6}} = 6 \times 1000 = 6000$

EXAMPLE 5

SKILLS
REASONING

By writing these numbers in standard form correct to 1 significant figure, work out an estimate for $\left(4.5 \times 10^{7}\right) + \left(4.5 \times 10^{6}\right)$.

Write your answer, correct to 1 s.f. in standard form.

$\left(4.5 \times 10^{7}\right) + \left(4.5 \times 10^{6}\right) = \left(45 \times 10^{6}\right) + \left(4.5 \times 10^{6}\right)$ (Make the **index** numbers the same)

$= 49.5 \times 10^{6}$ (Add **like terms**)

$\approx 5 \times 10^{7}$

EXERCISE 2

Estimate the answers to these.

1 ▶	3.1×47.9	**5** ▶	$(7.3 + 12.1) \times 15.9$	**9** ▶	$20.92 \div 0.11$
2 ▶	5.1×19.6	**6** ▶	$24.1 \times (17.9 - 8.3)$	**10** ▶	$315.71 \div 0.53$
3 ▶	$23.2 \div 7.8$	**7** ▶	79.868×0.101		
4 ▶	$394.82 \div 78.1$	**8** ▶	1239.32×0.24		

Use standard form to calculate these, giving each answer in standard form.

11 ▶	$(2 \times 10^{4}) \times (3 \times 10^{3})$	**15** ▶	$(2 \times 10^{4}) + (3 \times 10^{3})$	**19** ▶	$\sqrt{2.5 \times 10^{5}}$
12 ▶	$(4 \times 10^{5}) \times (3 \times 10^{3})$	**16** ▶	$(7 \times 10^{4}) + (2 \times 10^{3})$	**20** ▶	$\sqrt{8.1 \times 10^{5}}$
13 ▶	$(8 \times 10^{6}) \div (2 \times 10^{3})$	**17** ▶	$(9 \times 10^{4}) - (3 \times 10^{3})$		
14 ▶	$(6 \times 10^{7}) \div (3 \times 10^{2})$	**18** ▶	$(8 \times 10^{6}) - (3 \times 10^{5})$		

Use standard form to calculate an estimate for these, giving each answer in standard form correct to 1 significant figure.

21 ▶ 2670 × 760

22 ▶ 880 × 3420

23 ▶ 8490 ÷ 56.9

24 ▶ 6830 ÷ 29.5

25 ▶ $(6.8 \times 10^6) + (2.3 \times 10^5)$

26 ▶ $(4.1 \times 10^4) + (2.1 \times 10^5)$

27 ▶ $(4.8 \times 10^6) - (3.2 \times 10^5)$

28 ▶ $(9.1 \times 10^7) - (3 \times 10^6)$

29 ▶ $\sqrt{6.3 \times 10^5}$

30 ▶ $\sqrt{7.8 \times 10^7}$

EXERCISE 2*

Estimate the answers to these.

1 ▶ $\dfrac{3.1 \times 19.7}{14.8}$

2 ▶ $\dfrac{52.1 \times 94.3}{4.1}$

3 ▶ 1.98^3

4 ▶ $(4.1^3 \div 2.1^2) \times \sqrt{25.6}$

5 ▶ Estimate the volume and surface area of a closed box of dimensions 7.9 cm × 5.1 cm × 14.8 cm.

6 ▶ Estimate the area of the rectangle.

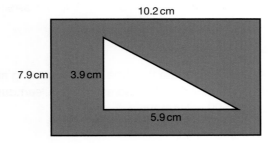

18.7 cm

5.4 cm

7 ▶ Estimate the shaded area.

10.2 cm

7.9 cm   3.9 cm

5.9 cm

8 ▶ A square has sides of length 7.23 cm. Estimate the length of its diagonal.

Use standard form to calculate these, giving each answer in standard form.

9 ▶ $(3 \times 10^3) \times (4 \times 10^5)$

10 ▶ $(6 \times 10^4) \times (4 \times 10^{-2})$

11 ▶ $(6 \times 10^8) \div (3 \times 10^5)$

12 ▶ $(3.5 \times 10^{-4}) \div (7 \times 10^{-2})$

13 ▶ $(7 \times 10^8) + (6 \times 10^6)$

14 ▶ $(2.8 \times 10^{-3}) - (7 \times 10^{-5})$

Use standard form to calculate an estimate for these, giving each answer as an ordinary number correct to 1 significant figure.

15 ▶ $(1.2 \times 10^2) \times (4.5 \times 10^2)$

16 ▶ $(6.8 \times 10^6) \times (3.1 \times 10^{-4})$

17 ▶ $(7.98 \times 10^{-4}) \div (3.79 \times 10^{-3})$

18 ▶ $(2.56 \times 10^{-3}) \div (6.28 \times 10^{-1})$

19 ▶ $\sqrt{3.2 \times 10^{-3}}$

20 ▶ $\sqrt{6.3 \times 10^7}$

21 ▶ A warehouse sells 8.7 million cups at an average price of $0.65 each. Use standard form to calculate an estimate of the total sales. Give your answer correct to 1 significant figure.

22 ▶ A human kidney has a volume of 120 cm³. It contains 1.35 million nephrons (small tubes). Use standard form to calculate an estimate of the average number of nephrons per cubic centimetre. Give your answer correct to 1 significant figure.

By writing these numbers in standard form correct to 1 significant figure, work out an estimate for the following in standard form to 1 s.f.

23 ▶ 5003×393

24 ▶ 0.041×5700

25 ▶ 47.8×0.0059

26 ▶ 0.00057×0.00287

27 ▶ $\dfrac{80\,920}{0.00418}$

28 ▶ $\dfrac{530}{0.000802}$

29 ▶ $\dfrac{0.6597}{729.8}$

30 ▶ $0.0678 \div 0.00321$

ROUNDING, UPPER AND LOWER BOUNDS

Rounding is often necessary as it can be impossible to give values exactly. Knowing the **degree of accuracy** of the numbers is useful. Unless requested, it is important not to round too much, otherwise the final answer can be too inaccurate.

We are often given information that is not exact.

For example, a scientific publication may state that 'the Earth is moving around the Sun at 66 000 miles/hour'. If this figure has been rounded to the nearest 1000 miles/hour, the exact speed will be between 65 500 miles/hour and 66 500 miles/hour.

This **range** can be shown on a number line.

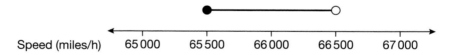

The range can also be written as 66 000 ± 500 miles/hour.

Numbers that can be expressed as $a \pm b$ have a given tolerance. The tolerance in the example above is 500.

This is a convenient way to express a number that can lie within a set range.

If x is given as 12 ± 0.5, x can lie between 11.5 and 12.5 (or $11.5 \leq x \leq 12.5$).

EXAMPLE 6

SKILLS

REASONING

$\sqrt{3}$ is shown rounded to a number of different degrees of accuracy.

$\sqrt{3}$	$=$	2	(1 significant figure)
	$=$	1.73	(3 s.f.)
	$=$	1.7321	(5 s.f.)
$\sqrt{3}$	$=$	1.7	(1 decimal place)
	$=$	1.732	(3 d.p.)
	$=$	1.732 05	(5 d.p.)

The difference between the first rounding (1 s.f. or 1 d.p.) and the last (5 s.f. or 5 d.p.) is relatively large, so take care when doing this operation.

Note: your calculator will produce 3 if you key in $\sqrt{3} \times \sqrt{3}$.

EXAMPLE 7

SKILLS

REASONING

Mario measures square bathroom tiles to be 12 cm to the nearest cm.

Find the greatest and smallest values for the side length of the tiles.

Therefore, find the greatest and smallest area for each tile.

Let L be the exact length of the tile in cm.

$$11.5 \leq L < 12.5$$

11.5 cm is the smallest length the tile can be: **lower bound**
(if the tile were 11.4 cm it would be rounded down to 11 cm).

12.5 cm is the greatest length the tile can be: **upper bound**
(if the tile were 12.5 cm it would be rounded up to 13 cm, so the < sign is used).

Lower bound area of a tile = 11.5 × 11.5 = 132.25 cm².

Upper bound area of a tile = 12.5 × 12.5 = 156.25 cm².

Let A be the exact area of the tile in cm².

$$132.25 \leq A < 156.25$$

KEY POINTS

- Measurements rounded to the nearest unit can be up to half a unit smaller or larger than the rounded value.

  If $x = 7$ (nearest **integer**), the exact value lies in the region $6.5 \leq x < 7.5$.

  If $y = 7.5$ (1 d.p.), the exact value lies in the region $7.45 \leq y < 7.55$.

- The upper bound is half a unit larger than the rounded measurement.

- The lower bound is half a unit smaller than the rounded measurement.

  If $z = 20$ (nearest 10), the exact value lies in the region: (lower bound) $15 \leq z < 25$ (upper bound).

The populations, rounded to the nearest thousand, of Cardiff and Nottingham are given as 350 000 and 314 000 respectively. Find the population difference.

The minimum (lower bound) and maximum (upper bound) populations are shown in the table and on the diagram.

CITY	LOWER BOUND POPULATION	UPPER BOUND POPULATION
Cardiff	349 500	350 500
Nottingham	313 500	314 500

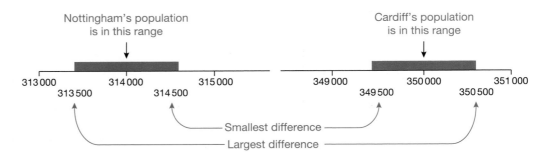

Largest population difference   (upper bound) = 350 500 − 313 500 = 37 000

Smallest population difference   (lower bound) = 349 500 − 314 500 = 35 000

The exact population difference between Cardiff and Nottingham lies between 35 000 and 37 000.

$c = \dfrac{a}{b}$ and $a = 2.3 \pm 0.1$ and $b = 4.5 \pm 0.5$.

Find the lower and upper bounds of c and write $c = p \pm q$ where p and q are numbers which need to be found.

The lower bound of c occurs when a is as small as possible and b is as large as possible.

Lower bound of $c = \dfrac{2.2 \text{ (min value of } a)}{5 \text{ (max value of } b)} = 0.44$

The upper bound of c occurs when a is as large as possible and b is as small as possible.

Upper bound of $c = \dfrac{2.4 \text{ (max value of } a)}{4 \text{ (min value of } b)} = 0.6$

The **mean** of 0.44 and 0.6 = 0.52 and half of the difference between the two bounds is 0.08 so c can be expressed as

$$c = 0.52 \pm 0.08$$

EXERCISE 3

Copy and complete the table.

	DIMENSION	ROUNDED TO NEAREST...	LOWER BOUND	UPPER BOUND	DIMENSION AS $a \pm b$
1 ▶	230 m	10 m			
2 ▶	70 kg	10 kg			
3 ▶	74°F	1°F			
4 ▶	19 m²	1 m²			
5 ▶	2.5 litres	0.5 litres			
6 ▶	10.5 cm	0.1 cm			
7 ▶	5465 g	5 g			
8 ▶	5470 g	10 g			
9 ▶	5500 g	100 g			
10 ▶	6000 g	1000 g			
11 ▶	____ m/s	____ m/s	12.0	12.4	
12 ▶	____ s	____ s	20.15	20.25	
13 ▶	____ m/s²	____ m/s²			10 ± 5
14 ▶	____ mph	____ mph			20 ± 1
15 ▶	____ kg/m³	____ kg/m³			30 ± 0.5

EXERCISE 3*

Write down the lower and upper bounds for each measurement, to the given degree of accuracy.

1 ▶ 6, 17, 123, to the nearest unit

2 ▶ 7, 40, 700, to 1 significant figure

3 ▶ 2.5, 14.5, 146.0, to the nearest 0.5

4 ▶ 50, 230, 4560, to the nearest 10

5 ▶ 0.2, 7.6, 12.4, to the nearest 0.2 of a unit

6 ▶ 0.34, 7.23, 12.89, to 2 decimal places

7 ▶ A sheep is weighed by a farmer as 43 kg to the nearest kg. What are the lower and upper bound weights for the sheep?

8 ▶ A milionaire estimates her wealth to be $2.2 × 10⁷ to the nearest million dollars. What are the lower and upper bounds for the millionaire's wealth?

9 ▶ A rectangular carpet measures 8 m by 10 m to the nearest m.

　　a Calculate the upper and lower bounds for the **perimeter** of the carpet.

　　b Calculate the upper and lower bounds for the area of the carpet.

10 ▶ If $p = \dfrac{x}{yz}$ and $x = 23.1 \pm 0.5$, $y = 12.1 \pm 0.3$ and $z = 1.2 \pm 0.1$, calculate correct to 3 significant figures the upper and lower bounds of p.

11 ▶ If $p = \dfrac{a+b}{c}$ and $a = 1.2 \pm 0.05$, $b = 3.7 \pm 0.03$ and $c = 1.1 \pm 0.1$, calculate correct to 3 significant figures the upper and lower bounds of p.

12 ▶ A circle has an area of 7.40 cm² to 2 significant figures. Find, correct to 3 significant figures, the upper bound of the **radius** and the lower bound of the **circumference**.

13 ▶ A square has a side length of 5.79 cm to 3 significant figures. Find, correct to 3 significant figures, the upper bound for its area and the lower bound of the diagonal length.

14 ▶ Find the lower and upper bounds of the perimeter of an **equilateral triangle** with area 100 cm² measured to the nearest 10 cm².

EXERCISE 4

REVISION

1 ▶ Calculate, giving your answers correct to 3 s.f.

a $7.5 + 7.5^2 + 7.5^3$

b $\dfrac{8.5 \times 10^4}{3.2 \times 10^7}$

c $\dfrac{\sqrt{2.5 \times 10^4}}{5.2 \times 10^3 - 1.5 \times 10^2}$

d $\dfrac{\sqrt{3.5 \times 10^6}}{\sqrt{1.3 \times 10^{-2}}}$

2 ▶ Estimate the value of $\dfrac{2.1 \times 5.8 \times 3.1}{2.9 \times (11.9 - 8.8)}$

3 ▶ Estimate the surface area of a **cube** of side 9.876 cm.

4 ▶ 80 ml is written to the nearest 10 ml. What is the maximum volume? What is the minimum volume?

5 ▶ The area of a circle is given as 45.5 ± 0.5 cm. Find, correct to 2 significant figures, the maximum possible radius and the minimum possible circumference. (Area of circle = πr^2, circumference of circle = $2\pi r$)

6 ▶ An engineer measures the distance along the ground to the base of a tree to be 12 m to the nearest metre. If the **angle of elevation** to the top of the tree is 40° to the nearest degree, find

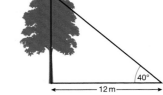

a the upper bound for the tree height

b the lower bound for the tree height.

EXERCISE 4*

REVISION

1 ▶ Calculate, giving your answers correct to 3 s.f.

a $2.5 + 2.5^2 + 2.5^3 + 2.5^4$

b $\dfrac{7.5 \times 10^5}{2.5^4}$

c $\dfrac{\sqrt{2500}}{9.2 \times 10^5 - 7.5 \times 10^5}$

d $\dfrac{\sqrt{7.5 \times 10^5}}{\sqrt{2.8 \times 10^{-5}}}$

2 ▶ Write the lower and upper bounds for the following to the given degrees of accuracy.

a 64 mins (nearest 1 min)

b 20 g (nearest 10 g)

c 30 m/s (nearest 5 m/s)

d 7500 mm (nearest 100 mm)

3 ▶ Given that $w = \dfrac{x - y}{z}$, $x = 9.5 \pm 0.1$, $y = 3.5 \pm 0.2$ and $z = 2.1 \pm 0.3$, find the lower and upper bounds of w.

4 ▶ Estimate the value of the following quantities in standard form to 1 s.f.

a $2.9 \times 10^2 \times 9.1 \times 10^5$

b $\dfrac{7.9 \times 10^6}{3.9 \times 10^4}$

c $\sqrt{4.1 \times 10^4}$

d $\dfrac{24.9\pi \times 10^7}{4.9^2}$

5 ▶ Elsa is in training for a swimming competition. She swims a distance of 400 m measured to the nearest 50 m. Her time is 6 mins measured to the nearest half a minute. Find the lower and upper bounds of Elsa's speed in m/s.

6 ▶ The area of a quarter circle is measured as 10 cm² to the nearest 1 cm². Find the lower and upper bounds for the perimeter of this quarter circle. (Area of circle = πr^2, circumference of circle = $2\pi r$)

EXAM PRACTICE: NUMBER 5

1 Calculate the following to 3 s.f.

    a $1.5 + 1.5^2 + 1.5^3$ **b** $\dfrac{1.5 \times 10^3}{1.5^3}$ **c** $\dfrac{\sqrt{165}}{7.2 \times 10^3 - 2.7 \times 10^2}$ **d** $\dfrac{\sqrt{6.5 \times 10^3}}{\sqrt{3.4 \times 10^{-5}}}$ **[4]**

2 State the lower and upper bounds for the following to the given degrees of accuracy.

    a 22 m (nearest 1 m)   **b** 50 kg (nearest kg)   **c** 750 s (nearest 10 s)   **d** 1400 km (nearest 100 km)   **[8]**

3 Given that $w = \dfrac{x + y}{z}$, $x = 2.5 \pm 0.5$, $y = 1.5 \pm 0.5$ and $z = 1.1 \pm 0.1$,

    find the lower and upper bounds of w.   **[4]**

4 Estimate the value of the following quantities in standard form to 1 s.f. Show your working.

    a $1.9 \times 10^3 \times 4.1 \times 10^2$ **b** $\dfrac{5.9 \times 10^4}{2.9 \times 10^2}$ **c** $\sqrt{8.9 \times 10^4}$ **d** $\dfrac{4.9\pi \times 10^3}{\sqrt{9.2}}$ **[4]**

5 Zac is in training for an athletics competition.

He runs a distance of 200 m measured to the nearest 10 m.

His time is 35s measured to the nearest 5 s.

Find the lower and upper bounds of his speed in m/s.

    [3]

6 The area of a semicircle is measured as 50 m² to the nearest 5 m².

Find the lower and upper bounds for the perimeter of this semicircle.

(Area of circle = πr^2, circumference of circle = $2\pi r$)   **[2]**

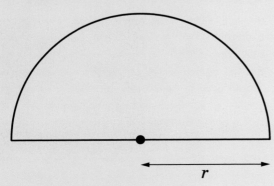

[Total 25 marks]

CHAPTER SUMMARY: NUMBER 5

CALCULATORS

Use the word **BIDMAS** to help you remember the order of calculations. Longer calculations will require brackets. Be familiar with your calculator and use the instruction booklet provided when you bought it.

ESTIMATING

To estimate the answer to a calculation, including calculations involving powers, round numbers to 1 s.f. and then perform the calculation.

For very large or very small numbers, it is often easier to estimate a calculation if the numbers are written in standard form.

ROUNDING, UPPER AND LOWER BOUNDS

Measurements rounded to the nearest unit can be up to half a unit smaller or larger than the rounded value.

If $x = 10$ (nearest integer), the exact value lies in the region $9.5 \leq x < 10.5$.

If $y = 10.5$ (1 d.p.), the exact value lies in the region $10.45 \leq y < 10.55$.

The upper bound is half a unit larger than the rounded measurement.

The lower bound is half a unit smaller than the rounded measurement.

If $z = 50$ (nearest 10), the exact value lies in the region:
(lower bound) $45 \leq z < 55$ (upper bound)

If $p = a \times b$ (where a and b are rounded values) and p_{min} and p_{max} are the lower and upper bounds for p then

$$p_{min} = a_{min} \times b_{min} \quad \text{and} \quad p_{max} = a_{max} \times b_{max}$$

If $q = \dfrac{a}{b}$ (where a and b are rounded values) and q_{min}

and q_{max} are the lower and upper bounds for q then

$$q_{min} = \frac{a_{min}}{b_{max}} \quad \text{and} \quad q_{max} = \frac{a_{max}}{b_{min}}$$

ALGEBRA 5

The quadratic equation has many applications and has played a fundamental role in human history, including the invention of the mobile phone and locating the orbits of objects in space. Solutions to quadratic equations were known to the ancient Babylonians and involve finding square roots. The Babylonians found these using a method of successive approximation to the answer which is identical to the method used by modern calculators and computers.

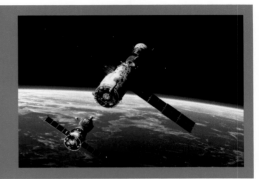

LEARNING OBJECTIVES

■ Expand the product of two or more linear expressions

■ Factorise quadratic expressions of the form $ax^2 + bx + c$

■ Solve quadratic equations by factorising

■ Solve problems involving quadratic equations

BASIC PRINCIPLES

■ **Simplifying** algebraic expressions such as $x^2 - 4x + x - 4$.

■ Multiplying out brackets such as $2(3 + x)$.

■ Finding **factors** of numbers.

■ Changing word problems into mathematical equations.

MULTIPLYING BRACKETS

TWO LINEAR BRACKETS

ACTIVITY 1

Finding the area of a rectangle involves multiplying two numbers together.

Multiplying $(x + 2)$ by $(x + 4)$ can also be done by finding the area of a rectangle.

This rectangular poster has sides $(x + 2)$ and $(x + 4)$.

Notice that the diagram shows the area of each part.

The total area is

$(x + 2)(x + 4) = x^2 + 4x + 2x + 8 = x^2 + 6x + 8$

Draw similar diagrams to calculate these:

$(x + 5)(x + 2)$ $\qquad$ $(x + 1)(x + 1)$

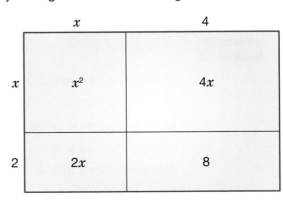

A very common mistake is to say that $(x + 2)^2 = x^2 + 2^2$.

Show that $(x + 2)^2 \neq x^2 + 2^2$ by substituting various numbers for x.

Are there any values of x for which $(x + 2)^2 = x^2 + 2^2$?

What does $(x + 2)^2$ equal?

Remember that $(x + 2)^2 = (x + 2)(x + 2)$.

With imagination, this method can be extended to deal with negative numbers.
$(x + 2)(x - 5) = x^2 - 5x + 2x - 10 = x^2 - 3x - 10$

Use diagrams to calculate these:
$(x + 4)(x - 3)$ $(x - 3)^2$ $(x + 2)(x - 2)$

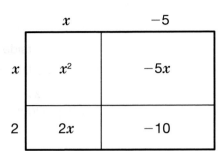

FIRST – OUTSIDE – INSIDE – LAST

Brackets can be multiplied without drawing diagrams:

$(x + 2) \times a = xa + 2a$

$\Rightarrow \qquad (x + 2) \times (x + 4) = x(x + 4) + 2(x + 4)$

giving $\quad (x + 2)(x + 4) = x^2 + 4x + 2x + 8 = x^2 + 6x + 8$

EXAMPLE 1

Multiply out and simplify $(x + 2)(x + 3)$.

Multiply the First terms	x^2
Multiply the Outside terms	$3x$
Multiply the Inside terms	$2x$
Multiply the Last terms	6
Add these terms to give	$(x + 1)(x + 2) = x^2 + 3x + 2x + 6 = x^2 + 5x + 6$

EXAMPLE 2

Multiply out and simplify $(x - 3)^2 = (x - 3)(x - 3)$.

Multiply the First terms	x^2
Multiply the Outside terms	$-3x$ (Note how the negative signs are dealt with)
Multiply the Inside terms	$-3x$
Multiply the Last terms	$+9$
Add these terms to give	$(x - 3)(x - 3) = x^2 + (-3x) + (-3x) + 9$
	$\qquad = x^2 - 6x + 9$

EXAMPLE 3

Multiply out and simplify $(2x + 3)(3x - 5)$.

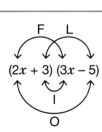

Multiply the First terms	$6x^2$
Multiply the Outside terms	$-10x$
Multiply the Inside terms	$9x$
Multiply the Last terms	-15
Add these terms to give	$(2x + 3)(3x - 5) = 6x^2 + (-10x) + 9x + (-15)$
	$\qquad = 6x^2 - x - 15$

The word (mnemonic) FOIL will remind you of the stages for multiplying out brackets.

FOIL stands for First, Outside, Inside, Last.

From each bracket:

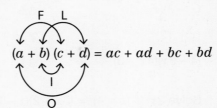

- multiply the First terms
- multiply the Outside terms
- multiply the Inside terms
- multiply the Last terms.
  Then add the four terms.

$$(a + b)(c + d) = ac + ad + bc + bd$$

EXERCISE 1

Expand and simplify these expressions.

1 ▶ $(x + 4)(x + 1)$

2 ▶ $(x - 7)(x + 3)$

3 ▶ $(2 + x)(x - 6)$

4 ▶ $(x - 3)(x - 5)$

5 ▶ $(x + 3)^2$

6 ▶ $(x - 4)^2$

7 ▶ $(x + 5)(x - 5)$

8 ▶ $(x + 2)(8 - x)$

9 ▶ $(3x - 2)(5x + 1)$

10 ▶ $(x^2 - 5)(x + 2)$

11 ▶ A rectangle with length $(x + 2)$ cm and width $(x + 1)$ cm has a square of length x cm cut out of it.

   a Find and simplify an expression for the area of the original rectangle.

   b Now find an expression for the shaded area.

   c Find x if the shaded area is 11 cm².

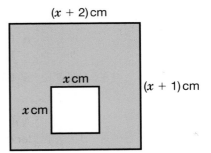

12 ▶ A concrete block is in the shape of a **cuboid** with length $(x + 3)$ cm, width $(x + 2)$ cm and height 5 cm.

   a Find and simplify an expression for the volume of the block.

   b Find and simplify an expression for the surface area of the block.

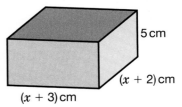

13 ▶ These two pictures have the same area. Find x.

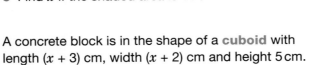

EXERCISE 1*

Expand and simplify these expressions.

1 ▶ $(x + 7)(x - 3)$

2 ▶ $(x - 3)(x + 3)$

3 ▶ $(x + 12)^2$

4 ▶ $(4 - 3x)(4x - 3)$

5 ▶ $(x - a)(x + b)$

6 ▶ $(4x - 5)^2$

7 ▶ $(3x^2 + 1)(5x + 7)$

8 ▶ $(x + 3)^2 - (x - 1)^2$

9 ▶ $\left(\dfrac{a}{2} - \dfrac{b}{5}\right)^2$

10 ▶ $x(5x^3 + 3x^2)(2x + 1)$

11 ▶ $\left(\dfrac{a}{b} + \dfrac{b}{a}\right)^2 - \left(\dfrac{a}{b} - \dfrac{b}{a}\right)^2$

12 ▶ Solve $2x^2 + (x + 4)^2 = (3x + 2)(x - 2)$.

13 ▶ If $(x + a)^2 + b = x^2 + 6x + 10$, find the values of a and b.

14 ▶ A circle of **radius** $(x + 6)$ cm has a circle of radius x cm cut out of it.

    a Find and simplify an expression for the area of the original circle.

    b Find x if the shaded area is 45π cm².

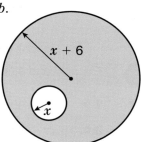

15 ▶ A rectangle with length $(4x + 5)$ cm and width $(x + 8)$ cm has four squares of side x cm cut out of its corners.

    a Find and simplify an expression for the area of the original rectangle.

    b Find x if the shaded area is 95.5 cm².

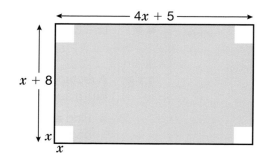

16 ▶ A right-angled triangle has lengths as shown. Find x.

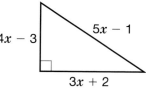

ACTIVITY 2

SKILLS

PROBLEM
SOLVING

Draw diagrams to show how to multiply out these expressions.

$(x^2 + 2x + 3)(x + 1)$

$(x + y + 3)(x - 2y)$

$(x^2 + 2x - 3)(x^2 + 3)$

Work out how to do the multiplication without using diagrams.

THREE LINEAR BRACKETS

EXAMPLE 4 ▶ Multiply out and simplify $x(x + 3)(x - 4)$.

First do $(x + 3)(x - 4) = x^2 - 4x + 3x - 12 = x^2 - x - 12$.

Then do $x(x^2 - x - 12) = x^3 - x^2 - 12x$.

The order of multiplying does not matter. You get the same answer if you first do $x(x + 3)$ and then multiply the answer by $(x - 4)$.

EXAMPLE 5 ▶ Expand and simplify $(x + 1)(x - 3)(x + 2)$.

First do $(x - 3)(x + 2) = x^2 + 2x - 3x - 6 = x^2 - x - 6$

Then do $(x + 1)(x^2 - x - 6) = x^3 - x^2 - 6x + x^2 - x - 6 = x^3 - 7x - 6$

The order of multiplying the brackets does not matter.

ACTIVITY 3

Multiply $(x + 1)(x - 3)(x + 2)$ by first multiplying out $(x + 1)(x - 3)$.

Then multiply the answer by $(x + 2)$.

Check your answer is the same as the answer in Example 5.

KEY POINT ▶ • The order of multiplication does not matter.

EXERCISE 2 ▶ Expand and simplify these expressions.

1 ▶ $(x - 1)(x^2 + 3x - 4)$	**5** ▶ $(x - 4)(x - 4)(x - 6)$
2 ▶ $x(x + 2)(x + 3)$	**6** ▶ $(x + 1)(3x - 2)(x - 1)$
3 ▶ $(x - 2)(x + 2)(x + 1)$	**7** ▶ $(x + 2)(x - 1)^2$
4 ▶ $(x - 3)(x - 1)(x + 4)$	**8** ▶ $(x + 1)^3$

EXERCISE 2* ▶ Expand and simplify these expressions.

1 ▶ $(2x + 3)(x^2 - 5x + 2)$	**5** ▶ $(x + 2)^2(2x - 3)$
2 ▶ $x(x + 2)(x - 5)$	**6** ▶ $(x^2 + 1)(2x + 5)(4x + 2)$
3 ▶ $(x - 7)(3x + 2)(x - 3)$	**7** ▶ $(2x - 3)^3$
4 ▶ $(3x - 4)(2x - 1)(4x - 3)$	**8** ▶ $(x + 4)(x - 2)(x + 3)(x - 1)$

FACTORISING QUADRATIC EXPRESSIONS

FACTORISING QUADRATIC EXPRESSIONS WITH TWO TERMS

Factorising quadratic expressions such as $x^2 + 2x$ is easy because x is always a common factor.

EXAMPLE 6

Factorise $x^2 - 12x$.

x is a common factor, and so

$x^2 - 12x = x(x - 12)$

Factorising $x^2 - 9$ is a little more difficult.

EXAMPLE 7

Expand $(x - 3)(x + 3)$ using FOIL.

$x^2 + 3x - 3x - 9 = x^2 - 9$

So factorising $x^2 - 9$ gives $(x - 3)(x + 3)$.

ACTIVITY 4

SKILLS

REASONING

Expand and simplify $(x - 3)(x + 3)$.

Expand and simplify $(x + 3)(x - 3)$.

What have you found?

What is the link between the numbers in the brackets and the number in the simplified expression?

Does the order of the brackets make a difference?

Use the result above to factorise $x^2 - 16$.

Can you factorise $x^2 + 9$ in the same way?

KEY POINTS

- $x^2 + ax = x(x + a)$ and $x^2 - ax = x(x - a)$.
- $x^2 - a^2 = (x + a)(x - a)$ This is called 'the difference of two squares'.
- $x^2 + a^2$ cannot be factorised.
- Always check your factorisation by multiplying out.

EXERCISE 3

Factorise these expressions.

1 ▶ $x^2 - 3x$ 3 ▶ $x^2 - 31x$ 5 ▶ $x^2 - 16$

2 ▶ $x^2 + 2x$ 4 ▶ $x^2 + 42x$ 6 ▶ $x^2 - 49$

EXERCISE 3*

Factorise these expressions.

1 ▶ $x^2 - 312x$ **3 ▶** $x^2 - 64$ **5 ▶** $x^2 - 225$

2 ▶ $x^2 + 51x$ **4 ▶** $x^2 - 121$ **6 ▶** $4x^2 - 16$

FACTORISING QUADRATIC EXPRESSIONS WITH THREE TERMS

Expanding $(x + 2)(x - 5)$ using FOIL gives $x^2 - 3x - 10$.

Factorising is the reverse process. $x^2 - 3x - 10$ factorises to $(x + 2)(x - 5)$.

EXAMPLE 8

Find a if $x^2 + 5x + 6 = (x + 3)(x + a)$.

Using FOIL, the last terms in each bracket are multiplied to give 6.

So $3 \times a = 6$ and $a = 2$.

Check: $(x + 3)(x + 2) = x^2 + 2x + 3x + 6$
$$= x^2 + 5x + 6$$

EXAMPLE 9

Find a if $x^2 + x - 12 = (x + 4)(x + a)$.

Using FOIL, the last terms in each bracket are multiplied to give −12.

So $4 \times a = -12$ and $a = -3$.

Check: $(x + 4)(x - 3) = x^2 + 4x - 3x - 12$
$$= x^2 + x - 12$$

EXERCISE 4

Find a.

1 ▶ $x^2 + 3x + 2 = (x + 2)(x + a)$ **4 ▶** $x^2 - 7x + 10 = (x - 5)(x + a)$

2 ▶ $x^2 + 7x + 12 = (x + 3)(x + a)$ **5 ▶** $x^2 + 4x + 4 = (x + 2)(x + a)$

3 ▶ $x^2 + 3x - 4 = (x + 4)(x + a)$ **6 ▶** $x^2 - 1 = (x + 1)(x + a)$

EXERCISE 4*

Find a.

1 ▶ $x^2 + 4x + 3 = (x + 1)(x + a)$ **4 ▶** $x^2 + 2x - 15 = (x + 5)(x + a)$

2 ▶ $x^2 + x - 12 = (x - 3)(x + a)$ **5 ▶** $x^2 - 64 = (x + 8)(x + a)$

3 ▶ $x^2 - 12x + 35 = (x - 5)(x + a)$ **6 ▶** $x^2 + 4\frac{1}{2}x + 2 = (x + 4)(x + a)$

When the number in the first bracket is not given, then try all the factors of the last number.
The two factors chosen must add up to the number in front of the x term.

KEY POINT

- If the last **sign** in the expression is +, then the numbers in both brackets will have the same sign as the middle term.

EXAMPLE 10 ▶ Factorise $x^2 + 5x + 6$.

The last sign is +, and so both brackets will have the same sign as +5x, giving $(x + \_)(x + \_)$.

The missing numbers are both positive, multiply to give +6, and add to +5.

The two numbers are +3 and +2.

So $x^2 + 5x + 6 = (x + 3)(x + 2)$.

EXAMPLE 11 ▶ Factorise $x^2 - 7x + 6$.

The last sign is +, and so both brackets will have the same sign as –7x, giving $(x - \_)(x - \_)$.

The missing numbers are both negative, multiply to give +6, and add to –7.

The numbers are –1 and –6.

So $x^2 - 7x + 6 = (x - 1)(x - 6)$.

EXERCISE 5 ▶ Factorise these. (Notice that the last sign is always +.)

1 ▶	$x^2 - 3x + 2$	**3** ▶	$x^2 - 7x + 12$	**5** ▶	$x^2 - 9x + 8$
2 ▶	$x^2 - 4x + 3$	**4** ▶	$x^2 + 8x + 16$	**6** ▶	$x^2 - 2x + 1$

 EXERCISE 5* ▶ Factorise these. (Notice that the last sign is always +.)

1 ▶	$x^2 + 10x + 21$	**3** ▶	$x^2 - 16x + 64$	**5** ▶	$x^2 + 14x + 45$
2 ▶	$x^2 - 8x + 12$	**4** ▶	$x^2 - 18x + 72$	**6** ▶	$x^2 + 24x + 144$

KEY POINT ▶ • If the last sign in the expression is –, then the numbers in the brackets will have opposite signs.

EXAMPLE 12 ▶ Factorise $x^2 - 5x - 6$.

The last sign is –, and so both brackets will have opposite signs, giving $(x + \_)(x - \_)$. The missing numbers multiply to give –6 and add to –5.

The two numbers are +1 and –6.

Thus $x^2 - 5x - 6 = (x + 1)(x - 6)$.

EXERCISE 6 ▶ Factorise these. (Notice that the last sign is always –.)

1 ▶	$x^2 + x - 6$	**3** ▶	$x^2 - 4x - 12$	**5** ▶	$x^2 + 5x - 14$
2 ▶	$x^2 - 3x - 10$	**4** ▶	$x^2 - 9x - 10$	**6** ▶	$x^2 + 7x - 8$

EXERCISE 6* ▶ Factorise these. (Notice that the last sign is always –.)

1 ▶	$x^2 + x - 30$	**3** ▶	$x^2 + 7x - 60$	**5** ▶	$x^2 - 7x - 120$
2 ▶	$x^2 - 2x - 24$	**4** ▶	$x^2 - 9x - 70$	**6** ▶	$x^2 + 10x - 75$

EXERCISE 7

Factorise these. (Notice that the last signs are mixed.)

1 ▶ $x^2 - 3x + 2$ **3 ▶** $x^2 + 13x + 12$ **5 ▶** $x^2 - 8x + 16$

2 ▶ $x^2 + 2x - 3$ **4 ▶** $x^2 - 8x + 12$ **6 ▶** $x^2 + x - 20$

EXERCISE 7*

Factorise these. (Notice that the last signs are mixed.)

1 ▶ $x^2 + 8x - 20$ **3 ▶** $x^2 + 13x + 36$ **5 ▶** $x^2 + 8x - 48$

2 ▶ $x^2 - 7x - 18$ **4 ▶** $x^2 - 12x + 32$ **6 ▶** $3 + 2x - x^2$

SOLVING QUADRATIC EQUATIONS BY FACTORISATION

ACTIVITY 5

SKILLS

ANALYSIS

If $a \times b = 12$ what can be said about either a or b?

If $a \times b = 0$ what can be said about either a or b?

A little thought should convince you that either $a = 0$ or $b = 0$ (or both are zero).

EXAMPLE 13

Solve $(x + 2)(x - 3) = 0$.

Either $(x + 2) = 0$ or $(x - 3) = 0$.

If $(x + 2) = 0$, then $x = -2$.

If $(x - 3) = 0$, then $x = 3$.

There are two solutions: $x = -2$ or $x = 3$.

EXAMPLE 14

Solve $(x - 5)^2 = 0$.

$(x - 5)^2 = 0$ is the same as $(x - 5)(x - 5) = 0$.

If the first bracket $(x - 5) = 0$, then $x = 5$.

If the second bracket $(x - 5) = 0$, then $x = 5$.

There is one solution: $x = 5$.

EXERCISE 8

Solve these equations.

1 ▶ $(x + 1)(x + 2) = 0$ **3 ▶** $0 = (x - 7)(x - 2)$ **5 ▶** $x(x - 10) = 0$

2 ▶ $(x + 4)(x - 1) = 0$ **4 ▶** $(x + 8)^2 = 0$

EXERCISE 8*

Solve these equations.

1 ▶ $(x + 8)(x - 4) = 0$ **3 ▶** $x(x - 8) = 0$ **5 ▶** $(x + 1)(x - 1)(2x + 5) = 0$

2 ▶ $0 = (x + 21)(x - 5)$ **4 ▶** $(2x + 3)(4x - 3) = 0$

EXAMPLE 15

Solve $x^2 + 5x + 6 = 0$.

$x^2 + 5x + 6 = 0$ factorises to $(x + 3)(x + 2) = 0$.   (See Example 10)

$\Rightarrow x = -3$ or $x = -2$.

EXAMPLE 16

Solve $x^2 - 7x + 6 = 0$.

$x^2 - 7x + 6 = 0$ factorises to $(x - 1)(x - 6) = 0$.   (See Example 11)

$\Rightarrow x = 1$ or $x = 6$.

KEY POINT

- To solve a **quadratic equation**, rearrange it so that the right-hand side is zero. Then factorise the left-hand side.

EXAMPLE 17

Solve $x^2 - 5x = 6$.

$x^2 - 5x = 6$ must first be rearranged to $x^2 - 5x - 6 = 0$.

Then $x^2 - 5x - 6 = 0$ factorises to $(x + 1)(x - 6) = 0$.   (See Example 12)

$\Rightarrow x = -1$ or $x = 6$.

EXERCISE 9

Solve these for x.

1 ▶ $x^2 - 3x + 2 = 0$

3 ▶ $x^2 + 6x + 8 = 0$

5 ▶ $x^2 - 8x + 15 = 0$

2 ▶ $x^2 + x - 2 = 0$

4 ▶ $x^2 - x - 12 = 0$

6 ▶ $x^2 + 8x + 16 = 0$

EXERCISE 9*

Solve these for x.

1 ▶ $x^2 - 9x + 20 = 0$

4 ▶ $x^2 - 18x + 56 = 0$

7 ▶ $x^2 + 7x - 78 = 42$

2 ▶ $x^2 - 5x - 24 = 0$

5 ▶ $x^2 + 22x + 96 = 0$

3 ▶ $x^2 + 21x + 108 = 0$

6 ▶ $24x^2 - 48x - 72 = 0$

If the quadratic equation has only two terms, the working is easier.

EXAMPLE 18

Solve $x^2 - 12x = 0$.

$x^2 - 12x$ factorises to $x(x - 12)$.   (See Example 6)

So $x^2 - 12x = 0 \Rightarrow x(x - 12) = 0$.

Now, either $x = 0$ or $x - 12 = 0$, giving the two solutions $x = 0$ or $x = 12$.

EXAMPLE 19

Solve $x^2 - 9 = 0$.

You could factorise $x^2 - 9$ and continue with the **working**, but the following is easier:

$x^2 - 9 = 0 \Rightarrow x^2 = 9$

Square-rooting both sides gives $x = \pm\sqrt{9}$, so $x = 3$ or $x = -3$.
(Do not forget the negative square root!)

EXERCISE 10

Solve these for x.

1 ▶ $x^2 - 2x = 0$ **3 ▶** $x^2 - 25x = 0$ **5 ▶** $x^2 - 4 = 0$

2 ▶ $x^2 + 7x = 0$ **4 ▶** $x^2 + 23x = 0$ **6 ▶** $x^2 - 25 = 0$

EXERCISE 10*

Solve these for x.

1 ▶ $x^2 - 125x = 0$ **3 ▶** $x^2 - 64 = 0$ **5 ▶** $x^2 - 7 = 0$

2 ▶ $x^2 + 231x = 0$ **4 ▶** $x^2 - 169 = 0$ **6 ▶** $x^2 + 9 = 0$

PROBLEMS LEADING TO QUADRATIC EQUATIONS

EXAMPLE 20

The **product** of two **consecutive** even numbers is 120. What are the numbers?

Let the first number be x. The second even number is two more than x and can be written as $x + 2$.

Then $x \times (x + 2) = 120$ (Multiply out the bracket)

$x^2 + 2x = 120$ (Rearrange to equal zero)

$x^2 + 2x - 120 = 0$

$(x - 10)(x + 12) = 0$ (Factorise)

$x = 10 \text{ or } -12$

So, the numbers are 10 and 12 or −12 and −10.

There are two possible answers. Answering the question by 'trial and improvement' would find the positive answer, but probably not the negative answer.

EXAMPLE 21

SKILLS

PROBLEM
SOLVING AND
REASONING

The length of a rectangular terrace is 3 m more than the width. If the area is 28 m², find the length and width of the terrace.

Let x be the width in metres. Then the length is $(x + 3)$ metres.

The area is $x \times (x + 3) = 28$ (Multiply out the bracket)

$x^2 + 3x = 28$ (Rearrange to equal zero)

$x^2 + 3x - 28 = 0$ (Factorise)

$(x + 7)(x - 4) = 0$

$x = -7 \text{ or } x = 4$

x

$x + 3$

As the answer cannot be negative, the width is 4 m and the length is 7 m.

> **KEY POINTS**
>
> To form and solve a quadratic equation in a problem-solving context:
> - If relevant, draw a diagram and write all the information on it.
> - Use x to represent one unknown and define the other **variables** from this.
> - Form an equation to represent the situation.
> - Solve to find the unknown(s).
>
> If x represents a measurement such as length, it cannot have a negative value.

EXERCISE 11

1 ▶   When x is added to its square, x^2, the answer is 12. Find the two possible values of x.

2 ▶   When x is subtracted from its square, the answer is 20. Find the possible values of x.

3 ▶   Simone thinks of a number. She squares the number and adds twice the original number. The answer is 35. What are the possible original numbers?

4 ▶   A rectangle has a length of $(x + 5)$ cm and a width of x cm.
     a   Write down an expression for the area of the rectangle.
     b   If the area is 24 cm², find the value of x.

5 ▶   The length of a mobile phone screen is 6 cm more than its width. The area of the screen is 40 cm². Find the length and width of the screen.

6 ▶   The rectangles shown have the same area. Find x.

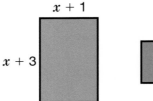
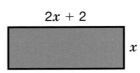

EXERCISE 11*

1 ▶   The product of two consecutive odd numbers is 143. Find two positive numbers and two negative numbers that **satisfy** the condition.

2 ▶   The length of a picture is 10 cm more than the width. The area is 1200 cm². Find the dimensions of the picture.

3 ▶   A ball is thrown vertically up so that its height above the ground after t seconds is $(15t - 5t^2)$ m. At what times is it 10 m above the ground?

4 ▶   The **sum** of the squares of two consecutive **integers** is 145. Find the two integers.

5 ▶   The sum of the first n integers 1, 2, 3, 4, …, n is given by the formula $\frac{1}{2}n(n+1)$. How many integers must be taken to add up to 210?

6 ▶   The sides of two **cubes** differ by 2 cm and their volumes differ by 152 cm³. Find the length of the side of the smaller cube.

EXERCISE 12

REVISION

Expand and simplify these.

1 ▶ $(x - 7)(x - 3)$ 2 ▶ $(x + 2)^2$ 3 ▶ $(x + 2)(x + 3)(x - 1)$

4 ▶ A rectangle with length $(x + 3)$ cm and width $(x + 2)$ cm has a square of length x cm cut out of it.

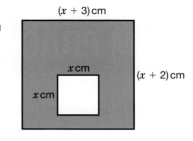

$(x + 3)$ cm

x cm

$(x + 2)$ cm

x cm

 a Find and simplify an expression for the area of the original rectangle.

 b Therefore, find an expression for the shaded area.

 c The shaded area is 26 cm². Find the value of x.

Factorise.

5 ▶ $x^2 - 36$ **6 ▶** $x^2 + 4x + 3$ **7 ▶** $x^2 + 2x - 8$

Solve for x.

8 ▶ $x^2 - 4x - 12 = 0$ **10 ▶** $x^2 - 36 = 0$

9 ▶ $x^2 - 5x = 0$ **11 ▶** $x^2 - x = 20$

12 ▶ The width of a laptop screen is 10 cm more than the height. The area of the screen is 600 cm². Find the dimensions of the screen.

EXERCISE 12* **REVISION**

Expand and simplify these.

1 ▶ $(x + 9)(x - 12)$ **2 ▶** $(2x - 3)^2$ **3 ▶** $(3x - 1)(2x + 3)$ **4 ▶** $(x + 3)(x - 2)(x + 5)$

5 ▶ The foot of a ladder is 2 m away from a vertical wall. The height that the ladder reaches up the wall is $\frac{1}{2}$ m less than the length of the ladder. Find the length of the ladder.

2 m

6 ▶ An abstract painting is a square of side 96 cm, and shows three circles that touch each other and the sides of the square. The top two circles have the same radius. What is the radius of the third circle?

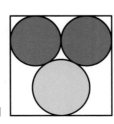

11 ▶ Two integers differ by 6. The sum of the squares of these integers is 116. Find the two integers.

12 ▶ The stopping distance of a car travelling at x kph is $\dfrac{x^2 + 30x}{150}$ m.

 a After braking, a car travels 12 m before stopping. Show that $x^2 + 30x = 1800$.

 b Find the value of x.

13 ▶ A square picture has a border 5 cm wide. The picture area is $\frac{4}{9}$ of the total area. Find the area of the picture.

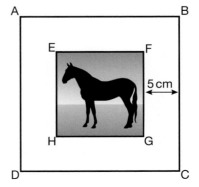

A   B

E   F

5 cm

H   G

D   C

Solve these for x.

7 ▶ $x^2 - 121 = 0$

8 ▶ $x^2 - 7x = 0$

9 ▶ $x^2 - x = 56$

10 ▶ $x^2 - 15x + 54 = 0$

EXAM PRACTICE: ALGEBRA 5

1 ▸ Expand and simplify these expressions.

   a $(x + 2)(x - 6)$

   b $(x - 7)^2$

   c $(x - 1)(x - 2)(x - 3)$ **[4]**

2 ▸ Factorise these expressions.

   a $x^2 - x$

   b $x^2 - 25$

   c $x^2 - 5x + 4$ **[5]**

3 ▸ Factorise and solve these for x.

   a $x^2 + 3x + 2 = 0$

   b $x^2 - 2x = 3$

   c $x^2 + 3x = 0$

   d $x^2 - 4 = 0$ **[8]**

4 ▸ A triangle has a base of $2x$ cm and a height of $(x + 1)$ cm.

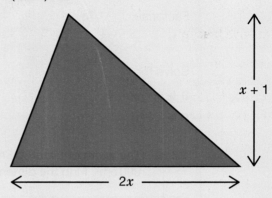

   a   Find and simplify an expression for the area of the triangle.

   b   Find x if the shaded area is 42 cm².   **[4]**

5 ▸ A rectangle with length $(2x + 1)$ cm and width $(x + 2)$ cm has a square of side x cut out of it.

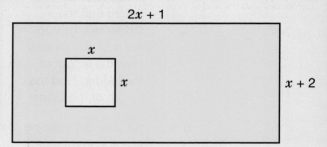

   a   Find and simplify an expression for the shaded area.

   b   The shaded area is 16 cm². Find the dimensions of the rectangle.   **[4]**

[Total 25 marks]

CHAPTER SUMMARY: ALGEBRA 5

MULTIPLYING BRACKETS

Use the word (mnemonic) FOIL.

From each bracket:

- multiply the First terms
- multiply the Outside terms
- multiply the Inside terms
- multiply the Last terms.

Then add the four terms and simplify.

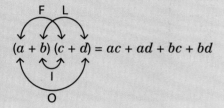

$$(a + b)(c + d) = ac + ad + bc + bd$$

You can multiply brackets in any order.

FACTORISING QUADRATIC EXPRESSIONS

With two terms:

$x^2 - ax = x(x - a)$
$x^2 - a^2 = (x - a)(x + a)$
$x^2 + a^2$ does not factorise.

With three terms:

The numbers in the brackets add up to the number in front of the x term.
If the number term is positive, then the numbers in the brackets will have the same sign as the x term.

$x^2 + 5x + 6 = (x + 3)(x + 2)$ $x^2 - 5x + 6 = (x - 3)(x - 2)$

If the number term is negative, then the numbers in the brackets will have opposite signs.

$x^2 - x - 6 = (x - 3)(x + 2)$ $x^2 + x - 6 = (x + 3)(x - 2)$

SOLVING QUADRATIC EQUATIONS BY FACTORISATION

Solve $x^2 - x = 6$.

$x^2 - x - 6 = 0$ — Rearrange the equation so that the right-hand side equals zero.

$(x - 3)(x + 2) = 0$ — Factorise the left-hand side.

$x = 3$ or $x = -2$ — Use the fact that $a \times b = 0 \Rightarrow a = 0$ or $b = 0$ (or both are zero) to solve.

PROBLEMS LEADING TO QUADRATIC EQUATIONS

Define your variable.

Change the word problem into a mathematical equation.

Solve the equation.

Choose the real-life solution.

GRAPHS 5

In computer-generated art and games, a picture can be drawn using straight lines to define regions which are then coloured in.

To do this mathematically you decide where to put the axes and then work out the equations of all the straight lines. To define the regions that will be coloured in, you need to use inequalities with two variables, usually x and y.

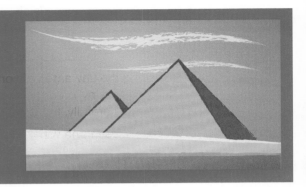

LEARNING OBJECTIVES

■ Represent inequalities on graphs

■ Interpret graphs of inequalities

■ Find the equations of lines perpendicular to a given line

■ Find the coordinates of the mid-point of a line

■ Find the length of a line

BASIC PRINCIPLES

■ Solving **inequalities** and showing the result on a number line: e.g. Solve $3x \geq x + 1$.

■ Positive and negative **gradients**: e.g. Find the gradient of the line passing through (1, 2) and (3, –4).

■ **Sketching** and plotting straight-line graphs: e.g. Sketch $y = 2x + 5$.

■ Rearranging equations: e.g. Make x the subject of $y = 3x - 7$.

REPRESENTING INEQUALITIES GRAPHICALLY

Inequalities in two **variables** can be represented on a graph. This makes them much easier to understand and solve.

EXAMPLE 1

Find the region representing $x + y \leq 4$.

First draw the line $x + y = 4$. This line divides the graph into two regions.

One of these regions **satisfies** $x + y \leq 4$.

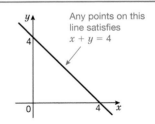

To decide which region satisfies $x + y \leq 4$, take any point in one of the regions, for example (1, 1).

Substitute $x = 1$ and $y = 1$ into $x + y$ to see if the result is less than or equal to 4.

$1 + 1 \leq 4$

So (1, 1) is in the required region, because it satisfies $x + y \leq 4$.

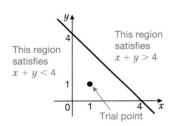

Therefore the required region is below the line $x + y = 4$.

Therefore this is the solution.

The line $x + y = 4$ is drawn as a solid line.

The unwanted region is shown shaded in the diagram.

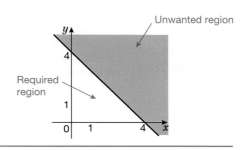

Shading the unwanted region makes it much easier to indentify regions when more than one inequality is involved. Sometimes you might be asked to shade the wanted region, so read the question carefully. In the work that follows, the unwanted region is always shown shaded.

Inequalities in one variable can also be represented on a graph.

EXAMPLE 2

Find the region that represents $y < 3$.

Draw the line $y = 3$ as a dotted line because points on the line do not satisfy $y < 3$.

Points below the line $y = 3$ have y values less than 3, so the required region is below the line, and the unwanted region above the line is shaded.

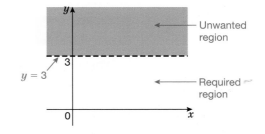

KEY POINTS

- Find the line representing the equality.
- If points on the line are required, draw a solid line. Otherwise, draw a dotted line.
- Find the required region by using any point that is not on the line.

EXERCISE 1

Describe the unshaded region in each graph.

1 ▶ 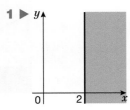 2 ▶ 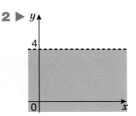 3 ▶ 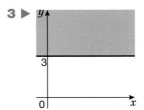 4 ▶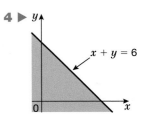

Illustrate each inequality on a graph.

5 ▶ $x < 1$ 6 ▶ $y \geq -2$ 7 ▶ $y \geq 8 - x$ 8 ▶ $y < 6 - 2x$

EXERCISE 1*

Describe the unshaded region in each graph.

1 ▶ 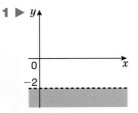 2 ▶ 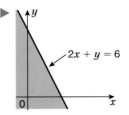 3 ▶ 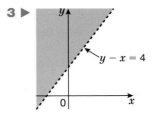 4 ▶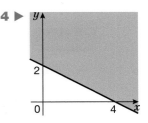

Illustrate each inequality on a graph.

5 ▶ $x \leq -5$ 6 ▶ $3x + 4y > 12$ 7 ▶ $y - 3x > 4$ 8 ▶ $2y - x \geq 4$

More than one inequality can be represented on a graph.

EXAMPLE 3 ▶ Illustrate on a graph the region that satisfies $1 \le x < 4$.

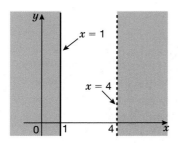

EXAMPLE 4 ▶ Find the region representing $x + y \le 4$ and $y - x < 2$.

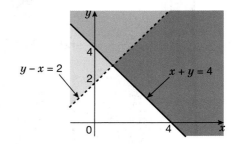

ACTIVITY 1

What would several inequalities drawn on one graph look like if the *wanted* region were shaded?

EXERCISE 2 ▶ Describe the unshaded region in the graph.

1 ▶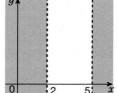

2 ▶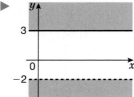

3 ▶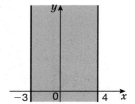

4 ▶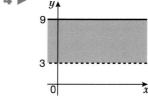

5 ▶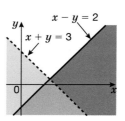

6 ▶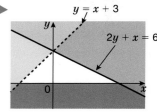

Illustrate each inequality on a graph.

7 ▶ $2 \le y < 5$

8 ▶ $x < -1$ or $x \ge 4$

9 ▶ $y > 5 - x$ and $y \ge 2x - 2$

10 ▶ $x \ge 0$, $y > 2x - 3$ and $y \le 2 - \dfrac{x}{2}$

EXERCISE 2* ▶ Describe the unshaded region in the graph.

1 ▶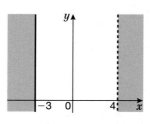

2 ▶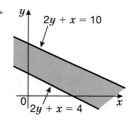

3 ▶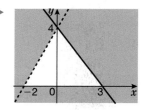

4 ▶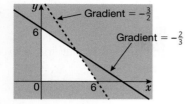

In Questions 5 and 6, illustrate each inequality on a graph.

5 ▶ $y \geq 2x$, $x + 2y \leq 4$ and $y + 2x > 1$

6 ▶ $x \geq 0$, $y \geq 0$, $y < \dfrac{x}{2} + 4$ and $y \leq 6 - 2x$

7 ▶   **a** On a graph, draw the triangle with **vertices** $(-2, 0)$, $(0, 2)$ and $(2, -2)$.

       b Find the three inequalities that define the region inside the triangle.

       c What is the smallest integer value of y that satisfies all three inequalities?

8 ▶   Illustrate on a graph the region that satisfies $y > x^2 - 4$ and $y \leq 0$.

9 ▶   Illustrate on a graph the region that satisfies both of the inequalities $y \geq x^2 - x - 2$ and $y < x + 6$.

10 ▶   Two numbers have a **sum** that is less than 16 and a **product** that is more than 36. Illustrate on a graph all the number pairs that satisfy these conditions, and list all the positive integers that satisfy these conditions.

PERPENDICULAR LINES

There is a simple connection between the gradients of **perpendicular** lines.

ACTIVITY 2

On graph paper draw axes with the x-axis labelled from 0 to 10 and the y-axis labelled from 0 to 6. Use the same **scale** for each axis.

Plot the points A (1, 0), B (3, 2) and C (0, 5). Join A to B and B to C.

Measure the angle between the lines AB and BC.

Find m_1, the gradient of AB and m_2, the gradient of CB. Multiply the two gradients together and put your results in a copy of this table.

Point A	Point B	Point C	m_1	m_2	$m_1 \times m_2$
(1, 0)	(3, 2)	(0, 5)			
(5, 0)	(3, 4)	(5, 5)			
(10, 3)	(7, 2)	(6, 5)			

Repeat for the two other sets of points in the table. Comment on your results.

Investigate if your conclusion is true for some other points.

Copy and complete this statement.
Lines which are .... have $m_1 \times m_2 = -1$.

KEY POINTS

- If $m_1 \times m_2 = -1$ then the two lines are perpendicular.
- If one line has a gradient m_1, the gradient of any perpendicular line is $m_2 = -\dfrac{1}{m_1}$. This is found by making m_2 the subject of $m_1 \times m_2 = -1$.
- If $m_1 = m_2$ then the lines are parallel.

EXAMPLE 5

a Find the gradient of a line perpendicular to a line of gradient –2.

b Find the gradient of a line perpendicular to a line of gradient $\dfrac{1}{3}$.

---

a Substituting in $m_2 = -\dfrac{1}{m_1}$ gives $m_2 = \dfrac{-1}{-2} = \dfrac{1}{2}$

b $m_2 = \dfrac{-1}{\frac{1}{3}} = -1 \times \dfrac{3}{1} = -3$

EXAMPLE 6

SKILLS

REASONING

Show that the line joining A (–2, 5) to B (–1, 1) is perpendicular to the line joining P (1, 3) to Q (5, 4).

Draw a sketch diagram and mark on the rise and run for each line.

The gradient of AB is $-\dfrac{4}{1} = -4$.

The gradient of PQ is $\dfrac{1}{4}$.

The product of the gradients is $-4 \times \dfrac{1}{4} = -1$

$\Rightarrow$ the lines AB and PQ are perpendicular.

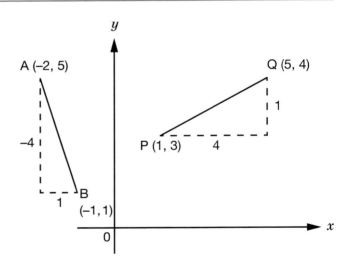

EXAMPLE 7

Find the equation of the straight line perpendicular to $y = 3x - 2$ that passes through (3, 1).

The diagram shows what is required.

The gradient of $y = 3x - 2$ is 3.

Perpendicular lines have a gradient of $-\dfrac{1}{3}$ $\left(m_2 = -\dfrac{1}{m_1}\right)$.

The required equation is $y = -\dfrac{x}{3} + c$.

Substitute $x = 3$, $y = 1$ to find c.

$1 = -\dfrac{3}{3} + c \Rightarrow c = 2$

The required equation is $y = -\dfrac{x}{3} + 2$.

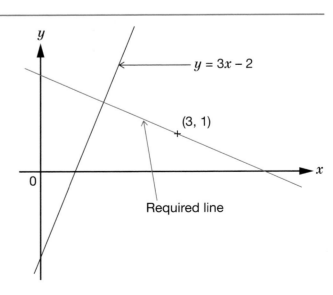

EXERCISE 3

Write down the gradients of lines perpendicular to the lines with gradient.

1 ▶   2
2 ▶   –3
3 ▶ $-\frac{1}{3}$
4 ▶ $1\frac{1}{2}$

For Questions 5 and 6, find the gradients of lines parallel and perpendicular to AB when

5 ▶   A is (1, 1) and B is (3, 2)

6 ▶   A is (1, 2) and B is (2, 5)

For Questions 7–9, decide whether AB is parallel, perpendicular or has no relationship to PQ.

7 ▶   A (1, 4) B (2, 0) P (0, 1) Q (5, 2)

8 ▶   A (3, 3) B (4, 6) P (4, 1) Q (6, 7)

9 ▶   A (0, 2) B (2, 1) P (3, 2) Q (5, 6)

10 ▶   Find the equation of the straight line perpendicular to $y = -2x + 1$ which passes through (4, 3).

11 ▶   A vertical pole for a lighting structure at an outdoor concert was held up during construction by wire ropes as shown in the diagram.

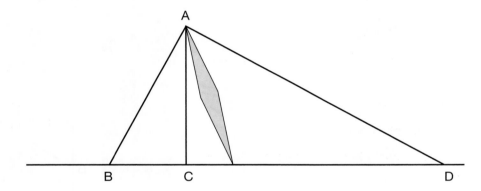

A is 6 m above the ground, C is vertically below A, BD is 15 m and BC is 3 m.

a Find the gradient of AB.

b Find the gradient of AD.

c Are AB and AD at right angles? Give a reason for your answer.

EXERCISE 3*

Write down the gradients of lines perpendicular to the lines with gradient

1 ▶   4
2 ▶ $-\frac{1}{5}$
3 ▶ $\frac{3}{2}$
4 ▶   –6

For Questions 5 and 6, find the gradients of the lines parallel and perpendicular to AB when

5 ▶   A is (–4, –1) and B is (4, 2)

6 ▶   A is (–3, 1) and B is (1, 6)

7 ▶   Find the equation of the line that is perpendicular to $y = 8x - 14$ and passes through (0, 8.4).

8 ▶ An architect is designing a roof on a building. The **cross-section** is shown in the diagram. The point D is vertically below A, BC and FE are 3 m and CD is 5 m.

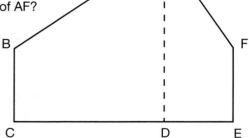

   a The gradient of AB is 0.8. How high is A above D?
   b AF is at right angles to AB. What is the gradient of AF?
   c What is the width of the building?

9 ▶ 'Speedy Pot' Joe has 'been snookered'. The situation is shown in the diagram where corner A of the snooker table has been taken as the origin.

Joe wants to hit the red ball R at (5, 8) with the white ball W at (2, 2) but the pink ball P at (4, 6) is in the way. He aims the white ball at a point B (0, 5) on the cushion at the edge of the table.

   a What is the gradient of the line BW?

The ball bounces back along the line BC which is perpendicular to BW.

   b What is the gradient of BC?
   c What is the equation of the line BC?
   d Does the white ball hit the red ball?

10 ▶ Find b such that the line from the origin to (3, 4b) is perpendicular to the line from the origin to (3, −b).

11 ▶ The vertices of a triangle are A (−2, 1), B (6.1, 3.7) and C (1, c). Find the value of c so that angle ABC is a right angle.

12 ▶ Find the value of p if the line joining (3, p) to (7, −4p) is perpendicular to the line joining (−1, −3) to (3, 7).

MID-POINTS

Example 8 shows how to find the point midway between two points.

EXAMPLE 8

Find the point midway between A (1, 3) and B (3, −1).

The x-coordinate of the **mid-point** is
the **mean** of the x-coordinates of A and B $=\dfrac{1+3}{2}=2$

The y-coordinate of the mid-point is
the mean of the y-coordinates of A and B $=\dfrac{3+-1}{2}=1$

The mid-point is (2, 1).

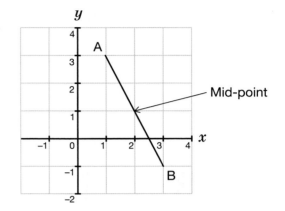

KEY POINTS

- The mid-point between (x_1, y_1) and (x_2, y_2) is $\left(\dfrac{x_1+x_2}{2}, \dfrac{y_1+y_2}{2}\right)$.
- Check your answer using a **sketch**.

EXAMPLE 9

Find the equation of the perpendicular **bisector** of the points A and B given in Example 8.

The gradient of AB is $\dfrac{-4}{2}=-2$.

The gradient of the perpendicular to AB is $\dfrac{-1}{-2}=\dfrac{1}{2}$.

The equation is $y=\dfrac{1}{2}x+c$.

From Example 8, the mid-point is (2, 1).

Substituting $x=2$ and $y=1$ gives $1=\dfrac{1}{2}\times 2+c \Rightarrow c=0$.

The equation is $y=\dfrac{x}{2}$.

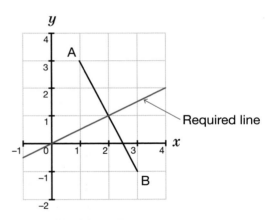

USING PYTHAGORAS' THEOREM

Pythagoras' Theorem can be used to find the distance between two points on a line.

EXAMPLE 10

Find the distance between A (−2, 1) and B (1, 5).

The diagram shows a right-angled triangle with AB as the **hypotenuse**.

AC is found by subtracting the x-coordinates.

AC = 1 − (−2) = 3

BC is found by subtracting the y-coordinates.

BC = 5 − 1 = 4

$AB^2 = 3^2 + 4^2 = 9 + 16 = 25 \Rightarrow AB = \sqrt{25} = 5$

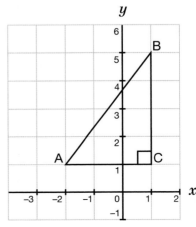

KEY POINTS

- The mean of the coordinates gives the coordinates of the mid-point.
- Use Pythagoras' Theorem to find the distance between two points.
- Draw a diagram to check if your answer is reasonable.

EXERCISE 4

1 ▶ Find the mid-point between A (2, 5) and B (10, 7).

2 ▶ Find the mid-point between A (−3, −4) and B (5, −2).

3 ▶ Find the distance between A (8, 1) and B (2, 6).

4 ▶ Find the distance between A (−5, 1) and B (−3,−4).

5 ▶ Find the equation of the perpendicular bisector of the line AB when A is (4, 1) and B is (−2, −1).

6 ▶ Show that the points A (−1, 1), B (11, 6), C (6, 18) and D (−6, 13) form a square.

EXERCISE 4*

1 ▶ Find the equation of the perpendicular bisector of the line AB when A is (4, 0) and B is (−2, 4).

2 ▶ The four points A (4, 2), B (10, 4), C (10, 8) and D (6, 10) form a **quadrilateral**. The mid-point of AB is P, the mid-point of BC is Q, the mid-point of CD is R and the mid-point of AD is S. Show that PQRS is a **parallelogram**.

3 ▶ A is (0, −4), B is (2, 2) and C is (−1, 3).

   a Show that the points A, B and C form a right-angled triangle by
    (i) showing that the triangle satisfies Pythagoras' Theorem
    (ii) showing that two of the sides are perpendicular.

   b Find the area of triangle ABC.

Q4 HINT
A median of a triangle is the line passing through a vertex and the mid-point of the opposite side.

4 ▶ A is (1, 5), B is (5, 3) and C is (6, 7). Find the equation of the median of the triangle ABC that passes through C.

5 ▶ l is the line $y = 2x + 2$ and A is (6, 4).

   a Find the equation of the straight line through A perpendicular to l.

   b The line in part a crosses l at the point B. Calculate the coordinates of B.

   c AB is the shortest distance from A to the line l. Calculate the distance AB.

Q5b HINT
Use simultaneous equations.

6 ▶ A is (5, 6), B is (7, 2) and C is (−2, 5).

   a Find the equation of the perpendicular bisector of AB.

   b Find the equation of the perpendicular bisector of AC.

Q6c HINT
Use simultaneous equations.

   c These two lines cross at point D. Calculate the coordinates of D.

   d Calculate the distances AD, BD and CD.

   e What is the geometrical connection between the points A, B, C and D?

EXERCISE 5

For Questions 1–4, describe the *unshaded* region in each graph.

1 ▶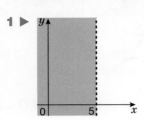

2 ▶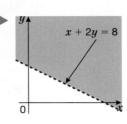

3 ▶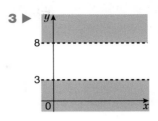

4 ▶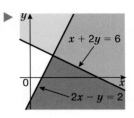

For Questions 5–8, illustrate each inequality on a graph.

5 ▶ $x \geq -1$ **6 ▶** $y < 10 - x$ **7 ▶** $-1 < x \leq 3$ **8 ▶** $y < 1$ or $y \geq 2$

9 ▶ Work out the mid-point of the line AB when A is (3, –5) and B is (–9, 6).

10 ▶ Work out the length of the line AB when A is (8, 1) and B is (1, 6).

11 ▶ Find the equation of the straight line perpendicular to $y = \frac{1}{3}x + 1$ that passes through (4, 0).

12 ▶ Find the equation of the perpendicular bisector of the line AB when A is (1, 1) and B is (5, –1).

EXERCISE 5*

For Questions 1–4, describe the *unshaded* region in each graph.

1 ▶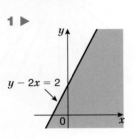

2 ▶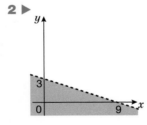

3 ▶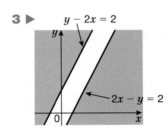

4 ▶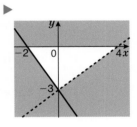

For Questions 5–8, illustrate each inequality on a graph.

5 ▶ $2x + 5y \leq 10$ **6 ▶** $y - 2x < -2$

7 ▶ $2y > x$, $y + 2x \leq 4$ and $y > 2x + 2$ **8 ▶** $x > 0$, $y \geq 0$, $3x + 4y \leq 12$ and $5x + 2y \leq 10$

9 ▶   **a** On a graph, draw the triangle with vertices (3, 4), (1, 0) and (0, 2.5).

     b Find the three inequalities that define the region inside the triangle.

     c What is the smallest integer value of x that satisfies all three inequalities?

10 ▶ Find the equation of the perpendicular bisector of the line AB when A is (–1, –2) and B is (1, 6).

11 ▶ A (5, 5), B (6, 12), C (1, 7) and the origin are the four vertices of a **rhombus**. Show that the diagonals **bisect** each other at right angles.

12 ▶ Find the shortest distance from the point A (–2, 1) to the line $x + 2y = 2$.

EXAM PRACTICE: GRAPHS 5

1   Illustrate on a graph the inequality $-1 < x \leq 3$, shading the unwanted regions.   **[2]**

2   **a** Draw a set of x and y axes from 0 to 10 units. On these axes, draw these graphs.
     (i) $x = 4$
     (ii) $y = 6$
     (iii) $3x + 2y = 18$

   b Use these lines to shade the regions not satisfied by the inequalities $x \leq 4$, $y \leq 6$, $3x + 2y \leq 18$, $x \geq 0$ and $y \geq 0$.

   c State the coordinates of the point with integer coordinates in the unshaded region that is furthest from the origin.   **[8]**

   HINT No calculation is required.

3   A is (1, –2) and B is (3, 6).

   a Find the length of AB.

   b Find the mid-point of AB.

   c Find the equation of the perpendicular bisector of AB.   **[7]**

4   A is (3, –2) and B is (5, 8). AB is the diameter of a circle and C is the centre.

   a Find the coordinates of C.

   b Find the radius of the circle.

   c Show that point D (–1, 2) lies on the circle.

   d A circle theorem says that AD is perpendicular to BD. Show that this is true.   **[8]**

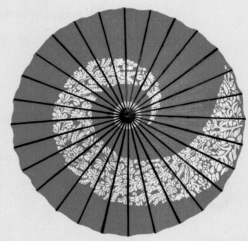

[Total 25 marks]

CHAPTER SUMMARY: GRAPHS 5

REPRESENTING INEQUALITIES GRAPHICALLY

Find the line representing the inequality.

If points on the line are required, draw a solid line. Otherwise draw a dotted line.

Find the required region by using any point that is not on the line.

- Find the region satisfied by the inequalities $x \geq 0$, $y \geq 0$, $x + y \leq 3$ and $y < 2$ by drawing suitable lines and shading the unwanted regions.

The solid line means that solutions can lie on the line ($\leqslant$)

Solutions in this region

The broken line means that the solutions cannot lie on the line ($<$)

PERPENDICULAR LINES

When two lines are perpendicular, the product of the gradients is −1.

If one line has a gradient m_1 then the gradient of any perpendicular line is $m_2 = -\dfrac{1}{m_1}$.

MID-POINTS

The mean of the coordinates gives the coordinates of the mid-point.

The mid-point between (x_1, y_1) and (x_2, y_2) is
$$\left(\frac{x_1 + x_2}{2}, \frac{y_1 + y_2}{2} \right).$$

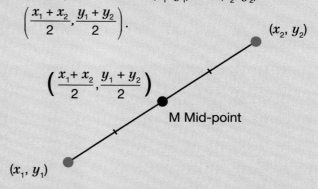

$\left(\dfrac{x_1 + x_2}{2}, \dfrac{y_1 + y_2}{2} \right)$

M Mid-point

(x_1, y_1)

(x_2, y_2)

USING PYTHAGORAS' THEOREM

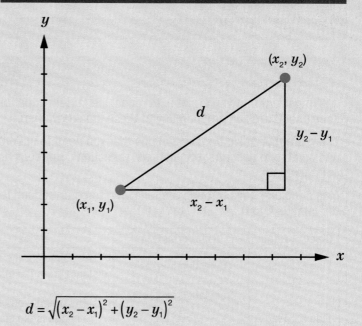

$$d = \sqrt{\left(x_2 - x_1\right)^2 + \left(y_2 - y_1\right)^2}$$

Use Pythagoras' Theorem to find the distance between two points.

SHAPE AND SPACE 5

Islamic art and architecture has many repeating shapes and patterns that have been turned (rotated), flipped (reflected), moved (translated) and enlarged to create beautiful images.

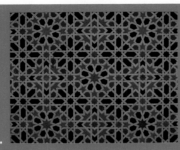

In computer graphics, reflections, rotations, enlargements and translations (sliding movements) are all used to position and shape objects and to change viewing positions.

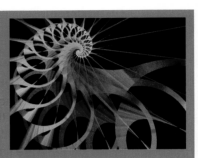

LEARNING OBJECTIVES

- Translate a shape using a vector
- Describe a translation
- Reflect a shape in a mirror line
- Describe a reflection
- Rotate a shape about a centre of rotation
- Describe a rotation
- Enlarge a shape about a centre of enlargement
- Describe an enlargement
- Carry out and describe combinations of transformations

TRANSFORMATIONS

BASIC PRINCIPLES

It is important that you are able to recognise certain equations of lines on a Cartesian graph. Many of these are shown here.

There are four basic transformations that you need to understand and be able to describe: translations, reflections, rotations and enlargements.

Flag F (object) goes through the following transformations to give the images A to D.

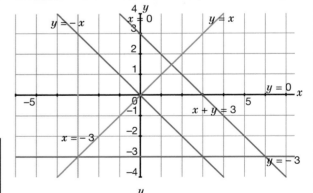

Object	Image	Transformation	Notes
Flag F	Flag A	Reflection in y-axis	All points are the same distance from the mirror line.
Flag F	Flag B	Translation by **vector** $\begin{pmatrix} -6 \\ -4 \end{pmatrix}$	The orientation of the image is the same after a translation.
Flag F	Flag C	Rotation of 90° clockwise about O	+ angles are anti-clockwise − angles are clockwise.
Flag F	Flag D	Enlargement of **scale factor** 2 about O	If the scale factor k is defined $(0 < k < 1)$ then the object is decreased in size.

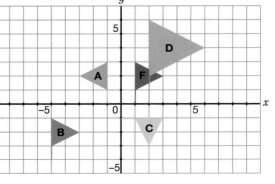

TRANSLATIONS

Transformations move a shape to a different position. Translation is a type of transformation. In a translation, all points of the shape move the same distance in the same direction.

HINT

To describe a translation fully, state the translation vector.

The lengths of the sides of the shape and the angles do not change, so the object and the image are said to be congruent.

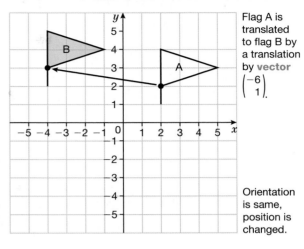

Flag A is translated to flag B by a translation by **vector** $\begin{pmatrix} -6 \\ 1 \end{pmatrix}$.

Orientation is same, position is changed.

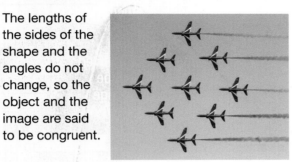

KEY POINT

• A column vector $\begin{pmatrix} x \\ y \end{pmatrix}$ is used to describe a translation.

The top number gives the movement parallel to the x-axis. The bottom number gives the movement parallel to the y-axis.

EXERCISE 1

7th

1 ▶ Describe the translation that moves each shape to its image where A is the object, A′ is the image.

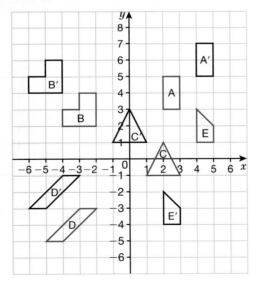

2 ▶ Copy this diagram.

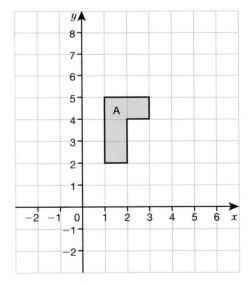

Translate shape A by the vector

a $\begin{pmatrix} 2 \\ 3 \end{pmatrix}$ to B

b $\begin{pmatrix} 3 \\ -4 \end{pmatrix}$ to C

c $\begin{pmatrix} -2 \\ 0 \end{pmatrix}$ to D

d $\begin{pmatrix} 0 \\ 3 \end{pmatrix}$ to E

e $\begin{pmatrix} -1 \\ -4 \end{pmatrix}$ to F.

3 ▶ Describe these translations using column vectors.

    a B to A

    b A to C

    c B to E

    d D to E

    e E to D

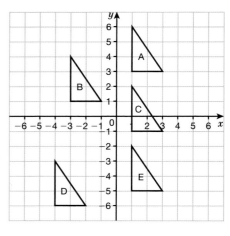

4 ▶ Copy the diagram.
Translate shape A by the vector

    a $\begin{pmatrix} 1 \\ 3 \end{pmatrix}$ to B   **b** $\begin{pmatrix} 2 \\ 3 \end{pmatrix}$ to C   **c** $\begin{pmatrix} 0 \\ -7 \end{pmatrix}$ to D

    d $\begin{pmatrix} -2 \\ 0 \end{pmatrix}$ to E   **e** $\begin{pmatrix} -5 \\ -3 \end{pmatrix}$ to F.

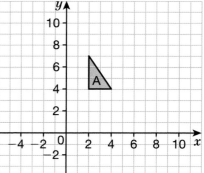

5 ▶ Describe these translations using column vectors.

    a A to B

    b C to E

    c D to C

    d F to B

    e B to F

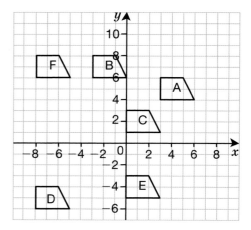

EXERCISE 1*

1 ▶ Draw a coordinate grid from −6 to +6 on both axes.

    a Plot a triangle with **vertices** at (1, 1), (3, 1) and (1, −2). Label the triangle P.

    b (i) Translate triangle P by vector $\begin{pmatrix} 1 \\ 4 \end{pmatrix}$. Label the image Q.

    (ii) Translate triangle Q by vector $\begin{pmatrix} -2 \\ 1 \end{pmatrix}$. Label the image R.

    c Describe the translation of triangle P to triangle R, using a single vector.

2 ▶ Draw a coordinate grid from −6 to +6 on both axes.

    a Plot a triangle with vertices at (−2, 3), (0, 1) and (1, 4). Label the triangle P.

b (i) Translate triangle P by vector $\begin{pmatrix} 2 \\ -7 \end{pmatrix}$.

(ii) Translate this new triangle by vector $\begin{pmatrix} -4 \\ 3 \end{pmatrix}$. Label the image Q.

c Describe the translation of triangle P to triangle Q, using a single vector.

3 ▶ a A shape is translated by vector $\begin{pmatrix} -2 \\ 3 \end{pmatrix}$ followed by a translation by vector $\begin{pmatrix} 3 \\ 1 \end{pmatrix}$.

What is the **resultant vector** (single vector that performs the translation in one step)?

b The resultant of two vectors is $\begin{pmatrix} 3 \\ -4 \end{pmatrix}$. The first vector is $\begin{pmatrix} -1 \\ 2 \end{pmatrix}$. What is the second vector?

4 ▶ a A shape is translated by vector $\begin{pmatrix} 3 \\ 4 \end{pmatrix}$ followed by a translation by vector $\begin{pmatrix} 1 \\ -3 \end{pmatrix}$.
What is the resultant vector?

b What is the resultant vector for a translation of $\begin{pmatrix} a \\ b \end{pmatrix}$ followed by a translation of $\begin{pmatrix} c \\ d \end{pmatrix}$?
Explain your answer.

5 ▶ Point Q (1, 2) is the image of point P after it has been translated by vector $\begin{pmatrix} 1 \\ 2 \end{pmatrix}$,

then vector $\begin{pmatrix} 5 \\ -3 \end{pmatrix}$. Find the coordinates of P.

REFLECTIONS AND ROTATIONS

Reflections and rotations are two other types of transformations.

In reflections and rotations, the lengths of the sides of the shape and the angles do not change, so the object and the image are said to be congruent.

EXAMPLE 1

SKILLS

REASONING

Describe the rotation that takes shape A onto shape B.

Rotation anti-clockwise 90° about (1, −1)

(Always give the direction, angle and centre of rotation.)

Trace the shape.

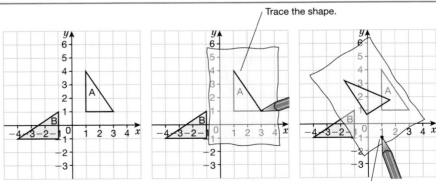

Rotate the tracing paper about a fixed point with your pencil. Repeat for different positions until your tracing ends up on top of the image.

• Reflection

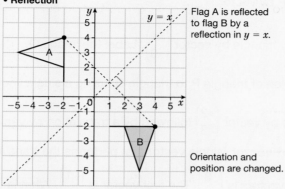

Flag A is reflected to flag B by a reflection in $y = x$.

Orientation and position are changed.

To describe a reflection fully, state the line of reflection.

• Rotation

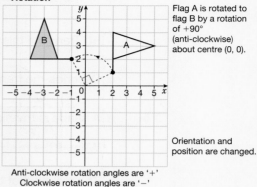

Flag A is rotated to flag B by a rotation of +90° (anti-clockwise) about centre (0, 0).

Orientation and position are changed.

Anti-clockwise rotation angles are '+'
Clockwise rotation angles are '−'

To describe a rotation fully, state the angle of rotation, direction and centre of rotation.

EXERCISE 2

1 ▶ Describe the reflection that maps
 a P onto Q   **b** P onto R
 c P onto S   **d** P onto T.

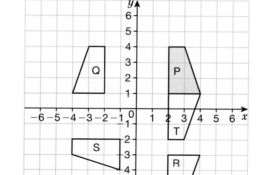

2 ▶ Describe the reflection that maps
 a A onto B   **b** A onto C.

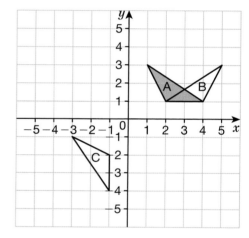

3 ▶ Describe the rotation that takes each shape to its image.

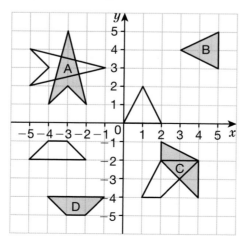

4 ▶ Describe the reflection that maps
 a P onto Q   **b** P onto R
 c P onto S   **d** P onto T.

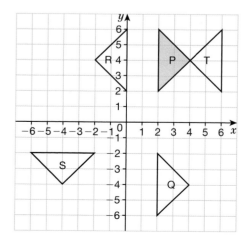

5 ▶ Describe the reflection that maps
   a A onto B   b A onto C.

6 ▶ Describe the rotation that takes each
   shape to its image.

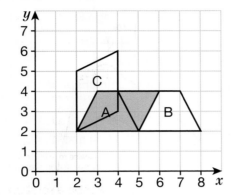

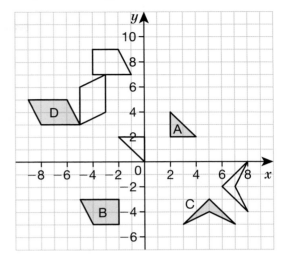

EXERCISE 2*

1 ▶ Draw a coordinate grid from −5 to +5 on both axes.

   a Draw rectangle Q with vertices at coordinates (1, 1), (1, 3), (5, 3) and (5, 1).

   b Reflect rectangle Q in the x-axis. Label the image R.

   c Reflect rectangle R in $x = 1$. Label the image S.

   d Reflect rectangle S in the x-axis. Label the image T.

   e Describe the single reflection that maps rectangle T onto rectangle Q.

2 ▶ Draw a coordinate grid from −5 to +5 on both axes.

   a Draw shape A with vertices at coordinates (−1, 2), (−1, 4), (1, 4) and (1, 2).

   b Reflect shape A in the line $y = x$. Label the image B.

   c Reflect shape A in the line $y = -x$. Label the image C.

   d Reflect shape A in the x-axis. Label the image D.

   e Describe the reflection that maps shape D onto shape B.

3 ▶ Draw a coordinate grid from −5 to +5 on both axes.

   a Draw shape A with vertices at coordinates (1, 1), (1, 3), (3, 3) and (4, 1).

   b Reflect shape A in the line $y = x$. Label the image B.

   c Reflect shape B in the y-axis. Label the image C.

   d Describe the transformation that takes shape A onto shape C.

4 ▶ Draw a coordinate grid from −8 to +8 on both axes.

   a Draw a rectangle Q with vertices at coordinates A (3, 2), B (1, 2), C (1, 5) and D (3, 5).

   b Reflect rectangle Q in the y-axis. Label the image R.

   c Reflect rectangle R in $y = -1$. Label the image S.

   d Reflect rectangle S in the y-axis. Label the image T.

   e Describe the single reflection that maps rectangle T onto rectangle Q.

5 ▶ Draw a coordinate grid from −5 to +5 on both axes.

    a Draw shape A with vertices at coordinates (−2, 1), (−4, 1) and (−3, 3).

    b Reflect shape A in the line $y = x$. Label the image B.

    c Reflect shape A in the line $y = -x$. Label the image C.

    d Reflect shape C in the x-axis. Label the image D.

    e Describe the reflection that maps shape D onto shape B.

6 ▶ Draw a coordinate grid from −8 to +8 on both axes.

    a Draw shape A with coordinates (2, 1), (4, 1), (4, 4) and (2, 4).

    b Rotate rectangle A
        (i)   90° anti-clockwise about (2, 1)
        (ii)   180° about (0, 0)
        (iii) 90° clockwise about (3, 1)
        (iv) 180° about (−1, 4)
        (v)   90° anti-clockwise about (1, 4)
        (vi) 180° about (−1, 0).

    Label your results **(i)**, **(ii)** etc.

ENLARGEMENTS

An enlargement changes the size of the object, but not the shape of the object. So the lengths of the sides of the shape change, but the angles of the shape do not change. To enlarge a shape, all the side lengths of the shape are multiplied by the same scale factor.

EXAMPLE 2

SKILLS

REASONING

Arrowhead A has been transformed into arrowhead B by an enlargement of scale factor 3 about centre (5, −2).

Note: all the points from the object (arrowhead A) have had their distances from the centre trebled (multiplied by 3) to transform onto their image points on arrowhead B.

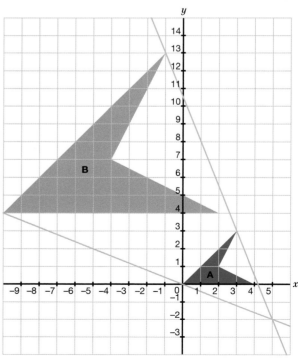

EXAMPLE 3

SKILLS

REASONING

Triangle A has been transformed into triangle B by an enlargement of scale factor $\frac{1}{2}$ about the origin.

Notes:

The distance between each point of the image and the origin is half the original distance.

Even though the image is smaller than the object, the transformation is still called 'an enlargement'.

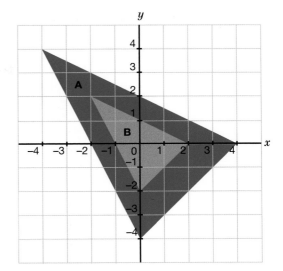

KEY POINTS

• **Enlargement**

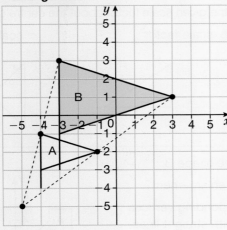

Flag A is enlarged to flag B by a scale factor 2 about centre $(-5, -5)$.

HINT To describe an enlargement fully, state the scale factor and centre of enlargement.

The orientation is the same*, the position has changed.

*If scale factor is positive.

EXERCISE 3

1 ▶ Copy the diagram, drawing the x-axis from −2 to 8 and the y-axis from −2 to 5.

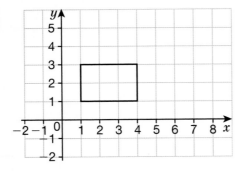

Enlarge the rectangle by scale factor 2, with these centres of enlargement.

a (1, 4)   **b** (1, 1)   **c** (3, 2)

2 ▶ Copy this diagram and draw

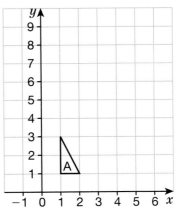

a an enlargement with scale factor 3, centre (0, 0)

b an enlargement with scale factor 1.5, centre (1, 1)

3 ▶ Copy the diagram.

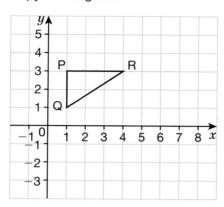

Enlarge the triangle by scale factor 2, with these centres of enlargement.

a (3, 5)   **b** (4, 3)   **c** (2, 2)

4 ▶ Copy these diagrams. Enlarge each shape by the scale factor given.

a scale factor $\frac{1}{2}$

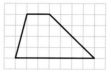

b scale factor $\frac{1}{3}$

5 ▶ Copy and enlarge each shape by the given scale factor about the centre of enlargement shown.

a scale factor $\frac{1}{3}$

b scale factor $\frac{1}{2}$

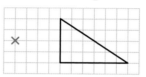

c scale factor $\frac{1}{3}$

EXERCISE 3*

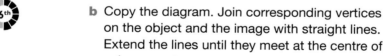

1 ▶ Shape A has been enlarged to give shape B.

     a What is the scale factor of the enlargement?

     b Copy the diagram. Join corresponding vertices on the object and the image with straight lines. Extend the lines until they meet at the centre of enlargement.

     c Write the coordinates of the centre of enlargement.

     d Copy and complete to describe the enlargement from A to B.
     Enlargement by scale factor __, centre (__, __).

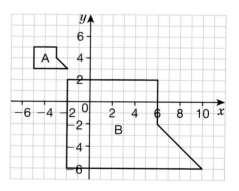

2 ▶ Triangle ABC has been enlarged to give triangle PQR.

     a What is the scale factor of the enlargement?

     b Copy the diagram. Join corresponding vertices on the object and the image with straight lines. Extend the lines (make the lines longer) until they meet at the centre of enlargement.

     c Write down the coordinates of the centre of enlargement.

     d Copy and complete to describe the enlargement from A to B.
     Enlargement by scale factor __, centre (__, __).

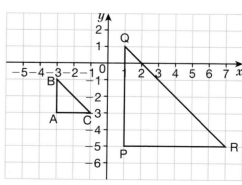

3 ▶ Copy and enlarge each shape by the given scale factor about the centre of enlargement shown.

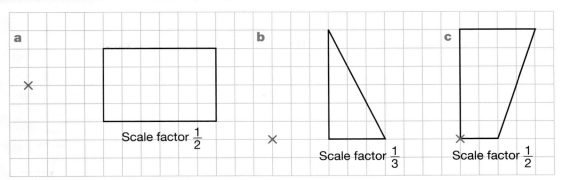

a Scale factor $\frac{1}{2}$

b Scale factor $\frac{1}{3}$

c Scale factor $\frac{1}{2}$

4 ▶   **a** Describe the enlargement that maps shape A onto shape P.

b Describe the enlargement that maps shape C onto shape R.

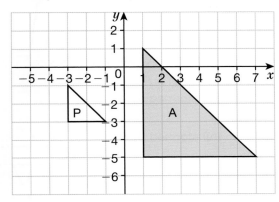

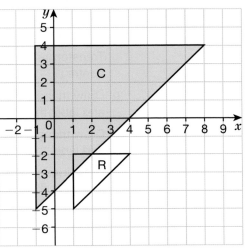

5 ▶ Describe the enlargement that maps shape A onto shape P.

a

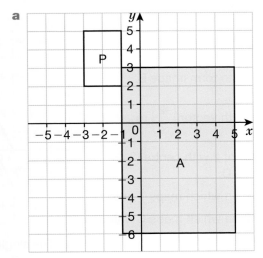

b

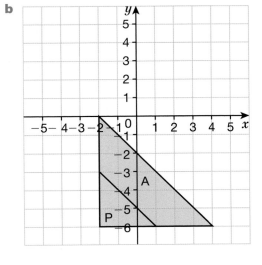

COMBINED TRANSFORMATIONS

Combined transformations are the result of a number of **successive transformations** one after the other.

The final image can be difficult to recognise when compared to the original object.

Note: if an operation is performed in reverse it is called the **inverse**. For example, the inverse of an enlargement of scale factor 3 about O is an enlargement of $\frac{1}{3}$ about O.

> **EXAMPLE 4**
>
> **SKILLS**
>
> **PPROBLEM SOLVING**

a Plot points (1, 2), (1, 4) and (2, 4) to form triangle P.

Transformation A is a translation of $\begin{pmatrix} -5 \\ -4 \end{pmatrix}$.

Transformation B is a reflection in $y = x$.

Transformation C is a clockwise rotation of 90° about centre (1, 1).

b Draw triangle P after it has been transformed by A and label this image Q.

c Draw triangle P after it has been transformed by B and label this image R.

d Draw triangle R after it has been transformed by C and label this image S.

e Describe fully the single transformation that maps P onto S.

a–d

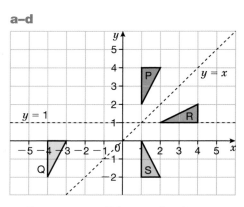

e S maps onto P by a reflection in $y = 1$.

> **EXAMPLE 5**
>
> **SKILLS**
>
> **PROBLEM SOLVING**

Triangle T is shown in the diagram.

a T is reflected in line M to form image A. Draw triangle A.

b A is reflected in the line $y = -1$ to form image B. Draw triangle B.

c T goes through a translation with vector $\begin{pmatrix} -2 \\ -3 \end{pmatrix}$ to form image C. Draw triangle C.

d T is enlarged by a scale factor of 2 with centre (3, 2) to form image D. Draw triangle D.

e Describe fully the transformation which maps T onto B.

f Describe fully the transformation which maps C onto D.

a–d

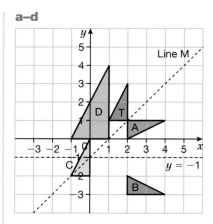

e The single transformation that maps T onto B is a clockwise rotation of 90° about centre (0, −1).

f The single transformation that maps C onto D is an enlargement of scale factor 2 about centre (−1, −4).

EXERCISE 4

1 ▶ Copy this diagram and shape A only on a coordinate grid from −6 to +6.

a Translate shape A by vector $\begin{pmatrix} -7 \\ 3 \end{pmatrix}$.
Label the image B.

b Reflect shape B in the line $x = -2$.
Label the image C.

2 ▶ Copy the diagram from Question 1 and shape P only.

a Translate shape P by vector $\begin{pmatrix} 6 \\ -2 \end{pmatrix}$.
Label the image Q.

b Reflect shape Q in the line $y = 1$. Label the image R.

c Translate shape R by vector $\begin{pmatrix} -6 \\ -2 \end{pmatrix}$.
Label the image S.

d Describe the reflection that maps shape P onto shape S.

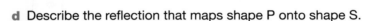

3 ▶ Copy the triangle from Question 1 and triangle V only.

a Rotate triangle V through 180° about the point (−1, 0). Label the image W.

b Reflect triangle W in the line $y = x$. Label the image X.

c Translate triangle X by vector $\begin{pmatrix} -9 \\ 0 \end{pmatrix}$. Label the image Y.

d Describe the single transformation that maps triangle V onto triangle Y.

4 ▶ A tessellation (pattern with shapes) is made by transforming shape A.

Copy the tessellation onto a coordinate grid with the vertices of
A at (0, 0), (3, 0), (3, 1), (1, 1), (1, 2) and (0, 2).

Describe the transformation that would move shape

a A to B   **b** B to C   **c** C to D   **d** A to E   **e** E to F.

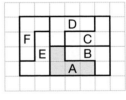

5 ▶ **a** Describe fully the single transformation that maps
triangle A onto triangle B.

b Reflect triangle B in the y-axis and label the
image C. Then translate shape C by vector $\begin{pmatrix} 4 \\ 0 \end{pmatrix}$
and label the image D.

c Describe the single transformation that maps
triangle B onto triangle D.

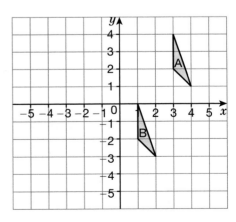

EXERCISE 4*

1 ▶ Copy this diagram and shape A only on a coordinate grid from −6 to +6 on both axes.

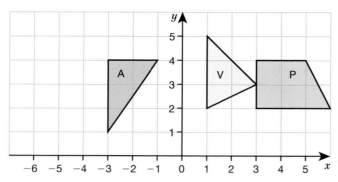

a Translate shape A by vector $\begin{pmatrix} 3 \\ -2 \end{pmatrix}$.
Label the image B.

b Reflect shape B in the line $y = -2$.
Label the image C.

2 ▶ Copy the diagram from Question 1 and shape P only on a coordinate grid from −6 to +6 on both axes.

a Reflect shape P in the line $y = 1$. Label the image Q.

b Rotate shape Q through 180° about the point (1, −1). Label the image R.

c Translate shape R by vector $\begin{pmatrix} 2 \\ 4 \end{pmatrix}$. Label the image S.

d Describe the single transformation that maps shape P onto shape S.

3 ▶ Copy the diagram from Question 1 and shape V only on a coordinate grid from −6 to +6 on both axes.

a Reflect triangle V in the line $y = x$. Label the image W.

b Translate triangle W by vector $\begin{pmatrix} -4 \\ -2 \end{pmatrix}$. Label the image X.

c Rotate triangle X through 90° anti-clockwise about the point (−2, 2). Label the image Y.

d Describe the single transformation that maps triangle V onto triangle Y.

4 ▶ A company has based its logo on a triangle.

Draw a coordinate grid from −6 to +6 on both axes.

a Plot the points (0, 0), (1, 2) and (2, 2) and join them to make a triangle.

b Reflect the triangle in the line $y = x$.

c Draw more reflections to complete the logo.

d The company now wants to make a version of the logo 12 units tall, to go on a desk sign. What transformation will convert the original logo into the larger one?

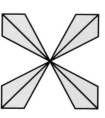

5 ▶ **a** Describe fully the single transformation that maps triangle P onto triangle Q.

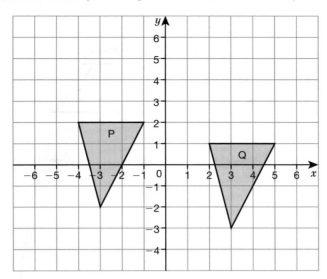

b Reflect triangle P in the x-axis and label the image S.

Then translate shape S by vector $\begin{pmatrix} 6 \\ 3 \end{pmatrix}$ and label the image R.

c Describe the single transformation that maps triangle Q onto triangle R.

EXERCISE 5

REVISION

1 ▶ Find the image of point A (1, 2) after it has been transformed by a

a reflection in the x-axis

b reflection in the y-axis

c rotation of 90° anti-clockwise about O

d translation by vector $\begin{pmatrix} 3 \\ 4 \end{pmatrix}$.

2 ▶ Find the image of point B (4, −1) after it has been transformed by a

a reflection in the x-axis

b reflection in the y-axis

c rotation of 90° clockwise about O

d translation by vector $\begin{pmatrix} 7 \\ -1 \end{pmatrix}$.

3 ▶ Draw a set of axes where $-4 \le x \le 7$ and $-5 \le y \le 5$ and draw the triangle A on these axes where the vertices are given by (1, 2), (3, 2) and (3, 4).

Find the image of triangle A after it has been

a reflected in the x-axis and label this triangle B

b reflected in the y-axis and label this triangle C

c translated by vector $\begin{pmatrix} -4 \\ -3 \end{pmatrix}$ and label this triangle D

d enlarged by a scale factor of 2 about centre (0, 4) and label this triangle E.

4 ▶   **a** Copy this diagram including flag F.

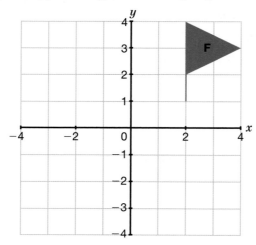

b Reflect flag F in the x-axis and label this flag A.

c Reflect flag F in the y-axis and label this flag B.

d Reflect flag A in the y-axis and label this flag C.

e Describe the single transformation that takes flag F to flag C.

5 ▶   Draw a coordinate grid from −6 to 6 on both axes.

Draw triangle A with vertices at (2, 1), (2, 2) and (4, 2).

a Translate triangle A by the vector $\begin{pmatrix} -2 \\ 4 \end{pmatrix}$. Label the image B.

b Reflect triangle A in the line $y = -1$. Label the image C.

c Reflect triangle A in the line $y = x$. Label the image D.

d Rotate triangle A 180° about (0, −2). Label the image E.

e Rotate triangle A 90° anti-clockwise about (−1, −2). Label the image F.

f Describe the single transformation that maps triangle B onto triangle E.

g Describe the single transformation that maps triangle D onto triangle C.

6 ▶   The image of point P (a, b) is at the point Q (5, 10) after it has been reflected in the line $x = 1$.
Find the values of a and b.

EXERCISE 5*   **REVISION**

1 ▶   The image of point P (a, b) is at point Q (5, 10) after it has been transformed in the
following order:

• Reflection in the y-axis

• Translation by vector $\begin{pmatrix} 3 \\ 4 \end{pmatrix}$

• Rotation by 90° in a clockwise direction about O.

Find the values of a and b.

2 ▶ The triangle A has vertices at (0, 4), (4, 0) and (4, 4) *after* it has been transformed from triangle B in the following order:

- Reflection in the line $y = x$.
- Enlargement by scale factor of 2 about O.
- Rotation of 180° about O.

Find the coordinates of triangle B.

3 ▶ **a** Copy this diagram including triangle A.

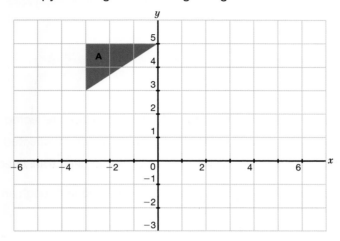

Triangle A goes through transformations in the following order:

- Reflection in $y = -x$ to produce image triangle B
- A 180° rotation about (0, 2) to produce image triangle C.

b Triangle D is the image of triangle C after a rotation of 180° about (3, 1). Draw triangles B, C and D on the same axes.

c Describe the single transformation that maps triangle D onto triangle B.

4 ▶ Draw a coordinate grid from −6 to 6 on both axes.

Draw **trapezium** P with vertices at (−4, −1), (−6, −1), (−6, −4) and (−4, −2).

a Reflect shape P in the line $y = x$. Label the image Q.

b Rotate shape Q 90° anti-clockwise about (0, −1). Label the image R.

c Translate shape R by the vector $\begin{pmatrix} -4 \\ 6 \end{pmatrix}$. Label the image S.

d Rotate shape S 90° anti-clockwise about (1, 6). Label the image T.

e Reflect shape T in the line $y = x$. Label the image U.

f Describe the single transformation that maps shape U onto shape P.

g Describe the single transformation that maps shape S onto shape Q.

5 ▶   **a** Copy this diagram including triangle A and line L.

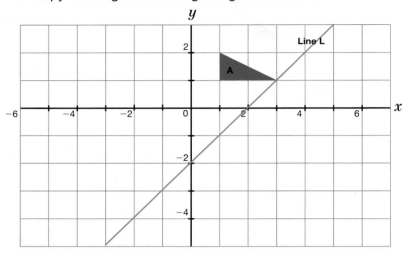

- Triangle B is the image of triangle A after it has been reflected in line L.
- Triangle C is the image of triangle B after it has been reflected in $x = -1$.
- Triangle D is the image of triangle A after it has been translated by vector $\begin{pmatrix} -3 \\ -4 \end{pmatrix}$.
- Triangle E is the image of triangle D after it has gone through an enlargement of scale factor $\frac{1}{2}$ with centre 0.

b Draw triangles B, C, D and E on the same axes.

c Describe the single transformations that map

    (i) triangle A onto triangle C

    (ii) triangle E onto triangle A.

6 ▶   The image of point P (x, y) is at point Q (a, b) after it has been transformed in the following order:

- Reflection in the x-axis
- Translation by vector $\begin{pmatrix} 4 \\ 3 \end{pmatrix}$
- Rotation by 90° in a clockwise direction about (0, 0).

Find the coordinates of P in terms of a and b.

EXAM PRACTICE: SHAPE AND SPACE 5

1 Draw a coordinate grid from –6 to 6 on both axes. Draw triangle J with vertices at (–2, 3), (2, 3) and (1, 5).

   a Translate triangle J by the vector $\begin{pmatrix} 3 \\ -3 \end{pmatrix}$. Label the image K.

   b Reflect triangle K in the line $y = -x$. Label the image L.

   c Reflect triangle L in the line $x = -3$. Label the image M.

   d Describe the single transformation that maps triangle M onto triangle J. **[8]**

2 Draw a coordinate grid from –6 to 6 on both axes. Draw triangle A at (–2, –1), (–1, –1) and (–1, 1).

   a Rotate triangle A 90° clockwise about (1, 2). Label the image B.

   b Enlarge triangle B by a scale factor of 2, centre of enlargement (–4, 6). Label your image C.

   c Translate triangle C by the vector $\begin{pmatrix} 2 \\ -6 \end{pmatrix}$. Label the image D.

   d Rotate triangle D 90° anti-clockwise about (–3, –5). Label the image E.

   e Describe the single transformation that maps triangle E onto triangle A. **[12]**

3 The image of point P (a, b) is at point Q (10, 10) *after* transformations in the following order:

   • Reflection in $y = x$

   • Rotation of 90° clockwise about O

   • Translation by vector $\begin{pmatrix} -2 \\ 4 \end{pmatrix}$

   • Enlargement of scale factor 2 about O.

Find the values of a and b. **[5]**

[Total 25 marks]

CHAPTER SUMMARY: SHAPE AND SPACE 5

TRANSFORMATIONS

The four basic transformations must be described clearly with the precise definitions shown below.

It is useful to know how some standard lines appear on a graph such as $y = x$, $y = -x$, $x = 1$, $y = 2$ and $x + y = 4$ etc.

Centres of rotation can usually be found by careful use of tracing (transparent) paper.

TRANSLATIONS

All points of the shape move the same distance in the same direction.

To describe a translation, use a column vector: $\begin{pmatrix} x \\ y \end{pmatrix}$.

REFLECTIONS

To describe a reflection, give the mirror line.

ROTATIONS

To describe a rotation, give the angle of rotation (turn), direction of rotation (clockwise or anti-clockwise) and centre of rotation.

All three pieces of information are required.
(+ angles are anti-clockwise and − angles are clockwise.)

ENLARGEMENTS

To describe an enlargement of a shape, the centre of enlargement and scale factor must be given.

All the side lengths of the shape are multiplied by the same scale factor.

When a centre of enlargement is given, multiply the distance from the centre to each point on the shape by the scale factor.

When the scale factor is a positive fraction less than 1, the image is smaller than the object.

To find the centre of enlargement, join corresponding points on the object and image.

The lengths of the sides of the shape change but the angles of the shape do not change.

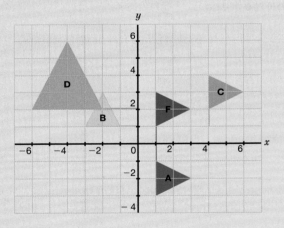

OBJECT	IMAGE	TRANSFORMATION
Flag F	Flag A	Reflection in x-axis ($y = 0$)
Flag F	Flag C	Translation by vector $\begin{pmatrix} 3 \\ 1 \end{pmatrix}$
Flag B	Flag D	Enlargement scale factor 2 centre O

HANDLING DATA 4

To be able to analyse random events and how likely they are to occur, mathematicians have used probability theory since the 16th century. One of the earliest known works on probability, '*On Casting the Die*', was written in the 16th century by an Italian mathematician, Cardano.

Girolamo Cardano (1501–1576) ▶

LEARNING OBJECTIVES

- Use a sample space diagram to record all possible outcomes
- Find the probability of mutually exclusive outcomes and events

- Find the probability of an event not happening
- Estimate probabilities from experimental data
- Find the expected number of outcomes

PROBABILITY – SINGLE EVENTS

BASIC PRINCIPLES

Consider these statements. They all involve a degree of uncertainty, which could be estimated through experiment or using previous knowledge.

- I doubt I will ever win the lottery.

- My dog will probably not live more than 5 years.
- It is unlikely to snow in the Sahara Desert.
- Roses will probably never grow at the South Pole.

EXPERIMENTAL PROBABILITY

It is possible to find the experimental probability, p(A), of A occurring through an experiment.
The experiment should include a number of **trials** to see how often event A happens.

KEY POINTS

- p(A) means the probability of event A happening.

- p(A') means the probability of event A not happening.

- p(A) = $\dfrac{\text{number of times } A \text{ occurs}}{\text{total number of trials}}$

EXAMPLE 1

SKILLS

REASONING

Event A is that the same bird lands on Mrs Leung's bird table before 9am each day. It does this on 40 days over a period of 1 year (365 days).

a Estimate the probability that tomorrow event A happens.

b Estimate the probability that tomorrow event A does not happen.

a $p(A) = \frac{40}{365} = \frac{8}{73}$

b $p(A') = \frac{325}{365} = \frac{65}{73}$

Note: $p(A) + p(A') = 1$

RELATIVE FREQUENCY

KEY POINT

- **Relative frequency** or experimental probability $= \dfrac{\text{number of successes}}{\text{total number of trials}}$

EXAMPLE 2

SKILLS

MODELLING

Bill is interested in analysing the probability that, when a piece of toast with butter falls, it will land with the buttered side facing up. He thinks that this event, A, is unlikely to happen.

He then carries out eight trials, with the results shown in this table.

Trial number	1	2	3	4	5	6	7	8
Butter lands upwards	✗	✓	✗	✗	✓	✓	✗	✗
Relative frequency	$\frac{0}{1} = 0$	$\frac{1}{2}$	$\frac{1}{3}$	$\frac{1}{4}$	$\frac{2}{5}$	$\frac{3}{6}$	$\frac{3}{7}$	$\frac{3}{8}$

He plots the results on a relative frequency diagram.

From these eight trials, Bill estimates that the probability of his toast landing buttered-side up is $\frac{3}{8}$.

How could he improve his estimation of $p(A)$? Comment on Bill's initial theory.

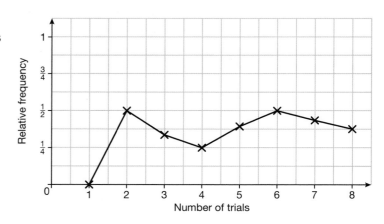

EXERCISE 1

1 ▶ Heidi believes that a particular die lands on the odd numbers more often than the even numbers, so she carries out ten trials. The results are given in this table.

Trial number	1	2	3	4	5	6	7	8	9	10
Odd number	☑	✓	✓	✗	✓	✗	✓	✗	✓	✓

a Draw a relative frequency diagram to investigate Heidi's suspicion.

b What conclusion do these results lead to? How could the experiment be improved?

2 ▶ In the UK, April has a reputation for being a particularly wet month. The data in this table was collected by a weather station in Edinburgh for the first 20 days in one April.

Day number	1	2	3	4	5	6	7	8	9	10
Rain	✓	✗	✗	✓	✓	✓	✗	✗	✓	✓
Day number	11	12	13	14	15	16	17	18	19	20
Rain	✗	✓	✓	✓	✓	✗	✗	✓	✓	✗

a Draw a relative frequency diagram to investigate the experimental probability of rain in Edinburgh in the first 20 days of April.

b What can you conclude from this data?

3 ▶ A spinner for a word game is an irregular pentagon that has five sections, each with a letter A, B, C, D or E. Sanjeev is a keen player, and he experiments to see if he can calculate an estimate of the probability that the spinner will land on a vowel. The results are shown as ticks (a vowel) and crosses (no vowel).

✓	✓	✗	✗	✗
✗	✗	✗	✓	✓
✓	✓	✗	✗	✓
✗	✗	✓	✗	✓

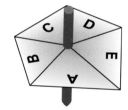

Draw a relative frequency diagram to investigate the experimental probability of the spinner landing on a vowel.

EXERCISE 1*

1 ▶ Pierre is a basketball shooter, and he practises hard to improve this particular skill. He makes 12 attempts from the left-hand side of the court and 12 from the right. His results are shown in these tables.

Left-hand side

✗	✗	✓	✗	✓	✓
✓	✓	✗	✓	✓	✓

Right-hand side

✗	✗	✗	✓	✗	✗
✗	✗	✓	✓	✗	✓

Event L is defined as a successful shot coming from the left-hand side of the court.

Event R is defined as a successful shot coming from the right-hand side.

a Draw a relative frequency diagram to estimate p(L) and p(R).

b What advice would you now give to Pierre based on this evidence?

2 ▶ The table shows the results of rolling a six-sided die.

NUMBER	FREQUENCY	RELATIVE FREQUENCY
1	23	
2	22	
3	21	
4	18	
5	9	
6	7	

a Copy and complete the table, calculating the relative frequency for each outcome.
b What is the experimental probability of rolling a 6?
c When the die is rolled 500 times, how many times would you expect to get a 6?
d Is the die fair? Give a reason for your answer.

3 ▶ A bag contains 100 marbles (small glass balls) of similar size and texture. The marbles are either white or purple, and the number of each is not known. A marble is **randomly** taken from the bag and replaced before another is taken out. 20 marbles are chosen in this way. The results are shown in this table.

W	W	P	P	W	W	W	P	W	W
P	P	W	W	W	W	W	P	P	P

Event W is defined as a white marble being taken out, and event P is defined as a purple one being taken out.

a Use these values to estimate the values of p(W) and p(P). Comment on your findings.
b Estimate how many marbles of each colour are in the bag.

ACTIVITY 1

A famous experiment in probability is Buffon's needle, in which a sewing needle of length x centimetres is dropped onto a sheet of paper with parallel lines drawn on it that are x centimetres apart. Event A is defined as the needle landing across a line.

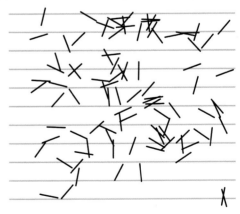

a Draw a relative frequency diagram to find an estimate of p(A) using at least 50 trials.
b Complicated probability theory predicts that

$$p(A) = \frac{2}{\pi}$$

Compare your result with the one above and carry out and record more trials yourself to see if your result becomes closer to the expected probability of event A.

THEORETICAL PROBABILITY

If all possible outcomes are equally likely, it is possible to find out how many of these outcomes should be event A. This means to calculate the theoretical probability of event A which is written as p(A).

KEY POINT

• $p(A) = \dfrac{\text{number of successful outcomes}}{\text{total number of possible outcomes}}$

EXAMPLE 3

A fair die is rolled. Calculate the probability of a **prime number** being rolled.

SKILLS

PROBLEM SOLVING

The prime numbers for this experiment are 2, 3 and 5.

Event A is the event of a prime number appearing.

$p(A) = \dfrac{3}{6}$ (3 is the number of desired outcomes, and 6 is the total number of possible outcomes)

$\quad\;\; = \dfrac{1}{2}$

EXAMPLE 4

A coin with heads on both sides is tossed. If event A is defined as the coin landing head side up, calculate $p(A)$ and $p(A')$.

SKILLS

PROBLEM SOLVING

$p(A) = \dfrac{2}{2} = 1$ (a certainty)

$p(A') = \dfrac{0}{2} = 0$ (an impossibility)

Heads

KEY POINT

• If A is an event, $0 \leq p(A) \leq 1$.

ACTIVITY 2

Copy this **scale** across your page.

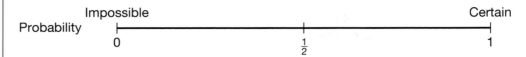

Impossible   Certain
Probability
0                                  $\frac{1}{2}$ 1

Label the scale, marking approximately where you think the probability of these five events $A–E$ should be placed.

- A hockey captain wins the toss at the start of a match (A).
- A heart is taken out from a pack of playing cards (B).
- A heart is not taken out from a pack of playing cards (C).
- You will be taken away by aliens on your way home from school today (D).
- Your teacher will be wearing shoes for your next geography lesson (E).

If A is an event, it either occurs (A) or it does not occur (A').

It is certain that nothing else can happen.

A card is randomly selected from a pack of 52 playing cards. Calculate the probability that a queen is not chosen.

Event Q is defined as a queen is chosen.

$$p(Q') = 1 - p(Q) = 1 - \frac{4}{52} = \frac{48}{52} = \frac{12}{13}$$

- $p(A) + p(A') = 1$

or, perhaps more usefully,

- $p(A') = 1 - p(A)$

EXPECTED FREQUENCY

If a die is rolled 60 times it would be reasonable to expect ten 6's to turn up.

This figure is obtained by multiplying the number of trials by the probability of the event.

Expected number of 6's = $60 \times \frac{1}{6} = 10$

Ten is not necessarily the exact number of 6's that will occur every time, but it is the most likely number.

- Expected frequency = number of trials × probability of the event

SAMPLE SPACE

A sample space (sometimes called a probability space) is a diagram showing all the possible outcomes. This enables probabilities to be easily calculated. This is useful when there are not too many outcomes to consider.

EXAMPLE 6

SKILLS

MODELLING

The diagram shows the probability space for a pack of 52 playing cards containing the four suits of hearts, diamonds, spades and clubs.

Ace	2	3	4	5	6	7	8	9	10	Jack	Queen	King
♥	♥	♥	♥	♥	♥	♥	♥	♥	♥	♥	♥	♥
♦	♦	♦	♦	♦	♦	♦	♦	♦	♦	♦	♦	♦
♠	♠	♠	♠	♠	♠	♠	♠	♠	♠	♠	♠	♠
♣	♣	♣	♣	♣	♣	♣	♣	♣	♣	♣	♣	♣

From the diagram it is a clear that if a single card is randomly taken from this 52-card pack then:

$p(\text{red card}) = \dfrac{26}{52} = \dfrac{1}{2}$ $p(\text{black king}) = \dfrac{2}{52} = \dfrac{1}{26}$

$p(\text{odd diamond}) = \dfrac{5}{52}$ $p(\text{black prime}) = \dfrac{8}{52} = \dfrac{2}{13}$

EXERCISE 2

1 ▶ Nelson is a keen collector of tropical fish. He collects different types of fish. He has four guppies, three angel fish, two cat fish, and one Siamese fighting fish. The tank has to be cleaned, so he randomly catches one of these fish in his net. Calculate the probability that the fish is

a a guppy

b an angel fish

c a tiger fish

d not a Siamese fighting fish.

2 ▶ A letter is chosen randomly from a collection of tiles with a single letter on each that spell the word PERIODONTOLOGY. Calculate the probability that it is

a an O

b a T

c a vowel

d a consonant.

3 ▶ A card is randomly selected from a pack of 52 playing cards. Calculate the probability that it is

a a red card

b a king

c a **multiple** of 3

d an ace, jack, queen or king.

4 ▶ The **bar chart** shows the colour of socks worn by pupils in class 5C.

If a pupil is chosen at random from 5C, calculate the probability that he or she will be wearing

a grey (G) socks

b white (W) socks

c red (R) or black (B) socks

d not red socks.

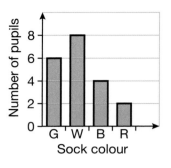

5 ▶ A fair ten-sided die with numbers from 1 to 10 on it is thrown. Calculate the probability of getting

a a 1

b an even number

c a number which has an **integer** square root

d a number of at most 7 and at least 4.

6 ▶ The table gives the numbers of boys and girls in a group who wear glasses.

	GLASSES	NO GLASSES	TOTAL
BOYS		10	
GIRLS	6		18
TOTAL			32

a Copy and complete the table.

A person is picked at random. What is the probability the person is

b a boy without glasses

c a girl?

d Given that a girl is picked at random, what is the probability that she does not wear glasses?

7 ▶ A coin is fixed so that it has the probability of $\frac{1}{3}$ of landing on a tail. If this coin is tossed 30 times, how many times would you expect to get heads?

8 ▶ It is estimated that the probability of a rainy day in Lagos, Nigeria in March is $\frac{1}{4}$. Work out an estimate for the number of dry days in Lagos from 1 March to 28 March.

EXERCISE 2*

1 ▶ A black die and a white die are thrown together and their scores are added. Copy and complete the sample space table showing all 36 possible outcomes.

a Use your table to calculate the probability of getting

(i) a total of 6

(ii) a total more than 10

(iii) a total less than 4

(iv) a prime number.

b What is the most likely total?

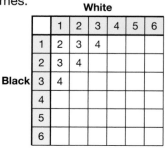

2 ▶ Four marbles are in a red bag. They are numbered 2, 3, 5 and 7. A green bag contains more marbles numbered 11, 13, 17 and 19. Two marbles, one from each bag, are randomly selected and the **difference** in the two scores is noted.

   a Construct a suitable sample space table to calculate the probability of obtaining

   (i) a score of 6   **(ii)** a score of at most 8

   (iii) a score of at least 12   **(iv)** a square number.

   b What are the least likely scores?

3 ▶ A regular five-sided spinner is spun twice and the scores are multiplied. Copy and complete the sample space table.

Use the table to calculate the probability of scoring

   a an odd number

   b a number less than 9

   c a number of at least 15

   d a triangular number.

First spin

		1	2	3	4	5
	1	1	2	3		
	2	2	4			
Second spin	3	3				
	4					
	5					

4 ▶ Three vets record the number of allergic reactions experienced by puppies given the same vaccination.

VET	NO. OF PUPPIES VACCINATED	NO. OF ALLERGIC REACTIONS
X	50	3
Y	60	7
Z	70	10

   a Calculate the probability that a puppy injected by vet X or Y will experience an allergic reaction.

   b Calculate the probability that a puppy injected by vet Y or Z will not experience any reaction.

   c If 7650 puppies are given this injection in a particular year, estimate how many of them will show signs of an allergy.

5 ▶ A regular three-sided spinner numbered 2, 4 and 6 is spun and a six-sided die is thrown. The highest number is noted; if the two numbers are equal, that number is noted.

Using a sample space or other method, calculate the probability of getting

   a a multiple of 3

   b a number less than 4

   c a non-prime number

   d two consecutive numbers.

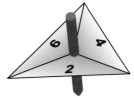

6 ▶ Five discs numbered 1, 2, 3, 4 and 5 are placed in bag X. Three discs numbered 1, 2 and 3 are placed in bag Y. One disc is taken out from X and one from Y. These represent the coordinates of a point on the positive x-axis and y-axis respectively, for example (1, 3). Calculate the probability that after one selection from each bag, the selected point

    a lies on the line $y = x$

    b lies on the line $x = 2$

    c lies on the line $y = 2x - 5$

    d lies on the curve $y = x^2 - 6$.

7 ▶ A pond contains 20 tadpoles, of which f are frog tadpoles and the others are toad tadpoles.

If 10 more frog tadpoles are added to the pond, the probability of catching a frog tadpole is doubled. Find f.

◀ Toad tadpole   ▶ Frog tadpole

8 ▶ A dartboard is in the shape of an **equilateral triangle** inside which a circle is perfectly inscribed. A dart is randomly thrown at the board (assume that it hits the board).

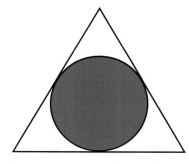 

    a Given that $\tan 60° = \sqrt{3}$ and $\sin 60° = \dfrac{\sqrt{3}}{2}$, show that the probability of the dart hitting the board inside the circle is $\dfrac{\pi}{3\sqrt{3}}$.

    b If 100 darts are thrown at the board, and they all hit the board, how many would you expect to land outside the circle?

9 ▶ The table gives the probability of getting each of 1, 2, 3 and 4 on a biased 4-sided spinner.

NUMBER	1	2	3	4
PROBABILITY	$4x$	$3x$	$2x$	x

Work out the probability of getting

    a 2 or 4   **b** 1 or 2 or 3.

ACTIVITY 3

The information in the table was compiled by the League of Dangerous Sports. Order the sports in terms of their safety.

Comment on your findings.

ACTIVITY	DEATHS OVER 5-YEAR PERIOD	PARTICIPATION OF ADULTS (MILLIONS)
Air sports	51	1
Badminton	3	59
Boating/sailing	69	23
Cricket	2	20
Fishing	50	37
Football	14	128
Golf	1	110
Gymnastics	1	14
Hockey	2	9
Horse riding	62	39
Motor sports	65	11
Mountaineering	51	6
Running	9	200
Rugby	2	12
Swimming/diving	191	370
Tennis	1	45

EXERCISE 3

REVISION

7th

1 ▶ Alec wants to estimate his chances of scoring a goal from a penalty.

He does this by taking 12 penalties in a row with these results.

✓	✗	✓	✓	✗	✓	✓	✓	✗	✗	✓	✓

Use a relative frequency diagram to estimate his chances of scoring. Comment on your answer.

2 ▶ The probability that a new truck gets a puncture in a tyre during its first 30 000 km is $\frac{2}{15}$. What is the probability of a puncture-free first 30 000 km for this vehicle?

3 ▶ One letter is randomly chosen from this sentence: 'All the world's a stage and all the men and women merely players.' What is the probability of the letter being

    a an 'a'   **b** a 't'   **c** a vowel   **d** an 'x'?

4 ▶ A $1 coin and a $2 coin are tossed. Write down all the possible outcomes in a sample space, and calculate the probability of getting

    a two tails   **b** a head and a tail.

5 ▶ Umberto has $1, $10, $20 and $50 notes in his wallet. He has one of each type. He randomly removes two notes together. Find the probability that these two notes total

    a $11   **b** $70   **c** $80   **d** at least $11.

6 ▶ Frances buys ten lottery tickets from 500 sold. If she does not win anything with any of the first six tickets selected, what is the probability that she will win with the seventh ticket? (Assume that there is only one prize in the lottery.)

7 ▶ The probability of a rainy day in Rome in April is $\frac{1}{3}$. How many dry days would you expect in Rome from 1 to 30 April?

8 ▶ Saul picks a ball from a bag containing a very large number of different coloured balls of the same size. Each ball is either red or black in the **ratio** of 1: 3 respectively.

Calculate an estimate of the probability that Saul picks out a ball which is

    a red   **b** not red   **c** white.

EXERCISE 3* **REVISION**

1 ▶ Germaine is a keen bird-watcher and sees an Australian magpie at the same place in a forest from 1 to 10 January for three years in a row. She keeps a record, shown below.

JAN YEAR	1	2	3	4	5	6	7	8	9	10
2014	1	0	1	0	1	1	1	0	1	1
2015	0	0	1	1	0	1	1	1	1	0
2016	0	0	1	0	0	1	0	0	1	1

    a Use these values to estimate the probability of seeing an Australian magpie in this place for each year.

    b Comment on your findings.

2 ▶ A black die and a red die are thrown at the same time. Both dice are numbered from 1 to 6. Their scores are multiplied together. Use a sample space diagram to calculate the probability of getting

    a 4   **b** an even number   **c** at least 16.

3 ▶ A region of Eastern China is called 'GUANGXI ZHUANGZU ZIZHIQU'. One letter is randomly chosen from this name.

    a Find the probability of the letter being **(i)** an A **(ii)** a Z **(iii)** a B.

    b What is the most likely letter to be chosen?

4 ▶ The **sets** A and B consist of the following numbers:

    A = {1, 3, 5, 7, 9, 11}   B = {1, 5, 9, 13, 17, 21}

    A whole number from 1 to 25 inclusive is randomly chosen. Find the probability that this number is in the set

    a A

    b B′

    c A∩B

    d A∪B.

5 ▶ A spinner is turned and a die is thrown. £5 is won when the score on the die is at least the score on the spinner. How much would you expect to win if this game were played 12 times in a row? (Assume that there is no cost to play the game.)

6 ▶ Three coins are tossed simultaneously. List all the possible outcomes in a sample space and use it to calculate the probability of getting

    a three heads

    b two heads and a tail

    c at least two heads.

Tails   Heads

7 ▶ In a game, two dice are rolled and their scores are added. This is done 12 times. How many times would you expect a seven to be scored?

8 ▶ Varoosha picks out a ball from a bag containing a very large number of different coloured balls of the same size. Each ball is either red, white or black in the ratio of 2 : 3 : 4 respectively.

    Calculate an estimate of the probability that Varoosha picks out a ball which is

    a red

    b black or white

    c not white.

EXAM PRACTICE: HANDLING DATA 4

1 Each of the six faces of a cube is coloured either red or blue.

Two faces are red (R) and four are blue (B).

The cube is rolled nine times with the following results.

Colour	B	R	B	B	R	B	B	R	B

a Plot these results on two relative frequency diagrams.

HINT Draw the two graphs on the same axes.

From these nine trials estimate the probability of getting

(i) a red face   (ii) a blue face.

b Comment on your results.   [7]

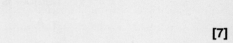

2 A single card is picked from a pack of 52 playing cards. Find the probability that this card is

a black   b a heart   c not a king   d a red prime.   [5]

3 The word 'floccinaucinihilipilification' is the habit of estimating a quantity as worthless. A letter is taken at random from this large mathematical word. Find the probability that this letter is

a o   b i   c x   d a vowel.   [4]

4 Two dice are thrown in a game and the score is the lowest common multiple of the two numbers rolled.

a Copy and complete the sample space, showing all the possible outcomes.

b Find the probability that the score is

(i) an odd number   (ii) a prime number

(iii) an integer   (iv) a square number.

c If this game is played 20 times, how many times would you expect to get an odd number?

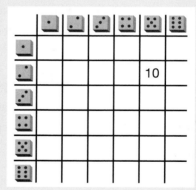

[9]

[Total 25 marks]

CHAPTER SUMMARY: HANDLING DATA 4

EXPERIMENTAL PROBABILITY

The experimental probability of an event happening can be measured by

$$\text{Relative frequency} = \frac{\text{number of successful outcomes}}{\text{total number of trials}} = \text{Estimated probability}$$

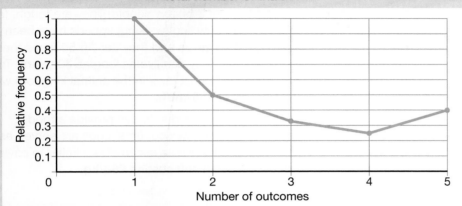

The estimated or experimental probability may be different from the theoretical probability.

THEORETICAL PROBABILITY

Theoretical probability is calculated without doing an experiment.

If p(E) is the theoretical probability of an event E happening

$$p(E) = \frac{\text{number of successful outcomes}}{\text{total number of possible outcomes}} \quad \text{if the outcomes are equally likely.}$$

p(E') is the probability of the event not happening.

$0 \le p(E) \le 1$

$p(E) + p(E') = 1$

Expected frequency = number of trials × probability of the event

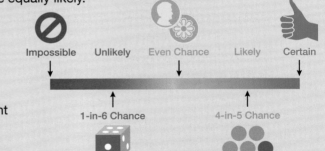

LISTING OUTCOMES: SAMPLE SPACES

A sample space is a diagram showing all possible results.
If two coins are tossed the probability space is as shown.

EVENT		Second toss	
		H	T
First toss	H	HH	HT
	T	TH	TT

$p(HH) = \frac{1}{4}$, $p(HT \text{ or } TH) = \frac{1}{2}$, $P(TT) = \frac{1}{4}$

FACT FINDER: ANTS

The study of ants is called myrmecology and it has revealed extraordinary facts about these creatures that are as old as dinosaurs. They evolved from the Cretaceous period **130 million years ago** and there are currently **11 800 species** in the world covering all the continents apart from Antarctica. They are a highly evolved and successful species and are an example of a superorganism. They behave within their nests (colonies) as a single organised body. Giant colonies of Argentine ants exist all over the world. One of the largest is along the Mediterranean coast which is **600 km** long and contains **1 billion** ants. This community behaves like a single colony with tolerance of and co-operation with each other.

The largest ant in the world is the African driver ant queen. She is **5 cm** long and can lay as many as **1.2 million eggs per month** to ensure the long life of the colony.

Ants are relatively small (**0.75 mm – 50 mm**), light (**500 milligrams**) and clever. They each have about **250 000 brain cells** compared with the **10 billion brain cells** of humans. Their strength is their organisation and huge population. It has been estimated that their total weight on the Earth is about the same as the weight of the global population of **7 billion** people. They are tough, fast and robust. Their crawling (walking) speeds have been estimated to be **75 mm/s** and they can lift **50** times their own body weight. They can live as long as **30 years**. Trap-jaw ants have the fastest jaws in the animal kingdom with a closing speed of **230 km/h**.

In some parts of the world ants can provide a food source for humans. In Mexico, ants' eggs are served as a luxury food dish known as escamoles, similar to caviar (expensive fish eggs) and costing **£60/kg**.

Source: Based on data from http://sciencekids.co.nz/

Give your answers to 3 s.ft. unless otherwise specified.

EXERCISE 1

SKILLS

ANALYSIS

1 ▶ How many ant species have evolved per million years since their existence?

2 ▶ Assuming the weight a man can lift is in the same proportion as the weight an ant can lift, what weight could a 90 kg man lift? Compare this to a typical car of weight 1 tonne. (1 tonne = 1000 kg)

3 ▶ Work out the number of ants per cm of coastline in the giant Mediterranean colony of Argentinian ants.

4 ▶ How many grams of escamoles would £1.50 buy in Mexico?

5 ▶ What size group of ants has the same total number of brain cells as a human?

EXERCISE 1*

SKILLS

REASONING/
ADAPTIVE
LEARNING/
ANALYSIS

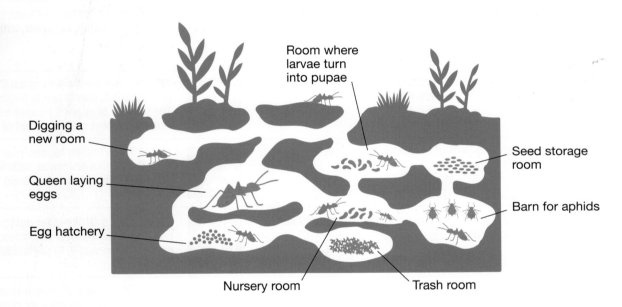

1 ▶ Ants can leave their nests and travel up to 200 m away. Find the time of their return journey on such a trip without a rest.

2 ▶ Calculate the closing speed of the trap-jaw ants' jaws in mm/s.

3 ▶ How many African driver queen ant eggs mature in a year if we know that 75% survive to adulthood?

4 ▶ The **mean** weight of a human is 70 kg. The total weight of all the ants on the Earth equals the total weight of the global human population.
Is the following statement true or false? There are approximately a quadrillion (10^{15}) ants on the Earth.

5 ▶ The surface area of a sphere $= 4\pi r^2$, where r is the **radius**. The radius of the Earth is 6370 km.

   a If 71% of the Earth's surface is covered with water, work out the area of land in km^2.

   b Work out the average number of **(i)** people per km^2 of land **(ii)** ants per km^2 of land.

   c What is the average number of ants per person on the Earth?

FACT FINDER: FRAGILE EARTH

During the last 15 years, our planet has gone through dramatic changes in terms of computing, population, pollution, global warming and other issues which have put pressure on its natural resources.

The Earth Summit in Abu Dhabi in 2015 highlighted a number of trends challenging world leaders.

2000

 POPULATION The Earth's population was **6.17 billion**. It was growing each year by **95 million**, which was the planet's entire population around 1000 BC.

 WAR AND REFUGEES Nations spent **$1100 billion** on weapons and armed forces. The number of refugees was **22.7 million**.

 COMPUTERS The number of people who had access to the internet was **400 million**.

 WATER Only **10%** of people had easy access to safe water.

 NUCLEAR POWER There were **428** nuclear reactors in **31** countries.

 TRANSPORT There were **740 million** vehicles on the road worldwide.

 MEGA-CITIES There were **17** cities with a population of over **10 million**. 50% of the world's population lived in towns and cities.

 RAINFORESTS The area of trees being destroyed was a worrying **190 000 km²/year**, which is an area the size of Senegal.

 SPECIES There were only about **525 000** African elephants left, mainly due to hunting and ivory poaching. The number of species disappearing from the planet was the highest since the start of the Ice Age.

 FISHING **126 million tonnes/year** of fish were taken from the Earth's oceans as nations expanded deep-sea fishing to catch protein from the sea.

 OZONE LAYER Ozone-layer-destroying chlorine had caused a hole over the Antarctic. Chlorine concentration was **3.79 parts/billion**.

 GLOBAL WARMING **26 billion tonnes** of carbon dioxide (the gas most responsible for climate-changing greenhouse gases) were released into the air from the burning of fossil fuels and cement manufacture. The concentration was **368 parts/billion**.

2015

 POPULATION There were **7.3 billion** people on the planet. The Earth's population was growing every year by **83 million**.

 WAR AND REFUGEES Global military spending was **$1600 billion**. Refugee numbers were estimated to be **59.5 million**.

 COMPUTERS Internet access was available to **3.2 billion** people.

 WATER **Half** of the world's population had access to safe water.

 NUCLEAR POWER There were **438** nuclear reactors in **31** countries.

 TRANSPORT There were **1.1 billion** motor vehicles on the road. Developed nations had the majority, but many cities in less economically developed countries had poor air quality due to motor vehicles.

2015 CONTINUED

 MEGA-CITIES There were **35** cities with over **10 million** people. **54%** of the world's population was urban.

 FISHING The number of fish caught went up to **156 million tonnes/year**. Some fish stocks are at serious risk of disappearing.

 RAINFORESTS The area of trees being destroyed has been reduced to **118 000 km²/year**.

 OZONE LAYER Chlorine concentration was reduced to about **3.45 parts/billion**.

 SPECIES The number of African elephants increased to **700 000** due to protection by some National Parks.

 GLOBAL WARMING 32.3 billion tonnes of carbon dioxide were released and the concentration was **400 parts/billion**. Forest burning continues to add more carbon dioxide.

Source: Based on data from *The Independent* (UK) and http://unep.org

Give your answers to 3 s.f. unless otherwise specified.

EXERCISE 1

SKILLS

PROBLEM SOLVING

1 ▶ How many more people had access to clean water in 2015 than in 2000?

2 ▶ Find the percentage of the world's population that had access to the internet in
a 2000 **b** 2015.

3 ▶ Calculate how much was spent (in US dollars) on weapons and military action per person in the world in
a 2000 **b** 2015.

4 ▶ Find the average increase in African elephants per day between 2000 and 2015.

5 ▶ Calculate the **mean** weight of fish (in kg) caught per person in
a 2000 **b** 2015.

EXERCISE 1*

SKILLS

REAL

1 ▶ What percentage of the world's population were refugees in
a 2000 **b** 2015?

2 ▶ The dimensions of a football pitch are 75 m × 110 m. Find how many areas equivalent to a football pitch of the world's rainforests were disappearing per minute in
a 2000 **b** 2015.

3 ▶ The Earth is a sphere of **radius** 6370 km. The area of a sphere is $4\pi r^2$ and 30% of the Earth's surface is land. Calculate the population density of the Earth in people per km² in
a 2000 **b** 2015.

4 ▶ The total length of roads in the USA in 2015 was 6.6 million km. The average motor vehicle is 5 m in length. Calculate the average spacing between vehicles if all the world's vehicles were placed one behind another on US roads in 2015.

5 ▶ The volume of the Earth's atmosphere (v km³) is given by

$$v = \frac{4\pi\left(R^3 - r^3\right)}{3} \text{ where } R = 6407 \text{ km and } r = 6370 \text{ km.}$$

Calculate the density of carbon dioxide in the atmosphere in kg/km³ in
a 2000 **b** 2015.

FACT FINDER: GREAT WHITE SHARK

Of the **350** species of shark, the great white shark is the most well known and feared, being large, aggressive and fast. It has extraordinary senses and is one of the most efficient hunters alive. The territory of the great white shark can cover an area of thousands of miles. They are fierce predators and have about **3000** razor-sharp teeth that are up to **7.5 cm** in length. Their body length averages **3–5 m**, although the biggest great white ever recorded was a massive **7 m** long and it weighed **3200 kg**. Even this is relatively small when compared with the great white's ancient, extinct ancestor, the *Carcharodon megalodon*, which was **18 m** long and had teeth up to **20 cm** long.

Great whites are powered through the water by their powerful tails. Their average speed is **2 miles/hour**, but they swim for short periods at **15 miles/hour**. Because of the speed of their prey, they rely heavily on stealth and surprise, often attacking from below. They can smell one drop of blood in **100 litres** of water and sense the tiny electrical charges generated by all animals by using a series of jelly-filled canals in their head called the ampullae of Lorenzi. A shark's lateral line (on their sides) can 'feel' vibrations that are up to **180 m** away. Great white sharks eat a lot less than you would imagine, consuming about **3–5%** of their body weight each time they eat. They do not chew their food. Their teeth rip prey into mouth-sized pieces which are swallowed whole. A large meal can satisfy the shark for up to **2 months**.

Sharks have survived for over **400 million years**; but within a period of **20 years**, man has dramatically reduced the population by killing them for sport and food, and overfishing the sea life that they eat. **100 million** sharks are killed each year. After the release of the film *Jaws*, the general public thought of these creatures as man-eaters. In fact, great whites rarely attack humans. In relation to the number of people who get close to them (knowingly or unknowingly), the ratio is very small. Of the **100 annual shark attacks**, great whites are responsible for about **one-third**, resulting in **10 deaths** worldwide. When attacks do occur, it is often a case of mistaken identity. A person on a surfboard looks a lot like a sea lion from below. However, the first bite is often deadly because of the shark's extraordinary bite strength. Humans can produce a bite of **11 kg/cm²**. A great white's jaws produce **310 kg/cm²**.

On average the great white lives for about **20–30 years**, but it is believed that they can live to be about **100 years** old. Despite the number of pups (baby sharks) born to each female (**2–14** fully formed babies that can be up to **1.5 m** in length), great whites are now an endangered species, because of ignorance and over-hunting by humans. They are a protected species along the coasts of the USA, Australia and South Africa. Their greatest threat is mankind.

Source: Based on data from *National Geographic*

Give your answers to 3 s.f. unless otherwise specified.

EXERCISE 1

SKILLS

ADAPTIVE LEARNING

1 ▶ How many sharks are killed in the world on average per second?

2 ▶ If all the teeth of one great white shark were laid end to end on the ground in a line, approximately how long would the greatest length of this line be in metres?

3 ▶ Thirty species of shark are responsible for attacks on humans. What percentage of the shark family could be called man-eaters?

4 ▶ Express the length of the largest ever recorded great white shark compared with your own height as a ratio of $1:x$. Find x.

5 ▶ Calculate the top speed of the great white shark in metres per second (1 mile $\simeq$ 1609 m).

EXERCISE 1*

SKILLS

ADAPTIVE LEARNING

1 ▶ Can the great white sense the vibrations of the paddling surfboarder shown?

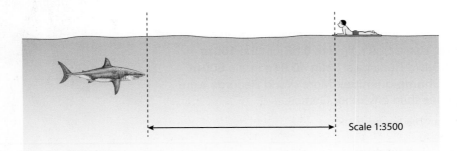

Scale 1:3500

2 ▶ The length of the extinct *Carcharodon megalodon* is $x\%$ of the biggest great white ever recorded. Find x.

3 ▶ The mako shark is the fastest of the species at 97 km/h. What percentage of this speed can the great white shark reach?

4 ▶ The weight ratio of the largest ever great white to the *Carcharodon megalodon* is $1:17$. What was the weight of the *Carcharodon megalodon* in kilograms?

5 ▶ Express the bite strength of humans as a percentage of the bite strength of the great white shark.

6 ▶ Calculate the bite strength of the great white shark in tonnes per square metre (1 tonne = 1000 kg).

7 ▶ Estimate the greatest **gross** weight of prey in tonnes consumed by a 1400 kg great white shark in a lifetime of 30 years. Give your answer in **standard form**.

FACT FINDER: LONDON 2012 OLYMPIC GAMES

The Opening Ceremony of the London **2012** Olympic Games took place in the Olympic Stadium which was full to its capacity of **80 000**. The cost of this single event was **£28 million**. The Games lasted **19 days** and the final cost of the entire Games was **£11.3 billion**.

10 568 athletes came from across the world; **5892** of the athletes were men. The majority of them slept and ate in the Olympic Village, which was home to **17 000** competitors for the duration of the Games. Over this period, the competitors consumed **19 tonnes** of eggs.

Worldwide interest was enormous with an estimated **4 billion** people watching the events across the globe via **350 miles** of broadcasting cable.

The total area of London used for the Olympic Park was **2.5 km²** and it was planted with **3000** trees.

Two World Records have caught the public imagination in the recent history of the Games: Usain Bolt's time of **9.58 s** in the **100 m** (**London 2012**) and David Rudisha's **1 min 40.91 s** in the **800 m** (**Berlin 2009 World Championships**). More World Records were broken at these Games than any other Games.

Source: Based on data from *The Telegraph* (UK)

CATEGORY	NUMBER OF WORLD RECORDS
Swimming	8
Athletics	4
Weight Lifting	5
Cycling	4
Shooting	3
Archery	2
Rowing	1

LONDON 2012 OLYMPIC GAMES MEDAL TABLE					
RANK BY GOLD	COUNTRY	GOLD	SILVER	BRONZE	POPULATION (MILLIONS)
1	USA	46	29	9	314
2	China	38	27	23	1350
3	UK	29	17	19	61
4	Russia	24	26	32	143
5	South Korea	13	8	7	50
6	Germany	11	19	14	80
7	France	11	11	12	53
8	Italy	8	9	11	51
9	Hungary	8	4	5	10
10	Australia	7	16	12	23

Give your answers to 3 s.f. unless otherwise specified.

EXERCISE 1

SKILLS

ADAPTIVE
LEARNING

1 ▶ What percentage of the athletes were women?

2 ▶ Work out the cost of

a the Opening Ceremony in £ per person at the event

b the whole Games in £ per second.

3 ▶ Find the density of trees on the Olympic Park in trees per m².

4 ▶ If the world population in 2012 was 7 billion people, calculate the percentage of people in the world who watched the London Olympics.

5 ▶ The Olympic Torch was accompanied around the U.K. by 8000 people, a total distance of 12 800 km. Find the **mean** distance in metres that the torch was carried by each person.

EXERCISE 1*

SKILLS

ADAPTIVE
LEARNING

Q3 HINT
1 tonne = 1000 kg

Q4 HINT
A marathon =
26.2 miles or
42.195 kilometres

1 ▶ Given 1 mile = 1609.34 m, write down the length of broadcasting cable used for the Games in mm in **standard form**.

2 ▶ What percentage of World Records at the Games were in a water-based sport?

3 ▶ What weight of eggs was consumed by each competitor in the Olympic Village?

4 ▶ If Usain Bolt and David Radisha could (impossibly) maintain their average speeds from their World Record performances (from the 100 m and 800 m events) over the length of a marathon, how much time would it take each of them to complete this event?

5 ▶ The medals table ranks (orders) the countries by the number of Gold medals won. Another way to order the countries could be to give each medal a points allocation of Gold = 3 pts, Silver = 2 pts, Bronze = 1 pt and to calculate a score of the number of points per 1 million people. Do this for each country and re-order the table.

FACT FINDER: THE INCREDIBLE HUMAN BODY

The human body is an amazing collection of organs, nerves, muscles and bones that is more complex and tough than any machine ever invented. You were born with **300** bones and when you become an adult you will have **206** bones. Your skull (the part of your head made of bone) has **29** bones, with **100 000** hairs on its surface. You lose about **70** hairs per day.

There are **45 miles** of nerves in the skin of an average person, and in each square centimetre of your skin there are **96 cm** of blood vessels (which carry blood around the body), **200** nerve cells and **16** sweat glands (organs which produce sweat). About **80%** of the body is made up of water. About **50 000** of the cells in your body will die and be renewed in the time it has taken for you to read this sentence, and **15 million** blood cells are destroyed per second.

Human blood travels 6×10^4 **miles per day** on its journey around the body, and in the same period, a human breathes **23 040** times, with each breath bringing in about **4.2 litres** of air.

Nerve signals to and from the brain travel at about **288 km/h**, while a sneeze leaves the head at **160 km/h** and a person blinks about **6 250 000** times a year.

A facial frown uses **43** muscles while a smile only uses **17** muscles, and every **200 000** frowns creates a single wrinkle.

In a lifetime of **70 years**, a person:

- walks a distance equivalent to **5** times around the equator
- experiences about **3 billion** heartbeats and in this time the heart pumps about **216 million litres** of blood
- produces **45 000 litres** of saliva
- drinks **72 000 litres** of water
- could grow a beard of **9 m** length (if the person is male).

We are truly remarkable creatures.

Source: Based on data from *Britannica Encyclopedia*

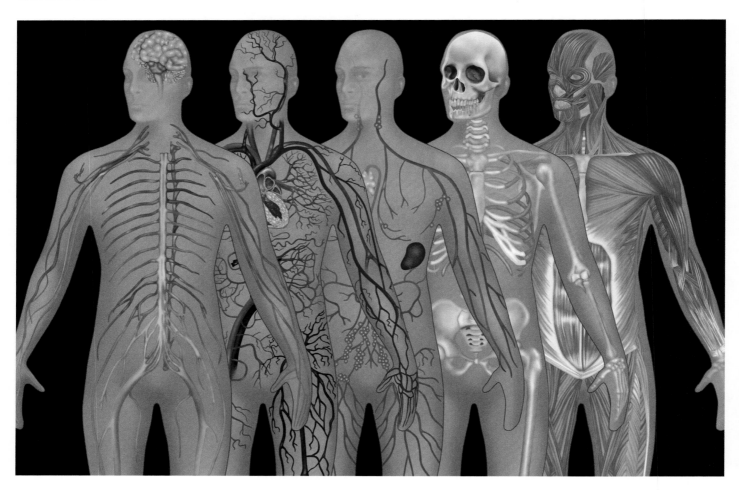

Give your answers to 3 s.f. unless otherwise specified.

1 ▶ What percentage of your bones as an adult are in your skull?

2 ▶ How many muscle movements are used to create 100 wrinkles (lines on your skin)?

3 ▶ Find the number of litres of blood that go around the human body per minute.

4 ▶ How many blinks will occur in a classroom of 20 children in a one-hour lesson?

5 ▶ A male can grow hair on his face from the age of 18 years. Find the speed of growth of a beard in mm per second, expressed in **standard form**.

1 ▶ Calculate the average heart **rate** of a human in beats per minute.

2 ▶ Given that the **radius** of the Earth is 6370 km, calculate the average speed, in m/s, that a human walks in a lifetime.

3 ▶ A glass of water is 250 cm³. How many glasses does a human drink per day on average?

4 ▶ Calculate the volume of air breathed by a human in mm³ in a lifetime of 70 years, expressed in standard form. Compare this to a rectangular classroom of dimensions 10 m × 8 m × 3 m.

5 ▶ A Maths teacher, Mr Quixote, is drawn to a **scale** of 1:60.

a If he stubs (hurts) his toe, how many seconds will it take before he feels any pain?

b Mr Quixote has an unusual reaction to stubbing his toe; he sneezes once his brain registers the event. Unfortunately Mr Quixote has a bad cold.

Jose is sitting 1 m away and he knows his teacher's reaction to pain in his toe. He can move away in 0.05 s from the moment Mr Quixote stubs his toe.

Is Jose likely to catch a cold?

CHALLENGES

1 ▶   **a** Evaluate

$$1\tfrac{1}{2} \times 1\tfrac{1}{3} \times 1\tfrac{1}{4} \times 1\tfrac{1}{5} \times 1\tfrac{1}{6} \times \ldots \times 1\tfrac{1}{2016}$$

     b Hence find an expression in terms of n (where n is an **integer**) for

$$1\tfrac{1}{2} \times 1\tfrac{1}{3} \times 1\tfrac{1}{4} \times 1\tfrac{1}{5} \times 1\tfrac{1}{6} \times \ldots \times 1\tfrac{1}{n}$$

2 ▶   Find p given that 5% of 15% of 20% of 25% of $p = 1$.

3 ▶   An intelligent ant is at a top corner of a solid **cube** of side x cm. It walks across the surface at x cm/s so that it reaches the furthest bottom corner in the fastest time possible.

     Show that this time is $\sqrt{5}$ secs.

4 ▶   Find the solution to these **simultaneous equations**.

$$2x + y - z = 1 \qquad\qquad 5x + y + z = 10 \qquad\qquad 3x - y + z = 4$$

5 ▶   Show that the **acute** angle between the lines given below is 15°.

$$x - y = 1 \qquad\qquad x - \sqrt{3}y = \sqrt{3}$$

6 ▶   The table lists some giant numbers.

Write down in **standard form** the value of

   a a million multiplied by a centillion

   b a vigintillion divided by a quintillion

   c a centillion squared.

Million	1×10^{6}
Quintillion	1×10^{30}
Vigintrillion	1×10^{120}
Centillion	1×10^{600}

7 ▶   In the universe, the distances are so vast that light years are used as units of length.

A light year is the distance travelled by light in one Earth year of 365 days.

Given that the speed of light is 3×10^{5} km/s, find out how many cubic millimetres there are in a volume of one cubic light year to 3 **significant figures** in standard form.

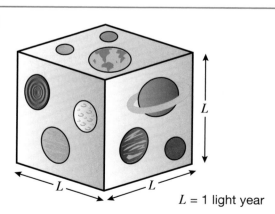

L = 1 light year

8 ▶ What is the value of $\sqrt{2+\sqrt{2+\sqrt{2+\sqrt{2+\sqrt{2+\ldots}}}}}$?

9 ▶ Can you complete the seating plan for a committee meeting around the table shown to meet these conditions?

- The chairman, Mr Grim, will sit at the head of the table.
- Anyone may sit next to him, except for Mrs Pain, who can sit next to Mr Nice, who can have Mrs Chatty on his other side.
- Mr Woof can sit on Mrs Hack's left.
- Mrs Smart must sit next to at least one male, but not the chairman.

10 ▶ Which is a better fit, a round peg that just fits in a square hole or a square peg that just fits in a round hole?

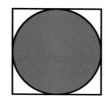
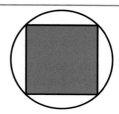

11 ▶ This vase shape is made from three-quarters of the **circumference** of a circle with **radius** 2 cm and three separate quarter-circle **arcs** with radius 2 cm. Find the shaded area.

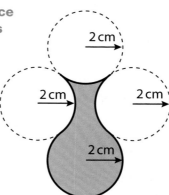

12 ▶ The diameters of the front and rear wheels of a penny farthing bicycle are 1.5 m and 0.5 m respectively. If it is ridden so that it travels at 4π km/h, show that the numbers of revolutions per minute of each wheel are given by $\dfrac{400}{p}$ and $\dfrac{400}{q}$ where p and q are constants to be found.
(Circumference of a circle = $2\pi r$)

GLOSSARY

acute angle (*noun*) an angle that is less than 90°

acute triangle (*noun*) a triangle that has all angles less than 90°

adjacent (*adjective*) next to

adjacent angles (*noun*) (*plural*) angles that share a common side and a common **vertex** (= corner point)

alternate angles (*noun*) (*plural*) two equal angles formed on opposite sides and at opposite ends of a line that crosses two parallel lines

angle of depression (*noun*) the angle measured downwards from the horizontal

angle of elevation (*noun*) the angle measured upwards from the horizontal

anomaly (*noun*) (*plural* **anomalies**) something that is noticeable because it is different from what is usual

appreciate (*verb*) to gain value over time

arc (*noun*) part of a curve or circle

axis of symmetry (*noun*) (or line of symmetry) a line through a shape such that each side is a mirror image of the other

bar chart (*noun*) a diagram using rectangles of equal width (bars) whose heights represent an amount or quantity

bearing (*noun*) an angle measured clockwise from north, used to describe a direction

bisect (*verb*) to divide something into two equal parts

bisector (*noun*) a straight line that divides an angle or another line into two equal parts

cancel down (*verb*) to simplify a fraction by dividing the **numerator** (= top number) and **denominator** (= bottom number) by the same number (a **common factor**)

chord (*noun*) a straight line joining two points on a curve

circumference (*noun*) the total distance around a circle

class (*noun*) a group of data in a collection of grouped data

clear (*verb*) to remove fractions in an equation by multiplying both sides of the equation by the lowest **common denominator**

common denominator (*noun*) a number that can be divided exactly by all the **denominators** (= bottom numbers) in a set of fractions

common factor (*noun*) a number (a **factor**) that two or more other numbers can be exactly divided by; for example, 2 is a common factor of 4, 6 and 8

compasses (*noun*) a V-shaped instrument with one sharp point and a pencil at the other end used for drawing circles

complement (*noun*) the complement of a **set** is all those members (objects) which are not in that set but which are in the universal set (all members being considered)

compound interest (*noun*) interest is the extra money that you must pay back when you borrow money or money paid to you by a bank or financial institution when you keep money in an account there; compound interest is calculated on both the sum of money lent or borrowed or saved and on the unpaid interest already earned or charged

consecutive (*adjective*) numbers follow each other in order, with no gaps, from smallest to largest

correct to (*adjective*) accurate to; a number given correct to '…' has been rounded, e.g. 3.592 is 3.6 correct to 1 decimal place and 3.59 correct to 2 decimal places

corresponding angles (*noun*) (*plural*) two equal angles that are formed when a line crosses two parallel lines; each angle is on the same side of the two parallel lines and on the same side of the line which they cross

cross-section (*noun*) something that has been cut in half so that you can look at the inside, or a drawing of this

cube (*noun*) a solid object that has 6 identical square **faces** (= flat surfaces)

cuboid (*noun*) a solid object that has 6 rectangular **faces** (= flat surfaces)

cumulative frequency (*noun*) the total of all the frequencies of a set of data up to any particular group of data; a 'running total' of the frequencies

decimal place (or **d.p.**) (*noun*) the position of a digit to the right of a decimal point

degree mode (*noun*) the angle mode setting on a scientific calculator

degree of accuracy (*noun*) tells you how accurate a number is; a number could be given to '…' decimal places or '…' significant figures

denominator (*noun*) the number below the line in a fraction

depreciate (*verb*) to lose value over time

diameter (*noun*) a straight line passing through the centre of a circle and joining two points that lie on the circle; a chord that passes through the centre of a circle

dispersion (*noun*) a measure of the way in which a set of data is spread out

dodecahedron (*noun*) a solid object that has 12 **faces** (= flat surfaces) which each have 5 edges

end-point (*noun*) the upper class boundary of a class of grouped data

equidistant (*adjective*) at an equal distance from two places or points

equilateral triangle (*noun*) a triangle whose 3 sides are all the same length and all the angles are 60°

expand (an expression) (*verb*) to **multiply out** brackets (= remove brackets)

exterior angle (*noun*) the angle formed outside a **polygon** between any one edge and the extended adjacent edge

face (*noun*) the flat surface of a solid object

factor (*noun*) a number that divides exactly into another number

factorise (*verb*) to put an expression into brackets; the reverse of expand

frequency polygon (*noun*) a diagram joining the mid-points of the tops of the bars of a **bar chart** with straight lines; frequency is on the vertical axis and the mid-points for each group are on the horizontal axis

gradient (*noun*) the measure of the slope of a straight line relative to the horizontal; for a straight line

$$\text{gradient} = \frac{\text{change in the } y \text{ coordinates}}{\text{change in the } x \text{ coordinates}} = \frac{\text{'rise'}}{\text{'run'}}$$

gross (*adjective*) before any deductions; a gross weight is the total weight of something

hypotenuse (*noun*) the longest side of a **right-angled triangle**; it is the side opposite the right angle

icosahedron (*noun*) a solid object that has 20 **faces** (= flat surfaces) which each have 3 edges

improper fraction (*noun*) a fraction such as $\frac{107}{8}$ in which the **numerator** (= top number) is larger than the **denominator** (= bottom number)

indices (*noun*) (*plural*) (*singular* **index**) (= **powers**) a number which tells you how many times to multiply the given number or term by itself; for example, the ^{2} in 4^2 is the index

inequality (*noun*) (*plural* **inequalities**) an expression containing one or more of the symbols $<$, $>$, $\leq$ or $\geq$

integer (*noun*) a whole number

intercept (*noun*) the point on a graph where the graph crosses an axis

interior angle (*noun*) an angle formed inside a **polygon** between two adjacent edges

inter-quartile range (*noun*) the difference between the upper and lower **quartiles** of a set of data

intersect (*verb*) if two lines intersect, they meet or cross over each other

inverse (*noun*) opposite in effect or the reverse of; for example, addition (+) is the inverse of subtraction (−)

inverted (*adjective*) in the opposite position to the one it was in before, often turned upside down (= the bottom is on the top and the top is on the bottom)

isosceles triangle (*noun*) a triangle with two equal sides and two equal angles

like terms (*noun*) terms whose **variables** (such as x or y) and **powers** (such as ^{2} or ^{3}) are exactly the same; for example, $2x$ and $5x$ are like terms, and $4x^2$ and $2x^2$ are like terms

linear simultaneous equations (*noun*) two equations, whose graphs are straight lines, that are solved together to find two unknowns

long division (*noun*) a method of dividing one large number by another

lower bound (*noun*) the value half a unit less than the rounded measurement

map (*noun*) the connection from one set to another

map (*verb*) to translate, reflect or rotate a shape so that it fits (maps) onto another shape exactly

mass (*noun*) a measure of how much matter is in an object

mean (*noun*) the numerical value found by adding together all the separate values of a data set and dividing by how many pieces of data there are

median (*noun*) the middle value of a set of values that have been arranged in size order

mid-point (*noun*) a point that is halfway along the line segment joining two points

mixed number (*noun*) a number that consists of a whole number and a fraction; for example $7\frac{1}{4}$

modal class (*noun*) the **class** of grouped data which has the highest frequency

mode (*noun*) the piece of data that occurs most often in a set of data

multiple (of a number) (*noun*) is the product of that number and an integer (whole number)

multiply out (*verb*) (= **expand**) to remove brackets; to multiply out a bracket, multiply each term inside the bracket by the term outside the bracket; to multiply out double brackets, multiply each term in one bracket by each term in the other bracket

multiplying factor (*noun*) a number which multiplies another number

numerator (*noun*) the number above the line in a fraction; for example 5 is the numerator in $\frac{5}{6}$

obtuse angle (*noun*) an angle that is greater than 90° but less than 180°

obtuse triangle (*noun*) a triangle that has an angle greater than 90°

octahedron (*noun*) a solid object that has 8 **faces** (= flat surfaces) which each have 3 edges

parabola (*noun*) a special curve, shaped like an arch (or upside-down arch); the path of an object that is thrown into the air follows a curve of this shape

parallelogram (*noun*) a flat shape with 4 sides (= a **quadrilateral**) in which opposite sides are parallel and the same length

percentile (*noun*) one of 100 equal groups into which a data set can be divided

perimeter (*noun*) the total distance around the edge of a shape

perpendicular (*adjective*) if one line is perpendicular to another line, they form an angle of 90° (= a **right angle**)

pictogram (*noun*) a diagram that shows numbers or amounts in the form of pictures or symbols

pie chart (*noun*) a diagram in which a circle is divided from its centre into sectors (parts) to show how the total is split up between the different categories

polygon (*noun*) a flat shape with 3 or more straight sides

power (*noun*) (= **index**) the small number written to the right and above another number

prime factor (*noun*) a factor that is a **prime number**

prime number (*noun*) a number that can only be divided by 1 and itself; for example, 3 and 7 are prime numbers

product (*noun*) the number you get by multiplying two or more numbers

protractor (*noun*) an instrument for measuring and drawing angles

quadratic curve (*noun*) another name for a **parabola**

quadratic equation (or **quadratic**) (*noun*) an equation where the highest power of x is 2; for example $3x^2 + 5x - 4 = 0$

quadratic graph (*noun*) the graph of a quadratic equation of the form $y = ax^2 + bx + c$ where a, b and c are numbers and the highest power of x is 2; its shape is that of a **parabola**

quadrilateral (*noun*) a flat shape with 4 straight sides

quartile (*noun*) each of 4 equal groups into which a data set can be divided

radius (*noun*) (*plural* **radii**) the distance from the centre to the curve which makes a circle; any straight line from the centre to the curve

random (*adjective*) happening or chosen by chance; a result is random if each possible result has the same chance of happening, and a selection is random if each object (or number) has the same chance of being chosen

range (*noun*) the difference between the lowest and highest values of a set of data

rate (*noun*) a fixed price paid or charged for something

rate (of change) (*noun*) how fast something changes over a period of time

rate (of inflation) (*noun*) percentage increase in the price of goods and services

ratio (*noun*) a ratio shows the relative sizes of two or more quantities

reading (*noun*) a value taken or found from a graph

reflex angle (*noun*) an angle that is greater than 180°

relative frequency (*noun*) (or experimental probability) an estimate of probability based on experimental data; it is how often something happens divided by the total number of **trials** (= experiments)

resultant vector (*noun*) a vector that is equivalent to two or more other vectors

retardation (*noun*) (= deceleration) the process of slowing down

rhombus (*noun*) a flat shape with 4 equal sides (= a quadrilateral) in which opposite sides are parallel and opposite angles are equal

right angle (*noun*) an angle that is 90° exactly

right-angled triangle (*noun*) a triangle that has a right angle (= 90°)

rotational symmetry (*noun*) the symmetry of a shape which can be turned and fitted onto itself within one full turn

round (*verb*) to alter an exact figure to one that is less exact

sample (*noun*) a small set of objects chosen from a larger set of objects which is examined to find out something about the larger set

satisfy (*verb*) to make an equation or an inequality true

scale (*noun*) a set of marks with regular spaces between them on the axes of a graph

scale (*noun*) a ratio such as 1:100 which shows the relationship between a length on a drawing or map and the actual length in real life

to scale (*adjective*) a uniform reduction or increase in size (according to a scale)

scale factor (*noun*) the scale factor of an enlargement is the number of times by which each original length has been multiplied

segment (*noun*) the part of a circle that is separated from the rest of the circle when you draw a straight line across it

set (*noun*) a collection of objects (numbers, letters, symbols, etc.)

sign (*noun*) a mathematical symbol such as +, −, ×, ÷

significant figure (or **s.f.**) (*noun*) each of the digits of a number that are used to express it to the required accuracy, starting from the first non-zero digit from the left-hand end of the number

similar triangles (*noun*) two triangles are similar if they are the same in shape but different in size

simplify (an expression) (*verb*) to collect all like terms so the expression is a collection of terms connected by + and − signs

simplify (a fraction) (*verb*) to divide the numerator (= top number) and denominator (= bottom number) by the same number (a common factor)

simultaneous equations (*noun*) two equations that are solved together to find two unknowns

sketch (*verb*) to make a rough drawing of a diagram, graph or shape

sketch (*noun*) a rough drawing of a diagram or graph which gives a general idea of the shape or relationship, or a rough drawing of a shape showing angles and lengths

standard form (*noun*) a number is written in standard form when it is expressed as $A \times 10^n$ where A is always between 1 and 10 and n is a positive or negative integer

subset (*noun*) a collection of objects (= set) which contains part of another set

subtended angle (*noun*) (in a circle) an angle in which the arms start and finish at the ends of an arc

successive transformations (*noun*) a combination of transformations (translation, reflection, rotation or enlargement) performed on a shape, followed one after another

sum (*noun*) the total resulting from the addition of two or more numbers, amounts or items

sum (*verb*) to add two or more numbers or amounts together

tangent (*noun*) a straight line that touches a curve at one point only

tetrahedron (*noun*) a solid object that has 4 faces (= flat surfaces) which each have 3 edges

trapezium (*noun*) (*British English*) a flat shape with 4 sides (= a quadrilateral) where one pair of opposite sides are parallel

trial (*noun*) an experiment (carried out a number of times to estimate the probability of an event)

upper bound (*noun*) the value half a unit greater than the rounded measurement

variable (*noun*) a letter such as x or y in a term, expression, formula or equation whose value can vary; a letter used to represent an unknown quantity to solve a problem using an equation(s)

vector (**column**) (*noun*) a vector such as $\begin{pmatrix} 3 \\ 8 \end{pmatrix}$ used to describe a translation; the top number gives the movement parallel to the horizontal axis (to the right or left); the bottom number gives the movement parallel to the vertical axis (up or down)

vertices (*noun*) (*plural*) (*singular* **vertex**) points where two or more edges meet (a corner)

working (*noun*) a record of the calculations made when solving a problem

UNIT 1 ANSWERS

UNIT 1: NUMBER 1

EXERCISE 1
1 ▶ $\frac{2}{3}$ 2 ▶ $\frac{2}{3}$ 3 ▶ $\frac{1}{3}$
4 ▶ $\frac{2}{3}$ 5 ▶ $\frac{1}{2}$ 6 ▶ $\frac{1}{3}$
7 ▶ 0.8 8 ▶ 0.375 9 ▶ $\frac{3}{4}$
10 ▶ $\frac{1}{5}$ 11 ▶ $2\frac{2}{3}$ 12 ▶ $3\frac{1}{4}$
13 ▶ $3\frac{2}{5}$ 14 ▶ $2\frac{5}{7}$ 15 ▶ $\frac{7}{3}$
16 ▶ $\frac{18}{5}$ 17 ▶ $\frac{11}{3}$ 18 ▶ $\frac{41}{7}$
19 ▶ $\frac{3}{10}$ 20 ▶ $1\frac{1}{2}$

EXERCISE 1*
1 ▶ $\frac{2}{7}$ 2 ▶ $\frac{2}{3}$ 3 ▶ $\frac{1}{6}$
4 ▶ $\frac{7}{11}$ 5 ▶ $\frac{1}{2}$ 6 ▶ $\frac{3}{8}$
7 ▶ 0.3125 8 ▶ 0.075 9 ▶ $\frac{7}{20}$
10 ▶ $\frac{3}{8}$ 11 ▶ $4\frac{1}{3}$ 12 ▶ $2\frac{1}{5}$
13 ▶ $3\frac{2}{7}$ 14 ▶ $4\frac{3}{4}$ 15 ▶ $\frac{14}{3}$
16 ▶ $\frac{45}{7}$ 17 ▶ $\frac{42}{5}$ 18 ▶ $\frac{188}{9}$
19 ▶ $\frac{13}{16}$ 20 ▶ $2\frac{2}{3}$

EXERCISE 2
1 ▶ $\frac{5}{6}$ 2 ▶ $\frac{3}{10}$ 3 ▶ 1
4 ▶ 2 5 ▶ $\frac{1}{4}$ 6 ▶ $\frac{2}{3}$
7 ▶ $\frac{1}{7}$ 8 ▶ $\frac{2}{3}$ 9 ▶ $\frac{1}{3}$
10 ▶ $\frac{1}{6}$

EXERCISE 2*
1 ▶ $\frac{3}{4}$ 2 ▶ $\frac{1}{4}$ 3 ▶ $3\frac{3}{4}$
4 ▶ 36 5 ▶ $\frac{1}{6}$ 6 ▶ 6
7 ▶ a 8 ▶ 1 9 ▶ $\frac{1}{12}$
10 ▶ $10\,000\,\text{m}^2$

EXERCISE 3
1 ▶ $\frac{6}{7}$ 2 ▶ $\frac{3}{8}$ 3 ▶ $\frac{3}{25}$
4 ▶ 12 5 ▶ $4\frac{1}{2}$ 6 ▶ $\frac{3}{10}$
7 ▶ $\frac{5}{9}$ 8 ▶ $1\frac{1}{9}$ 9 ▶ 6
10 ▶ 12

EXERCISE 3*
1 ▶ $\frac{21}{430}$ 2 ▶ $\frac{4}{9}$ 3 ▶ 56
4 ▶ $\frac{2}{9}$ 5 ▶ $\frac{5}{6}$ 6 ▶ $1\frac{3}{5}$
7 ▶ 6 8 ▶ $8\frac{1}{3}$ 9 ▶ 26
10 ▶ 64

EXERCISE 4
1 ▶ $\frac{6}{7}$ 2 ▶ $\frac{1}{3}$ 3 ▶ $\frac{1}{2}$
4 ▶ $\frac{1}{4}$ 5 ▶ $\frac{23}{24}$ 6 ▶ $\frac{1}{12}$
7 ▶ $4\frac{5}{12}$ 8 ▶ $2\frac{1}{10}$ 9 ▶ $4\frac{7}{12}$
10 ▶ $8\frac{1}{8}$ 11 ▶ $2\frac{3}{34}$ 12 ▶ $3\frac{19}{24}$

13 ▶ $\frac{5}{12}$ 14 ▶ $\frac{1}{3}$

EXERCISE 4*
1 ▶ $\frac{3}{4}$ 2 ▶ $\frac{7}{10}$ 3 ▶ $\frac{3}{5}$
4 ▶ $\frac{7}{12}$ 5 ▶ $\frac{19}{20}$ 6 ▶ $\frac{3}{8}$
7 ▶ $7\frac{2}{3}$ 8 ▶ $13\frac{11}{15}$ 9 ▶ $6\frac{1}{2}$
10 ▶ $1\frac{4}{9}$ 11 ▶ $6\frac{7}{9}$ 12 ▶ $1\frac{23}{60}$
13 ▶ $1\frac{17}{24}$
14 ▶ Total length is $7\frac{1}{9}$, $7\frac{1}{18} < 7\frac{1}{9} < 7\frac{1}{6}$ so it will fit.

EXERCISE 5
1 ▶ 20 2 ▶ 32 3 ▶ 2
4 ▶ 0 5 ▶ 4 6 ▶ 25
7 ▶ −1 8 ▶ 5
9 ▶ $4 \times (5 - 3) + 2 = 10$
10 ▶ $(7 - 5) \times 3 = 6$

EXERCISE 5*
1 ▶ 12 2 ▶ 8 3 ▶ 1
4 ▶ 1 5 ▶ 20 6 ▶ 1
7 ▶ 6 8 ▶ $\frac{1}{2}$
9 ▶ $8 - ((2 + 1) \times (5 - 3)) = 2$
10 ▶ $(8 + (6 \times 2)) \div 4 = 5$

EXERCISE 6
1 ▶ 800 2 ▶ 90 000 3 ▶ 3740
4 ▶ 80 300 5 ▶ 0.44 6 ▶ 0.56
7 ▶ 0.506 8 ▶ 0.105 9 ▶ 34.78
10 ▶ 0.65 11 ▶ 3.0 12 ▶ 9.1
13 ▶ a 300 000 000 m/s
   b 299 792 000 m/s
14 ▶ a 0.02 mm b 0.019 mm
15 ▶ $179 400 000
16 ▶ 40 000 km

EXERCISE 6*
1 ▶ 10 2 ▶ 5000
3 ▶ 45.7 4 ▶ 89 500
5 ▶ 0.069 6 ▶ 0.0068
7 ▶ 0.0495 8 ▶ 0.000 568
9 ▶ 9.00 10 ▶ 2.08
11 ▶ 7.0 12 ▶ 78.2
13 ▶ a 0.000 b 0.000 498
14 ▶ a 1.414 214 b 1.414 21
15 ▶ a $10 000 b $12 721.9
16 ▶ a 0.000 000 1 mm
   b 0.000 000 052 917 72 mm

EXERCISE 7 REVISION

1 ▶ a $\frac{2}{3}$ b $\frac{1}{15}$

2 ▶ a $\frac{1}{4}$ b 2

3 ▶ a $2\frac{13}{20}$ b $2\frac{1}{20}$

4 ▶ a 4   b 2   c 4

5 ▶ $12 \div (4 + 2) + 3 = 5$

6 ▶ $(3 + 5) \div 2 = 4$

7 ▶ a 12.000 50   b 12.000

8 ▶ a 4.5   b 5

9 ▶ 16

10 ▶ a $\frac{1}{3}$ b 4000

EXERCISE 7* REVISION

1 ▶ a $\frac{1}{3}$ b $\frac{1}{300}$

2 ▶ a $\frac{2}{3}$ b $1\frac{1}{12}$

3 ▶ a $1\frac{11}{20}$ b $1\frac{1}{24}$

4 ▶ a 2   b 7   c 4

5 ▶ $((2 \times 3) + 3) \div 3 = 3$

6 ▶ $(7 + 2) \times 2 \div 3 = 6$

7 ▶ a 8.999   b 9.00

8 ▶ a 2.718 281 8   b 2.718 281 83

9 ▶ 14

10 ▶ a $\frac{49}{80}$
     b Space left is 918 gigabytes so yes.

EXAM PRACTICE: NUMBER 1

1 ▶ a $\frac{1}{3}$ b $3\frac{1}{3}$ c $\frac{1}{30}$

2 ▶ a $\frac{4}{9}$ b 6

3 ▶ $1\frac{1}{9}$

4 ▶ a 53   b $1\frac{1}{10}$

5 ▶ a 21 196.2 km   b 20 000 km

6 ▶ a $\frac{1}{4}$ b 96

7 ▶ 32

UNIT 1: ALGEBRA 1

EXERCISE 1

1 ▶ $4ab$ 2 ▶ $7xy$

3 ▶ $-3pq$ 4 ▶ $y - xy$

5 ▶ $2 - 6x$ 6 ▶ $2cd$

7 ▶ $-4xy$ 8 ▶ $2ab + 5bc$

9 ▶ 0   10 ▶ $2gh - 5jk + 7$

11 ▶ $-3p^2 - 2p$ 12 ▶ $5x^2y - 3xy^2$

EXERCISE 1*

1 ▶ $-xy$ 2 ▶ $4ab - b$

3 ▶ $6ab$ 4 ▶ 0

5 ▶ $3ab + 3bc$ 6 ▶ $3q^2$

7 ▶ $x + 1$

8 ▶ $a^3 + 2a^2 + a = a(a^2 + 2a + 1)$

9 ▶ $h^3 + h^2 + 3h + 4$

10 ▶ $7a^2b - 3ab$

11 ▶ $a^2b^3c - 0.6a^3b^2c + 0.3$

12 ▶ $4pq^2r^5 - 2pq^2r^4$

EXERCISE 2

1 ▶ $6a$ 2 ▶ $2x^2$

3 ▶ $3x^3$ 4 ▶ $15a^5$

5 ▶ $6st$ 6 ▶ $4rs^2$

7 ▶ $2a^2b^2$ 8 ▶ $4y^3$

9 ▶ $12x^3$ 10 ▶ $20a^3$

EXERCISE 2*

1 ▶ $8a^3$ 2 ▶ $15x^4y^2$

3 ▶ $6a^7$ 4 ▶ $18y^3$

5 ▶ $36x^5y^3$ 6 ▶ $30a^3b^3c^5$

7 ▶ $56xy^4$ 8 ▶ $10x^3y^3$

9 ▶ $3x^3y^4 - 2x^3y^2 = x^3y^2(3y^2 - 2)$

10 ▶ $14a^4b^6$

EXERCISE 3

1 ▶ $10 + 15a$ 2 ▶ $2b - 8c$

3 ▶ $-6a - 24$ 4 ▶ $4x - 12$

5 ▶ $2b - a$ 6 ▶ $5a + 4b$

7 ▶ $3t - 18$ 8 ▶ $6x + y$

9 ▶ $1.4x + 0.3y$ 10 ▶ $2.1a - 11.7$

EXERCISE 3*

1 ▶ $12m - 8$

2 ▶ $2x - 2y + 2z$

3 ▶ $15a + 5b - 20c$

4 ▶ $2x - 3y + 4$

5 ▶ $3y - x$

6 ▶ $-1.4x - 2.2$

7 ▶ $-6x - 3y$

8 ▶ $4.6x - 6.2y - 0.4z$

9 ▶ $-0.6a - 4.2b + 0.7$

10 ▶ $-0.44x^2 - 3.8xy - 1.2y^2$

EXERCISE 4

1 ▶ $x = 4$ 2 ▶ $x = 15$

3 ▶ $x = 25$ 4 ▶ $x = 100$

5 ▶ $x = 12$ 6 ▶ $x = 15$

7 ▶ $x = 2.4$ 8 ▶ $x = 13.5$

9 ▶ $x = 26.6$ 10 ▶ $x = 1.4$

11 ▶ $x = 0.985$ 12 ▶ $x = 6.8$

EXERCISE 4*

1 ▶ $x = 99.9$

2 ▶ $x = 5.13$ (to 2 d.p.)

3 ▶ $x = 40.664$

4 ▶ $x = 580.39$

5 ▶ $x = 8.49$ (to 2 d.p.)

6 ▶ $x = 38.84$

EXERCISE 5

1 ▶ $x = 3$

2 ▶ $x = -1$

3 ▶ $x = -2$

4 ▶ $x = -2$

5 ▶ $x = 2$

6 ▶ $x = 8$

7 ▶ $x = 1$

8 ▶ $x = -6$

9 ▶ $x = -10$

10 ▶ $x = 1$

11 ▶ $x = 1$

12 ▶ $x = -2$

13 ▶ $x = -1$

14 ▶ $x = \frac{2}{3}$

EXERCISE 5*

1 ▶ $x = 4$

2 ▶ $x = 11$

3 ▶ $x = -2$

4 ▶ $x = -5$

5 ▶ $x = -4$

6 ▶ $x = -4$

7 ▶ $x = 5$

8 ▶ $x = 2$

9 ▶ $x = 0$

10 ▶ $x = 1$

11 ▶ $x = \frac{5}{9}$

12 ▶ $x = \frac{4}{3}$

13 ▶ $x = -1$

14 ▶ $x = -\frac{2}{7}$

EXERCISE 6

1 ▶ $x = 1$

2 ▶ $x = 2$

3 ▶ $x = 2$

4 ▶ $x = 5$

5 ▶ $x = 4$

6 ▶ $x = -3$

7 ▶ $x = 1$

8 ▶ $x = -1$

9 ▶ $x = 0$

10 ▶ $x = -\frac{1}{2}$

EXERCISE 6*

1 ▶ $x = 4$

2 ▶ $x = -2$

3 ▶ $x = 1\frac{1}{2}$

4 ▶ $x = \frac{4}{5}$

5 ▶ $x = \frac{7}{9}$

6 ▶ $x = 3$

7 ▶ $x = 5$

8 ▶ $x = -9$

9 ▶ $x = 0.576$ (3 s.f.)

10 ▶ $x = 1.28$ (3 s.f.)

EXERCISE 7

1 ▶ $x = 13$

2 ▶ $x = 36$

3 ▶ $x = 3$

4 ▶ $x = 7$

5 ▶ $x = 2$

6 ▶ $x = 6$

7 ▶ $x = 4$

8 ▶ $x = 4$

9 ▶ $x = \frac{5}{2}$

10 ▶ $x = -\frac{5}{3}$

EXERCISE 7*

1 ▶ $x = 8$

2 ▶ $x = 5$

3 ▶ $x = 5$

4 ▶ $x = 1$

5 ▶ $x = 4$

6 ▶ $x = 3$

7 ▶ $x = 9$

8 ▶ $x = 5$

9 ▶ $x = \frac{3}{4}$

10 ▶ $x = \frac{3}{5}$

EXERCISE 8

1 ▶ 238, 239

2 ▶ $x = 10$, 40°, 80°, 60°

3 ▶ $x = 2, 38$

4 ▶ 13

5 ▶ a $20x - 10(30 - x) = 180$

    b $x = 16$

6 ▶ a $3x + 5(x - 10) + 2(x + 20) = 890$

    b   90c

EXERCISE 8*

1 ▶ 72, 74, 76

2 ▶ 11 kg, 44 kg, 67 kg

3 ▶ 42 years old

4 ▶ 6

5 ▶ 15

6 ▶ 4

EXERCISE 9   REVISION

1 ▶ $3x - 2$

2 ▶ ab

3 ▶ $6a$

4 ▶ $2a^2$

5 ▶ a^3

6 ▶ $2a^4$

7 ▶ $4a^4$

8 ▶ $-5a - 4ab$

9 ▶ $x + 7y$

10 ▶ $x = 7$

11 ▶ $x = 4.8$

12 ▶ $x = 2$

13 ▶ 145, 146, 147

14 ▶ a $4x + 12 = 54$

     b   10.5, 16.5

EXERCISE 9*   REVISION

1 ▶ $4xy^2 - 3x^2y$

2 ▶ $2x^3y^3$

3 ▶ 1

4 ▶ $2x^3y + xy^3 + x^4$

5 ▶ $x = 20$

6 ▶ $x = 1.25$

7 ▶ $x = -6$

8 ▶ $x = 2$

9 ▶ $x = 4$

10 ▶ 72 m²

11 ▶ 11 years old

12 ▶ 6 m/s

13 ▶ $294

EXAM PRACTICE: ALGEBRA 1

1 ▶ $-3xy$

2 ▶ $3ab^3 - 2ab^2$

3 ▶ $8b^6$

4 ▶ $32p^4$

5 ▶ $10x - 2y$

6 ▶ $x = 108$

7 ▶ $x = 12$

8 ▶ $x = 1$

9 ▶ $x = 2$

10 ▶ $x = 4$

11 ▶ $x + (x + 1) + (x + 2) = 219 \Rightarrow x = 72$
so numbers are 72, 73 and 74

12 ▶ $(5x - 50) + (2x) + (80 - x) = 180 \Rightarrow x = 25$
so angles are 75°, 50° and 55°

13 ▶ $4x - 3 = 9 - 2x \Rightarrow x = 2 \Rightarrow$ perimeter is 16

UNIT 1: GRAPHS 1

EXERCISE 1

1 ▶ 1   2 ▶ –0.5

3 ▶ 3   4 ▶ $\frac{1}{4}$

5 ▶ $-\frac{1}{4}$ 6 ▶ 2

7 ▶ –1   8 ▶ 3 m

9 ▶ 10 km   10 ▶ 2.325 m

11 ▶ 2 m

12 ▶ a 14 m   b $\frac{1}{30}$

EXERCISE 1*

1 ▶ $\frac{3}{8}$

2 ▶ $-\frac{6}{7}$

3 ▶ 0.5

4 ▶ –3

5 ▶ 652

6 ▶ a –2   b 159 m

7 ▶ a $\frac{1}{6}$ cm   b 0.1 cm

8 ▶ a 4 m   b 8.2 m

9 ▶ No, the gradients between pairs of points
are different.

10 ▶ $\frac{s-q}{r-p}$

11 ▶ $p = -2$

12 ▶ $q = 2.5$

13 ▶ 26 m

EXERCISE 2

1 ▶ a

x	–2	–1	0	1	2	3
y	–7	–5	–3	–1	1	3

b
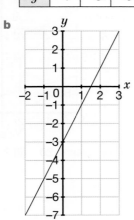

c Gradient = 2, y-intercept = –3

d –1.8; reading from a graph is not exact

2 ▶ a $y = 4x - 2$

b $y = -3x + 5$

c $y = 2x + 3$ and $y = 2x - 4$

3 ▶ a
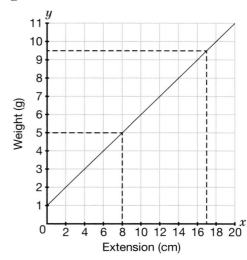

b (i) 9.5 g   (ii) 8 cm

c 1998 cm, outside validity range

4 ▶ a
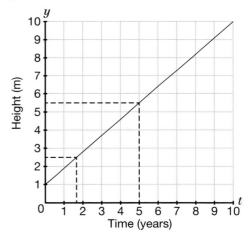

b (i) 1 m and 2.5 m   (ii) 5 years

c $t = 20$ years, outside validity range

5 ▶ a
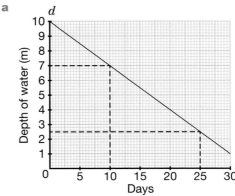

b (i) 2.5 m   (ii) 10 December

c $t \approx 33.3$ days, outside validity range

6 ▶ a

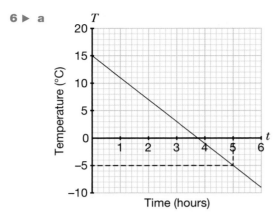

b (i) 15°C   (ii) 3:45pm, 5pm

c −15°C, outside validity range

EXERCISE 2*

1 ▶ a

x	−2	0	2	4
$y = \frac{1}{2}x + 1$	0	1	2	3
$y = \frac{1}{2}x - 2$	−3	−2	−1	0

b

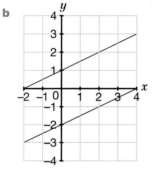

c For $y = \frac{1}{2}x + 1$ gradient $= \frac{1}{2}$,
y-intercept = 1; for $y = \frac{1}{2}x - 2$
gradient $= \frac{1}{2}$, y-intercept = −2

d No, they are parallel lines.

2 ▶ a

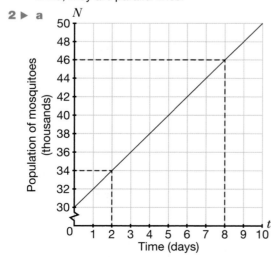

b (i) 34 000   (ii) 8 June

c 59 000

3 ▶ a $C = 40t + 60$

b

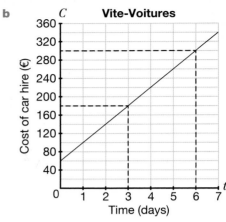

c (i) €300   (ii) 3 days

4 ▶ a $V = -1.5x + 9$

b

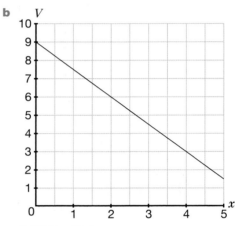

c (i) $525   (ii) 4 years

d 6 years

5 ▶ a Zenith: $V = -5x + 25$
Bubble: $V = -2x + 10$

b

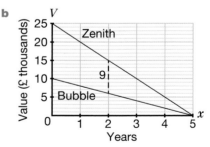

c (i) 5 years, £0   (ii) 2 years, £9000

EXERCISE 3

1 ▶ (3, 0), (0, 6)

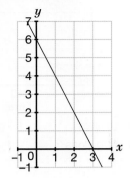

2 ▶ (4, 0), (0, 6)

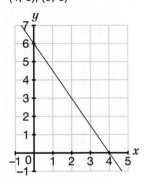

3 ▶ (4, 0), (0, –2)

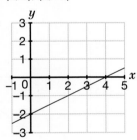

4 ▶ (–8, 0), (0, 6)

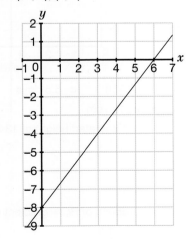

5 ▶ a

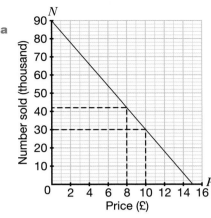

b £10   **c** 42 000

d £0; no, not a sensible value

EXERCISE 3*

1 ▶ (6, 0) and (0, –12)

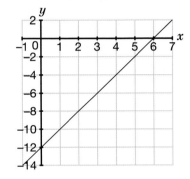

2 ▶ (3.5, 0), (0, 5.25)

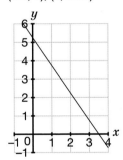

3 ▶ (–10.5, 0), (0, 3)

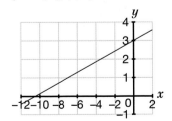

4 ▶ (−3.5, 0), (0, 3)

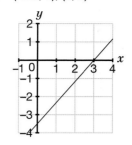

5 ▶ a

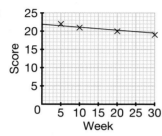

b ≈23

c $-\frac{3}{25}$, 23; about $25H + 3W = 575$

d 92 weeks; no, longer, unlikely to continue linear

6 ▶ a = any number, $b = 0$, $c \neq 0$

7 ▶ a $2x + y = 4$ **b** $\left(\frac{4}{3}, \frac{4}{3}\right)$

EXERCISE 4

1 ▶ a ¥12 000   **b** €60   **c** ¥7333

2 ▶ a $130   **b** 220 units

c No units

3 ▶ a 3 hr 40 mins   **b** 1.8 kg

c No, graph should end at around $\frac{1}{2}$ kg

4 ▶ a

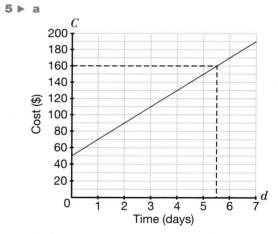

b 85 feet   **c** 6.1 m   **d** 0.61 m

EXERCISE 4*

1 ▶ a 56 mph   **b** 120 kph

c 1220 kph

2 ▶ a 132 cm   **b** 73 cm

c Suspect is running

3 ▶ a 3.6°C   **b** 40 ppm   **c** 200 ppm

4 ▶ a

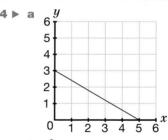

b 18 litres   **c** 1.1 gallons

d 11 gallons

EXERCISE 5   REVISION

1 ▶ a 2   **b** −1

2 ▶ 4.5 m

3 ▶ a 7 m   **b** 8.2 m

4 ▶ a

b $-\frac{3}{5}$

5 ▶ a

b $50   **c** 5.5 days   **d** $330

6 ▶ a 163 cm

b Estimated height of 134 cm so no.

EXERCISE 5*   REVISION

1 ▶ 5 m

2 ▶ Gradient of BC = gradient of AD = $-\frac{5}{6}$

3 ▶ $b = \pm 1.5$

4 ▶ 2

5 ▶ a

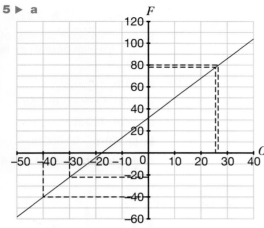

b (i) 27°C   (ii) 77°F   (iii) –30°C

c –40

6 ▶ a (i) $F = 40K + 20$ (ii) $S = 75K + 35$

b

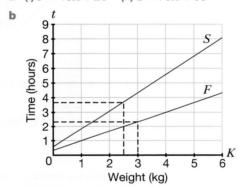

c (i) 222.5 min   (ii) 140 min

d 5.125 kg

e approx 13.30

EXAM PRACTICE: GRAPHS 1

1 ▶ a 2   **b** –4

2 ▶ 45 m

3 ▶ a

t	1	5	10
c	9	25	45

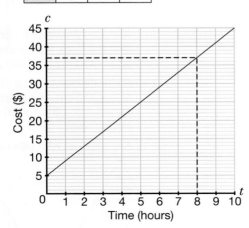

b 4   **c** $t = 8$

4 ▶ a

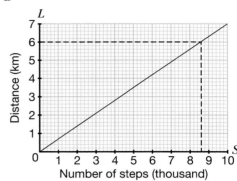

b around 6000 m

c around 8600 steps

5 ▶ a $v = 500 - 10t$

b

t	0	25	50
v	500	250	0

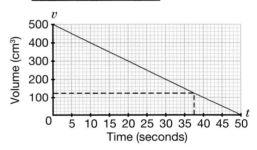

c $v = 125$, $t = 37.5$

UNIT 1: SHAPE AND SPACE 1

EXERCISE 1

1 ▶ $a = b = c = 60°$; $d = e = 45°$; $f = 135°$; $g = 33°$

2 ▶ a 75°   **b** 68°   **c** 68°   **d** 7°

3 ▶ a $y = 103°$ **b** $y = 148°$

    c $y = 111°$

4 ▶ 110°

5 ▶ $\angle ACB = 94°$

6 ▶ a $x = 110°$ **b** $y = 120°$

EXERCISE 1*

1 ▶ a 112°   **b** 99°   **c** 99°   **d** 13°

2 ▶ a $y = 107°$ **b** $z = 51°$

    c $x = 104°$ **d** $v = 120°$, $w = 120°$

3 ▶ $\angle AED = 38°$ (alternate angles are equal)

$\angle ADE = \dfrac{180 - 38}{2} = 71°$ (the angle sum of a triangle is 180°)

$\angle EAD$ and $\angle ADE$ are equal (base angles of an isosceles triangle)

$\angle ADC = 180 - 71 = 109°$ (angles on a straight line sum to 180°)

4 ▶ $2x - 20 + x + 5 = 2x + 35$ so $x = 50°$
(the exterior angle of a triangle is equal to
the sum of the two interior angles at the
other vertices)

5 ▶ 80°, 50°, 50° and 50°, 65°, 65°

6 ▶ 36°, 36°, 108°

EXERCISE 2

1 ▶ Parallelogram

2 ▶ 38°

3 ▶ a 92°   b 71°   c 55°

4 ▶ 174°

5 ▶ 128°

6 ▶ 84°

EXERCISE 2*

1 ▶ Kite

2 ▶ 35°

3 ▶ ∠BCE + ∠CBE = 132° (exterior angles of
a triangle is equal to the sum of the two
interior angles at the other two vertices)

∠BCE = ∠CBE (triangle BEC is isosceles)

∠BCE = ∠CBE = $\frac{132}{2}$ = 66°

∠CBA = 66° (alternate angles)

∠DAB = ∠CBA (trapezium is an isosceles
trapezium)

∠DAB = 66°

4 ▶ ∠CBE = 110° (corresponding angles)

∠CBA = 70° (angles on a straight line sum
to 180°)

∠ACB = 180 − (74 + 70) = 36° (angles in a
triangle sum to 180°)

5 ▶ a Angle PSR = $\frac{4}{7}x = \frac{4}{7} \times 105 = 60°$

b Angle QPS = $\frac{6}{7}x = \frac{6}{7} \times 105 = 90°$

6 ▶ a 38°   b $\frac{x}{2}$

EXERCISE 3

1 ▶ a (i) 360° (ii) 156° b (i) 540° (ii) 142°

c (i) 720° (ii) 146°

2 ▶ a (i) 720° (ii) 120° b (i) 540° (ii) 108°

c (i) 2880° (ii) 160°

3 ▶ a 11 sides   b 14 sides

c 17 sides   d 24 sides

4 ▶ 9   5 ▶ 54°   6 ▶ 112.5°

EXERCISE 3*

1 ▶ n

2 ▶ No, the equation $180 - \frac{360}{n} = 145$ gives a
number of sides that is not an integer.

3 ▶ 117°   4 ▶ 99°

5 ▶ 16 sides   6 ▶ 6

EXERCISE 4

1 ▶ a 20 m   b 2.5 cm

2 ▶ a Accurate scale drawing of right-angled
triangle with base 6 cm, hypotenuse
10 cm

b 36 m

3 ▶ a 072°   b 255°

4 ▶ a 1 cm : 120 m

b (i) 360 m (ii) 600 m

c Answers between 4 and 4.24 minutes

EXERCISE 4*

1 ▶
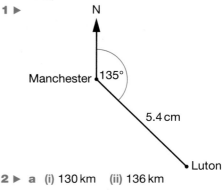

2 ▶ a (i) 130 km (ii) 136 km

b Sligo

3 ▶ a 2.5 km   b 16 cm

4 ▶ 323°

EXERCISE 5

1 ▶ Accurate construction of triangle with sides
6 cm, 7 cm and 10 cm

2 ▶ Accurate construction of triangle with sides
7 cm, 8 cm, 9 cm

3 ▶ Accurate construction of triangle with sides
4 cm, 5 cm, 7 cm

4 ▶ a–c Accurate drawings of the triangles

5 ▶ Accurate drawing of an equilateral triangle
with sides 6.5 cm

6 ▶ The sum of the two shorter sides is less
than the longest side so the triangle will not
be possible.

EXERCISE 5*

1 ▶ Accurate drawing of triangle with sides of
length 5.5 cm, 5.5 cm and 10 cm (for real-life
sides of 11 m, 11 m and 200 m respectively)

2 ▶ Accurate drawing of a triangle with sides
of length 5 cm, 15 cm and 17 cm (for real-
life sides of 100 cm, 300 cm and 340 cm
respectively)

3 ▶ Accurate net with sides of length 6 cm

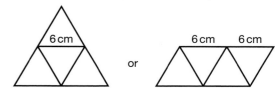

4 ▶

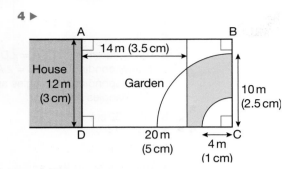

5 ▶

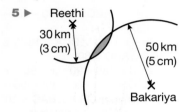

6 ▶

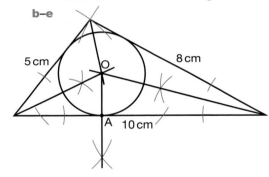

EXERCISE 6

1 ▶ Accurate construction of the perpendicular bisector of a line of length 12 cm

2 ▶ Accurate construction of the perpendicular bisector of a line of length 7 cm

3 ▶ Perpendicular bisector accurately constructed on a line of length 10 cm

4 ▶ a, b Perpendicular bisector of line segment AB of length 7 cm drawn accurately

    c AP is the same distance as BP.

EXERCISE 6*

1 ▶ a, b Perpendicular bisector accurately constructed of 2 points, S and T, 10 cm apart. The perpendicular bisector shows possible positions of the lifeboat.

2 ▶ a, b, c Perpendicular bisector from point P to the line AB accurately constructed

3 ▶ a, b, c Perpendicular at point P on a line accurately constructed

4 ▶ a Shortest distances to sides accurately drawn

    b 2.5 m   c 10 seconds

EXERCISE 7

1 ▶ Accurate construction of angle bisector of 70° angle

2 ▶ Angles accurately drawn and bisected

3 ▶ a Accurate construction of 90° angle

    b Accurate construction of 45° angle

4 ▶ a Accurate construction of 60° angle

    b Accurate construction of 30° angle

EXERCISE 7*

1 ▶ a Accurate scale drawing with sides 3 cm and 5 cm

    b Accurate construction of 30° angle

    c 115 m^2

2 ▶ a Accurate construction of triangle

    b Accurate construction of line perpendicular to AB that passes through C

    c 16 cm^2

3 ▶ Accurate scale drawing

4 ▶ a Accurate construction of triangle

    b–e

EXERCISE 8

1 ▶ a (i) AB and ED, DF and BC, AC and EF

      (ii) ∠ABC = ∠EDF, ∠ACB = ∠EFD, ∠CAB = ∠FED

    b (i) IK and IJ, GI and HI, GK and HJ

      (ii) ∠IJH = ∠IKG, ∠KIG = ∠JIH, ∠IHJ = ∠IGK

    c (i) LM and OP, MN and PQ, LN and OQ

      (ii) ∠OPQ = ∠LMN, ∠POQ = ∠MLN, ∠PQO = ∠MNL

    d (i) SR and WU, ST and WT, RT and UT

      (ii) ∠RST = ∠UWT, ∠SRT = ∠WUT, ∠STR = ∠WTU

2 ▶ C and E

3 ▶ a 5   b 60 cm

4 ▶ a = 4 cm, b = 20 cm, c = 12 cm, d = 6 cm

5 ▶ a 7.0 cm   b 13.2 cm

1 ▶ ∠EDC = ∠EBA (alternate);
∠DCE = ∠EAB (alternate); ∠CED = ∠AEB
(vertically opposite). Therefore all angles are
equal and the triangles are similar.

2 ▶ **a** ∠RPQ = ∠RTS (alternate); ∠PQR
= ∠RST (alternate); ∠PRQ = ∠SRT
(vertically opposite). Therefore all angles
are equal and the triangles are similar.

   b 10 cm

3 ▶ **a** ∠F is common; ∠FGH = ∠FJK
(corresponding); ∠FHG = ∠FKJ
(corresponding). Therefore all angles are
equal and the triangles are similar.

   b 60 mm

   c 64 mm

4 ▶ 308 m tall

5 ▶ **a** ∠PQN = 52°; ∠LMN = 102°

   b ∠L is common; ∠MNL = ∠PQL
(corresponding); ∠LMN = ∠LPQ
(corresponding). Therefore all angles are
equal and the triangles are similar.

   c 44 cm   **d** 22 cm   **e** 18 cm

REVISION

1 ▶ $a = 23°$, $b = 157°$, $c = 44°$, $d = 116°$

2 ▶ 68°

3 ▶ $a = 145°$

4 ▶ **a** 24 sides   **b** 20°

5 ▶
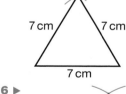

6 ▶
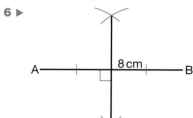

7 ▶ **a**
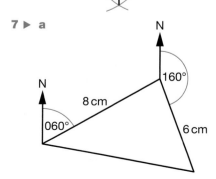

b 27 km

c 280°

8 ▶ **a** ∠A is common; ∠EBA = ∠DCA
(corresponding); ∠ADC = ∠AEB
(corresponding). All angles are equal so
the triangles are similar.

   b CD = 32 cm

REVISION

1 ▶ ∠CBD = ∠BCD = (180 − 2(x − 30)) ÷ 2
= 120 − x
120 − x + x + ∠BCA = 180°, ∠BCA = 60°
and ∠ABC = 60°
∠EAC = 180 − 90 − x = 90 − x
∠BAC = 180 − (x + 30) − (90 − x) = 60°
∠ABC = ∠ACB = ∠BAC = 60° means
triangle ABC is equilateral

2 ▶ Angle ABC = interior angle
Exterior angle of a regular octagon
 = 360° ÷ 8 = 45°
Interior angle = 180 − 45 = 135°
Angle BAC = angle BCA (triangle ABC is
isosceles)
Angle BAC = (180 − 135) ÷ 2
= 22.5° (angles in a triangle)

3 ▶ $x = 50°$ giving exterior angles of 70°, 50°,
90°, 50° and 100°

4 ▶ 8

5 ▶
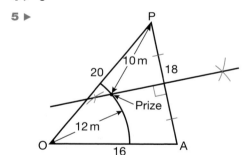

6 ▶ 55 m approx

7 ▶
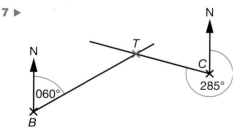

8 ▶ **a** ∠PQR = ∠RST (alternate);
∠QPR = ∠RTS (alternate)

   ∠PRQ = ∠SRT (vertically opposite). All
angles are equal so the triangles are
similar.

   b $x = 40$ cm; $y = 19.5$ cm

EXAM PRACTICE: SHAPE AND SPACE 1

1 ▶ a 112°   **b** 81°   **c** 31°

2 ▶ 69°

3 ▶ 110°

4 ▶ 162°

5 ▶ a (i) 37.5 km   (ii) 25 km

    b St Peter's Port or Vale

6 ▶ a Accurate construction of an angle of 45°

    b Accurate construction of the perpendicular bisector of an 8 cm line

7 ▶ 93 m

8 ▶ a ∠PQN = 65°, ∠LMN = 72°

    b All corresponding angles are equal so the triangles are similar.

    c 21 cm   **d** 7 cm   **e** 6.65 cm

UNIT 1: SETS 1

EXERCISE 1

1 ▶ a Any two vegetables

    b Any two colours

    c Any two letters

    d Any two odd numbers

2 ▶ a {Sunday, Monday, Tuesday, Wednesday, Thursday, Friday, Saturday}

    b {1, 4, 9, 16, 25, 36, 49, 64, 81, 100}

    c For example {Mathematics, Science, English, …}

    d {2, 3, 5, 7, 11, 13, 17, 19}

3 ▶ a {first four letters of the alphabet}

    b {days of the week beginning with T}

    c {first four square numbers}

    d {even numbers}

4 ▶ a False   **b** False

    c False   **d** True

5 ▶ b and c

EXERCISE 1*

1 ▶ a Any two planets

    b Any two polygons

    c Any two elements

    d Any two square numbers

2 ▶ a {2, 3, 4}   **b** {1, 4, 6}

    c {1, 5, 7, 35}

    d {10, 100, 1000, 10 000, 100 000}

3 ▶ a {seasons of the year}

    b {conic sections}

    c {first 5 powers of 2}

    d {Pythagorean triples}

4 ▶ a True   **b** False   **c** True   **d** False

5 ▶ a and d

EXERCISE 2

1 ▶ a 16

    b $n(S) = 14$; 14 pupils like sweets.

    c $n(C \cap S) = 12$; 12 pupils like both chocolate and sweets.

    d 21

2 ▶ a 6   **b** 15   **c** 58   **d** 85

3 ▶ a ℰ

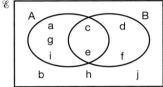

    b {c, e}, 2   **c** Yes

    d No, d ∈ B but d ∉ A for example.

4 ▶ a Pink Rolls-Royce cars

    b Cars that are not Rolls Royces

    c There are no pink Rolls-Royce cars in the world.

EXERCISE 2*

1 ▶ a ℰ

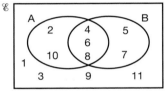

    b {4, 6, 8}, 3   **c** Yes

    d {1, 2, 3, 5, 7, 9, 10, 11}   **e** Yes

2 ▶ a ℰ

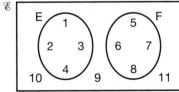

    b { } or ∅

    c The sets don't overlap (*disjoint*)

3 ▶ a ℰ

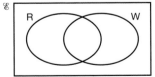

    b White roses in the shop

    c There are no white roses in the shop.

4 ▶ a ℰ

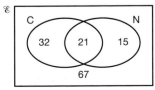

    b 32   **c** 47   **d** 135

5 ▶ 2^n

6 ▶ A ∩ B ∩ C gives multiples of 30, so 𝒞 must be a set that includes one and only one multiple of 30.

EXERCISE 3

1 ▶ a 𝒞

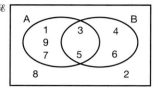

b {1, 3, 4, 5, 6, 7, 9}, 7

c Yes

d {2, 8}

e No

2 ▶ a 𝒞

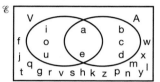

b {a, e}

c Consonants

d {a, e, i, o, u, b, c, d}

3 ▶ a 𝒞

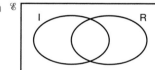

b

c Isosceles right-angled triangles

d Non-right-angled isosceles triangles

4 ▶ 21

EXERCISE 3*

1 ▶ a 𝒞

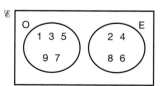

b {1, 2, 3, 4, 5, 6, 7, 8, 9}

c E ∩ F = ∅

d E ∪ F = 𝒞

2 ▶ a All pizzas containing olives or cheese or both

b All pizzas containing olives and cheese

c All pizzas contain either olives or cheese or both

3 ▶ 6

4 ▶ B is a subset of A

5 ▶ Yes

EXERCISE 4 REVISION

1 ▶ a {4, 9, 16, 25}

b {1, 2, 3, 4, 6, 8, 12, 24}

c {a, e, i}

d {April, June, September, November}

2 ▶ a {first four prime numbers}

b {even numbers between 31 and 39}

c {days of the week beginning with S} or {days of the weekend}

d {vowels}

3 ▶ a False (51 = 3 × 17)

b False (2 ∉ O)

c True

d True

4 ▶ a 𝒞

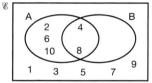

b {1, 3, 5, 7, 9}, odd integers between 1 and 9 inclusive

c 8

d Yes – all multiples of 4 are also multiples of 2

5 ▶ a 𝒞

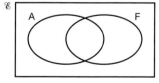

b All members of the expedition who were born in Africa or are female or both

c The leader is a female who was born in Africa.

6 ▶ 7

EXERCISE 4* REVISION

1 ▶ a {4, 8, 12, 16}

b {red, orange, yellow, green, blue, indigo, violet}

c {CAT, CTA, ACT, ATC, TCA, TAC}

d {2, 3, 6}

2 ▶ a {factors of 12}

    b {first five Fibonacci numbers}

    c {suits in a pack of cards}

    d {five regular solids}

3 ▶ 9

4 ▶ a, d ℰ

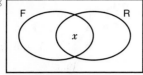

    b All regular four-sided polygons

    c All irregular four-sided polygons

5 ▶ 11

6 ▶ a {20}

    b 12 or 24

    c Yes. The first integer that is a multiple of both 5 and 6 is 30

EXAM PRACTICE: SETS 1

1 ▶ b and **c**

2 ▶ a Clothes that aren't yellow

    b Yellow jeans

    c There are no yellow jeans.

3 ▶ a 50   **b** 25

    c 42; there are 42 animals that are either black or sheep or both in the field.

    d 17

4 ▶ a $E' = \{1, 3, 5, 7, 9, 11\}$, $E \cap T = \{6, 12\}$ and $F \cap T = \{12\}$

    b E' is odd numbers less than 13, $E \cap T$ is multiples of 6 less than 13, $F \cap T$ is multiples of 12 less than 13

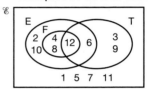

5 ▶ 8

UNIT 2 ANSWERS

UNIT 2: NUMBER 2

EXERCISE 1

1 ▶ 4.56×10^2 2 ▶ 6.78×10^1
3 ▶ 1.2345×10^2 4 ▶ 6.7×10^7
5 ▶ 5.68×10^2 6 ▶ 3.84×10^1
7 ▶ 7.0605×10^2 8 ▶ 1.23×10^8
9 ▶ 4000   10 ▶ 56 000
11 ▶ 4 090 000   12 ▶ 678 900
13 ▶ 560   14 ▶ 65 000
15 ▶ 7 970 000   16 ▶ 987 600
17 ▶ 1000   18 ▶ 10 000
19 ▶ 8.4×10^9 20 ▶ 1.4×10^2
21 ▶ 5×10^1 22 ▶ 2.75×10^5

EXERCISE 1*

1 ▶ 4.5089×10^4 2 ▶ 8.705×10^4
3 ▶ 2.983×10^7 4 ▶ 7.654×10^7
5 ▶ 1×10^3 6 ▶ 1×10^6
7 ▶ 1×10^5 8 ▶ 1×10^1
9 ▶ 1×10^{21} 10 ▶ 1×10^8
11 ▶ 1×10^0 or 1   12 ▶ 1×10^6
13 ▶ 6.16×10^6 14 ▶ 2.7×10^8
15 ▶ 4×10^1 16 ▶ 7.083×10^4
17 ▶ 9.1125×10^{16} 18 ▶ 2.43×10^{42}
19 ▶ 2.5×10^4 20 ▶ 3.46×10^8
21 ▶ 9.653×10^8 22 ▶ 4×10^3
23 ▶ 1×10^{10} 24 ▶ 1000
25 ▶ Saturn 10 cm, Andromeda Galaxy 1 million km, OQ172 1000 million km

EXERCISE 2

1 ▶ 1×10^{-1} 2 ▶ 1×10^{-2}
3 ▶ 1×10^{-3} 4 ▶ 1×10^{-4}
5 ▶ 1×10^{-3} 6 ▶ 1×10^{-2}
7 ▶ 1×10^1 8 ▶ 1×10^0
9 ▶ 0.001   10 ▶ 0.000 01
11 ▶ 0.0012   12 ▶ 0.87
13 ▶ 0.000 001   14 ▶ 0.0001
15 ▶ 0.0467   16 ▶ 0.000 34
17 ▶ 5.43×10^{-1} 18 ▶ 7.08×10^{-2}
19 ▶ 7×10^{-3} 20 ▶ 9×10^{-4}
21 ▶ 6.7×10^{-1} 22 ▶ 7.07×10^{-4}
23 ▶ 1×10^2 24 ▶ 1×10^3
25 ▶ 100   26 ▶ 100
27 ▶ 10 000   28 ▶ 1 000 000
29 ▶ 128   30 ▶ 0.03

EXERCISE 2*

1 ▶ 10   2 ▶ 0.001
3 ▶ 0.011   4 ▶ 0.099
5 ▶ 0.01   6 ▶ 0.0001
7 ▶ 0.0011   8 ▶ −0.099
9 ▶ 1×10^3 10 ▶ 1×10^4
11 ▶ 1×10^1 12 ▶ 1×10^{-1}
13 ▶ 1×10^4 14 ▶ 1×10^{-4}
15 ▶ 1×10^2 16 ▶ 1×10^{-3}
17 ▶ 6.25×10^{-6} 18 ▶ 1.6×10^{-3}
19 ▶ 6.9×10^7 20 ▶ 5×10^{-2}
21 ▶ 4×10^{-6} 22 ▶ 2.5×10^{-3}
23 ▶ 4.8×10^5 24 ▶ 3×10^{10}
25 ▶ 5000 viruses   26 ▶ 66 000 viruses
27 ▶ 4.7×10^{10} 28 ▶ 2×10^7
29 ▶ $(3.4 \times 10^{23}) + (0.34 \times 10^{23}) = 3.74 \times 10^{23}$
30 ▶ a 1×10^{27}, 27 zeros
     b $\sqrt[3]{1 \times 10^{-27}} = 1 \times 10^{-9}$
     c 1×10^7
     d 2×10^{23}
     e 2×10^{16} cm
     f $(2 \times 10^{16}) \div (4 \times 10^9) \approx 5 \times 10^6$ times!

EXERCISE 3

1 ▶ 20%   2 ▶ 12.5%
3 ▶ 5%   4 ▶ 4%
5 ▶ 5.5 km/h   6 ▶ 12°C
7 ▶ 126 m²   8 ▶ 16.8 hrs
9 ▶ +25%   10 ▶ −25%

EXERCISE 3*

1 ▶ 5%   2 ▶ 16.7%
3 ▶ 2.5%   4 ▶ 2.5%
5 ▶ 21.6 cm²   6 ▶ 1468.8 cm³
7 ▶ 2500 m³   8 ▶ 810 db
9 ▶ +0.04%   10 ▶ a   −11.3%
                         b   −22.9%

EXERCISE 4

1 ▶

Original value	Percentage increase	Multiplying factor	New value
20	5	1.05	21
180	95	1.95	351
360	30	1.30	468
2500	70	1.70	4250

2 ▶

Original value	Percentage decrease	Multiplying factor	New value
20	5	0.95	19
180	95	0.05	9
360	30	0.70	252
2500	70	0.30	750

3 ▶ a $1515 **b** $2985 **c** $1650 **d** $2850

4 ▶ a 495 kg **b** 5 kg **c** 450 kg **d** 50 kg

5 ▶ 68 kg　　　　**6 ▶** 624 kg

7 ▶ $13 440　　　**8 ▶** $39 600

9 ▶ €129 600　　**10 ▶** €2300

EXERCISE 4*

1 ▶

Original value	Percentage increase	Multiplying factor	New value
60 secs	25	1.25	75 secs
50 kg	60	1.60	80 kg
100 km/h	25	1.25	125 km/h
1250 m	20	1.20	1500 m

2 ▶

Original value	Percentage decrease	Multiplying factor	New value
75 secs	20	0.80	60 secs
80 kg	37.5	0.625	50 kg
120 km/h	40	0.60	72 km/h
1500 m	20	0.80	1200 m

3 ▶ $24.48　　　**4 ▶** $39.60

5 ▶ £6762　　　**6 ▶** £5940

7 ▶ 39.6°C　　　**8 ▶** 120 db

9 ▶ 554 cm^2　　**10 ▶** 22.8 cm

EXERCISE 5　REVISION

1 ▶ 2.75×10^5　　　**2 ▶** 2.75×10^{-2}

3 ▶ 3500　　　　　**4 ▶** 0.0035

5 ▶ $64 800　　　**6 ▶** 2%

7 ▶ $33\frac{1}{3}$%　　　**8 ▶** +5%

9 ▶ $411.25　　　**10 ▶** $288.75

EXERCISE 5*　REVISION

1 ▶ 22 500 000　　**2 ▶** 1.23×10^{-1}

3 ▶ 58 300　　　　**4 ▶** 5×10^{11}

5 ▶ 19.2 m　　　　**6 ▶** 1.16×10^{-3}%

7 ▶ +10%　　　　**8 ▶** $\frac{y-x}{x} \times 100$%

9 ▶ €445.50

10 ▶ a 20% profit　**b** 20% loss

1 ▶ a 4.5×10^3　　**b** 3×10^6

　　c 7.5×10^{-3}　**d** 2.5×10^{-1}

2 ▶ a 1200　　　**b** 5 800 000

　　c 0.45　　　**d** 0.0093

3 ▶ a 4.25×10^7　**b** 3.48×10^3

　　c 8.03×10^5

4 ▶ 45 kg

5 ▶ a 17.5%　　**b** 6.61%

6 ▶ 21%

7 ▶ 2 hrs 15 mins 25 secs

UNIT 2: ALGEBRA 2

EXERCISE 1

1 ▶ 4　　**2 ▶** $3y$　　**3 ▶** 2　　**4 ▶** $\frac{3a}{b}$

5 ▶ $\frac{b}{2}$　**6 ▶** $\frac{3a}{b}$　**7 ▶** $4c$　**8 ▶** $\frac{a}{2}$

9 ▶ $\frac{4}{x}$　**10 ▶** $2b$　**11 ▶** $\frac{1}{5b^2}$　**12 ▶** $\frac{a}{4}$

EXERCISE 1*

1 ▶ $\frac{1}{2}$　**2 ▶** $\frac{2}{b}$　**3 ▶** $\frac{x}{4}$　**4 ▶** $\frac{a}{2}$

5 ▶ $\frac{2}{b}$　**6 ▶** $\frac{6}{b^2}$　**7 ▶** $\frac{a}{2b}$　**8 ▶** $\frac{3}{abc}$

9 ▶ $\frac{a}{4b^2}$　**10 ▶** $\frac{1}{a^2 b^2}$　**11 ▶** $\frac{3a}{8b}$　**12 ▶** $\frac{3z^2}{10x^2}$

EXERCISE 2

1 ▶ $\frac{5x^2}{4}$　**2 ▶** $\frac{x^3 z}{y}$　**3 ▶** 1　**4 ▶** $\frac{4c^2}{5}$

5 ▶ 6　**6 ▶** $\frac{ab}{2}$　**7 ▶** $\frac{b}{6}$　**8 ▶** 1

9 ▶ $\frac{2}{y}$　**10 ▶** $\frac{b}{2c}$

EXERCISE 2*

1 ▶ $2a^3$　　**2 ▶** $\frac{3x}{z}$　　**3 ▶** $\frac{9pq^2}{10}$

4 ▶ $\frac{1}{2x}$　　**5 ▶** $\frac{5xy^3}{z^2}$　　**6 ▶** y

7 ▶ $\frac{3x^4}{8y}$　　**8 ▶** $\frac{1}{2a^2 b^2}$

EXERCISE 3

1 ▶ $\frac{7x}{12}$　**2 ▶** $\frac{a}{12}$　**3 ▶** $\frac{4a+3b}{12}$

4 ▶ $\frac{5x}{12}$　**5 ▶** $\frac{a}{2}$　**6 ▶** $\frac{3a+4b}{12}$

7 ▶ $\frac{a}{6}$　**8 ▶** $\frac{3a+8b}{12}$

EXERCISE 3*

1 ▶ $\frac{7x}{18}$　**2 ▶** $\frac{5a}{21}$　**3 ▶** $\frac{14x+20y}{35}$

4 ▶ $\frac{a}{4}$　**5 ▶** $\frac{17}{6b}$　**6 ▶** $\frac{2d+3}{d^2}$

7 ▶ $\frac{7-3x}{10}$　　**8 ▶** $\frac{y-2}{30}$

9 ▶ $\frac{3x+5}{12}$　　**10 ▶** $\frac{2a-1}{a(a-1)}$

EXERCISE 4

1 ▶ $x = \pm 3$ 2 ▶ $x = \pm 6$

3 ▶ $x = \pm 4$ 4 ▶ $x = \pm 8$

5 ▶ $x = \pm 3$ 6 ▶ $x = \pm 1$

7 ▶ $x = 13$ 8 ▶ $x = \pm 4$

9 ▶ $x = 16$ 10 ▶ $x = 81$

EXERCISE 4*

1 ▶ $x = \pm 5$ 2 ▶ $x = \pm 7$

3 ▶ $x = \pm 9$ 4 ▶ $x = 0$

5 ▶ $x = 7$ 6 ▶ $x = \pm 4$

7 ▶ $x = \pm 5$ 8 ▶ $x = 10$ or $x = -16$

9 ▶ $x = \pm 3$ 10 ▶ $x = 1$ or $x = 97$

EXERCISE 5

1 ▶ $2^{10} = 1024$ 2 ▶ $4^7 = 16\,384$

3 ▶ $2^6 = 64$ 4 ▶ $7^3 = 343$

5 ▶ $2^{12} = 4096$ 6 ▶ $6^8 = 1\,679\,616$

7 ▶ a^5 8 ▶ c^4 9 ▶ e^6 10 ▶ a^9

11 ▶ c^5 12 ▶ $12a^6$ 13 ▶ $6a^5$ 14 ▶ $2e^8$

EXERCISE 5*

1 ▶ $6^{12} \approx 2.18 \times 10^9$ 2 ▶ $7^6 \approx 1.18 \times 10^5$

3 ▶ $8^{12} \approx 6.87 \times 10^{10}$ 4 ▶ $4^{17} \approx 1.72 \times 10^{10}$

5 ▶ a^{12} 6 ▶ $3c^6$

7 ▶ $5e^8$ 8 ▶ $8g^{12}$

9 ▶ $48j^{12}$ 10 ▶ $24m^7$

11 ▶ $27a^6$ 12 ▶ 2

13 ▶ $8b^4$ 14 ▶ 6

EXERCISE 6

1 ▶ $<$ 2 ▶ $<$ 3 ▶ $>$ 4 ▶ $<$

5 ▶ $x \le 0, x > 2$ 6 ▶ $-3 < x \le 3$

7 ▶ $x > 5$

8 ▶ $x \le 4$

9 ▶ $x < 3$

10 ▶ $x \ge \frac{3}{2}$

11 ▶ $x \ge 9$

12 ▶ $x < 4$

13 ▶ $x < 0$

14 ▶ $x > 3$

15 ▶ $x < -2$ 16 ▶ $x \ge -5$

17 ▶ $x < -1$ 18 ▶ $x \le -2$

19 ▶ $x \ge -\frac{2}{3}$ 20 ▶ $x \ge -7$

21 ▶ $\{5, 6\}$ 22 ▶ $\{3, 4\}$

23 ▶ $\{0, 1\}$ 24 ▶ $\{1, 2, 3, 4\}$

25 ▶ $\{2, 3\}$

EXERCISE 6*

1 ▶ $x \le 0$ or $x > 3$; $0 \ge x > 3 \Rightarrow 0 \ge 3$

2 ▶ $x \le 2.5$

3 ▶ $x < 5\frac{1}{3}$

4 ▶ $x < \frac{3}{2}$

5 ▶ $x < -3\frac{1}{5}$

6 ▶ $x \le 2$

7 ▶ $-1\frac{2}{3} < x \le 4\frac{1}{3}$

8 ▶ $-1 < x \le 3$

9 ▶ 23

10 ▶ $\{1, 2, 3\}$ 11 ▶ $x \le 7$; $\{7, 6, 5, 4\}$

EXERCISE 7 REVISION

1 ▶ 3 2 ▶ x 3 ▶ $3x$ 4 ▶ 4

5 ▶ a 6 ▶ $6x$ 7 ▶ $\frac{9y}{20}$ 8 ▶ $\frac{2x}{15}$

9 ▶ $\frac{4a + b}{10}$ 10 ▶ $x = \pm 4$ 11 ▶ $x = \pm 6$

12 ▶ $x = 20$ 13 ▶ a^{10} 14 ▶ b^2 15 ▶ c^{12}

16 ▶ $>$ 17 ▶ $<$ 18 ▶ $<$ 19 ▶ $=$

20 ▶ $-3 < x \le 2$; -2 21 ▶ $x > 5$

22 ▶ $x \le 4.5$ 23 ▶ $x \ge 2$

24 ▶ $x \ge 1$ 25 ▶ $\{3, 4\}$

EXERCISE 7* REVISION

1 ▶ $\frac{4a}{b}$ 2 ▶ $\frac{5x}{y}$ 3 ▶ $\frac{b}{4a}$

4 ▶ $\frac{b}{2}$ 5 ▶ $\frac{5}{xy}$ 6 ▶ $\frac{18b}{a}$

7 ▶ $\frac{8a}{5}$ 8 ▶ $\frac{7}{12b}$ 9 ▶ $\frac{2x + 6}{21}$

10 ▶ $x = \pm 3$ 11 ▶ $x = 2$ 12 ▶ $x = \pm 4$

13 ▶ a^4 14 ▶ $4b^6$ 15 ▶ $81c^7$

16 ▶ $-3 < x \le 0$; -2 17 ▶ $x < -4.4$

18 ▶ $x > -4$ 19 ▶ $x \le 4.5$

20 ▶ 37 21 ▶ $\{-3, -2, -1, 0\}$

EXAM PRACTICE: ALGEBRA 2

1 ▶ $4y^2$ **2** ▶ $\dfrac{y}{3x}$ **3** ▶ 1

4 ▶ $\dfrac{3}{y}$ **5** ▶ $\dfrac{x}{12}$ **6** ▶ $\dfrac{7x}{9}$

7 ▶ $x = \pm 5$ **8** ▶ $x = \pm 9$ **9** ▶ $x = 12$

10 ▶ **a** $3q^6$ **b** p^2 **c** x^{20}

11 ▶ $x \le -3$

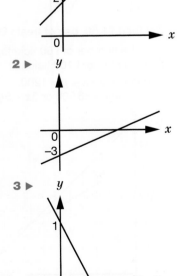

12 ▶ $1, 2$

UNIT 2: GRAPHS 2

EXERCISE 1

1 ▶ $y = x + 1$ **2** ▶ $y = 0.5x - 1$

3 ▶ $y = -2x + 3$ **4** ▶ $y = -x$

5 ▶ $y = x + 1$ **6** ▶ $y = x + 3$

7 ▶ $y = 2x - 3$ **8** ▶ $y = \frac{1}{3}x$

9 ▶ $y = -x + 4$ **10** ▶ $y = -2x - 1$

EXERCISE 1*

1 ▶ $y = 3x + 12$ **2** ▶ $y = -0.5x$

3 ▶ $y = \frac{5}{2}x - 3.5$ **4** ▶ $y = \frac{9}{5}x - 12$

5 ▶ $y = 3x + 7$ **6** ▶ $y = -\frac{1}{3}x + 3$

7 ▶ $y = 1$

8 ▶ **a** $y = -0.5x$ **b** Collinear

9 ▶ **a** $y = \frac{1}{2}x + 3$ **b** $y = \frac{1}{2}x + 3$ **c** Collinear

10 ▶ $y = -3x + 3,\ y = \frac{1}{2}x - \frac{1}{2}$

EXERCISE 2

1 ▶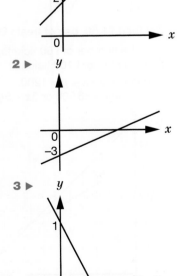

2 ▶

3 ▶

4 ▶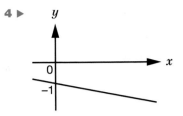

5 ▶ $3, 5$

6 ▶ $1, -7$

7 ▶ $-2, 3$

8 ▶ $-\frac{1}{2}, -1$

9 ▶ Crosses axes at $(2, 0)$ and $(0, 3)$

10 ▶ Crosses axes at $(4, 0)$ and $(0, -2)$

11 ▶ Crosses axes at $(-3, 0)$ and $(0, 4)$

12 ▶ For example

   a $y = x - 1$

   b $y = -\frac{1}{2}x + 2$

   c $y = 1$

EXERCISE 2*

1 ▶ $5, \frac{1}{2}$

2 ▶ $-2, 4$

3 ▶ $2, 2.5$

4 ▶ $-3, 2.5$

5 ▶ $3.5, -7$

6 ▶ $-2, 10$

7 ▶ Crosses axes at $(\frac{1}{2}, 0)$ and $(0, -\frac{1}{3})$

8 ▶ Crosses axes at $(\frac{3}{2}, 0)$ and $(0, -\frac{3}{4})$

9 ▶ For example

   a $x = 2$

   b $2x + y = 2$

   c $y = \frac{1}{2}x - 1$

10 ▶ **a**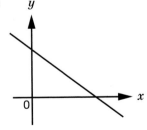

   b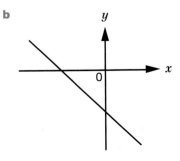

c

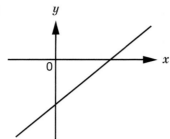

EXERCISE 3

1 ▶

x	0	2	4
$y = x + 1$	1	3	5
$y = 2x - 2$	−2	2	6

Intersection point is (3, 4)

2 ▶ (2, 5)

3 ▶ (3, 8)

4 ▶ (2, 2)

5 ▶ a Logan: $3x + 2y = 12$ Max: $5x + y = 13$

b

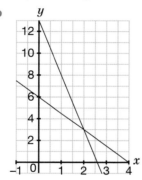

c Big Wheel $2, Pirate Ship $3

6 ▶ Numbers of coins: $x + y = 18$
Value: $\frac{1}{2}x + y = 13$

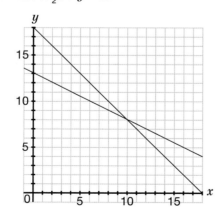

Freya has ten 50p coins (and eight £1 coins).

EXERCISE 3*

1 ▶ (6, 13)

2 ▶ (0.53, −0.9)

3 ▶

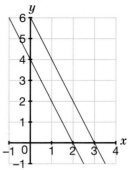

No solutions as lines are parallel and never cross.

4 ▶

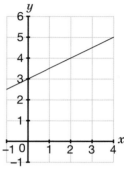

Infinite number of solutions (e.g. (0, 3), (2, 4), $(p, \frac{1}{2}p + 3)$) as the lines are the same.

5 ▶ Approx (700, 2900) and (7400, 2300)

6 ▶ Equations are $4x + 2y = 7$ and $3x + 3y = 6$

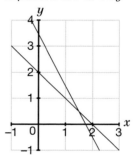

Cat food £1.50, bag of treats £0.50

7 ▶ Let x be number of £60 tickets, y be number of £100 tickets.

Equations are $x + y = 1200$,
$60x + 100y = 88\,000$ or $3x + 5y = 4400$

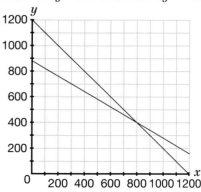

Number of £60 tickets is 800

8 ▶ a Angles: 0°, 90°, 180°, 270°, 0°, 90°, 180°, 270°, 0°, 90°, 180°

b, c

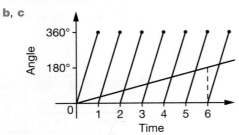

d 1 h 5.45 min; 2 h 10.9 min; 3 h 16.4 min; 4 h 21.8 min; 5 h 27.3 min

EXERCISE 4 REVISION

1 ▶ a $y = 2x$ **b** $y = -3x + 6$
2 ▶ a $y = 2x - 2$ **b** $y = -x + 1$
3 ▶ a

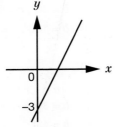

b

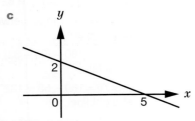

c

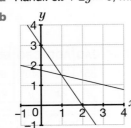

4 ▶ $x = 2, y = 1$
5 ▶ $x = -1, y = 3$
6 ▶ a Rahul: $3x + 2y = 6$, Mia: $x + 4y = 7$

b

c Banana $1, Musedown $1.50

EXERCISE 4* REVISION

1 ▶ $3y = x + 6$
2 ▶ a $3y + x = -7$
    b $y = 2x - 4$
3 ▶ a

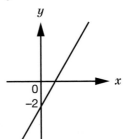

b

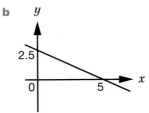

c

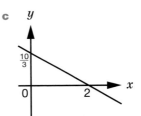

4 ▶ $x = -1.4, y = -0.8$
5 ▶ Let x be number correct, y be number wrong. Then $x + y = 20$ and $4x - y = 50$.

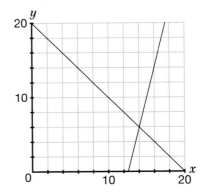

From graph number wrong is 6.

6 ▶ $y = 3x + 9 - 6p$

EXAM PRACTICE: GRAPHS 2

1 ▶ $y = 5x - 3$
2 ▶ a $y = -\frac{1}{2}x$
    b $y = -\frac{1}{2}x - \frac{1}{2}$

3 ▶ a

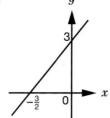

b

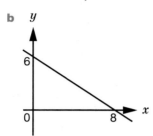

c

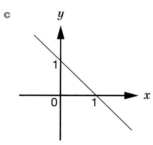

4 ▶ $x = 3, y = 5$

5 ▶ Theo: $6x + 4y = 14$, Erin: $4x + 6y = 16$

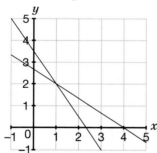

a Apple costs $1   **b** Avocado costs $2

UNIT 2: SHAPE AND SPACE 2

EXERCISE 1

1 ▶ 10.3 cm	**2 ▶** 8.06 cm
3 ▶ 8.94 cm	**4 ▶** 13.0 cm
5 ▶ 11.8 cm	**6 ▶** 15.3 cm
7 ▶ 70.7 m	**8 ▶** 69.2 km
9 ▶ 3.16 m	**10 ▶** 10.4 m

EXERCISE 1*

1 ▶ 12.4 cm	**2 ▶** 4.90 cm
3 ▶ 8.77 m	**4 ▶** 11.0 m
5 ▶ 13.9	**6 ▶** 200 cm²
7 ▶ 17 : 28 : 20	
8 ▶ a 75 m	**b** 43.3 m

9 ▶ a $\sqrt{y^2 - r^2}$

b Both tangents to circle from same point

10 ▶ 11.6 cm   **11 ▶** 27.5 m   **12 ▶** 3.92 m

ACTIVITY 2

Circle | Angle	BAO	ABO	AOB	BOC	OBC+OCB	OBC	ABC
C_1	25°	25°	130°	50°	130°	65°	90°
C_2	$x°$	$x°$	$180° - x°$	$2x°$	$180° - 2x°$	$90° - x°$	90°

EXERCISE 2

1 ▶ $a = 50°, b = 280°$
2 ▶ $a = 90°, b = 30°$
3 ▶ $a = 70°, b = 20°$
4 ▶ $a = 55°, b = 70°$
5 ▶ $a = 25°, b = 25°, c = 65°$
6 ▶ $x = 30°, 2x = 60°$
7 ▶ $a = 90°, b = 30°, c = 60°$
8 ▶ $a = 90°, b = 130°, c = 65°$
9 ▶ $a = 55°$
10 ▶ $a = 70°$

EXERCISE 2*

1 ▶ $a = 60°, b = 300°$
2 ▶ $a = 90°, b = 45°$
3 ▶ $2a = 36°, 3a = 54°$
4 ▶ $a = 55°, b = 35°$
5 ▶ $a = 70°, b = 70°, c = 20°, d = 20°$
6 ▶ $a = 70°, b = 55°, c = 125°$
7 ▶ $x = 130°, y = 25°, z = 65°$
8 ▶ $x = 70°, y = 55°, z = 35°$
9 ▶ $x = 124°, y = 34°, z = 62°$
10 ▶ $\angle OTP = 90°$ (angle between tangent and radius is 90°)

$\angle TOP = 180 - (90 + 32) = 58°$ (angles in a triangle)

$\angle SOT = 180 - 58 = 122°$ (angles on a straight line)

OS = OT (radii of same circle)

$x = (180 - 122) \div 2 = 29°$ (angles in an isosceles triangle)

ACTIVITY 3

Circle | Angle	OCA	OCB	CAO	AOD	CBO	BOD	ACB	AOB
C_1	35°	40°	35°	70°	40°	80°	75°	150°
C_2	$x°$	$y°$	$x°$	$2x°$	$y°$	$2y°$	$x° + y°$	$2(x° + y°)$

$k = 2$

EXERCISE 3

1 ▶ $a = 60°$

2 ▶ $a = 140°$

3 ▶ $a = 50°$

4 ▶ $a = 140°$

5 ▶ $a = 40°, b = 20°$

6 ▶ $a = 120°, b = 30°$

7 ▶ $a = 65°, b = 115°$

8 ▶ $a = 50°, b = 130°$

9 ▶ $a = 72°$ (opposite angles of a cyclic quadrilateral add to 180°)

$b = 108°$ (angles on a straight line add to 180°)

$c = 93°$ (angles in a quadrilateral add to 360°)

10 ▶ $k = 46°$ and $m = 38°$ (angles subtended by the same arc)

$l = 54°$ (angles in a triangle add to 180°)

EXERCISE 3*

1 ▶ $a = 100°$

2 ▶ $a = 80°$

3 ▶ $a = 290°$

4 ▶ $a = 102°$

5 ▶ $a = 40°, b = 60°$

6 ▶ $a = 35°, b = 25°$

7 ▶ $a = 110°, b = 70°$

8 ▶ $a = 60°, b = 60°$

9 ▶ $\angle ADC = \frac{y}{2}$ (angle at centre is twice the angle at the circumference)

$\angle ABC = 180 - \frac{y}{2}$ (opposite angles in cyclic quadrilateral add to 180°)

10 ▶ Angle TAO = 90° (angle between tangent and radius = 90°)

Angle OAB = angle OBA = 32° (base angles of isosceles triangle are equal)

Angle ABT = 81° (angles in a triangle add to 180°)

Angle OBT = 32 + 81 = 113°

EXERCISE 4   REVISION

1 ▶ **a** 13.0 cm   **b** 11.2 cm

2 ▶ 44.7 cm

3 ▶ **a** 2.5 m   **b** 6.5 m²

4 ▶ $a = 60°$ (OBC is an equilateral triangle)

OA = OB so OAB is isosceles (radii same circle)

$c = \angle OBA = 130° - 60° = 70°$ (base angles of an isosceles triangle are equal)

$b = 180 - 70 - 70 = 40°$ (angles in a triangle add to 180°)

5 ▶ $\angle ABC = 90°$; $\angle ACB = 36°$; $\angle BAC = 54°$

6 ▶ OB = OC = OA (radii same circle)

$\angle OAC = \angle OCA$ (base angles of isosceles triangle are equal)

$\angle OCB = (180° - 40° - 70°) \div 2 = 35°$

$\angle OBC = \angle OCB$ (base angles of isosceles triangle are equal)

$\angle OCB = (180° - 40°) \div 2 = 70°$

$= 2 \times \angle ACO$

Hence AC bisects $\angle OCB$

7 ▶ $\angle ODC = 66°$ (opposite angles of a cyclic quadrilateral add to 180°)

OC = OD (radii same circle)

$\angle ODC = \angle OCD$ (base angles of isosceles triangle are equal)

$\angle COD = 180° - 66° - 66° = 48°$ (angles in a triangle add to 180°)

8 ▶ $\angle BCD = 30°$ (opposite angles of a cyclic quadrilateral add to 180°)

$\angle BOD = 60°$ (angle at the centre is twice angle at the circumference when both are subtended by the same arc)

OB = OD (radii same circle)

$\angle OBD = \angle ODB = (180° - 60°) \div 2 = 60°$ (base angles of isosceles triangle are equal and angles in a triangle add to 180°)

In triangle OBD all the angles are 60° so it is equilateral.

EXERCISE 4*   REVISION

1 ▶ 2 m

2 ▶ 3.71 cm

3 ▶ OA = OB radii same circle.
Angle OAB = angle OBA (base angles of isosceles triangle are equal)
Angle OAB = (180° - 124°) ÷ 2 = 28° (angles in a triangle add to 180°)
Angle OAT = 90° (angle between tangent and radius is 90°)
Angle BAT = 90° - 28° = 62°
(Note: these angles may be annotated on the diagram.)

4 ▶ Angle BAD = 70°. Angle BOD = 140°.
Opposite angles of cyclic quadrilateral add to 180° and angle at centre equals twice angle at circumference when both are subtended by the same arc.

5 ▶ **a** Angle BAD = 90° (the angle in a semicircle is a right angle). Angle ABD = 180 - 90° - 19° = 71° (angles in a triangle add to 180°)

b Angle ACB = 19° (angles subtended at the circumference by the same arc are equal)

6 ▶ Angle ABC = 90°, $6y$ = 90°, angle BAC = 75°

7 ▶ **a** Let angle BAO = x. Angle CDO = angle
BAO = x (both subtended by arc BC)
Angle BOC = 2 × angle BAO = $2x$ (angle
at centre = 2 × angle at circumference)
So angle BAO + angle CDO = $x + x = 2x$
= angle BOC

b Angle BAO = angle ABO (base angles
of isosceles triangle OAB, equal radii)
Angle CDO = angle DCO (base angles of
isosceles triangle OCD, equal radii)
Since angle BAO = angle CDO = x, all
four angles = x

8 ▶ Angle ABC = 180° – x (angles on a straight
line). Also angle ABC = 180° – angle ADC
(opposite angles of a cyclic quadrilateral
are supplementary). So angle ADC = x
Angle ADC + angle CDT = 180° (angles on a
straight line). So $x + y$ = 180°

EXAM PRACTICE: SHAPE AND SPACE 2

1 ▶ 2.98 m

2 ▶ **a** $a = b$ = 40° (angles subtended by same
arc)

Angle adjacent to 35° = 40° (alternate
angles)

So $c = b$ + 75 = 115° (exterior angle
property)

b Angle adjacent to d = 74° (opposite
angles of a cyclic quadrilateral are
supplementary)

d = 106° (angles on a straight line)

e = 102° (opposite angles of a cyclic
quadrilateral are supplementary)

c f = 65° (angles subtended by same arc)

g = 102 – f = 37° (exterior angle property)

3 ▶ Angle OBA = 90° – $3x$ (angle between
tangent and radius = 90°)

Angle OAB = 90° – $3x$ (base angle of
isosceles triangle OAB, equal radii)

Angle OAC = x (base angle of isosceles
triangle OAC, equal radii)

Therefore
angle BAC = 90° – $3x + x$ = 90° – $2x$

Angle BOC = 2 × angle BAC = 180°
– $4x$ (angle at centre = 2 × angle at
circumference)

Angle TBO = angle TCO = 90° (angles
between tangent and radii)

In quadrilateral TBOC,
y + 90 + 180 – $4x$ + 90 = 360°

Therefore $y = 4x$ (There are at least four
other ways to prove this result.)

4 ▶ 43.3 cm^2

UNIT 2: HANDLING DATA 1

EXERCISE 1

1 ▶ **a** Categorical

b Discrete

c Discrete

d Continuous

e Categorical

f Continuous

2 ▶ **a**

Grade Rating	Tally	Frequency
A	ЖH IIII	9
B	ЖH	5
C	II	2
D	ЖH I	6
E	ЖH III	8
Total		30

b 30

c Students either loved or hated the event.

3–4 Students' own answers

EXERCISE 1*

1 ▶ **a** Continuous

b Categorical

c Discrete

d Continuous

e Categorical

f Discrete

2 ▶ **a**

Score	Tally	Frequency
1	ЖH II	7
2	ЖH ЖH	10
3	ЖH	5
4	ЖH ЖH	10
5	ЖH I	6
6	ЖH ЖH II	12
Total		50

b No clear bias. (Sample is too small to
draw conclusions from)

3–4 Students' own answers

EXERCISE 2

1 ▶

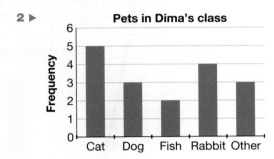

2 ▶

3 ▶ a

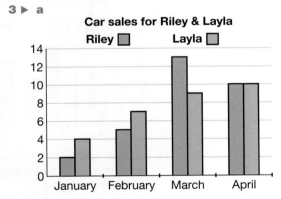

b Both have increasing sales, but Riley did very well in March.

4 ▶ a Hot chocolate 80°, milkshake 60°, coffee 100°, tea 120°

b Accurate pie chart drawn with hot chocolate 80°, milkshake 60°, coffee 100°, tea 120°

5 ▶ a Any suitable two-way table

b No since only 54% are in favour.

EXERCISE 2*

1 ▶ a

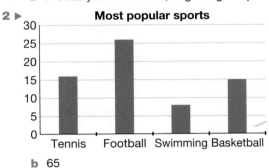

b Probably end of March, beginning of April

2 ▶

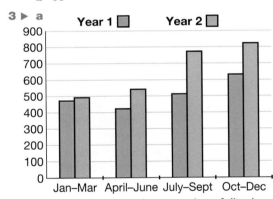

b 65

3 ▶ a

b Year 2 sales are better and are following the same trend as Year 1.

4 ▶ Accurate pie chart drawn with France 144°, Spain 108°, Germany 45°, Italy 63°

5 ▶ a

	No change	Improved	Much improved	Total
Drug A	10	45	5	60
Drug B	7	20	13	40
Total	17	65	18	100

b $\frac{2}{5}$

c Students' own answer, e.g. Drug B had a greater proportion much improved but Drug A had a greater proportion improved.

EXERCISE 3

1 ▶ Mean = 4, median = 4, mode = 4
2 ▶ Mean = 5, median = 4, mode = none
3 ▶ Mean = 6, median = 4, mode = 0
4 ▶ Mean = 4.75, median = 5, mode = 7 and 9
5 ▶ Mean = 30.5, median = 31, mode = 31
6 ▶ 4
7 ▶ 43
8 ▶ 1

EXERCISE 3*

1 ▶ Mean = 3, median = 2, mode = 0
2 ▶ Mean = 66, median = 70.5, mode = 72
3 ▶ Mean = 82.375, median = 71, mode = none
4 ▶ Mean = 0.62, median = 0.575, mode = 0.46
5 ▶ Mean = 12.9, median = 12, mode = none
6 ▶ Mean = 92.9
7 ▶ 11 and 15, 12 and 14, or 13 and 13
8 ▶ $x = 3$, $y = 6$, $z = 9$

EXERCISE 4

1 ▶ a Mean £19 400, median £15 000, mode £12 000
   b Median; mean is distorted by one high salary and mode is lowest salary so neither of these gives a typical salary.
2 ▶ a Median; the low value of 6 s distorts the mean, making it too low, and the mode gives the longest time so neither of these is typical.
   b Mode; the data is qualitative so you cannot work out the mean or median.
3 ▶ a Mean = 14.2, median = 13, mode = 12
   b Size 12; the most popular size is the one that is most likely to be purchased.
4 ▶ a Mean = 194, mode = 180, median = 180
   b Mean. This takes into account lower and higher values throughout the week.

EXERCISE 4*

1 ▶ a Mean = 8.375, median = 7.75, mode = 7
   b Mode; this is the most popular shoe size so it makes sense to order what customers are likely to want to buy. The values of mean and median aren't proper shoe sizes.
2 ▶ a Mean = 53, median = 47, mode = 47
   b Mean. This is the highest therefore they will wish to work on a 'worst case scenario'. They will also want an excuse to charge more!

3 ▶ a Mean = £212, median = £190, mode = £180
   b Mean, which takes into account all five values and could be used to work out the total bill.
4 ▶ a Mode. Data is non-numerical.
   b Median. The mean would not give a whole number and the mode is the lowest value so not representative of the data set.

EXERCISE 5   REVISION

1 ▶ Accurate pie chart drawn with strawberries 125°, banana 75°, yoghurt 100°, iced water 60°

2 ▶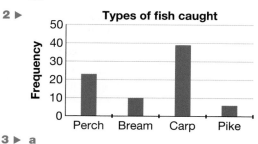

3 ▶ a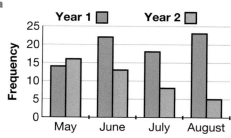
   b Second year started with roughly the same number of sunny days, but then rapidly deteriorated.

4 ▶

	French	German	Mandarin	Total
History	57	51	18	126
Geography	45	12	17	74
Total	102	63	35	200

   b 17.5%
   c History

5 ▶ a The vertical scale does not start from zero. This makes a small difference look like a big difference.

b

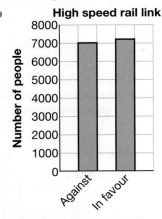

High speed rail link

Very similar numbers in favour of and against the rail link.

6 ▶ Mean = 5, median = 6, mode = none

7 ▶ a Mean = $1150, mode = $700, median = $750

b Median

8 ▶ 36

EXERCISE 5* REVISION

1 ▶ 540

2 ▶ a

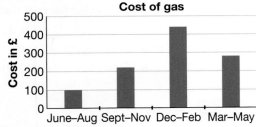

Cost of gas

b £86.67

3 ▶ a

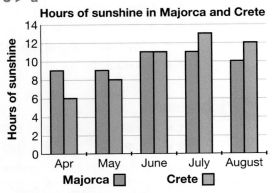

Hours of sunshine in Majorca and Crete

Majorca ▢ Crete ▢

b Majorca is sunnier before June, Crete is sunnier after June.

4 ▶

	Men	Women	Total
More spaces	23	42	65
Adequate spaces	37	18	55
Total	60	60	120

No, only 54% want more spaces.

5 ▶ The bar for 'Nutty Oats' is wider than the rest. The vertical axis has no scale or unit.

6 ▶ a Mean = 47, mode = 70, median = 49

b Mean or median

7 ▶ 1.74 m

8 ▶ 9.37 m (to 3 s.f.)

EXAM PRACTICE: HANDLING DATA 1

1 ▶ a 8   **b** 60°

2 ▶ 14

3 ▶ a

Year 1 ▢   Year 2 ▢

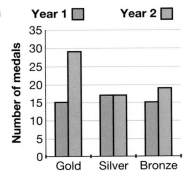

b Year 2 was much better, especially the number of gold medals won.

4 ▶

	Chicken	Vegetarian	Total
Cheese	15	8	23
Ice cream	22	5	27
Total	37	13	50

5 ▶ (1) The blocks have different widths. (2) The scale on the y-axis does not start at zero.

6 ▶ Mean = 6, median = 6, mode = none

7 ▶ 82

8 ▶ 1.803… = 1.80 (3 s.f.)

UNIT 3 ANSWERS

UNIT 3: NUMBER 3

EXERCISE 1

1 ▶ 7, 14, 21, 28, 35
2 ▶ 6, 12, 18, 24, 30
3 ▶ 1, 2, 3, 4, 6, 12
4 ▶ 1, 2, 3, 6, 9, 18
5 ▶ 1, 2, 3, 5, 6, 10, 15, 30
6 ▶ $2 \times 2 \times 7$
7 ▶ $2 \times 5 \times 7$
8 ▶ $2 \times 2 \times 3 \times 5$
9 ▶ $2 \times 2 \times 2 \times 2 \times 2 \times 3$
10 ▶ $n = 4$
11 ▶ a $2^2 \times 3^2 \times 7$ b $2^3 \times 3^3 \times 7$
12 ▶ 6 mm by 6 mm

EXERCISE 1*

1 ▶ 5, 10, 15, 20, 25
2 ▶ 9, 18, 27, 36, 45
3 ▶ 13, 26, 39, 52, 65
4 ▶ 1, 3, 5, 15, 25, 75
5 ▶ 1, 2, 4, 5, 8, 10, 20, 40
6 ▶ 1, 2, 3, 6, 9, 18, 27, 54
7 ▶ $3 \times 5 \times 7 \times 11$
8 ▶ a $3 \times 7 \times 19$ b $2^2 \times 3^3 \times 7 \times 19$
9 ▶ $2^3 \times 3 \times 7; 2^6 \times 3^2 \times 7^2$
10 ▶ a $60 = 2 \times 2 \times 3 \times 5 = 2^2 \times 3 \times 5$
     b $60 = 2 \times 2 \times 3 \times 5 = 2^2 \times 3 \times 5$
     c $48 = 2 \times 2 \times 2 \times 2 \times 3 = 2^4 \times 3$
11 ▶ 200 cm
12 ▶ 168

EXERCISE 2

1 ▶ 2   2 ▶ 5   3 ▶ 22
4 ▶ 6   5 ▶ 30   6 ▶ 30
7 ▶ 9 bags each with 2 chocolates and 3 mints
8 ▶ LCM is 45 and 75 is 225 mins so 12:45
9 ▶ $2x$ 10 ▶ $4y^2$ 11 ▶ $6ab$
12 ▶ $12xy$

EXERCISE 2*

1 ▶ HCF = 6   2 ▶ HCF = 15
    LCM = 36   LCM = 210
3 ▶ HCF = y 4 ▶ HCF = $2xy$
    LCM = $6xyz$ LCM = $12xy$
5 ▶ HCF = xy 6 ▶ HCF = xy
    LCM = x^2yz LCM = x^3y^4

7 ▶ HCF = $3xyz$
    LCM = $18x^2y^2z^2$
8 ▶ 12, 15 120   9 ▶   420, 924
10 ▶ a 300 mins
     b Next possible is 600 mins which is too long for a school day
11 ▶ 1920 secs or 32 mins
12 ▶ 42 parcels each containing 6 tins of beans, 4 chocolate bars and 7 packets of soup

EXERCISE 3

1 ▶ $45 : $75   2 ▶ 111 ml
3 ▶ 30°, 60°, 90°   4 ▶ $32
5 ▶ a 11.5 : 1   b The first school
6 ▶ Julie (Julie uses 5 parts water to 1 part squash. Hammad uses 5.7 parts water)
7 ▶ £84
8 ▶ a 5 : 2   b 22.5 g resin
    c 4.8 g hardener

EXERCISE 3*

1 ▶ €50 : €300   2 ▶ 519 g
3 ▶ 256 tonnes : 192 tonnes : 128 tonnes
4 ▶ 1 mg
5 ▶ a $\frac{25}{3}$: 1 or 8.3333… : 1
    b 637 customers to 70 staff gives a ratio of 9.1 : 1, so the store with 70 staff has more customers per staff member.
6 ▶ Jon   7 ▶ £20 400
8 ▶ a 5 : 2 or 2.5 : 1 or 1 : 0.4
    b 24 kg   c 187.5 kg

EXERCISE 4 REVISION

1 ▶ $2^2 \times 3^3 \times 7$ 2 ▶ 6, 72
3 ▶ 12 cm by 12 cm   4 ▶ 30
5 ▶ 168 cm
6 ▶ a $\frac{4}{7}$ b $\frac{3}{7}$
    c Carlotta £200, Hannah £150
7 ▶ 350 students

EXERCISE 4* REVISION

1 ▶ $2^4 \times 3^2 \times 7$ 2 ▶ 6, 720
3 ▶ 144, 216   4 ▶ 180 seconds
5 ▶ 15, each with 5 pink, 7 yellow and 3 white
6 ▶

Size	Blue	Red	White
1 litre	0.1	0.1875	0.7125
2.5 litre	0.25	0.468 75	1.781 25

7 ▶ a 300 : 1   b 81 cm

EXAM PRACTICE: NUMBER 3

1 ▶ $2 \times 3 \times 5^2 \times 7$

2 ▶ 18, 252

3 ▶ **a** 120 questions

    b 4 tests

4 ▶ 84

5 ▶ Ben £315, Terry £120, Anne £105

6 ▶ **a** 1:5   **b** 9.6 litres

UNIT 3: ALGEBRA 3

EXERCISE 1

1 ▶ $x(x + 3)$ 2 ▶ $x(x - 4)$

3 ▶ $5(a - 2b)$ 4 ▶ $x(y - z)$

5 ▶ $2x(x + 2)$ 6 ▶ $3x(x - 6)$

7 ▶ $ax(x - a)$ 8 ▶ $3xy(2x - 7)$

9 ▶ $3pq(3p + 2)$ 10 ▶ $a(p + q - r)$

11 ▶ $a^2x^2(1 + ax)$ 12 ▶ $2ab(2b^2 + 3a)$

EXERCISE 1*

1 ▶ $5x^3(1 + 3x)$

2 ▶ $3x^2(x - 6)$

3 ▶ $3x^2y^2(3x - 4y^2)$

4 ▶ $x(x^2 - 3x - 3)$

5 ▶ $\pi(r + 2h)$

6 ▶ $ab(c^2 - b + ac)$

7 ▶ $4pq(pqr^2 - 3r + 4q)$

8 ▶ $3x(10x^2 + 4y - 7z)$

9 ▶ $0.1h(2h + g - 3g^2h)$

10 ▶ $\dfrac{xy(2x^2 - 4y + xy)}{16}$

11 ▶ $4pqr(4pr^2 - 7 - 5p^2q)$

12 ▶ $(a + b)(x + y)$

13 ▶ $(x - y)^2(1 - x + y)$

14 ▶ $x^2(x + 3)(x + 5)$

EXERCISE 2

1 ▶ $x + 1$ 2 ▶ $1 - a^2$

3 ▶ $\dfrac{(x + y)}{z}$ 4 ▶ $\dfrac{(a - b)}{c}$

5 ▶ 2   6 ▶ 5

7 ▶ $\dfrac{(a - b)}{b}$ 8 ▶ $\dfrac{(x + y)}{y}$

9 ▶ $\dfrac{t}{r}$ 10 ▶ $\dfrac{a}{z}$

11 ▶ $\dfrac{x}{z}$ 12 ▶ $\dfrac{a}{c}$

EXERCISE 2*

1 ▶ $x + y$ 2 ▶ $3a + b$

3 ▶ $\dfrac{1}{z + 1}$ 4 ▶ $\dfrac{2}{m - 2}$

5 ▶ $2 + 3x^2$ 6 ▶ $\dfrac{2}{3}(x - 3y^2)$

7 ▶ y 8 ▶ $\dfrac{2x}{z}$ 9 ▶ 1

10 ▶ $\dfrac{b}{a}$ 11 ▶ 5   12 ▶ $-x$

EXERCISE 3

1 ▶ $x = 8$ 2 ▶ $x = -10$

3 ▶ $x = 2$ 4 ▶ $x = 0$

5 ▶ $x = -6$ 6 ▶ $x = 5$

7 ▶ $x = -4$ 8 ▶ $x = 6$

9 ▶ $x = 14$ 10 ▶ $x = 3$

11 ▶ $x = 0$ 12 ▶ $x = 0$

13 ▶ $x = 10$ 14 ▶ 6 km

EXERCISE 3*

1 ▶ $x = 9$ 2 ▶ $x = \frac{3}{5}$

3 ▶ $x = 9$ 4 ▶ $x = -6$

5 ▶ $x = 0$ 6 ▶ $x = \frac{1}{9}$

7 ▶ $x = 3$ 8 ▶ $x = -1$

9 ▶ $x = 5.6$ 10 ▶ $x = -\frac{5}{13}$

11 ▶ $x = 7$ 12 ▶ 84 years

EXERCISE 4

1 ▶ $x = 2$ 2 ▶ $x = -3$

3 ▶ $x = \frac{3}{5}$ 4 ▶ $x = -8$

5 ▶ $x = 10$ 6 ▶ $x = -2.4$

7 ▶ $x = 50$ 8 ▶ $x = -25$

9 ▶ $x = \frac{5}{3}$ 10 ▶ $x = \pm 3$

11 ▶ $x = \frac{6}{7}$ 12 ▶ $x = \pm 5$

EXERCISE 4*

1 ▶ $x = 4$ 2 ▶ $x = -8$

3 ▶ $x = \frac{1}{6}$ 4 ▶ $x = -64$

5 ▶ $x = 4$ 6 ▶ $x = \pm 8$

7 ▶ $x = \pm 2$ 8 ▶ $x = 0.32$

9 ▶ $x = \frac{5}{6}$ 10 ▶ $x = \dfrac{a + b}{ab}$

11 ▶ $x = \frac{7}{12}$ 12 ▶ $x = \dfrac{b - a}{ab}$

EXERCISE 5

1 ▶ $x = 3, y = 1$ 2 ▶ $x = 2, y = 1$

3 ▶ $x = 1, y = 4$ 4 ▶ $x = 2, y = 4$

5 ▶ $x = 1, y = 6$ 6 ▶ $x = 2, y = 5$

7 ▶ $x = -1, y = 2$ 8 ▶ $x = -2, y = 2$

9 ▶ $x = 3, y = -1$ 10 ▶ $x = 2, y = -2$

EXERCISE 5*

1 ▶ $x = 1, y = 2$ 2 ▶ $x = 1, y = 2$

3 ▶ $x = 4, y = 1$ 4 ▶ $x = 3, y = 1$

5 ▶ $x = 2, y = 1$ 6 ▶ $x = 5, y = 3$

7 ▶ $x = 1, y = -2$ 8 ▶ $x = 4, y = 5$

9 ▶ $x = -3, y = \frac{1}{2}$ 10 ▶ $x = -2, y = 1$

EXERCISE 6

1 ▶ (5, 3)
2 ▶ (1, 1)
3 ▶ (3, 2)
4 ▶ (2, 1)
5 ▶ (1, 2)
6 ▶ (−1, 3)
7 ▶ (1, 1)
8 ▶ (−2, 1)
9 ▶ (1, −1)
10 ▶ (−1, 2)

EXERCISE 6*

1 ▶ (8, 3)
2 ▶ (2, −1)
3 ▶ (4, 5)
4 ▶ $(3, -\frac{1}{2})$
5 ▶ (1, 5)
6 ▶ (8, 5)
7 ▶ (0, −2)
8 ▶ (−7, 0)
9 ▶ (−1, 5)
10 ▶ (1, 1)

EXERCISE 7

1 ▶ (2, 5)
2 ▶ (4, 1)
3 ▶ (5, 1)
4 ▶ (−2.75, −0.75)
5 ▶ (1, 3)
6 ▶ (−2, 1)
7 ▶ (5, −1)
8 ▶ (3, −2)
9 ▶ (2, 1)
10 ▶ (1, 2)

EXERCISE 7*

1 ▶ (3, −1)
2 ▶ (4, −2)
3 ▶ (1, 2)
4 ▶ (4, −3)
5 ▶ (−0.4, 2.6)
6 ▶ (1, 1)
7 ▶ (7, 3)
8 ▶ (4, −1)
9 ▶ (0.5, 0.75)
10 ▶ (0.2, −0.6)
11 ▶ (4, 6)
12 ▶ (−5, 4)
13 ▶ $a = -0.6, b = -0.8$
14 ▶ $c = 0.6, d = -0.2$
15 ▶ (0.4, 0.5)
16 ▶ (4, −6)

EXERCISE 8

1 ▶ 29, 83
2 ▶ 12, 16
3 ▶ 9, 4
4 ▶ $x = 2, y = 3$, area = 180
5 ▶ Burger 99p, cola 49p
6 ▶ Rollercoaster £1.50, water slide 90p
7 ▶ 27 @ 20p, 12 @ 50p
8 ▶ 420
9 ▶ 11
10 ▶ 39

EXERCISE 8*

1 ▶ (2, 3)
2 ▶ $m = 2, c = -1$
3 ▶ $\frac{12}{17}$
4 ▶ 1.5 m/s
5 ▶ 16 years
6 ▶ 7.5 km
7 ▶ 150 km
8 ▶ 37
9 ▶ 84 m
10 ▶ Urban 63 km, Motorway 105 km, total 168 km

EXERCISE 9   REVISION

1 ▶ $x(x - 8)$
2 ▶ $3x(x + 4)$
3 ▶ $6xy(y - 5x)$
4 ▶ $3x(4x^2 + 3x - 5)$
5 ▶ $x - 1$
6 ▶ $\frac{x + y}{x - y}$
7 ▶ $x = 4$
8 ▶ $x = 6$
9 ▶ $x = -4$
10 ▶ $n = 2$
11 ▶ 24
12 ▶ (−1, 3)
13 ▶ (0, 3)
14 ▶ (2, 2)
15 ▶ (1, 3)
16 ▶ CD £7.50, USB stick £3.50
17 ▶ 19 @ 10p, 11 @ 20p

EXERCISE 9*   REVISION

1 ▶ $3x^3(x - 4)$
2 ▶ $\frac{2}{3}pr^2(2r + 1)$
3 ▶ $6x^2y(4xy - 3)$
4 ▶ $3a^2b^2c^2(5b - 3a + 7c)$
5 ▶ $\frac{x}{y}$
6 ▶ x
7 ▶ $x = \frac{1}{3}$
8 ▶ $x = -4$
9 ▶ $x = 6$
10 ▶ $x = \frac{1}{2}$
11 ▶ 70 years
12 ▶ (2, 3)
13 ▶ (4, 1)
14 ▶ (4, 1.5)
15 ▶ $(3\frac{1}{3}, 2)$
16 ▶ $a = \frac{3}{11}, b = \frac{2}{11}$
17 ▶ Abdul is 38, Pavel is 14

EXAM PRACTICE: ALGEBRA 3

1 ▶ a $3x(x + 2)$ b $7ab(4b - 3a)$
2 ▶ a $\frac{x - 2}{2}$ b $\frac{x}{y}$
3 ▶ a $x = -5$ b $x = 7$
    c $x = 15$ d $x = -15$
4 ▶ a $x = -1, y = 2$ b $x = 3, y = -2$
5 ▶ An orange costs 50 cents, a mango costs 70 cents.

UNIT 3: GRAPHS 3

EXERCISE 1

1 ▶ a   65 km/h   b   50 km/h
    c   12:00   d   72.5 km
    e   11:08 approx
2 ▶ a   09:30 for half an hour
    b   09:00 and 10:54
    c   20 miles   d   80 mph; yes!
    e   53.3 mph   f   53.3 mph

3 ▶ a

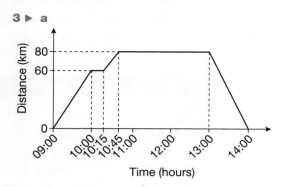

b 14:00

4 ▶ a

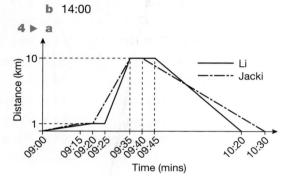

b Li at 10:20, Jacki at 10:30

c 09:20, 09:35–09:40, 09:57

d Li: 18.5 km/h, Jacki: 15 km/h

EXERCISE 1*

1 ▶ a d_A **b** d_B

c d_C **d** d_D

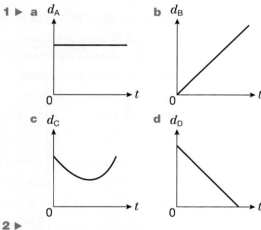

2 ▶

| Exercise 1 | Exercise 2 | Exercise 3 diagonal route: |

3 ▶ a (i) B & C joint 1st, A 2nd

    (ii) C 1st, B 2nd, A 3rd

    (iii) A 1st, B 2nd, C 3rd

b 28.5 s   **c** B

d (i) A (ii) C

4 ▶ a

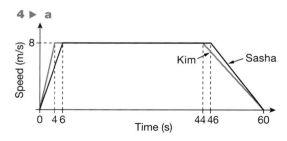

b 09:47   **c** A: 48 km/h, B: 80 km/h

d A: 57 km/h, B: 67 km/h

EXERCISE 2

1 ▶ a 2 m/s²   **b** 4 m/s²

    c 150 m   **d** 10 m/s

2 ▶ a 3.5 km/h²   **b** 7 km/h²

    c 10.5 km   **d** 3.5 km/h

3 ▶ a 2 m/s²   **b** 1 m/s²

    c 8000 m   **d** 50 m/s

4 ▶ a 30 m/s   **b** 10 s

    c 570 m approx **d** 23 m/s approx

EXERCISE 2*

1 ▶ a

b 0.6 m/s²

c −0.5 m/s²

d 4.43 m/s (3 s.f.)

2 ▶ a $S = 120$ m/s

b 9600 m

c 80 m/s

3 ▶ a $t = 10$ s, so distance = 1900 m

b −3 m/s²

c 47.5 m/s

4 ▶ a

b Dead heat

c 6.67 m/s (to 3 s.f.) for both runners

d 400 m

e (i) Sasha reaches 100 m after 15.5 s. Kim reaches 100 m after 14.5 s. Kim is in the lead at 100 m.

(ii) Sasha reaches 300 m after 40.5 s. Kim reaches 300 m after 39.5 s. Kim is in the lead at 300 m.

5 ▶ Bee cannot have two speeds at any given time.

EXERCISE 3 REVISION

1 ▶ a 20 min **b** 10:00
c 10 km/h **d** $3\frac{1}{3}$ km

2 ▶ a 0.4 m/s **b** 10 min **c** 0.2 m/s

3 ▶ a

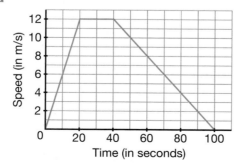

b $\frac{2}{15}$ m/s^2 **c** 0 m/s^2
d $\frac{4}{15}$ m/s^2 **e** $3\frac{1}{7}$ m/s

4 ▶ a 400 m **b** 1050 m
c 10.5 m/s **d** 0.33 m/s

EXERCISE 3* REVISION

1 ▶ b Daniela home at 12:00, Alberto home at 12:00
c Daniela 1.48 m/s, Alberto 2.22 m/s

2 ▶ a 50 m/s **b** 0.53 s approx at 30 m/s

3 ▶ a False; it is constant at $\frac{2}{3}$ m/s^2
b True **c** True
d False; it is 72 km/h

4 ▶ a 32 m **b** $\frac{2}{3}$ m/s^2 **c** 3.2 m/s

EXAM PRACTICE: GRAPHS 3

1 ▶ a 1 km/min **b** 5 mins **c** 120 km/h
2 ▶ a

b (i) 0.6 m/s^2 (ii) 0.2 m/s^2 (iii) 7.2 m/s

3 ▶ a 9.8 m/s **b** 35.4 km/h
c 11.2 m/s **d** 2.2 m/s^2

UNIT 3: SHAPE AND SPACE 3

EXERCISE 1

1 ▶ x: hyp, y: opp, z: adj
2 ▶ x: hyp, y: adj, z: opp
3 ▶ x: opp, y: adj, z: hyp
4 ▶ $\frac{3}{4}$ **5 ▶** $\frac{4}{3}$
6 ▶ $\frac{5}{12}$ **7 ▶** 5.77
8 ▶ 74.6 **9 ▶** 86.6
10 ▶ 16 **11 ▶** 99.9
12 ▶ 99.9 **13 ▶** 6.66 cm
14 ▶ 7.14 cm **15 ▶** 8.20 cm
16 ▶ 4.04 cm **17 ▶** 11.3 cm
18 ▶ 2.58 cm **19 ▶** 87.5 m
20 ▶ 86.6 m **21 ▶** 100 m^2

EXERCISE 1*

1 ▶ 14.4 cm **2 ▶** 4.00 m
3 ▶ 200 cm **4 ▶** 173 cm
5 ▶ 8.45 m **6 ▶** 10.4 m
7 ▶ 100 m **8 ▶** 37.3 m
9 ▶ 22.4 m
10 ▶ BX = 2.66 m, BC = 4.00 m
11 ▶ x = 8.40 cm, y = 4.85 cm
12 ▶ x = 10.9 cm, y = 6.40 cm
13 ▶ x = 7.28 cm, y = 4.27 cm
14 ▶ x = 27.5 cm, y = 9.24 cm
15 ▶ a 25.4 m **b** 18.3 km/h
16 ▶ 6.88 cm

EXERCISE 2

1 ▶ 45° **2 ▶** 30°
3 ▶ 15° **4 ▶** 60.0°
5 ▶ 70.0° **6 ▶** 75.0°
7 ▶ 45.0° **8 ▶** 60.0°
9 ▶ 75.0° **10 ▶** 36.9°
11 ▶ 37.9° **12 ▶** 32.0°
13 ▶ 28.2° **14 ▶** 56.7°
15 ▶ 27.1°
16 ▶ a = 27.2°, b = 62.8°
17 ▶ 23.4°
18 ▶ 15°

EXERCISE 2*

1 ▶ $a = 69°$, $b = 138°$

2 ▶ 113°

3 ▶ 60°

4 ▶ 15°

5 ▶ 160°

6 ▶ **a** 125°   **b** 305°

7 ▶ **a** 080.5°   **b** 260.5°

    c 108.4°   **d** 236.3°

8 ▶ 13.9°   9 ▶ 101°

10 ▶

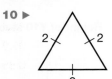

11 ▶

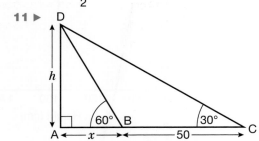

From $\triangle ABC$ $x = \dfrac{h}{\tan 60°} = \dfrac{h}{\sqrt{3}} = \dfrac{h\sqrt{3}}{3}$ ①

From $\triangle ACD$ $50 + x = \dfrac{h}{\tan 30°} = h\sqrt{3}$ ②

Sub ① into ② gives $50 + \dfrac{h\sqrt{3}}{3} = h\sqrt{3}$

$50 = h\sqrt{3} - \dfrac{h\sqrt{3}}{3}$

$50 = \dfrac{2\sqrt{3}}{3}h$

$h = 25 \times \dfrac{3}{\sqrt{3}}$

$h = 25\sqrt{3}$

EXERCISE 3   **REVISION**

1 ▶ 7.00   2 ▶ 6.71

3 ▶ 6.99   4 ▶ 11.0

5 ▶ 8.57   6 ▶ 6.93

7 ▶ 59.0°   8 ▶ 32.5°

9 ▶ 58.0°   10 ▶ 5.19 cm²

11 ▶ 30°

EXERCISE 3*   **REVISION**

1 ▶ 549 m

2 ▶ **a** 063.4°   **b** 243°

3 ▶ **a** 1.01 m

    b Undesirable to have too large a blind distance

4 ▶ Proof

5 ▶ $\tan 30° = \dfrac{1}{\sqrt{3}}$, $\tan 45° = 1$

$x = \left(\dfrac{25 \div 1}{\sqrt{3}}\right) - (25 \div 1) = 25\sqrt{3} - 25$

$= 25(\sqrt{3} - 1)$

EXAM PRACTICE: SHAPE AND SPACE 3

1 ▶ 10.3   2 ▶ 36.9°   3 ▶ 11.7 m

4 ▶ **a** $h_1 = 140$ m , $h_2 = 380$ m

    b 1.44 m/s

5 ▶ **a** 237°

    b Arrives at 5:14:10 approx so arrives safely!

UNIT 3: HANDLING DATA 2

EXERCISE 1

1 ▶ **a**

Score x	Tally	Frequency f	$f \times x$
1	|||	3	$3 \times 1 = 3$
2	|||	3	$3 \times 2 = 6$
3	|||	3	$3 \times 3 = 9$
4	||||	4	$4 \times 4 = 16$
5	|||	3	$3 \times 5 = 15$
6	|||	3	$3 \times 6 = 18$
7	||	2	$2 \times 7 = 14$
8	|||	3	$3 \times 8 = 24$
9	|||	3	$3 \times 9 = 27$
10	|||	3	$3 \times 10 = 30$
		$\sum f = 30$	$\sum fx = 162$

    b Mean $= \dfrac{162}{30} = 5.4$

    c Modal score = 4, median = 5

2 ▶ **a**

Number x	Tally	Frequency f	$f \times x$
4	||	2	$2 \times 4 = 8$
5	||	2	$2 \times 5 = 10$
6			1	$1 \times 6 = 6$
7	||||	4	$4 \times 7 = 28$
8	|||	3	$3 \times 8 = 24$
9	|||	3	$3 \times 9 = 27$
10			1	$1 \times 10 = 10$
11			1	$1 \times 11 = 11$
12	|||	3	$3 \times 12 = 36$
		$\sum f = 20$	$\sum fx = 160$

    b Mean $= \dfrac{160}{20} = 8$

    c Modal number = 7, median = 8

3 ▶ **a** Mean = 2.52   **b** Mode = 3, median = 2

4 ▶ **a** Mean = 7.3   **b** Mode = 8, median = 8

EXERCISE 1*

1 ▶ a

Time t (secs)	Tally	Frequency f
$30 \le t < 35$	|||	3
$35 \le t < 40$	||||	4
$40 \le t < 45$	||||	4
$45 \le t < 50$	||||	5
$50 \le t < 55$		0
$55 \le t < 60$	||||	4

b Mean $= \dfrac{885}{20} = 44.25$ s

c Median: $40 \le t < 45$,
modal class: $45 \le t < 50$

2 ▶ a Mean $= \dfrac{4775}{25} = 191$ kg

b Median: $150 \le w < 200$,
mode: $150 \le w < 200$

3 ▶ a Mean $= \dfrac{496}{100} = 4.96$

b Median: $4 \le t < 6$, mode: $4 \le t < 6$

4 ▶ a $t = 2$ **b** Mean $= \dfrac{44.3}{30} = 1.48$

c Median: $1.4 \le h < 1.6$,
mode: $1.4 \le h < 1.6$

EXERCISE 2 REVISION

1 ▶ a

Time	$0 \le t < 2$	$2 \le t < 4$	$4 \le t < 6$	$6 \le t < 8$	$8 \le t < 10$
Frequency	1	3	9	5	2
Mid-points	1	3	5	7	9

b

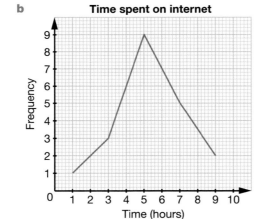

Time spent on internet

2 ▶

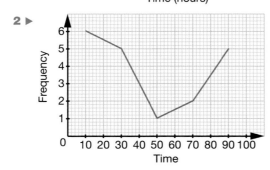

3 ▶ a 9.265   **b** $5 \le x < 110$

c 25   **d** $5 \le x < 10$

4 ▶ a 5   **b** 35

c 2.1

d On average families in rural communities have 1 child more than those living in the city.

EXERCISE 2* REVISION

1 ▶ a Continuous

b $x = 5$, $y = 4$

c

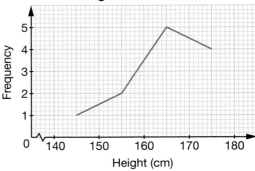

Height of Y10 students

2 ▶ a 36

b The total number of items is 36, so the median is at item $\dfrac{36 + 1}{2} = 18.5$

c $7.5 \le d < 8.0$

d $7.0 \le d < 7.5$

e Ben

f $7.5 \le d < 8.0$

g Jamie; he has jumped over 8.0 m more times in training than Ben has.

3 ▶ a

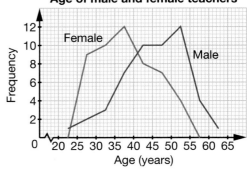

Age of male and female teachers

b The mean age of male teachers is 45.2 and the mean age of female teachers is 38.1, showing that the male teachers are, on average, 7 years older than the female teachers.

c The male frequency polygon is to the right of the female frequency polygon.

4 ▶ $x = 15$

EXAM PRACTICE: HANDLING DATA 2

1 ▶ Previous mean = 2 baskets/game,
current mean = 2.7 baskets/game

2 ▶ **a**

t mins	Tally	Frequency f
0 ≤ t < 5	||	2
5 ≤ t < 10	ЦЖ ||||	9
10 ≤ t < 15	ЦЖ ||	7
15 ≤ t ≤ 20	||	2

(i)

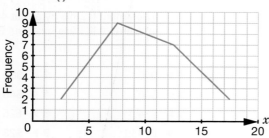

(ii) Estimated mean = 9.75 mins,
modal class is 5 ≤ t < 10

b Exact mean = 9.9 mins

c Difference as grouped data uses mid-
points as a best estimate of each value.

3 ▶ **a** $p = 15$

Time t hrs	0 ≤ t < 4	4 ≤ t < 6	6 ≤ t < 8	8 ≤ t < 12
Frequency f	15	24	45	16

b (i)

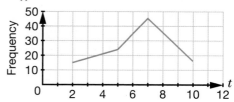

(ii) Estimated mean = 6.25 hrs,
modal class = 6 ≤ t < 8

(iii) 38.5%

UNIT 4 ANSWERS

UNIT 4: NUMBER 4

EXERCISE 1

1 ▶

Original value	Compound percentage p.a	Time (yrs)	New value
100	+2	3	106.1
500	+4	5	608.3
360	+6	7	541.3
1250	+8	9	2498.8

2 ▶

Original value	Compound percentage p.a	Time (yrs)	New value
100	−2	3	94.1
500	−4	5	407.7
360	−6	7	233.5
1250	−8	9	590.2

3 ▶ **a** £13 112.72 **b** £13 911.29 **c** £16 127.00

4 ▶ **a** $2205 **b** $2431.01 **c** $3257.79

5 ▶ €216.65

6 ▶ 8280

7 ▶ $1 310 796

8 ▶ €38 689

EXERCISE 1*

1 ▶

Original value (€)	Compound percentage p.a	Time (yrs)	New value (€)
128.1	+12	3	180
1985.6	+8	12	5000
13 522.5	−15	5	6000
1670.18	−5	10	1000

2 ▶ £1495.05

3 ▶ €4 317 850

4 ▶ €48.23

5 ▶ $3 102 512

6 ▶ €5 150 976

7 ▶ 14.2 yrs so 15 yrs

8 ▶ 9.6 yrs so 10 yrs

ACTIVITY 1

Number of years n	0	1	2	3	4	5
Investment I (€)	100	105	110	116	122	128
Investment II (€)	100	110	121	133	146	161

Looking carefully both graphs are curves.

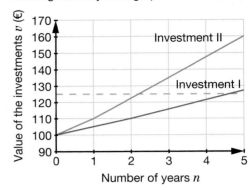

Investment I: 25% by about 4.6 yrs.
Investment II: 25% by about 2.3 yrs.

EXERCISE 2

1 ▶ $40	**2 ▶** $30
3 ▶ $60	**4 ▶** $40
5 ▶ $74.11	**6 ▶** €25 100
7 ▶ €2430	**8 ▶** $23
9 ▶ $180 000	**10 ▶** $3.50

EXERCISE 2*

1 ▶ $60	**2 ▶** $400
3 ▶ 62.5 cm	**4 ▶** €73 000
5 ▶ 5000	**6 ▶** 20
7 ▶ 80	**8 ▶** 4000
9 ▶ 3 747 759	**10 ▶** £995 662

EXERCISE 3 REVISION

1 ▶ 2800 RM	**2 ▶** 4400 ₹
3 ▶ £1 687 500	**4 ▶** $1.88
5 ▶ £15 315.38	**6 ▶** 1800

EXERCISE 3* REVISION

1 ▶ 9775 ¥

2 ▶ $1 012 000

3 ▶ 64 200 ₦

4 ▶ $11 375

5 ▶ **a** £9261 **b** Graph A **c** £3700

6 ▶ 583 217.59

EXAM PRACTICE: NUMBER 4

1 ▶ **a** $1344

b $1056

2 ▶ $28 350 **3 ▶** 824 500

4 ▶ £28 800 000 **5 ▶** $64 739 928

6 ▶ 78.6 km/h **7 ▶** 5 265 680

UNIT 4: ALGEBRA 4

EXERCISE 1

1 ▶ 4.5 cm
2 ▶ 44 cm; 154 cm²
3 ▶ $h = 8$ cm
4 ▶ YZ = 4 cm
5 ▶ $h = 4.7$ cm
6 ▶ 11.7 km
7 ▶ 150 million km
8 ▶ **a** 9.42×10^8 km   **b** 1.08×10^5 km/h

EXERCISE 1*

1 ▶ 14 cm
2 ▶ $x = 10$ cm
3 ▶ $h = 5.5$ cm
4 ▶ 5.30 cm²
5 ▶ 5.83 units
6 ▶ 10.5 cm² for each
7 ▶ 39 800 km
8 ▶ Obtuse
9 ▶ 3.71 cm
10 ▶ 8.37 cm

EXERCISE 2

1 ▶ $x = a - 2$
2 ▶ $x = 5 + p$
3 ▶ $x = c - a$
4 ▶ $x = \dfrac{b}{5}$
5 ▶ $x = \dfrac{(b - a)}{3}$
6 ▶ $x = \dfrac{(t - s)}{2}$
7 ▶ $x = \dfrac{4 - b}{a}$
8 ▶ $x = \dfrac{f + g}{e}$
9 ▶ $x = \dfrac{c}{a + b}$
10 ▶ $x = \dfrac{(d - 8b)}{c}$
11 ▶ $x = \dfrac{(a - 3b)}{3}$
12 ▶ $x = \dfrac{c - ab}{a}$
13 ▶ $x = ab$
14 ▶ $x = \dfrac{qr}{p}$
15 ▶ $x = r(p + q)$
16 ▶ $x = qr - p$

EXERCISE 2*

1 ▶ $x = \dfrac{c - b}{a}$
2 ▶ $x = cd + b$
3 ▶ $x = \dfrac{cd}{b}$
4 ▶ $x = \dfrac{e}{a} - c$
5 ▶ $x = \dfrac{P - b^2}{\pi}$
6 ▶ $x = \dfrac{Td^2}{b}$
7 ▶ $x = \pi - b$
8 ▶ $x = \dfrac{ab - c}{d}$
9 ▶ $\dfrac{a}{b}$
10 ▶ $\dfrac{a + b}{c}$
11 ▶ $\dfrac{s}{(p - q)}$
12 ▶ $r = \dfrac{A}{2\pi}$
13 ▶ $h = \dfrac{3V}{\pi r^2}$
14 ▶ $x = \dfrac{(y - c)}{m}$
15 ▶ $s = \dfrac{(v^2 - u^2)}{2a}$
16 ▶ $a = 2m - b$
17 ▶ $a = \dfrac{S}{n} - \dfrac{(n - 1)d}{2}$
18 ▶ $a = \dfrac{S(1 - r)}{(1 - r^n)}$

EXERCISE 3

1 ▶ $x = \pm\sqrt{\dfrac{b}{a}}$
2 ▶ $x = \pm\sqrt{ab}$
3 ▶ $x = \pm\sqrt{2D - C}$
4 ▶ $x = \pm\sqrt{a(c - b)}$
5 ▶ $x = \pm\sqrt{\dfrac{c - 2b}{a}}$
6 ▶ $x = \dfrac{t}{a + d}$
7 ▶ $x = \dfrac{ab}{a - 1}$
8 ▶ $x = \dfrac{2b - a}{a - b}$
9 ▶ $r = \pm\sqrt{\dfrac{A}{4\pi}}$
10 ▶ $v = \pm\sqrt{ar}$
11 ▶ $r = \pm\sqrt[3]{\dfrac{3V}{4\pi}}$
12 ▶ $l = \left(\dfrac{T}{2\pi}\right)^2$

EXERCISE 3*

1 ▶ $x = \pm\sqrt{\dfrac{S}{R}}$
2 ▶ $x = \pm\sqrt{\dfrac{g - a}{c}}$
3 ▶ $x = \dfrac{c}{b - a}$
4 ▶ $x = \dfrac{c - f}{e + d}$
5 ▶ $x = \dfrac{\tan b + ac}{1 - a}$
6 ▶ $x = t(p^2 - s)$
7 ▶ $x = \pm\sqrt{Ab - Da}$
8 ▶ $x = \pm\sqrt{\dfrac{3V}{\pi h}}$
9 ▶ $v = \pm\sqrt{2gh}$
10 ▶ $x = \pm\sqrt{\dfrac{1}{y} - a^2}$
11 ▶ $a = b \pm\sqrt{12s}$
12 ▶ $Q = \dfrac{1}{p}\left(\dfrac{S}{r}\right)^2$
13 ▶ $d = \left(\dfrac{k}{F}\right)^3$
14 ▶ $x = \pm\sqrt{1 - \dfrac{1}{y^2}}$
15 ▶ $c = \dfrac{b^2 - (2ax + b)^2}{4a}$
16 ▶ $x = \dfrac{p(y + 1)}{y - 1}$

EXERCISE 4

1 ▶ **a** 18   **b** 10
2 ▶ **a** 0.15   **b** 200
3 ▶ **a** 155 min   **b** 2 kg
4 ▶ **a** 2350   **b** 25 750
5 ▶ **a** $A = \dfrac{\pi r^2}{4}, P = r\left(2 + \dfrac{\pi}{2}\right)$
   b $A = 19.6$ cm², $P = 17.9$ cm
   c 11.28   **d** 14.0   **e** 4.55

EXERCISE 4*

1 ▶ **a** 339   **b** 4
2 ▶ **a** 53.75 m   **b** 80 km/h
3 ▶ **a** 16 km   **b** 195 m
4 ▶ **a** 6.67   **b** 20
5 ▶ **a** $A = r^2(1 + \pi), P = 2r(2 + \pi)$
   b $A = 265$ cm², $P = 82.3$ cm
   c 4.91   **d** 3.89   **e** 2.48

EXERCISE 5 REVISION

1 ▶ $x = \dfrac{b}{a}$ **2 ▶** $x = ac$

3 ▶ $x = \dfrac{a - c}{b}$ **4 ▶** $y = \pm\sqrt{\dfrac{d}{b}}$

5 ▶ $y = \dfrac{b^2}{a}$ **6 ▶** $y = \dfrac{d}{a - c}$

7 ▶ $y = \dfrac{bc}{c - 1}$

8 ▶ **a** 35 km   **b** 200 m   **c** 27 km

9 ▶ **a** $26   **b** 100   **c** $1800

10 ▶ **a** $A = \dfrac{\pi r^2}{2}, P = r(2 + \pi)$

     b $A = 39.3, P = 25.7$

     c 3.57   **d** 11.7   **e** 3.27

EXERCISE 5* REVISION

1 ▶ $x = \dfrac{c - b}{a}$ **2 ▶** $x = \dfrac{b}{a - d}$

3 ▶ $x = \dfrac{ab - \tan c}{a}$ **4 ▶** $y = \pm\sqrt{\dfrac{a}{b - c}}$

5 ▶ $y = \dfrac{ac - d}{a - b}$ **6 ▶** $y = b - d(c - a)^2$

7 ▶ **a** $A = \dfrac{r^2}{2}(1 + \pi), P = r(2 + \sqrt{2} + \pi)$

     b $A = 18.6, P = 19.7$

     c 2.41   **d** 5.19   **e** 3.17

8 ▶ **a** $\frac{2}{3}$ **b** 3 s   **c** 2.45 m

9 ▶ 3 : 1

10 ▶ **a** 0.75   **b** $\dfrac{m_1 - t}{m_1 t + 1}$ **c** 1

EXAM PRACTICE: ALGEBRA 4

1 ▶ **a** $x = \dfrac{d - f}{3}$

     b $x = \dfrac{p}{2} - q$ or $x = \dfrac{p - 2q}{2}$

     c $x = bc - a$

2 ▶ **a** $x = \sqrt{3C + B}$

     b $x = \sqrt{y(a + z)}$

     c $x = \dfrac{pq}{p - 1}$

3 ▶ **a** $a = \dfrac{2(s - ut)}{t^2}$

     b $a = 7.2 \text{ m/s}$

4 ▶ **a** $P = r(\pi + 2)$

     b $A = \dfrac{\pi r^2}{2}$

     c $2 + \dfrac{4}{\pi} = 3.27$ to 3 s.f.

UNIT 4: GRAPHS 4

EXERCISE 1 **1 ▶**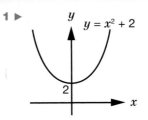

2 ▶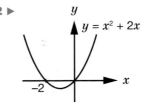

3 ▶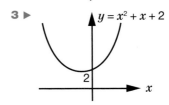

4 ▶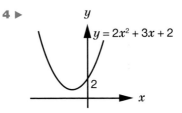

5 ▶ **b**

x	0	0.4	0.8	1.2	1.6	2.0
V	0	0.32	1.28	2.88	5.12	8

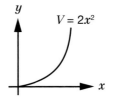

     c 1.41 m × 1.41 m

     d 0.72 m³

     e $1.23 \le x \le 1.8$

6 ▶

t	0	1	2	3	4	5	6
y	5	2.5	1	0.5	1	2.5	5

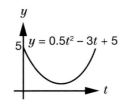

     b 5 m   **c** 0.5 m, 3 s

     d 0 m   **e** $0 \le t \le 0.76, 5.24 \le t \le 6$

EXERCISE 1*

1 ▶
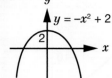
$y = -x^2 + 2$

2 ▶
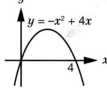
$y = -x^2 + 4x$

3 ▶
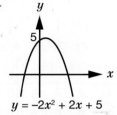
$y = -2x^2 + 2x + 5$

4 ▶ a $k = 1.75 \Rightarrow P = 1.75t^2 + t + 1$

t	2	4	6	8	10	12
P	10	33	70	121	186	265

b
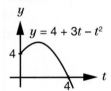
$P = 1.75t^2 + t + 1$

c Accurate answer is 49 750 000. Only approximate answers will be available from the graph.

d 7.2 days approx

5 ▶ a

t	0	1	1.5	2	3	4
y	4	6	6.25	6	4	0

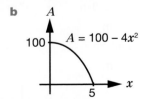
$y = 4 + 3t - t^2$

b 4 m   **c** 4 pm

d 6.25 m, 1:30 pm

e Between 12:23 pm and 2:37 pm

6 ▶ a $A = (10 - 2x)^2 + 4x(10 - 2x) = 100 - 4x^2$

b
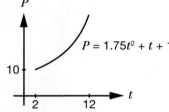
$A = 100 - 4x^2$

c $2.5 \le x \le 3.5$

7 ▶ a

x	20	30	40	50	60	70	80
y	12	22.5	36	52.5	72	94.5	120

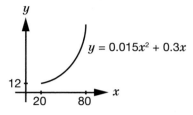
$y = 0.015x^2 + 0.3x$

b 61.9 m   **c** 48.6 mph   **d** 0.7 s

EXERCISE 2

1 ▶ $x = -2$ or $x = 3$ **2 ▶** $x = 3$ or $x = 2$

3 ▶ $x = -1$ or $x = 3$ **4 ▶** $x = 2$ or $x = 5$

5 ▶ $x = 0$ or $x = 5$

EXERCISE 2*

1 ▶ $x = -1$ or $x = \frac{1}{2}$ **2 ▶** $x = \frac{1}{2}$ or $x = 2$

3 ▶ $x = \frac{1}{2}$ or $x = -\frac{1}{2}$ **4 ▶** $y = x^2 - 6x + 5$

5 ▶ $y = x^2 - 7x + 10$

6 ▶ $y = x^2 - 6x + 9$

7 ▶ $y = x^2 - 3x - 4$

8 ▶

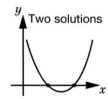 Two solutions
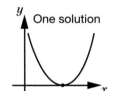 One solution
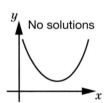 No solutions

EXERCISE 3   REVISION

1 ▶
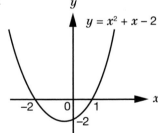
$y = x^2 + x - 2$

2 ▶ $x \approx 0.6$ or 3.4

3 ▶ b $x \approx -1.4$ or 3.4

4 ▶ a 4.9 cm²   **b** 4.5 cm   **c** 12.96 cm

5 ▶ a
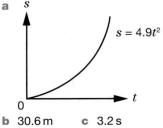
$s = 4.9t^2$

b 30.6 m   **c** 3.2 s

EXERCISE 3* REVISION

1 ▶
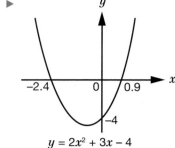
$y = 2x^2 + 3x - 4$

2 ▶ $x \approx -2.6$ or 1.1

3 ▶ b $x \approx -2.6$ or 1.1

4 ▶ b $28.3\,m$

5 ▶ a
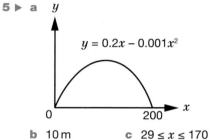
$y = 0.2x - 0.001x^2$

b $10\,m$ **c** $29 \leq x \leq 170$

1 ▶

x	−4	−3	−2	−1	0	1	2	3	4
y	6	0	−4	−6	−6	−4	0	6	14

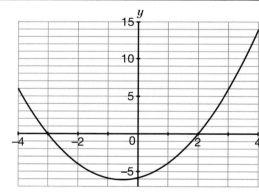

2 ▶ a

x	−3	−2	−1	0	1	2	3
$2x^2$	18	8	2	0	2	8	18
$-3x$	9	6	3	0	−3	−6	−9
-2	−2	−2	−2	−2	−2	−2	−2
y	25	12	3	−2	−3	0	7

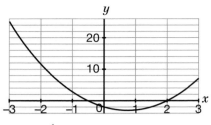

b $x = -\frac{1}{2}$ or 2

3 ▶ a If $p = 4t - kt^2 : t = 4, p = 8$
$\Rightarrow 8 = 16 - 16k, k = \frac{1}{2}$

t	0	2	4	6	8
p	0	6	8	6	0

b
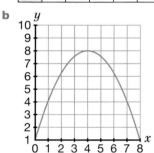

c (i) $p_{max} = \$8$ million at $t = 4$ years

(ii) $2 \leq t \leq 6$

EXERCISE 1

1 ▶ 2.46 **2 ▶** 5.07

3 ▶ 8.09 **4 ▶** 9.44 cm

5 ▶ 8.76 cm **6 ▶** 10.1 m

7 ▶ 1.61 m **8 ▶** 67.6 m

EXERCISE 1*

1 ▶ 6.57 m

2 ▶ 6.60 cm

3 ▶ a 2.5 m **b** 4.33 m

c 20.6 m² **d** 31.7°

4 ▶ 6.93 m²

5 ▶ a 1070 m **b** 797 m

6 ▶ 155 m

7 ▶ 5.88 cm

8 ▶ 452 m

EXERCISE 2

1 ▶ 48.6° **2 ▶** 41.4°

3 ▶ 46.1° **4 ▶** 71.2°

5 ▶ 19.5° **6 ▶** 80.1°

7 ▶ 78.9° **8 ▶** 23.6°

9 ▶ 1.72° **10 ▶** 70.5°

EXERCISE 2*

1 ▶ 37.8° 2 ▶ 37.7°
3 ▶ 58.6° 4 ▶ 29.6°
5 ▶ 57.3° 6 ▶ 29.0°
7 ▶ 014.9°; 194.9° 8 ▶ 72.7°
9 ▶ 33.6° 10 ▶ 57.3°

EXERCISE 3

1 ▶ $x = 5$ 2 ▶ $x = 8.66$
3 ▶ $x = 5.18$ 4 ▶ $a = 30.0°$
5 ▶ $a = 60.0°$ 6 ▶ 9.24
7 ▶ 32.2° 8 ▶ 49.7°
9 ▶ 1.308 cm 10 ▶ 41.6°
11 ▶ 62.3° 12 ▶ 250 m
13 ▶ 10.0° 14 ▶ 5.47 km
15 ▶ 63.6°

EXERCISE 3*

1 ▶ $x = 18$ 2 ▶ $x = 22$
3 ▶ $x = 100$ 4 ▶ $x = 10$
5 ▶ $x = 20$ 6 ▶ $x = 200$
7 ▶ $a = 45°$ 8 ▶ $a = 10°$
9 ▶ $a = 30°$
10 ▶ $a = 30°$, $x = 8.7$, $y = 2.5$
11 ▶ a 4.66 km N b 17.4 km W
12 ▶ 195 m, 442 m
13 ▶ $H = 22.2$ m 14 ▶ $d = 611$ m
15 ▶ 7.99 km 16 ▶ 1.5 m

EXERCISE 4 REVISION

1 ▶ $x = 14.1$ cm, $\theta = 70.5°$
2 ▶ $x = 7.87$ m, $\theta = 10.2°$
3 ▶ $x = 16.8$ km, $\theta = 39.9°$
4 ▶ $x = 11.7$ cm, $\theta = 31.2°$
5 ▶ $x = 2.38$ m, $\theta = 4.62°$
6 ▶ $x = 14.3$ km, $\theta = 79°$
7 ▶ 43.3 cm²
8 ▶ 33.7°

EXERCISE 4* REVISION

1 ▶ a 0.5 b $\theta = 30°$
2 ▶ a 20.5 m b 19.1 m c 20.7 m
3 ▶ Ascends in 3 min 52 s, so reaches surface with 8 seconds to spare.
4 ▶ a 17.2 km, 284°
    b 18:11:10
5 ▶ 3.56 m

6 ▶ a 16.2 m
    b 16.2 s
    c 432 m
7 ▶ $p = 25$
8 ▶ $q = 5$

EXAM PRACTICE: SHAPE AND SPACE 4

1 ▶ a 4.91 m b 0.382 m
2 ▶ a (i) 51.3° (ii) 321.3° (iii) 141.3°
    b 6.24 km
3 ▶ a (i) 4880 km (ii) 4090 km
    (iii) 38 200 km (iv) 123°
    b Tangent is perpendicular to radius. Therefore the smallest possible value of angle ODS is 90°, since a smaller value would mean that the signal would pass back into Earth before reaching Delhi.
    c 77 000 km
    d 0.26 s

UNIT 4: HANDLING DATA 3

EXERCISE 1

1 ▶ $Q_1 = 1$, $Q_2 = 6$, $Q_3 = 9$, IQR = 8
2 ▶ $Q_1 = 2$, $Q_2 = 7$, $Q_3 = 12$, IQR = 10
3 ▶ $Q_1 = -1.5$, $Q_2 = 1$, $Q_3 = 5$, IQR = 6.5
4 ▶ $Q_1 = \frac{3}{8}$, $Q_2 = \frac{1}{2}$, $Q_3 = \frac{3}{4}$, IQR = $\frac{3}{8}$
5 ▶ $Q_1 = 12.5$ cm, $Q_2 = 25$ cm, $Q_3 = 45$ cm, IQR = 32.5 cm
6 ▶ 1.5, 4, 7, 5.5
7 ▶ 0.5, 4, 6.5, 6
8 ▶ 1.5, 3.5, 8, 6.5

EXERCISE 1*

1 ▶ $Q_2 = 50.5$, IQR = 64.5, range = 120
2 ▶ $Q_2 = 14.2$, IQR = 2.1, range = 3.5
3 ▶ $Q_2 = 4$, IQR = 2.5, range = 5
4 ▶ $Q_2 = 12$, IQR = 17, range = 27
5 ▶ a Mean = 1150, mode = 700, median = 750; median
    b Range = 3300, IQR = 100; IQR
6 ▶ a Mean = 47, mode = 70, median = 49; mean or median
    b Range = 70, IQR = 25.5; IQR
7 ▶ a $x = 6$ b $x = 2$
    c $x = 3$ d $x = 4$
8 ▶ a $x \geq 5$ b $x = 8$
    c $x = 7$ d $x = 6$

EXERCISE 2

1 ▶ a   26 minutes

   b   29 – 21 = 8 minutes

2 ▶ a   37 cm

   b

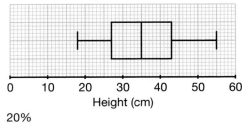

Heights of shrubs

20%

3 ▶ a   80 tomatoes

   b   Minimum = 155 g, maximum = 205 g

   c   Median = 186 g, IQR = 191 – 176 = 15 g

   d   100 tomatoes

   e   Minimum = 160 g, maximum = 210 g

   f   Median = 178 g, IQR = 183 – 174 = 9 g

   g   The median for variety X (186) is greater than the median for variety Y (178) so, on average, tomatoes from variety X weigh more than tomatoes from variety Y. The range is the same for both varieties (50 g), but the IQR for variety Y (9) is significantly smaller than the IQR for variety X (15), so the masses of tomatoes from variety Y are more consistent.

4 ▶ a

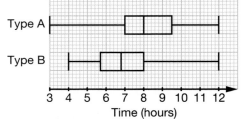

Battery Life for different mobile phones

Type A: Median = 8 hours, LQ = 7 hours, UQ = 9.5 hours

Type B: Median = 6.8 hours, LQ = 5.7 hours, UQ = 8 hours

   b   Type B is more likely to last longer (median is higher). However, its range is also larger so the length of time it lasts is more variable.

EXERCISE 2*

1 ▶ a

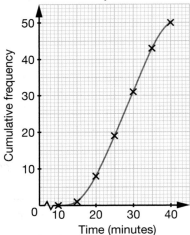

Time to complete homework

   b   27 to 28 minutes

   c   22 to 23 minutes

   d   32 to 33 minutes

   e   10 to 11 minutes

2 ▶ a

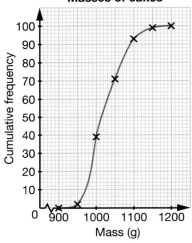

Masses of cakes

   b   Median = 1010 g to 1020 g, LQ = 990 g, UQ = 1060 g

   c   Approximately 85 cakes

   d   90 cakes are estimated to weigh less than 1090 g

3 ▶ a

Marks, x, out of 150	F
$0 < x \le 30$	5
$30 < x \le 60$	13
$60 < x \le 90$	27
$90 < x \le 120$	40
$120 < x \le 150$	50

b   (i) $Q_2 = 87$

     (ii) $Q_1 = 58$

     (iii) $Q_3 = 115$

     (iv) IQR = 57

c   Approx $\frac{6}{50}$ = top 12%

4 ▶ a

Weight, x kg per day	F
$50 < x \le 70$	8
$70 < x \le 90$	23
$90 < x \le 110$	37
$110 < x \le 130$	46
$130 < x \le 150$	50

b   (i) $Q_2 = 95$ (ii) $Q_1 = 77$ (iii) $Q_3 = 110$

     (iv) IQR = 33

c   100 kg corresponds to $F = 30$, so only 20 days > 100 kg therefore not 'healthy'.

EXERCISE 3   REVISION

1 ▶ a $Q_1 = 2$, $Q_2 = 4.5$, $Q_3 = 9$, IQR = 7, range = 9

    b $Q_1 = 3$, $Q_2 = 9$, $Q_3 = 17$, IQR = 14, range = 16

2 ▶ $Q_1 = 5$, $Q_2 = 11$, $Q_3 = 17$, IQR = 12, range = 18

3 ▶ a $Q_1 = 19.5$, $Q_2 = 27.5$, $Q_3 = 33.5$, IQR = 14, range = 37

    b   C, D, E. F

4 ▶ a

x	$0 < w \le 2$	$2 < w \le 4$	$4 < w \le 6$	$6 < w \le 8$	$8 < w \le 10$
Frequency	4	8	12	10	6
F	4	12	24	34	40

    b   (i) $Q_2 = 5.5$

       (ii) $Q_1 = 3.5$

       (iii) $Q_3 = 7.5$

       (iv) IQR = 2

EXERCISE 3*   REVISION

1 ▶ $Q_1 = 6.5$, $Q_2 = 30.5$, $Q_3 = 72.5$, IQR = 66, range = 99

2 ▶   2, 5

3 ▶ a $Q_2 = 42$, IQR = 12.5, range = 21

    b   (i) D, E   (ii) F, G

4 ▶ a $x = 5$

    b

h	$0.5 < w \le 1.0$	$1.0 < w \le 1.5$	$1.5 < w \le 2.0$	$2.0 < w \le 2.5$
Frequency	6	9	$2x$	x
F	6	15	25	30

    c   (i) $Q_2 = 1.5$ (ii) IQR = 0.8

    d   Mean = 1.48 m

EXAM PRACTICE: HANDLING DATA 3

1 ▶ a   R = 27

    b $Q_2 = 9.5$

    c   IQR = 22.5

2 ▶ a   R = 15

    b $Q_2 = 10$

    c   IQR = 7.5

3 ▶ a

Marks, x%	Boys F	Girls F
$0 < x \le 20$	2	1
$20 < x \le 40$	10	3
$40 < x \le 60$	19	11
$60 < x \le 80$	25	21
$80 < x \le 100$	30	30

Correct cumulative frequency curves × 2

Boys: $Q_2 =$ 53   Girls: $Q_2 =$ 70

      IQR = 40   IQR = 30

    b   The girls' median of 17% is higher than the boys' median, so they are better at Chinese in general.

       Girls are also more consistent than boys since their IQR is smaller than the boys' IQR.

UNIT 5 ANSWERS

UNIT 5: NUMBER 5

EXERCISE 1

1 ▶ 11.9	2 ▶ 8.10	3 ▶ 7.81
4 ▶ 6.57	5 ▶ 49.9	6 ▶ 0.779
7 ▶ 17.0	8 ▶ 40.0	9 ▶ 6.53
10 ▶ 11.3	11 ▶ 10.2	12 ▶ 8.75
13 ▶ 20.5	14 ▶ 1.36	15 ▶ 161 000
16 ▶ 306	17 ▶ 530	18 ▶ 68 100 000
19 ▶ 693 000	20 ▶ 21 800	

EXERCISE 1*

1 ▶ 30.1	2 ▶ 18.1
3 ▶ 0.005 77	4 ▶ 2.17×10^{-4}
5 ▶ 0.122	6 ▶ 9.05
7 ▶ 4.84	8 ▶ 2.26
9 ▶ 74.4	10 ▶ 456
11 ▶ 3.80×10^{-3}	12 ▶ 7140
13 ▶ 707	14 ▶ 18 900
15 ▶ 1.62×10^{8}	16 ▶ 2.36×10^{29}
17 ▶ 7.21	18 ▶ 18.1
19 ▶ 2.34	20 ▶ 2.68

EXERCISE 2

1 ▶ 150	2 ▶ 100	3 ▶ 3
4 ▶ 5	5 ▶ 300	6 ▶ 240
7 ▶ 8	8 ▶ 300	9 ▶ 200
10 ▶ 600	11 ▶ 6×10^{7}	
12 ▶ 1.2×10^{9}	13 ▶ 4×10^{3}	
14 ▶ 2×10^{5}	15 ▶ 2.3×10^{4}	
16 ▶ 7.2×10^{4}	17 ▶ 8.7×10^{4}	
18 ▶ 7.7×10^{6}	19 ▶ 5×10^{2}	
20 ▶ 9×10^{2}	21 ▶ 2×10^{6}	
22 ▶ 3×10^{6}	23 ▶ 1×10^{2}	
24 ▶ 2×10^{2}	25 ▶ 7×10^{6}	
26 ▶ 2×10^{5}	27 ▶ 4×10^{6}	
28 ▶ 9×10^{7}	29 ▶ 8×10^{2}	
30 ▶ 9×10^{3}		

EXERCISE 2*

1 ▶ 4	2 ▶ 1250
3 ▶ 8	4 ▶ 80
5 ▶ 600 cm³, 470 cm²	6 ▶ 100 cm²
7 ▶ 68 cm²	8 ▶ 10 cm
9 ▶ 1.2×10^{9}	10 ▶ 2.4×10^{3}
11 ▶ 2×10^{3}	12 ▶ 5×10^{-3}
13 ▶ 7.06×10^{8}	14 ▶ 2.73×10^{-3}

15 ▶ 50 000	16 ▶ 2000	
17 ▶ 0.2	18 ▶ 0.004	
19 ▶ 0.06	20 ▶ 8000	
21 ▶ $6 000 000	22 ▶ 10 000	
23 ▶ 2×10^{6}	24 ▶ 2×10^{2}	
25 ▶ 3×10^{-1}	26 ▶ 2×10^{-6}	
27 ▶ 2×10^{7}	28 ▶ 7×10^{5}	
29 ▶ 1×10^{-3}	30 ▶ 2×10^{1}	

EXERCISE 3

	Dimension	Rounded to nearest...	Lower bound	Upper bound	Dimension as $a \pm b$
1 ▶	230 m	10 m	225	235	230 ± 5
2 ▶	70 kg	10 kg	65	75	70 ± 5
3 ▶	74°F	1°F	73.5	74.5	74 ± 0.5
4 ▶	19 m²	1 m²	18.5	19.5	19 ± 0.5
5 ▶	2.5 litres	0.5 litres	2.25	2.75	2.5 ± 0.25
6 ▶	10.5 cm	0.1 cm	10.45	10.55	10.5 ± 0.05
7 ▶	5465 g	5 g	5462.5	5467.5	5465 ± 2.5
8 ▶	5470 g	10 g	5465	5475	5470 ± 5
9 ▶	5500 g	100 g	5450	5550	5500 ± 50
10 ▶	6000 g	1000 g	5500	6500	6000 ± 500
11 ▶	12.2 m/s	0.2 m/s	12.0	12.4	12.2 ± 0.2
12 ▶	20.2 s	0.1 s	20.15	20.25	20.2 ± 0.05
13 ▶	10 m/s²	10 m/s²	5	15	10 ± 5
14 ▶	20 mph	2 mph	19	21	20 ± 1
15 ▶	30 kg/m³	1 kg/m³	29.5	30.5	30 ± 0.5

EXERCISE 3*

1 ▶ 5.5 and 6.5; 16.5 and 17.5; 122.5 and 123.5

2 ▶ 6.5 and 7.5; 35 and 45; 650 and 750

3 ▶ 2.25 and 2.75; 14.25 and 14.75; 145.75 and 146.25

4 ▶ 45 and 55; 225 and 235; 4555 and 4565

5 ▶ 0.1 and 0.3; 7.5 and 7.7; 12.3 and 12.5

6 ▶ 0.335 and 0.345; 7.225 and 7.235; 12.885 and 12.895

7 ▶ 42.5 kg and 43.5 kg

8 ▶ 2.15×10^{7} and 2.25×10^{7}

9 ▶ Max perimeter = 38 m, min perimeter = 34 m
Max area = 89.25 m², min area = 71.25 m²

10 ▶ p(max) = 1.82, p(min) = 1.40

11 ▶ p(max) = 4.98, p(min) = 4.02

12 ▶ Radius = 1.54 cm, circumference = 9.61 cm

13 ▶ A_{max} = 33.6 cm²; d_{min} = 8.18 cm

14 ▶ 44.4 cm, 46.7 cm

EXERCISE 4   REVISION

1 ▶ a 486
   b 2.66×10^{-3}
   c 3.13×10^{-2}
   d 16 400
2 ▶ 4
3 ▶ 600 cm²
4 ▶ Max = 85 ml; min = 75 ml
5 ▶ Max radius = 3.8 cm, min circumference = 24 cm
6 ▶ a 10.7 m   b 9.48 m

EXERCISE 4*   REVISION

1 ▶ a 63.4   b 19 200
   c 2.94×10^{-4} d 164 000
2 ▶ a 63.5 mins, 64.5 mins
   b 15 g, 25 g
   c 27.5 m/s, 32.5 m/s
   d 7450 mm, 7550 mm
3 ▶ $w_{min} = 2.38$, $w_{max} = 3.5$
4 ▶ a 3×10^8 b 2×10^2
   c 2×10^2 d 3×10^7
5 ▶ 1 m/s, 1.23 m/s
6 ▶ 12.4 cm, 13.1 cm

EXAM PRACTICE: NUMBER 5

1 ▶ a 7.13   b 444
   c 1.85×10^{-3} d 13 800
2 ▶ a 21.5 m, 22.5 m
   b 49.5 kg, 50.5 kg
   c 745 s, 755 s
   d 1350 km, 1450 km
3 ▶ $w_{min} = 2.5$, $w_{max} = 5$
4 ▶ a 8×10^5 b 2×10^2
   c 3×10^2 d 5×10^3
5 ▶ 5.2 m/s, 6.3 m/s
6 ▶ 28.3 m, 29.7 m

UNIT 5: ALGEBRA 5

EXERCISE 1

1 ▶ $x^2 + 5x + 4$ 2 ▶ $x^2 - 4x - 21$
3 ▶ $x^2 - 4x - 12$ 4 ▶ $x^2 - 8x + 15$
5 ▶ $x^2 + 6x + 9$ 6 ▶ $x^2 - 8x + 16$
7 ▶ $x^2 - 25$ 8 ▶ $-x^2 + 6x + 16$
9 ▶ $15x^2 - 7x - 2$ 10 ▶ $x^3 + 2x^2 - 5x - 10$
11 ▶ a $x^2 + 3x + 2$ b $3x + 2$ c $x = 3$
12 ▶ a $5x^2 + 25x + 30$ b $2x^2 + 30x + 62$
13 ▶ $x = 6$

EXERCISE 1*

1 ▶ $x^2 + 4x - 21$
2 ▶ $x^2 - 9$
3 ▶ $x^2 + 24x + 144$
4 ▶ $-12x^2 + 25x - 12$
5 ▶ $x^2 + x(b - a) - ab$
6 ▶ $16x^2 - 40x + 25$
7 ▶ $15x^3 + 21x^2 + 5x + 7$
8 ▶ $8x + 8 = 8(x + 1)$
9 ▶ $\frac{a^2}{4} - \frac{ab}{5} + \frac{b^2}{25}$
10 ▶ $10x^5 + 11x^4 + 3x^3$
11 ▶ 4
12 ▶ $x = -\frac{5}{3}$
13 ▶ $a = 3, b = 1$
14 ▶ a $\pi(x^2 + 12x + 36)$
    b $x = 0.75$
15 ▶ a $4x^2 + 37x + 40$
    b $x = 1.5$
16 ▶ $x = 6$

EXERCISE 2

1 ▶ $x^3 + 2x^2 - 7x + 4$
2 ▶ $x^3 + 5x^2 + 6x$
3 ▶ $x^3 + x^2 - 4x - 4$
4 ▶ $x^3 - 13x + 12$
5 ▶ $x^3 - 14x^2 + 64x - 96$
6 ▶ $3x^3 - 2x^2 - 3x + 2$
7 ▶ $x^3 - 3x + 2$
8 ▶ $x^3 + 3x^2 + 3x + 1$

EXERCISE 2*

1 ▶ $2x^3 - 7x^2 - 11x + 6$
2 ▶ $x^3 - 3x^2 - 10x$
3 ▶ $3x^3 - 28x^2 + 43x + 42$
4 ▶ $24x^3 - 62x^2 + 49x - 12$
5 ▶ $2x^3 + 5x^2 - 4x - 12$
6 ▶ $8x^4 + 24x^3 + 10x^2 + 24x + 10$
7 ▶ $8x^3 - 36x^2 + 54x - 27$
8 ▶ $x^4 + 4x^3 - 7x^2 - 22x + 24$

EXERCISE 3

1 ▶ $x(x - 3)$ 2 ▶ $x(x + 2)$
3 ▶ $x(x - 31)$ 4 ▶ $x(x + 42)$
5 ▶ $(x - 4)(x + 4)$ 6 ▶ $(x - 7)(x + 7)$

EXERCISE 3*

1 ▶ $x(x - 312)$ 2 ▶ $x(x + 51)$
3 ▶ $(x - 8)(x + 8)$ 4 ▶ $(x - 11)(x + 11)$
5 ▶ $(x + 15)(x - 15)$ 6 ▶ $4(x + 2)(x - 2)$

EXERCISE 4

1 ▶ $a = 1$ **2 ▶** $a = 4$
3 ▶ $a = -1$ **4 ▶** $a = -2$
5 ▶ $a = 2$ **6 ▶** $a = -1$

EXERCISE 4*

1 ▶ $a = 3$ **2 ▶** $a = 4$
3 ▶ $a = -7$ **4 ▶** $a = -3$
5 ▶ $a = -8$ **6 ▶** $a = \frac{1}{2}$

EXERCISE 5

1 ▶ $(x - 2)(x - 1)$ **2 ▶** $(x - 1)(x - 3)$
3 ▶ $(x - 4)(x - 3)$ **4 ▶** $(x + 4)(x + 4)$
5 ▶ $(x - 1)(x - 8)$ **6 ▶** $(x - 1)(x - 1)$

EXERCISE 5*

1 ▶ $(x + 7)(x + 3)$ **2 ▶** $(x - 2)(x - 6)$
3 ▶ $(x - 8)(x - 8)$ **4 ▶** $(x - 6)(x - 12)$
5 ▶ $(x + 9)(x + 5)$ **6 ▶** $(x + 12)(x + 12)$

EXERCISE 6

1 ▶ $(x + 3)(x - 2)$ **2 ▶** $(x + 2)(x - 5)$
3 ▶ $(x + 2)(x - 6)$ **4 ▶** $(x + 1)(x - 10)$
5 ▶ $(x + 7)(x - 2)$ **6 ▶** $(x + 8)(x - 1)$

EXERCISE 6*

1 ▶ $(x + 6)(x - 5)$ **2 ▶** $(x + 4)(x - 6)$
3 ▶ $(x + 12)(x - 5)$ **4 ▶** $(x + 5)(x - 14)$
5 ▶ $(x + 8)(x - 15)$ **6 ▶** $(x - 5)(x + 15)$

EXERCISE 7

1 ▶ $(x - 1)(x - 2)$ **2 ▶** $(x + 3)(x - 1)$
3 ▶ $(x + 1)(x + 12)$ **4 ▶** $(x - 2)(x - 6)$
5 ▶ $(x - 4)(x - 4)$ **6 ▶** $(x - 4)(x + 5)$

EXERCISE 7*

1 ▶ $(x + 10)(x - 2)$ **2 ▶** $(x + 2)(x - 9)$
3 ▶ $(x + 9)(x + 4)$ **4 ▶** $(x - 4)(x - 8)$
5 ▶ $(x + 12)(x - 4)$ **6 ▶** $(3 - x)(x + 1)$

EXERCISE 8

1 ▶ $x = -1$ or $x = -2$ **2 ▶** $x = -4$ or $x = 1$
3 ▶ $x = 7$ or $x = 2$ **4 ▶** $x = -8$
5 ▶ $x = 0$ or $x = 10$

EXERCISE 8*

1 ▶ $x = -8$ or $x = 4$ **2 ▶** $x = -21$ or $x = 5$
3 ▶ $x = 0$ or $x = 8$ **4 ▶** $x = -\frac{3}{2}$ or $x = \frac{3}{4}$
5 ▶ $x = -1$ or $x = 1$ or $x = -\frac{5}{2}$

EXERCISE 9

1 ▶ $x = 1$ or $x = 2$ **2 ▶** $x = -2$ or $x = 1$
3 ▶ $x = -2$ or $x = -4$ **4 ▶** $x = 4$ or $x = -3$
5 ▶ $x = 5$ or $x = 3$ **6 ▶** $x = -4$

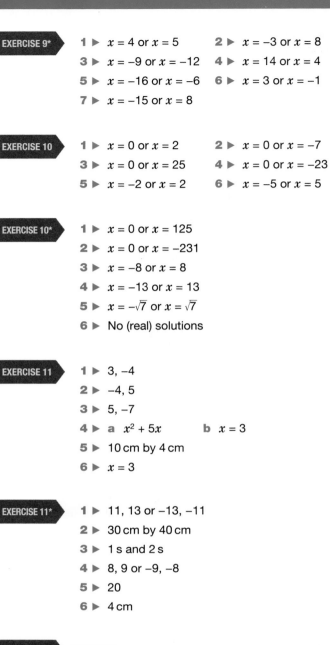

EXERCISE 9*

1 ▶ $x = 4$ or $x = 5$ **2 ▶** $x = -3$ or $x = 8$
3 ▶ $x = -9$ or $x = -12$ **4 ▶** $x = 14$ or $x = 4$
5 ▶ $x = -16$ or $x = -6$ **6 ▶** $x = 3$ or $x = -1$
7 ▶ $x = -15$ or $x = 8$

EXERCISE 10

1 ▶ $x = 0$ or $x = 2$ **2 ▶** $x = 0$ or $x = -7$
3 ▶ $x = 0$ or $x = 25$ **4 ▶** $x = 0$ or $x = -23$
5 ▶ $x = -2$ or $x = 2$ **6 ▶** $x = -5$ or $x = 5$

EXERCISE 10*

1 ▶ $x = 0$ or $x = 125$
2 ▶ $x = 0$ or $x = -231$
3 ▶ $x = -8$ or $x = 8$
4 ▶ $x = -13$ or $x = 13$
5 ▶ $x = -\sqrt{7}$ or $x = \sqrt{7}$
6 ▶ No (real) solutions

EXERCISE 11

1 ▶ $3, -4$
2 ▶ $-4, 5$
3 ▶ $5, -7$
4 ▶ **a** $x^2 + 5x$ **b** $x = 3$
5 ▶ 10 cm by 4 cm
6 ▶ $x = 3$

EXERCISE 11*

1 ▶ 11, 13 or $-13, -11$
2 ▶ 30 cm by 40 cm
3 ▶ 1 s and 2 s
4 ▶ 8, 9 or $-9, -8$
5 ▶ 20
6 ▶ 4 cm

EXERCISE 12   REVISION

1 ▶ $x^2 - 10x + 21$
2 ▶ $x^2 + 4x + 4$
3 ▶ $x^3 + 4x^2 + x - 6$
4 ▶ **a** $x^2 + 5x + 6$ **b** $5x + 6$
    c $x = 4$
5 ▶ $(x - 6)(x + 6)$
6 ▶ $(x + 3)(x + 1)$
7 ▶ $(x + 4)(x - 2)$
8 ▶ $x = 6$ or $x = -2$
9 ▶ $x = 0$ or $x = 5$
10 ▶ $x = -6$ or $x = 6$
11 ▶ $x = -4$ or $x = 5$
12 ▶ 20 cm by 30 cm

EXERCISE 12*　REVISION

1 ▶ $x^2 - 3x - 108$

2 ▶ $4x^2 - 12x + 9$

3 ▶ $6x^2 + 7x - 3$

4 ▶ $x^3 + 6x^2 - x - 30$

5 ▶ 4.25 m

6 ▶ 27 cm

7 ▶ $x = -11$ or $x = 11$

8 ▶ $x = 0$ or $x = 7$

9 ▶ $x = -7$ or $x = 8$

10 ▶ $x = 9$ or $x = 6$

11 ▶ $-4, -10$ and $4, 10$

12 ▶ b　$x = 30$

13 ▶ 400 cm²

EXAM PRACTICE: ALGEBRA 5

1 ▶ a　$x^2 - 4x - 12$　　b　$x^2 - 14x + 49$

c　$x^3 - 6x^2 + 11x - 6$

2 ▶ a　$x(x - 1)$　　　b　$(x - 5)(x + 5)$

c　$(x - 4)(x - 1)$

3 ▶ a　$(x + 1)(x + 2) = 0$, $x = -1$ or -2

b　$(x + 1)(x - 3) = 0$, $x = -1$ or 3

c　$x(x + 3) = 0$, $x = 0$ or -3

d　$(x - 2)(x + 2) = 0$, $x = -2$ or 2

4 ▶ a　$x(x + 1)$

b　$x^2 + x - 42 = 0 \Rightarrow (x + 7)(x - 6) = 0$
$\Rightarrow x = 6$

5 ▶ a　$x^2 + 5x + 2$

b　$x^2 + 5x - 14 = 0 \Rightarrow x = -7$ or $x = 2$
$\Rightarrow$ dimensions are 5 cm by 4 cm

UNIT 5: GRAPHS 5

EXERCISE 1

1 ▶ $x \leq 2$　　　　　2 ▶ $y > 4$

3 ▶ $y \leq 3$　　　　　4 ▶ $x + y \geq 6$

5 ▶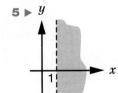

6 ▶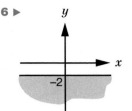

7 ▶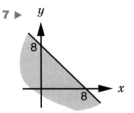

8 ▶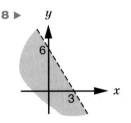

EXERCISE 1*

1 ▶ $y > -2$　　　　2 ▶ $2x + y \geq 6$

3 ▶ $y - x < 4$　　　4 ▶ $2y + x \leq 4$

5 ▶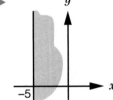

6 ▶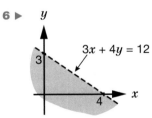

7 ▶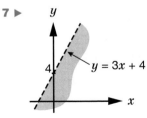

8 ▶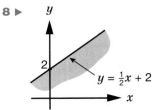

EXERCISE 2

1 ▶ $2 < x < 5$ 2 ▶ $-2 < y \le 3$

3 ▶ $x \ge 4$ or $x \le -3$ 4 ▶ $y \ge 9$ or $y < 3$

5 ▶ $x + y > 3$ and $x - y \le 2$

6 ▶ $y < x + 3$, $2y + x \le 6$ and $y \ge 0$

7 ▶

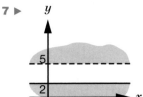

8 ▶

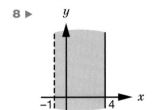

9 ▶

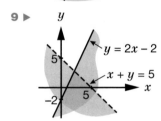

10 ▶

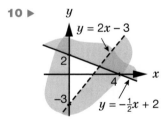

EXERCISE 2*

1 ▶ $-3 \le x < 4$

2 ▶ $2y + x \ge 10$ or $2y + x \le 4$

3 ▶ $4x + 3y \le 12$, $y \ge 0$ and $y < 2x + 4$

4 ▶ $x \ge 0$, $y \ge 0$, $y < -\dfrac{3x}{2} + 9$ and $y \le -\dfrac{2x}{3} + 6$

5 ▶

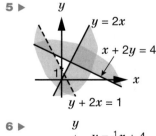

6 ▶

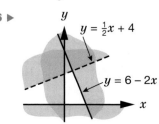

7 ▶ b $y < x + 2$, $y < -2x + 2$ and $2y + x > -2$

   c $y = -1$

8 ▶

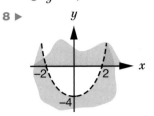

9 ▶

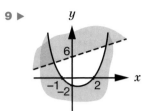

10 ▶

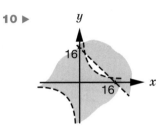

4 and 10, 4 and 11, 5 and 8, 5 and 9, 5 and 10, 6 and 7, 6 and 8, 6 and 9, 7 and 6, 7 and 7, 7 and 8, 8 and 5, 8 and 6, 8 and 7, 9 and 5, 9 and 6, 10 and 4, 10 and 5, 11 and 4

ACTIVITY 2

Point A	Point B	Point C	m_1	m_2	$m_1 \times m_2$
(1, 0)	(3, 2)	(0, 5)	1	-1	-1
(5, 0)	(3, 4)	(5, 5)	-2	$\frac{1}{2}$	-1
(10, 3)	(7, 2)	(6, 5)	$\frac{1}{3}$	-3	-1

Comment: The lines are at right angles.

Completed statement: Lines that are perpendicular have $m_1 \times m_2 = -1$

EXERCISE 3

1 ▶ $-\frac{1}{2}$ 2 ▶ $\frac{1}{3}$ 3 ▶ 3   4 ▶ $-\frac{2}{3}$

5 ▶ $\frac{1}{2}$, -2 6 ▶ 3, $-\frac{1}{3}$

7 ▶ Nothing   8 ▶ Parallel

9 ▶ Perpendicular   10 ▶ $y = \dfrac{x}{2} + 1$

11 ▶ a 2

   b $-\frac{1}{2}$

   c Product is -1 so yes

EXERCISE 3*

1 ▶ $-\frac{1}{4}$ 2 ▶ 5

3 ▶ $\frac{3}{2}$ 4 ▶ $\frac{1}{6}$

5 ▶ $\frac{3}{8}$, $-\frac{8}{3}$ 6 ▶ $\frac{5}{4}$, $-\frac{4}{5}$

7 ▶ $y = -\dfrac{x}{8} + 8.4$

8 ▶ **a** 7 m   **b** $-\dfrac{5}{4}$ **c** 8.2 m

9 ▶ **a** $-\dfrac{3}{2}$ **b** $\dfrac{2}{3}$

   c $y = \dfrac{2x}{3} + 5$ **d** No

10 ▶ $\dfrac{3}{2}$ or $-\dfrac{3}{2}$ **11** ▶ 19   **12** ▶ 0.32

EXERCISE 4

1 ▶ (6, 6)

2 ▶ (1, −3)

3 ▶ $\sqrt{61}$

4 ▶ $\sqrt{29}$

5 ▶ $y = -3x + 3$

EXERCISE 4*

1 ▶ $y = \dfrac{3}{2}x + \dfrac{1}{2}$

2 ▶ Gradient of PQ = gradient of SR = 1,
gradient of SP = gradient of RQ = $-\dfrac{3}{2}$

3 ▶ **a** (i) $AB^2 = 40$, $BC^2 = 10$, $AC^2 = 50$,
$AB^2 + BC^2 = AC^2$

   (ii) Gradient of AB is 3, gradient of BC
is $-\dfrac{1}{3}$, product of the gradients is −1

   b 10

4 ▶ $y = x + 1$

5 ▶ **a** $y = -\dfrac{1}{2}x + 7$

   b (2, 6)

   c $\sqrt{20}$ or 4.47 to 3 s.f.

6 ▶ **a** $y = \dfrac{1}{2}x + 1$

   b $y = -7x + 16$

   c (2, 2)

   d AD = BD = CD = 5

   e A, B and C lie on a circle of radius 5
centre at D.

EXERCISE 5

REVISION

1 ▶ $x > 5$

2 ▶ $x + 2y < 8$

3 ▶ $3 < y < 8$

4 ▶ $x + 2y \leq 6$ and $2x - y \leq 2$

5 ▶

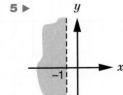

6 ▶

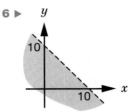

7 ▶

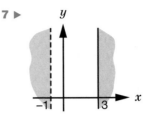

8 ▶

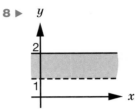

9 ▶ $(-3, \dfrac{1}{2})$

10 ▶ $\sqrt{74}$ or 8.60 to 3 s.f.

11 ▶ $y = -3x + 12$

12 ▶ $y = 2x - 6$

EXERCISE 5*

REVISION

1 ▶ $y - 2x \geq 2$

2 ▶ $3y + x > 9$

3 ▶ $-2 \leq 2x - y \leq 2$

4 ▶ $y > \dfrac{3x}{4} - 3$, $y \leq 0$ and $y \geq -\dfrac{3x}{2} - 3$

5 ▶

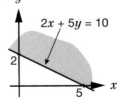

6 ▶

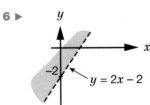

7 ▶

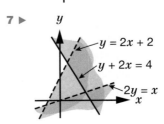

8 ▶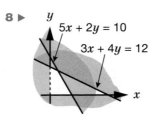

$5x + 2y = 10$

$3x + 4y = 12$

9 ▶ b $2y < x + 5$, $y > 2x - 2$ and $2y > 5 - 5x$

   c $x = 1$

10 ▶ $y = -\frac{1}{4}x + 2$

11 ▶ Gradient OB = 2, gradient of AC = $-\frac{1}{2}$
   $\Rightarrow$ OB is perpendicular to AC as $2 \times -\frac{1}{2} = -1$

   Mid-point of OB is (3, 6), mid-point of AC is (3, 6) so diagonals bisect each other.

12 ▶ $\sqrt{0.8}$ or 0.894 to 3 s.f.

EXAM PRACTICE: GRAPHS 5

1 ▶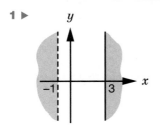

2 ▶ a, b

   c (2, 6)

3 ▶ a $\sqrt{68}$

   b (2, 2)

   c $y = -\frac{1}{4}x + 2\frac{1}{2}$

4 ▶ a (4, 3)

   b $\sqrt{26}$ or 5.10 to 3 s.f.

   c DC = $\sqrt{26}$

   d Gradient of AD is −1, gradient of BD is 1, product of gradients is −1
      $\Rightarrow$ perpendicular

UNIT 5: SHAPE AND SPACE 5

EXERCISE 1

1 ▶ A 2 square right, 2 squares up
   B 2 squares left, 2 squares up
   C 2 squares left, 2 squares up
   D 1 square left, 2 squares up
   E 2 squares left, 5 squares down

2 ▶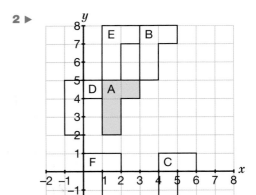

3 ▶ a $\begin{pmatrix} 4 \\ 2 \end{pmatrix}$ b $\begin{pmatrix} 0 \\ -4 \end{pmatrix}$

   c $\begin{pmatrix} 4 \\ -6 \end{pmatrix}$ d $\begin{pmatrix} 5 \\ 1 \end{pmatrix}$

   e $\begin{pmatrix} -5 \\ -1 \end{pmatrix}$

4 ▶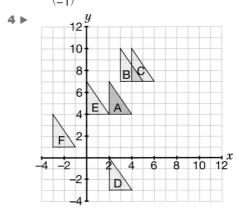

5 ▶ a $\begin{pmatrix} -6 \\ 2 \end{pmatrix}$ b $\begin{pmatrix} 0 \\ -6 \end{pmatrix}$ c $\begin{pmatrix} 8 \\ 7 \end{pmatrix}$

   d $\begin{pmatrix} 5 \\ 0 \end{pmatrix}$ e $\begin{pmatrix} -5 \\ 0 \end{pmatrix}$

EXERCISE 1*

1 ▶ a, b

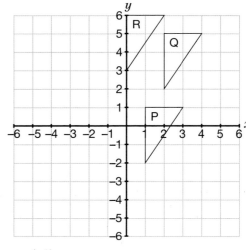

   c $\begin{pmatrix} -1 \\ 5 \end{pmatrix}$

2 ▸ a, b

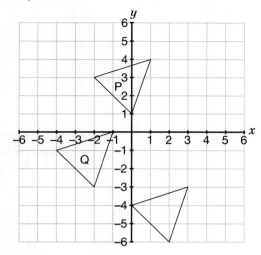

c $\begin{pmatrix} -2 \\ -4 \end{pmatrix}$

3 ▸ a $\begin{pmatrix} 1 \\ 4 \end{pmatrix}$ **b** $\begin{pmatrix} 4 \\ -6 \end{pmatrix}$

4 ▸ a $\begin{pmatrix} 4 \\ 1 \end{pmatrix}$

b $\begin{pmatrix} a + c \\ b + d \end{pmatrix}$, e.g. because this is the total horizontal movement and total vertical movement.

5 ▸ P (–5, 3)

EXERCISE 2

1 ▸ a Reflection in the y-axis or the line $x = 0$
b Reflection in the line $y = -1$
c Reflection in the line $y = -x$
d Reflection in the line $y = 1$
2 ▸ a Reflection in the line $x = 3$
b Reflection in the line $y = -x$
3 ▸ a Rotation 90° clockwise about (–3, 3)
b Rotation 90° clockwise about (1, 4)
c Rotation 90° anti-clockwise about (3, –3)
d Rotation 180° about (–3, –3)
4 ▸ a Reflection in x-axis
b Reflection in the line $x = 1$
c Reflection in the line $y = -x$
d Reflection in the line $x = 4$
5 ▸ a Reflection in the line $x = 5$
b Reflection in the line $y = x$
6 ▸ A: Rotation 180° about (1, 2)
B: Rotation 180° about (–3, 2)
C: Rotation 90° anti-clockwise about (5, –2) (or 270° clockwise)
D: Rotation 90° clockwise about (–5, 3) (or 270° anti-clockwise)

EXERCISE 2*   **1 ▸ a–d**

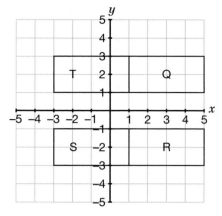

e Reflection in the line $x = 1$

2 ▸ a–d

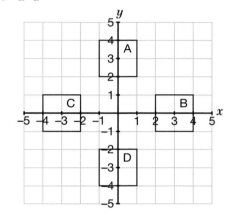

e Reflection in the line $y = -x$

3 ▸ a–d

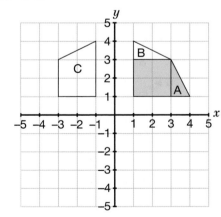

d Rotation 90° anti-clockwise about (0, 0)

4 ▶ a–d

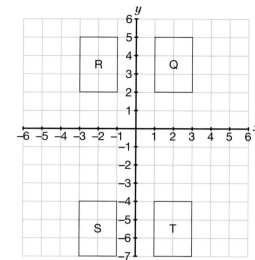

e Reflection in the line $y = -1$

5 ▶ a–d

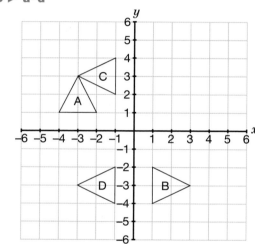

e Reflection in the y-axis

6 ▶

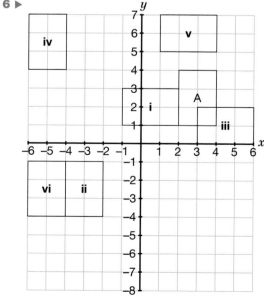

1 ▶ a–c

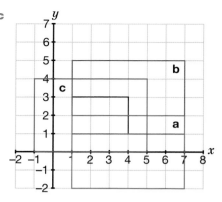

2 ▶ a, b

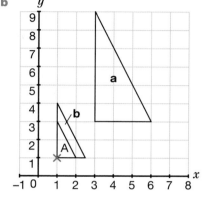

3 ▶ a–c

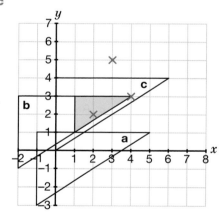

4 ▶ a **b**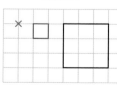

5 ▶ a

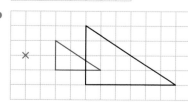

b

c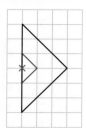

EXERCISE 3*

1 ▶ a 4   b Students' own drawings

    c (−6, 6)

    d Enlargement by scale factor 4, centre (−6, 6)

2 ▶ a Scale factor 3

    b Correct construction lines

    c (−5, −2)

    d Enlargement by scale factor 3, centre (−5, −2)

3 ▶ a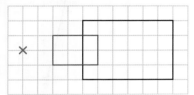

    b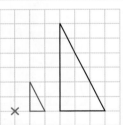

    c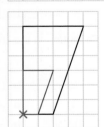

4 ▶ a Enlargement, scale factor $\frac{1}{3}$, centre (−5, −2)

    b Enlargement, scale factor $\frac{1}{3}$, centre (2, −5)

5 ▶ a Enlargement scale factor $\frac{1}{3}$, centre (−4, 6)

    b Enlargement scale factor $\frac{1}{2}$, centre (−2, −6)

EXERCISE 4

1 ▶ a, b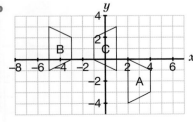

2 ▶ a–c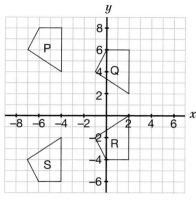

    d Reflection in the line $y = 1$

3 ▶ a–c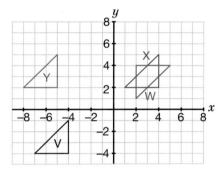

    d Translation by $\begin{pmatrix} -1 \\ 6 \end{pmatrix}$

4 ▶ a Rotation 180° about (2, 1)

    b Reflection in the line $y = 2$

    c Rotation 180° about (2, 3)

    d Rotation 90° anti-clockwise about (0, 0)

    e Rotation 180° about (−1, 2)

5 ▶ a Translation by $\begin{pmatrix} -2 \\ -4 \end{pmatrix}$

    b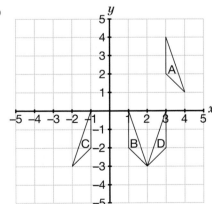

    c Reflection in the line $x = 2$

EXERCISE 4*

1 ▶ a, b

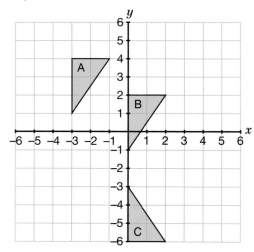

2 ▶ a–c

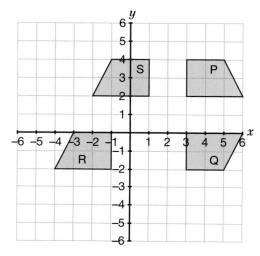

d Reflection in the line $x = 2$

3 ▶ a–c

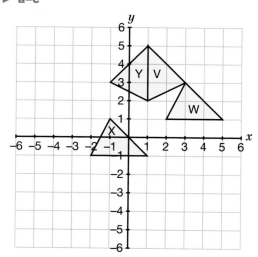

d Reflection in the line $x = 1$

4 ▶ a–c

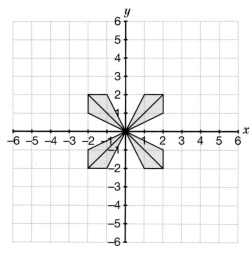

d Enlargement scale factor 3, centre (0, 0)

5 ▶ a Translation by $\begin{pmatrix} 6 \\ -1 \end{pmatrix}$

b

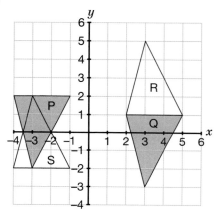

c Reflection in the line $y = 1$

EXERCISE 5 **REVISION**

1 ▶ a (1, −2) **b** (−1, 2)

   c (−2, 1) **d** (4, 6)

2 ▶ a (4, 1) **b** (−4, −1)

   c (−1, −4) **d** (11, −2)

3 ▶ a–d

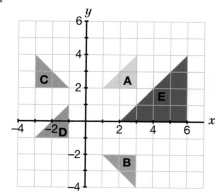

4 ▶ a–d

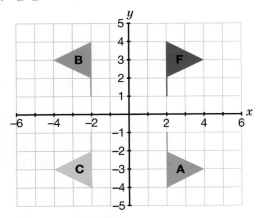

  e   180° rotation about (0, 0)

5 ▶ a–e

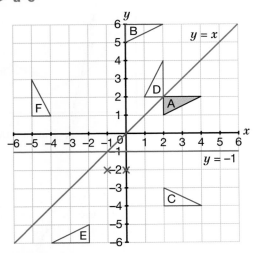

  f   Rotation 180° about (–1, 0)

  g   Rotation 90° clockwise about (–1, –1)

6 ▶ $a = -3, b = 10$

EXERCISE 5*   **REVISION**

  1 ▶ $a = 13, b = 1$

  2 ▶

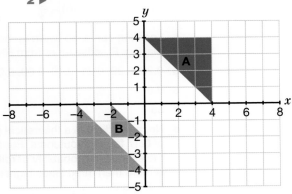

3 ▶

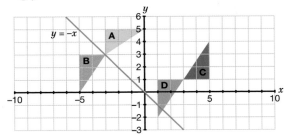

  c   Translation by $\begin{pmatrix} -6 \\ 2 \end{pmatrix}$

4 ▶ a–e

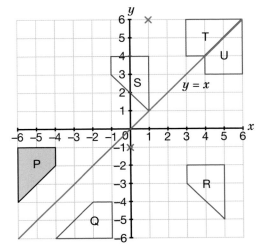

  f   Rotation 180° about (0, 1)

  g   Rotation 90° clockwise about (–5, 0)

5 ▶ a, b

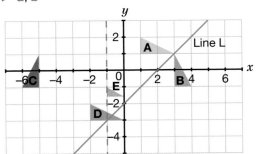

  c   (i) Rotation 90° anti-clockwise about (–1, –3)

       (ii) Enlargement scale factor 2 about (–3, –4)

6 ▶   P $(-b - 4, 3 - a)$

EXAM PRACTICE: SHAPE AND SPACE 5

1 ▶ **a–c**

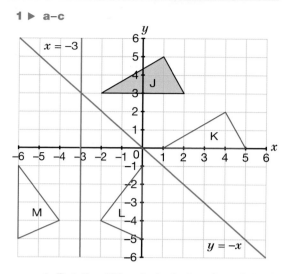

d Rotation 90° anti-clockwise about (–6, 3)

2 ▶ **a–d**

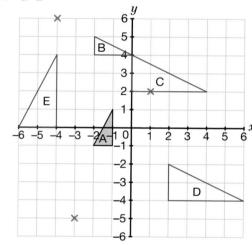

e Enlargement, scale factor $\frac{1}{2}$, centre of enlargement (2, –2)

3 ▶ $a = 7$, $b = -1$

UNIT 5: HANDLING DATA 4

EXERCISE 1

1 ▶ **a**

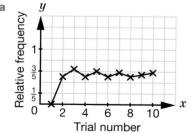

b p(biased) $= \frac{3}{5}$

Heidi's suspicion seems to be true. More trials would improve the experiment.

2 ▶ **a** p(rain) $= \frac{3}{5}$

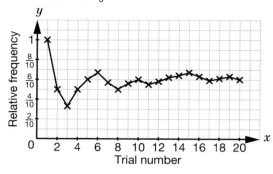

b More likely than not to rain in first 20 days of April.

3 ▶ p(vowel) $= \frac{9}{20}$

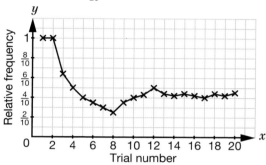

EXERCISE 1*

1 ▶ **a**

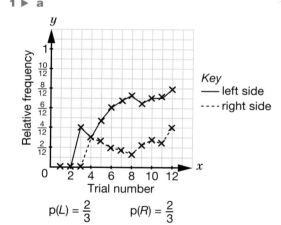

p(L) $= \frac{2}{3}$ p(R) $= \frac{2}{3}$

b Learning curve, so warm up before playing. Practise more from RHS.

2 ▶ **a** 0.23, 0.22, 0.21, 0.18, 0.09, 0.07

b 0.07

c 35

d No, a fair die has a theoretical probability of 0.17 for each outcome. For this die, the estimated probability of rolling a 1 is more than three times higher than of rolling a 6.

3 ▶ a $p(W) = \frac{12}{20} = \frac{3}{5}$; $p(P) = \frac{8}{20} = \frac{2}{5}$

   b Number of white $\approx \frac{3}{5} \times 100 = 60$

      $\Rightarrow$ number of purple ≈ 40

EXERCISE 2

1 ▶ a $p(g) = \frac{4}{10} = \frac{2}{5}$

   b $p(a) = \frac{3}{10}$

   c $p(t) = 0$

   d $p(\bar{S}) = \frac{9}{10}$

2 ▶ a $p(O) = \frac{4}{14} = \frac{2}{7}$

   b $p(T) = \frac{1}{14}$

   c $p(vowel) = \frac{6}{14} = \frac{3}{7}$

   d $p(consonant) = \frac{8}{14} = \frac{4}{7}$

3 ▶ a $p(R) = \frac{1}{2}$

   b $p(K) = \frac{1}{13}$

   c $p(\text{mult of } 3) = \frac{3}{13}$

   d $p(AJQK) = \frac{4}{13}$

4 ▶ a $\frac{3}{10}$ **b** $\frac{2}{5}$ **c** $\frac{3}{10}$ **d** $\frac{9}{10}$

5 ▶ a $\frac{1}{10}$ **b** $\frac{1}{2}$ **c** $\frac{3}{10}$ **d** $\frac{2}{5}$

6 ▶ a

	Glasses	No glasses	Total
Boys	4	10	14
Girls	6	12	18
Total	10	22	32

   b $\frac{5}{16}$ **c** $\frac{9}{16}$ **d** $\frac{2}{3}$

7 ▶ 20

8 ▶ 21

EXERCISE 2*

1 ▶ a

	1	2	3	4	5	6
1	2	3	4	5	6	7
2	3	4	5	6	7	8
3	4	5	6	7	8	9
4	5	6	7	8	9	10
5	6	7	8	9	10	11
6	7	8	9	10	11	12

   (i) $\frac{5}{36}$ (ii) $\frac{1}{12}$ (iii) $\frac{1}{12}$ (iv) $\frac{5}{12}$

   b 7

2 ▶ a

Green \ Red	2	3	5	7
11	9	8	6	4
13	11	10	8	6
17	15	14	12	10
19	17	16	14	12

   (i) $\frac{1}{8}$ (ii) $\frac{5}{16}$ (iii) $\frac{7}{16}$ (iv) $\frac{3}{16}$

   b 4, 9, 11, 15, 16, 17; all with probability $\frac{1}{16}$

3 ▶

2nd spin \ 1st spin	1	2	3	4	5
1	1	2	3	4	5
2	2	4	6	8	10
3	3	6	9	12	15
4	4	8	12	16	20
5	5	10	15	20	25

   a $\frac{9}{25}$ **b** $\frac{14}{25}$ **c** $\frac{6}{25}$ **d** $\frac{9}{25}$

4 ▶ a $\frac{10}{110} = \frac{1}{11}$ **b** $\frac{113}{130}$ **c** 850

5 ▶

Spinner \ Die	1	2	3	4	5	6
2	2	2	3	4	5	6
4	4	4	4	4	5	6
6	6	6	6	6	6	6

   a $\frac{1}{2}$ **b** $\frac{3}{18} = \frac{1}{6}$ **c** $\frac{13}{18}$ **d** $\frac{5}{18}$

6 ▶ a $\frac{1}{5}$ **b** $\frac{1}{5}$ **c** $\frac{2}{15}$ **d** $\frac{1}{15}$

7 ▶ $f = 5$

8 ▶ a 0.4   **b** 0.9

9 ▶ b Approx. 40 darts

EXERCISE 3   REVISION

1 ▶ $\frac{2}{3}$; More trials for a better estimate

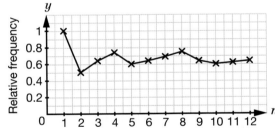

2 ▶ $\frac{13}{15}$

3 ▶ a $\frac{7}{51}$ **b** $\frac{1}{17}$ **c** $\frac{1}{3}$ **d** 0

4 ▶ HH, HT, TH, TT

   a $\frac{1}{4}$ **b** $\frac{1}{2}$

5 ▶ a $\frac{1}{8}$ **b** $\frac{1}{8}$ **c** 0   **d** 1

6 ▶ $\frac{10}{494} = \frac{5}{247}$

7 ▶ 20

8 ▶ a $\frac{1}{4}$ **b** $\frac{3}{4}$ **c** 0

EXERCISE 3*   REVISION

1 ▶ a 2014, $\frac{7}{10}$; 2015, $\frac{6}{10}$; 2016, $\frac{4}{10}$

   b Decrease in numbers from 2014 is suggested by the data

2 ▶ **a** $\frac{1}{12}$ **b** $\frac{3}{4}$ **c** $\frac{11}{36}$

3 ▶ **a** (i) $\frac{1}{11}$ (ii) $\frac{2}{11}$ (iii) 0

b Z or U, $\frac{2}{11}$

4 ▶ **a** $\frac{6}{25}$ **b** $\frac{19}{25}$ **c** $\frac{3}{25}$ **d** $\frac{9}{25}$

5 ▶ £45

6 ▶ HHH, HHT, HTH, THH, HTT, THT, TTH, TTT

a $\frac{1}{8}$ **b** $\frac{3}{8}$ **c** $\frac{1}{2}$

7 ▶ 2

8 ▶ **a** $\frac{2}{9}$ **b** $\frac{7}{9}$ **c** $\frac{2}{3}$

EXAM PRACTICE: HANDLING DATA 4

1 ▶ **a**

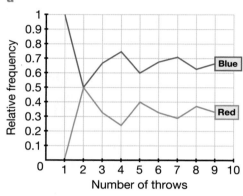

b p(R) = $\frac{1}{3}$, p(B) = $\frac{2}{3}$; both as expected!

2 ▶ **a** p(B) = $\frac{1}{2}$ **b** p(H) = $\frac{1}{4}$

c p(k') = $\frac{12}{13}$ **d** p(rp) = $\frac{1}{13}$

3 ▶ **a** p(o) = $\frac{2}{29}$ **b** p(i) = $\frac{9}{29}$

c p(x) = 0 **d** p(vowel) = $\frac{14}{29}$

4 ▶ **a**

	1	2	3	4	5	6
1	1	2	3	4	5	6
2	2	2	6	4	10	6
3	3	6	3	12	15	6
4	4	4	12	4	20	12
5	5	10	15	20	5	30
6	6	6	6	12	30	6

b (i) p(odd) = $\frac{1}{4}$ (ii) p(prime) = $\frac{1}{4}$

(iii) p(integer) = 1 (iv) p(square) = $\frac{1}{6}$

c 5 times

OTHER ANSWERS

FACT FINDER: ANTS

EXERCISE 1

1 ▶ 90.7 species per million years

2 ▶ 4500 kg ≈ 4.5 cars!

3 ▶ 16.7 ants/cm

4 ▶ 25 g of escamoles

5 ▶ 40 000 ants

EXERCISE 1*

1 ▶ 1 hr 28 mins 53 secs

2 ▶ 63 900 mm/s

3 ▶ 1.08×10^7 eggs = 10.8 million eggs

4 ▶ Weight of humans = 4.9×10^{11} kg

Number of ants = 9.8×10^{14}
$\approx 10^{15}$ = a quadrillion, so true!

5 ▶ **a** 1.48×10^8 km²

b (i) 47.3 people/km²

(ii) 6 630 000 ants/km²

c 140 000 ants/person

FACT FINDER: FRAGILE EARTH

EXERCISE 1

1 ▶ 3.03 billion

2 ▶ **a** 6.48%

b 43.8%

3 ▶ **a** $178 per person

b $219 per person

4 ▶ 32.0 elephants per day

5 ▶ **a** 20.4 kg per person

b 21.4 kg per person

EXERCISE 1*

1 ▶ **a** 0.368% **b** 0.815%

2 ▶ **a** 43.8 pitches per min

b 27.2 pitches per min

3 ▶ **a** 40.3 people per km²

b 47.7 people per km²

4 ▶ 1 m

5 ▶ **a** 1370 kg/km³ **b** 1700 kg/km³

FACT FINDER: GREAT WHITE SHARK

EXERCISE 1

1 ▶ 3.17 sharks per sec approx.

2 ▶ 225 m

3 ▶ 8.57%

4 ▶ For a 1.6 m pupil, $x \approx 4.38$

5 ▶ 6.67 m/s

EXERCISE 1*

1 ▶ 5 cm × 3500 ≈ 17 500 cm = 175 m. Yes!

2 ▶ 257%

3 ▶ 24.9%

4 ▶ 54 400 kg

5 ▶ 3.55%

6 ▶ 3.1×10^3 tonnes/m²

7 ▶ 1.26×10 tonnes

FACT FINDER: LONDON 2012 OLYMPICS

EXERCISE 1

1 ▶ 44.2%

2 ▶ a £350 per person

     b £6880 per sec

3 ▶ 1.2×10^{-3} trees/m²

4 ▶ 57.1%

5 ▶ 1600 m

EXERCISE 1*

1 ▶ 5.63×10^8 mm

2 ▶ $33\frac{1}{3}$%

3 ▶ 1118 g per person

4 ▶ Bolt: 1 hr 7 mins 22 secs

     Radisha: 1 hr 28 mins 42 secs

5 ▶

Rank by points/ million	Country	Points/ million	Previous rank (by Gold)
1	Hungary	3.70	9
2	Australia	2.83	10
3	U.K.	2.30	3
4	France	1.26	7
5	South Korea	1.24	5
6	Russia	1.09	4
7	Italy	1.04	8
8	Germany	1.06	6
9	U.S.A.	0.65	1
10	China	0.14	2

FACT FINDER: THE HUMAN BODY

EXERCISE 1

1 ▶ 14.1%

2 ▶ 8.6×10^8

3 ▶ 5.87 litres/min

4 ▶ 14 300

5 ▶ 5.49×10^{-6} mm/s

EXERCISE 1*

1 ▶ 81.5 beats/min

2 ▶ 0.0907 m/s

3 ▶ 11.3

4 ▶ 2.47×10^{15} mm³,
10 300 × volume of the classroom

5 ▶ a 0.0225 s   b Yes

CHALLENGES

1 ▶ a $\frac{2017}{2}$ b $\frac{n+1}{2}$

2 ▶ $\frac{8000}{3}$

4 ▶ $x = 1, y = 2, z = 3$

6 ▶ a 1×10^{606} b 1×10^{90} c 1×10^{1200}

7 ▶ 8.47×10^{56} mm³ (to 3 s.f.)

8 ▶ 2

9 ▶

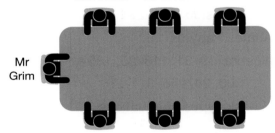

Mrs Hack   Mr Woof   Mrs Smart

Mr Grim

Mrs Chatty   Mr Nice   Mrs Pain

10 ▶ Ratio of areas for round peg in square hole
is $\frac{\pi}{4} \approx 0.785$

     Ratio of areas for square peg in round hole
is $\frac{2}{\pi} \approx 0.637$

     So a round peg in a square hole is the better fit.

11 ▶ 16 cm²

12 ▶ $p = 9$ (front), $q = 3$ (rear)

INDEX

area of 248

travel graphs 201–12

   distance–time 202–5, 212

   speed–time 205–9, 212

trials 357

triangles 51–7, 82

   angle sum 51–2, 54

   constructing 68–9, 83

   dividing polygons into 61, 62, 63

   dividing quadrilaterals into 57

   equilateral 51, 53, 54

   exterior angle 51–2

   interior angle 51–2

   isosceles 51, 53, 54, 137

   similar 73–8, 83

   special 53–7

   see also right-angled triangles

trigonometry 213–23, 271–84

   calculating angles 218–20, 275–8

   calculating sides 215–17, 273–5

   cosine ratio 271–2

   inverse functions 218, 275

   sine ratio 271–2

   tangent ratio 214–23

Turing, Alan 225

two-way tables 156, 172

U

union of sets 91–2

unit ratios 180

universal set 87, 89

upper bounds 304–7, 310

upper quartile 286, 287, 288

V

variables 38

vectors 339–41

Venn diagrams 87–92, 95, 178

volume

   cylinder 247

   pyramid 252

X

x-axis 32

x-intercept 265

Y

y-axis 32

y-intercept 37, 38

The author and publisher would like to thank the following individuals and organisations for permission to reproduce photographs:

(Key: b-bottom; c-centre; l-left; r-right; t-top)

123RF.com: 48cr, 93cr, 162t, 296cr, 361r, 369b, Aaron Amat 8c, 9br, Agnieszka Murphy 374 (fishing), 375 (fishing), Andrey Golubev 252, Andrey Pavlov 372, Brenken 295t, Corey A Ford 376, crisferra 241t, Dan Iacob 288b, Darko Novakovic 195cr, Eduard Kim 247, Ferli Achirulli 111b, gkuna 295b, greyjj 374 (mega-cities), 375 (mega-cities), homestudio 363l, Igor Shkvara 269cr, Ihor Obraztsov 374 (transport), Inspirestock International 232br, James Weston 375 (ozone layer), Joerg Hackemann 207cr, Kirill Cherezov 46br, Konstantin Shaklein 311tr, mocker 183l, myvector 374 (population), Oleksandr Galata 374 (water), Olexandr Moroz 109b, ozaiachin 294bl, photopiano 109t, rabbit75123 263cr, rioblanco 16t, Robert Nyholm 367tc, Sergey Leonov 374 (nuclear power), siraphol 242, Tatiana Mihaliova 246br, Tim Hester 368b, Tomas Marek 367tr, tomwang 164br, Tul Chalothonrangsee 374 (global warming), 375 (global warming), vasilevki 375 (species), Vladimir Yudin 375 (rainforests), vselenka 275cr, Yulia Kireeva 374 (computers); **Alamy Images:** Anna Curnow 182b, Blend Images 285b, Boaz Rottem 152cl, catherinka 288t, Cultura RM 7t, Enigma 228, epa european pressphoto agency b.v. 245tl, Ian Shaw 11, Jamie Pham Photography 131cr, Janine Wiedel Photolibrary 211br, Juniors Bildarchiv GmbH 96, Mauritius images GmbH 205tl, Paul Shawcross / LGPL 209tr, PCN Photography 308b, Pictorial Press Ltd 84t, World History Archive 259tr, ZUMA Press Inc 227b; **Fotolia.com:** Africa Studio 170b, baibaz 6c, 8tr, bennymarty 44, BillionPhotos.com 15, Boggy 42, Budimir Jevtic 163t, carballo 240b, chekky 133, Dariusz Kopestynski 241b, davehanlon 47b, dracozlat 113tr, DragonImages 135l, eagle20ita 50t, fotoliaxrender 102t, giulianax 292cl, Igor Mojzes 24, kletr 40t, lzf 289, Maksim Shebeko 90cr, Marco Tiberio 6t, 6b, markrhiggins 234cr, ndoeljindoel 209br, nobeastsofierce 102c, NOBU 158br, oles_photo 104b, pilipphoto 166, ray8 177, redche 229b, Stephanie Friedman 305, tilpich 355, winston 16b, Zarya Maxim 154tr; **Getty Images:** Andrew Holt 339tl, Apic 175, Asanka Brendon Ratnayake 296t, ChinaFotoPress 105br, Daryl Benson 2, Fred Stein Archive 238t, Gurpal Singh Dutta 225, Hemera Technologies 366br, Heritage Images 224tr, JEKESAI NJIKIZANA 286cr, Keith Ladzinski 93t, LOCOG 379, Miles Willis 41tr, Mouse-ear 224tl, Print Collector 240t, Science & Society Picture Library 299t, 357, SEBASTIEN BOZON 110, The Asahi Shimbun 33tc, ullstein bild 97l, UniversalImagesGroup 140cl; **IOC Museums Collection © IOC :** 378tr; **Jacques Rodrigue:** Living in the Spotlight 2013, acrylic on canvas, 40x60, George Rodrigue 174; **Michael Poulton:** Number 5 and Floating Stones. Installation on Grass Creek, by Michael Poulton, Museum of Temporary Art, Victoria Road, Ontario, CA. Photograph by the artist 298; **Pearson Education Ltd:** Studio 8 84b, Gareth Boden 171br, Trevor Clifford 338tl, Coleman Yuen. Pearson Education Asia Ltd 29; **Press Association Images:** Mike Derer / AP 106tr; **Science Photo Library Ltd:** Gwen Shockey 380, Martyn F. Chillmaid 39t, NASA / ESA / JPL-CALTECH 97r, Royal Astronomical Society 185t; **Shutterstock.com:** 85050 117, absolutimages 87b, Africa Studio 8br, Alica Q 48bl, Ander Dylan 41tl, Andrew Scherbackov 182t, Angel Simon 233b, AnnaDe 181b, Antonio Abrignani 150t, arek_malang 38, artpritsadee 286cl, baloon111 293tl, bibiphoto 9cr, bikeriderlondon 151, Bikeworldtravel 237tr, Breadmaker 245bl, BRG.photography 367bl, BUGNUT23 332cl, CandyBox Images 104t, cesc_assawin 98, Christian Kieffer 271tr, Daniel Prudek 210cr, Danin Tulic 47t, Dziurek 245tr, El Nariz 92cr, Eric Isselee 162b, 224c, 348t, 366tr, 366c, EurngKwan 65cr, Everett Historical 285t, Evgenyi 135r, Fisherss 99, FoodStocker 85, Georgios Kollidas 32, Hung Chung Chih 17l, Iasmina Calinciuc 9bl, icsnaps 259tl, Igor Kolos 152c, Irafael 245br, Jag_cz 7b, Jagodka 87t, Jan Martin Will 107br, Jennifer Gottschalk 338tr, Joggie Botma 367tl, Joshua Resnick 183r, katatonia82 169b, Kesu 181t, Kiev.Victor 290, Ksenia Palimski 108br, lexaarts 283br, liza1879 94cl, Ljupco Smokovski 210tr, LU JINRONG 341cr, Luis Fernando Curci Chavier 222tr, Malcolm Chapman 111t, Manfred Ruckszio 366tl, MARGRIT HIRSCH 39b, Matt Jones 17r, Microstock Man 86b, Milkovasa 243, Milles Studio 180, Molodec 86t, Monkey Business Images 126tr, Natali Glado 199, Nataliya Nazarova 244b, Nejron Photo 229t, nui7711 336, oksana2010 190b, Oleksiy Mark 130cr, Ondrej Prosicky 28, Pablo77 132, Pal2iyawit 234tr, Pamela D. Maxwell 89cr, patpitchaya 361l, Peter Bernik 309cr, PeterVrabel 236, Photosebia 211bl, Piti Tan 10, pkchai 198, Racheal Grazias 33tr, Rafa Irusta 8bl, Rahmo 19, rayjunk 268b, Reha Mark 46bl, Richard Griffin 3, Rido 89br, S.Borisov 179t, SergeyDV 201t, Skylines 5t, SpeedKingz 114, successo images 40b, suravid 152cr, TachePhoto 179b, Tyler Olson 9tr, unclepepin 383br, urosr 196, Vaclav Volrab 5b, Valentina Razumova 257r, vdLee 176b, Vitaliy Netiaga 238b, Vogel 33tl, Volodymyr Burdiak 222bl, Waj 217tr, Wasu Watcharadachaphong 226cr, wavebreakmedia 286t, Yingko 178cr, You Touch Pix of EuToch 102b

Cover images: _Front_: **Shutterstock.com:** Filip Fuxa
Inside front cover: **Shutterstock.com:** Dmitry Lobanov

All other images © Pearson Education

Glossary terms have been taken from _The Longman Dictionary of Contemporary English Online_.